Introduction to

OPERATIONS
RESEARCH

C. WEST CHURCHMAN

Professor of Business Administration
University of California, Berkeley

RUSSELL L. ACKOFF

Director, Operations Research Group
and Professor

E. LEONARD ARNOFF

Assistant Director, Operations Research Group
and Associate Professor

Department of Engineering Administration
Case Institute of Technology

In collaboration with:

LESLIE C. EDIE, *The Port of New York Authority*

LAWRENCE FRIEDMAN, *Operations Research Group, Case Institute of Technology*

R. J. D. GILLIES, *Arms and Ammunition Service, Olin Mathieson Chemical Corporation* *

VAN COURT HARE, *Experimental Towing Tank, Stevens Institute of Technology* *

JOSEPH F. MCCLOSKEY, *Operations Research Group, Case Institute of Technology*

LORING G. MITTEN, *Department of Industrial Engineering, The Ohio State University*

ELIEZER NADDOR, *Department of Industrial Engineering, The Johns Hopkins University* *

BERTRAM E. RIFAS, *Operations Research Staff, Pacific Intermountain Express Company* *

ELIZABETH A. SMALL, *Operations Research Group, Case Institute of Technology*

PAUL STILLSON, *Operations Research Group, Shell Development Company*

WALTER R. VAN VOORHIS, *Operations Research Group, Case Institute of Technology*

RAM VASWANI, *Operations Research Group, Engineering Experiment Station, The Ohio State University* *

* *Formerly with Operations Research Group, Case Institute of Technology.*

Introduction to

OPERATIONS
RESEARCH

New York · John Wiley & Sons, Inc.

London

Library of Congress Catalog Card Number: 57-5907

To T. Keith Glennan
   President, Case Institute of Technology

*Royalties received from the sale of this
book for the first two years are to be part
of a Faculty gift to establish the T. Keith
Glennan Laboratory of Industrial Electronics.*

*Subsequent royalties will be used to
establish graduate scholarships in Operations Research at Case.*

Preface

This text grew from the lecture material for the "Short Course in Operations Research" which has been offered annually (since 1952) by Case Institute of Technology. This course, and therefore this text, has two objectives:

1. To provide prospective consumers of Operations Research with a basis for evaluating the field and for understanding its potentialities and procedures.

2. To provide potential practitioners with a survey of the field and a basis on which they can plan the further education required for competence with the methods and techniques.

Our aim in both cases has been to create an understanding of the application of scientific method to Operations Research, and not a listing of "techniques."

The prospective consumer will find Parts I, II, III, and X, and the case studies offered in the other Parts, of particular interest. The potential practitioner should work through all the material.

It should be emphasized that this book is an introduction. It is not intended to be a reference work for experienced practitioners. An effort has been made to simplify the technical material without distorting it.

A high degree of mathematical maturity is not required. Parts I, II, III, and X require only elementary training in mathematics, even if that training took place in the "distant past"—if the reader is not afraid of symbolism and abstraction. Some of the material in Parts IV–IX will require a higher degree of mathematical sophistication, in particular a knowledge of elementary calculus.

The chapters of this book were initially prepared by different persons:

Chapter 3 by Loring G. Mitten, Chapter 4 by Van Court Hare, the case study in Chapter 4 by R. J. D. Gillies, Chapters 8 and 18 by Eliezer Naddor, Chapters 10 and 17 by Bertram E. Rifas, Chapters 12 and 16 by Ram Vaswani, Chapter 14 by Walter R. Van Voorhis, Chapter 19 by Lawrence Friedman, the case study in implementation in Chapter 21 by Elizabeth A. Small, and Chapter 22 by Joseph F. McCloskey. Case I in Chapter 6 is reprinted in part from an article by Paul Stillson. Chapter 15 is reprinted from an article by Leslie C. Edie. These reprints are made with the kind permission of the authors and editors of *Industrial Quality Control* and *Operations Research* respectively.

The material initially prepared has been revised in an effort to obtain a connected and consistent text. In a number of instances these revisions have been quite extensive. The ultimate blame for inaccuracy and inconsistency is ours.

We have emphasized here the application of Operations Research to industrial problems because this application has been our experience. We fully realize that Operations Research has had an extensive application to military problems. We also realize that it has an enormous potential application to community problems, as is evidenced by Chapter 15. Indeed, two of the authors of this book spent considerable time and effort in attempting to apply research to city planning and to union problems. We still feel that the future development of Operations Research should occur in all areas of administration. The fact stands, however, that military and industrial management have shown more extensive interest in supporting and receiving aid from Operations Research-type projects than has civil government.

We are indebted to the following for their constructive criticism during preparation of this book: W. W. Cooper, Alfred W. Jones, J. S. Minas, John F. Muth, Leon Pritzker, Richard S. Rudner, and Max A. Woodbury. Invaluable editorial assistance was received from Beverly Bond, Richard E. Deal, and Arthur J. Yaspan.

For their encouragement and enthusiastic support of this and other activities of the Operations Research Group, we are particularly indebted to our department chairman, Clay H. Hollister, and to Deans Elmer H. Hutchisson and Karl B. McEachron.

Finally, we wish to express our appreciation to Carol Mara Prideaux and Grace White for their work in preparing the manuscript.

C. WEST CHURCHMAN
RUSSELL L. ACKOFF
E. LEONARD ARNOFF

Cleveland, Ohio
October 25, 1956

Contents

ix

PART

I

INTRODUCTION

Part I of this book is concerned with the meaning of Operations Research. In Chapter 1, the subject is defined and its characteristics are explored. Central to this discussion is the notion that the *aim* of Operations Research is to obtain a *systems* or *over-all* approach to problems. This idea is illustrated in the case presented in Chapter 2. The case given in Chapter 3 dramatically illustrates the reason for including a variety of disciplines in an Operations Research team. A discussion dealing specifically with the composition of an Operations Research team is deferred to Chapter 22.

Chapter 1

The General Nature

of

Operations Research

THE ESSENTIAL CHARACTERISTICS OF O.R.

No science has ever been born on a specific day. Each science emerges out of a convergence of an increased interest in some class of problems and the development of scientific methods, techniques, and tools which are adequate to solve these problems. Operations Research (O.R.) is no exception. Its roots are as old as science and the management function. Its name dates back only to 1940.* O.R.'s initial development began in the United Kingdom during World War II and was quickly taken up in the United States. This start took place in a military context. After the war O.R. moved into business, industry, and civil government. This movement was slower in the United States than in the United Kingdom but in 1951 industrial O.R. took hold in this country and has since developed very rapidly.

Although the activity called Operations Research began in a military context, its evolution or emergence can be described in terms of the well-known development of industrial organization. Before the industrial revolution most business and industry consisted of small enterprises, each directed by a single boss who did the purchasing, planned and supervised production, sold the product, hired and fired personnel, etc. The mechanization of production led to such rapid growth of industrial enterprises that it became impossible for one man to perform all these managerial functions. Consequently, a division of the management function took place. Managers of production, marketing, fi-

* For a brief history of O.R. see Trefethen.[8]

3

nance, personnel, and the like appeared. Continued mechanization, supplemented in part by automation, resulted in still further industrial growth which manifested itself in decentralization of operations and still further division of the management function. For example, production departments were subdivided into sections having the function of maintenance, quality control, production planning, purchasing, stock, and other sections which were frequently supervised by persons of managerial status. Multiple plant operations created many new plant managers. Today a decreasing number of production department managers have direct contact with manufacturing operations. They have, in effect, become production executives.

Along with the increased differentiation and segmentation of the management function came increased attention by scientists to the problems generated in the various functional divisions of industrial operations. For example, scientists applied themselves increasingly to production problems and out of their efforts arose several new branches of applied science: mechanical, chemical, and industrial engineering, and statistical quality control. In other functions marketing research, industrial economics, econometrics, personnel psychology, industrial sociology, and similar applied scientific disciplines appeared.

During this period of differentiation and segmentation of the management function a new class of managerial problems began to appear and assert themselves, problems which can be called executive-type problems. These problems are a direct consequence of the functional division of labor in an enterprise, a division which results in *organized* activity. In an organization each functional unit (division, department, or section) has a part of the whole job to perform. Each part is necessary for the accomplishment of the *over-all objectives* of the organization. A result of this division of labor, however, is that each functional unit develops objectives of its own. For example, the production department generally assumes the objectives of minimizing the cost of production and maximizing production volume. The marketing department tries to minimize the cost of unit sales and maximize sales volume. The finance department attempts to optimize the capital investment policy of the business. The personnel department tries to hire good people at minimum cost, and to retain them, etc. These objectives are not always consistent; in fact, they frequently come into direct conflict with one another.

Consider, for example, the attitudes of the various departments with regard to the inventory policy of a business. The production department is interested in long uninterrupted production runs, because such runs reduce setup costs and hence minimize manufacturing costs, but such long runs may result in large inventories of in-process and finished goods in relatively few product lines. Marketing wants to give immediate delivery over a wide variety of products. Hence it wants a more diverse but still large inventory. It would also like a flexible productive department that can fill small special orders on short notice. Finance wants to minimize inventory because it wants to minimize capital investments that tie up assets for indeterminate periods. Personnel wants to stabilize labor and this can only be accomplished when goods are produced for inventory during slack periods, etc.

Inventory policy affects the operations of each functional unit of an industrial organization. The policy most favorable to one department is seldom most favorable to the others. The problem is: What inventory policy is best for the organization as a whole? This is an executive-type problem because (*a*) it involves the effectiveness of the organization as a whole, and (*b*) it involves a conflict of interests of the functional units of the organization.

A similar type of problem can and does arise within a department of an industrial organization. For example, a conflict of interests over the inventory problem can arise within the production department alone and hence can be an executive-type problem for the production department manager. For example, one section of the production department may be interested in reducing setup costs, but such reduction may increase inventories of certain products beyond the capacity of the existing warehouses. This introduces a conflict of interest within the production department, the solution of which we call an executive-type problem for this department.

It is important to note that this division of organizational objectives is not "bad." If a large group of persons attempts to accomplish some task, it may not be possible for them to act as a single person would. Thus it is pointless to develop a plan for a large industrial organization which assumes that everyone knows and can evaluate what everyone else does. Division of function seems to be the only solution in this situation. The executive-type problem thus arises out of the need to subdivide functions. Its solution is rarely of the form: "Let's all try to understand the other fellow's problem." Rather, the solution demands a highly refined balance of departmental objectives and over-all objectives; departments need to be motivated to pursue their own goals and excessive interest in the good of the whole may lead to stagnation of effort. Therefore, when we talk of an "over-all optimum" we mean a policy that takes account of the necessity of a split function in the organization.

With the emergence of executive-type problems came the development of a profession of management consultants. These consultants sought to aid executives confronted with such problems by applying their experience with similar problems in other contexts. The method they introduced consisted of observing what was common in certain executive-type problems and analyzing proposed solutions. It was only natural that efforts should eventually be made to try to find a common structure ("model") in these solutions, and the bases on which such structures could be tested. These efforts amounted to the use of science in the study of executive-type problems. Applications of science in this area had been made from time to time prior to O.R.

During World War II, military management called on scientists in large numbers to assist in solving strategic and tactical problems. Many of these problems were what we have called executive-type problems. Scientists from different disciplines were organized into teams which were addressed initially to optimizing the use of resources. These were the first "O.R. teams."

An objective of O.R., as it emerged from this evolution of industrial organization, is to provide managers of the organization with a scientific basis for solving problems involving the interaction of components of the organization in the best interest of the organization as a whole. A decision which is best for the organization as a whole is called an optimum decision; one which is best relative to the functions of one or more parts of the organization is called a suboptimum decision. The problem of establishing criteria for an optimum decision is itself a very complex and technical one. The complexities and technicalities are discussed in detail in Chapter 5.

O.R. tries to find the best decisions relative to as large a portion of a total organization as is possible. For example, in attempting to solve a maintenance problem in a factory O.R. tries to consider the effect of alternative maintenance policies on the production department as a whole. If possible it also tries to consider how this effect on the production department in turn affects other departments and the business as a whole. It may even try to go further and investigate how the effect on this particular business organization in turn affects the industry as a whole, etc. O.R. attempts to consider the interactions or chain of effects as far out as these effects are significant. In particular practical applications, however, the scope of O.R. is usually restricted either because access to higher and higher levels of organization is closed off or because of the limitations of time, money, or resources. This point is important to bear in mind in reading this book. There is always a difference between what one tries to do and what one actually does. O.R.

is here defined in terms of its important goal: an over-all understanding of optimal solutions to executive-type problems in organizations.

The comprehensiveness of O.R.'s aim is an example of a "systems" approach, since "system" implies an interconnected complex of functionally related components. Thus a business organization is a social or man-machine system. But not all systems involve human or social components. An automobile, for example, is a mechanical system. It is made up of such functional units as a motor, transmission, radiator, and generator. These and other units are combined to form a mechanism which can satisfy a set of interests. The effectiveness of each unit depends on how it fits into the whole, and the effectiveness of the whole depends on the way each unit functions. Problems of optimizing the design of a mechanical system are similar to but not identical with those involving man-machine systems. Both systems involve a conflict of interests. The users of automobiles want fast, safe, economical, comfortable, roomy, and attractive vehicles. All of these desires cannot be served perfectly at the same time. Hence the design problem involves optimizing over a set of at least partially conflicting objectives. The "division of labor" aspect of human organizations is different from the component functioning of machine systems, however, because in human organizations there is the critical problem of motivating the divisions to perform their respective functions.

The application of science to the design of mechanical and man-machine systems is sometimes called systems analysis, and this is often equated with O.R. In this sense, the design and evaluation of weapons and communications systems is O.R. But this text is oriented toward human organizations since this has been the emphasis in the practice of O.R. in business and industry.

The systems approach to problems does not mean that the most generally formulated problem must be solved in one research project. However desirable this may be, it is seldom possible to realize it in practice. In practice, parts of the total problem are usually solved in sequence. In many cases the total problem cannot be formulated in advance but the solution of one phase of it helps define the next phase. For example, a production control project may require determination of the most economic production quantities of different items. Once these are found it may turn out that these quantities cannot be produced on the available equipment in the available time. This, then, gives rise to a new problem whose solution will affect the solution obtained in the first phase. In brief, then, although simultaneous optimization of all phases of a system is desirable, practical restrictions usually require sequential optimization of parts of the system accompanied by adjustments of the "phase-optima" to approach an over-all optimum.

To assert that O.R. is concerned with as much of the whole system as it can encompass does not mean it necessarily *starts* with the system as a whole. Most O.R. projects begin with familiar problems of restricted scope. But in the course of the research the scope is enlarged as much as circumstances permit. In effect, the scope of the research is a scale on which one of the dimensions of "O.R.ness" can be measured. Consequently, O.R. frequently begins with the same problem a mechanical, industrial, or chemical engineer or market researcher might start with, but it seldom ends with the same problem. This aspect of O.R. will be illustrated in the case study presented in Chapter 2.

It is characteristic of O.R. that in the solution of each problem new problems are uncovered. Consequently, O.R. is not effectively used if it is restricted to one-shot projects. Greatest benefits can be obtained through continuity of research; i.e., by "following through." This follows from the aims of O.R. as specified above.

The concern of O.R. with finding an *optimum* decision, policy, or design is one of its essential characteristics. It does not seek merely to find a better solution to a problem than the one in use; it seeks the *best* solution. It may not always find it because of limitations imposed by the present state of science or by lack of time, funds, or opportunity. But O.R.'s efforts are continually directed to getting to the optimum or as close to it as possible.

In some circumstances O.R. cannot specify an optimum decision because one or more of the essential aspects of the system cannot be evaluated within the limitations imposed upon the problem. For example, it may not be able to assign a cost to the time customers must wait to receive service. In such cases, however, it can specify the optimum decision for each value which such waiting time may assume. It is then left to the decision-maker to use his judgment and assign a value to such waiting time. Once this is done, an optimum decision is specified relative to the judgment. In this procedure O.R. can show the quantitative effect of such judgment on the system's operations. For example, it can state what the total expected cost of operating a service facility is for each possible value assigned to customer waiting time. In all cases, the final decision rests with those in control of the operations, *not* with the operations researchers. The team can only recommend solutions or the basis on which solutions can be selected. It can, however, assist in implementing the solution once the decision is made.

Summarizing this discussion, O.R. in the most general sense can be characterized as the application of scientific methods, techniques, and tools to problems involving the operations of systems so as to provide those in control of the operations with optimum solutions to the problems. This text restricts itself to the application of O.R. to executive-type problems in organizations.

This does not mean that we will ignore other forms of systems analysis; but the purpose of constructing a model, e.g., of a production system will be to enable the researcher to understand how production fits into the organizational activity. Hence we begin our discussion in Chapter 4 with the aspects of formulating the problem—which is essentially an attempt to get as much of an over-all viewpoint as possible. The student should keep this chapter in mind in all subsequent discussions that deal with specific aspects of the problem-solution. Thus a careful reader will not think of "solving" inventory problems as such, but of solving an organizational problem in which inventory plays an important part. As we shall see later, an inventory model is a "technique," and the manner in which it fits into the whole research project is a "method." As the chapters on models are read, the reader should keep asking himself how the model can be used within a specific system with which he is acquainted. In this way, the reader can avoid becoming "technique" oriented.

THE TEAM APPROACH

Because O.R. has emerged out of other sciences it borrows from them quite heavily. This same pattern has been followed in the "birth" of each scientific discipline. It is always difficult to distinguish a new field from those out of which it arises because of the overlap of problems, methods, and concepts. In time the differentiation becomes more complete and practitioners are no longer plagued with the question: "How does this differ from such and such a field?" The rapid growth of O.R. under its own name testifies to an increasing recognition of its uniqueness. But the differentiation is far from complete.

The overlap of methods, techniques, and tools between O.R. and other fields is largely due to the way in which O.R. was initially and is still carried on. It is research performed by teams of scientists whose individual members have been drawn from different scientific and engineering disciplines. One might find, for example, a mathematician, physicist, psychologist, and economist working together on a problem of optimizing capital expansion. The effectiveness of such interdisciplinary teams in tackling the type of problem characterized as the subject matter of O.R. is not accidental.

When a scientist is confronted by a new type of problem, he, like anyone else so confronted, tries to abstract the essence of the problem and determine whether or not he has faced a similarly structured problem in a different context, particularly in his field of specialization. Once he finds an analogous problem in his special field he can inquire as to whether or not the methods he would use on the analogous problem in his own field are applicable to the new problem with which he is faced. In this way he brings to bear on the new problem methods of attack which might not otherwise be thought of in this connection. When scientists from different disciplines do this collectively, the pool of possible approaches to the problem grows.

For example, an electronics engineer examining the problem of production and inventory control may quickly perceive that the fluctuations in inventory are a function of the length of time that elapses between changes in the market and adjustment of the production level. In effect he sees the problem as one of designing a servo-control system in which necessary information concerning changes in the market is fed back quickly and accurately to the production control center. At this center, adjustments in production can be made in such a way as to minimize some cost function. He has in effect translated the problem into one of servo theory and he knows how to solve such problems. This example is not at all hypothetical.

On the other hand, a chemical engineer may look at the same problem and formulate it in terms of flow theory, and once this is done he has methods available for solving it.

Which of the alternative methods of approach is most fruitful depends on the circumstances. The research team examines the alternatives and selects an approach or develops a new one which borrows from several methods of attack.

One of the major reasons for O.R. teams is to bring the most advanced scientific procedures to bear on the problem or to develop new procedures which are more effective in approaching the problem than any that are available. The idea is that no one mind can hold all the potentially useful scientific information, but a "team mind" may.

Another important advantage of the team approach lies in the fact that most man-machine systems have physical, biological, psychological, sociological, economic, and engineering aspects. These phases of the system can best be understood and analyzed by those trained in the appropriate fields. Those in control of a system may be unaware of one or more of these aspects and hence have an incomplete picture of their system. That is, to see a system as a whole means not only to see all its components and their interrelationships but also all aspects of its operations. A mixed team increases the number of aspects of the operation which can be examined in detail. This point will be illustrated by the case study presented in Chapter 3.

THE DEVELOPMENT OF O.R. METHODS, TECHNIQUES, AND TOOLS

As certain classes of problems appear more and more frequently in O.R. it is only natural that these should be singled out for more intensive study. The result is that for many types of repetitive problems new methods of attack or modification of old ones have been developed. Gradually the body of methods, techniques, and tools developed or adopted specifically for O.R.-type problems has grown. It has already grown to the point where it is extremely difficult for one person to keep well informed on all these developments. This fact has some important consequences.

Ten years ago any interested person with a creative mind and a good training in science or engineering could easily become an operations researcher. He did not need any special training or education. This easy movement into O.R. is going by the wayside because as O.R. develops it requires more and more time to catch up with what has gone on and to learn what methods, techniques, and tools are available. As this body of knowledge develops, however, O.R. becomes increasingly teachable. Numerous universities, colleges, and technological institutes give such courses, and a few even offer graduate curricula leading to advanced degrees. It is this development of an increasingly unique body of methods, techniques, and tools which makes a text like this possible.

This book will concentrate on the growing body of O.R. knowledge. It will make no effort to cover the large number of general tools that operations researchers are required to have available to do their job. For example, there will be no attempt made here to provide the knowledge of mathematics and statistics which are necessary for the effective practice of O.R. Nor will this text consider such other areas as cost analysis, economics, forecasting, and the use of computers, which are also important in the practice of O.R. These are all things with which an operations researcher must become familiar and their omission here is not to be interpreted as a minimization of their importance. It would be impossible to cover all this material in one book and it is not really necessary to do so. Good material on these topics is readily available. What is not available at this time is an introduction to the methods, concepts, and techniques which have developed in O.R.

or which have been developed elsewhere and have been adapted for use in O.R. It is to this task that this text is addressed.

The terms "tools," "techniques," and "methods," which are frequently used interchangeably in science, are carefully differentiated here. As employed in this book, they are related much as are the tools used in constructing a building, the ways of handling these tools, and the design or method of the building which requires the use of the tools in prescribed ways. For example, a table of random numbers is a tool of science. The way in which this tool is used (e.g., in Monte Carlo procedures to be discussed in Chapter 7) is a technique of science. The research plan which involves the use of Monte Carlo procedures and a table of random numbers is a method of science. Similarly, calculus is a scientific tool; employing calculus to find an optimum value of a variable in a mathematical model of a system is a scientific technique; the plan of utilizing a mathematical model to optimize a system is a scientific method.

Though it is true that all sciences have certain aspects of methods, techniques, and tools in common, it is also true that each science employs unique methods, techniques, and tools which reflect the distinctiveness of the subject matter which it investigates. To the extent that a science develops methods, techniques, and tools well adapted to its special subject matter, that science itself develops.

Textbooks on established research areas such as physics and chemistry deal with scientific method in only a cursory way. Their emphasis is on techniques and tools. In the present book there is considerable emphasis on methods. This is because the way of approaching a problem is critical in a new area of research, more important than the techniques or tools employed. Before O.R. began to develop its own techniques and tools, it was useful because of the power of its approach to problems. As we remarked earlier, the reader should always consider each technique as an aspect of the entire problem, not as a device that is valuable in itself. In this way he will avoid becoming committed to one or a set of techniques and tools. An openness of mind about techniques, together with a broad knowledge of their usefulness and an appreciation of the over-all problem, are essentials of sound method in science.

THE PHASES OF O.R.

Ten years ago it would have been difficult to get an operations researcher to describe a procedure for conducting O.R. Today it is difficult to keep one from doing it. Each practitioner's version of O.R.'s method (if recorded) would differ in some respects. But there would also be a good deal in common. For example, most would agree that the following are the major phases of an O.R. project:

1. Formulating the problem.
2. Constructing a mathematical model to represent the system under study.
3. Deriving a solution from the model.
4. Testing the model and the solution derived from it.
5. Establishing controls over the solution.
6. Putting the solution to work: implementation.

Each of these phases will be discussed in detail in subsequent chapters but it may be helpful to provide an orientation by summarizing the material here.

Formulating the Problem

Both the consumer's and the researchers' problem must be formulated. The research consumer is the person (or group) who controls the operations under study. (He is also referred to as the decision-maker.) In formulating the consumer's problem an analysis must be made of the system under his control, his objectives, and alternative courses of action. Others affected by the decisions under study must be identified and their pertinent objectives and courses of action must also be uncovered. What we have called the over-all viewpoint is closely connected with the attempt to define objectives. O.R. tries to take into account as broad a scope of objectives as possible. In most general terms, the research problem is to determine which alternative course of action is most effective relative to the set of pertinent objectives. Consequently, in formulating the research problem a measure of effectiveness must be specified and its suitability must be established.

Constructing a Mathematical Model

This model expresses the effectiveness of the system under study as a function of a set of variables at least one of which is subject to control. The general form of an O.R. model is

$$E = f(x_i, y_j)$$

where E represents the effectiveness of the system, x_i the variables of the system which are subject to control, and y_j those variables which are not subject to control. The restrictions on values of the variables may be expressed in a supplementary set of equations and/or inequations.

Deriving a Solution from the Model

There are essentially two types of procedures for deriving an optimum (or an approximation to an optimum) solution from a model: *analytic* and *numerical*. Analytic procedures consist of the use of mathematical deduction. This involves the application of various branches of mathematics such as calculus or matrix algebra. Analytic solutions are obtained "in the abstract"; i.e., the substitution of numbers for symbols is generally made after the solution has been obtained.

Numerical procedures consist essentially of trying various values of the control variables in the model, comparing the results obtained, and selecting that set of values of the control variables which yields the best solution. Such procedures vary from simple trial and error to complex *iteration*. An iterative procedure is one in which successive trials tend to approach an optimum solution. In addition, an iterative procedure usually provides a set of rules which identify the optimum solution as such when it has been obtained.

Some expressions in a model cannot be numerically evaluated with exactness because of either mathematical or practical considerations. In many such cases a particular application of random sampling, called the Monte Carlo technique, can be used to obtain approximate evaluations of the expressions.

Testing the Model and Solution

A model is never more than a partial representation of reality. It is a good model if, despite its incompleteness, it can accurately predict the effect of changes in the system on the system's over-all effectiveness. The adequacy of the model can be tested by determining how well it does predict the effect of these changes. The solution can be evaluated by comparing results obtained without applying the solution with results obtained when it is used. These evaluations may be performed retrospectively by the use of past data, or by a trial run or pretest. Testing requires careful analysis as to what are and what are not valid data.

Establishing Controls over the Solution

A solution derived from a model remains a solution only as long as the uncontrolled variables retain their values and the relationship between the variables in the model remains constant. The solution itself goes "out of control" when the value of one or more of the uncontrolled variables and/or one or more of the relationships between variables has changed significantly. The significance of the change depends on the amount by which the solution is made to deviate from the true optimum under the changed conditions and the cost of changing the solution in operation. To establish controls over the solution, then, one must develop tools for determining when significant changes occur and rules must be established for modifying the solution to take these changes into account.

Putting the Solution to Work

The tested solution must be translated into a set of operating procedures capable of being understood and applied by the personnel who will be responsible for their use. Required changes in existing procedures and resources must be specified and carried out.

The steps enumerated are seldom if ever conducted in the order presented. Furthermore the steps may take place simultaneously. In many projects, for example, the formulation of the problem is not completed until the project itself is virtually completed. There is usually a continuous interplay between these steps during the research.

RECURRENT PROCESSES AND PROBLEMS

The techniques and tools which will be discussed fall into certain classes depending on the type of process to which they are applicable. In most cases these processes have conventionally accepted names; in a few they do not. In the latter situation the authors have had to assign to classes terms which appear to be appropriate.

Briefly the classes of processes and related problems to be discussed are as follows:

Inventory Processes

By an inventory process O.R. has come to mean a process involving one or both of the following decisions: a. how many (or much) to order (i.e., produce or purchase), and b. when to order. These decisions involve balancing inventory carrying costs against one or more of the following: order or run setup costs, shortage or delay costs, and costs associated with changing the level of production or purchasing. Some of the tools applicable to these problems are economic-order-quantity equations, and linear, dynamic, and quadratic programming.

Allocation Processes

These processes arise when (a) there are a number of activities to be performed and there are alternative ways of doing them, and (b) resources or facilities are not available for performing each activity in the most effective way. The problem, then, is to combine activities and resources in such a way as to maximize over-all effectiveness. The resources and/or the activities may be specified. If only one is specified the problem is to determine what mixture of the other will yield maximum effectiveness.

The tools which have come to be most closely associated with allocation problems are linear and other types of mathematical programming.

Waiting-Time Processes

These processes involve the arrival of units which require service at one or more service units. Except in very rare cases, waiting is required of either the units requiring service and/or the service units. Costs are associated with both types of waiting time. The problem is to control arrivals or to determine the amount or organization of service facilities which minimizes the sum of these two types of cost.

Queuing theory is applicable to problems involving determination of the number of service facilities required and/or the timing (i.e., *scheduling*) of arrivals. Sequencing theory is applicable to problems which involve determining the order in which units available for receiving service should be serviced. Finally, line-balancing theory is applicable to the problems which involve the grouping of work elements of the service activity into a sequence of servicing stations.

Replacement Processes

Replacement processes fall into two classes depending on the life-pattern of the equipment involved; i.e., whether the equipment deteriorates or becomes obsolete (i.e., becomes less efficient) with use or new developments (e.g., machine tools) or does not deteriorate but is subject to failure or "death" (e.g., light bulbs).

For deteriorating items the problem consists of timing the replacement so as to minimize the sum of the cost of new equipment, the cost of maintaining efficiency on the old, and/or the cost of loss of efficiency. For items that fail, the problem is one of determining which items to replace (e.g., all but those installed in the last week) and how frequently to replace them in such a way as to minimize the sum of the cost of the equipment involved, the cost of replacing the units, and the cost associated with failure of the unit.

Maintenance problems can be considered a special class of replacement problems since maintenance usually involves the replacement of a component of a facility or resource rather than the whole. Consequently, the same type of approach is applicable to both maintenance and replacement problems.

Competitive Processes

A competitive process is one in which the efficiency of a decision by one party is capable of being decreased by the decision of another party. The most discussed competitive situation in O.R. circles is a "game." A game is specified by a number of players, rules for play such that all possible permissible actions can be specified, a set of end states (e.g., win, lose, and draw), and the payoffs associated with these end states. The basic set of techniques applicable to this class of problems is known as the theory of games.

Another type of competitive situation is one in which bidding takes place. It differs from a game in the following ways: a. the number of competitors is not usually known; b. the possible "plays" are generally unlimited in number; c. the payoffs are not known with certainty but can only be estimated; and d. the outcome of a play (win or lose) can usually only be estimated. The beginning of a theory of bidding has just been started but already some useful tools are available.

Combined Processes

Real systems seldom involve only one of the processes discussed above. For example, a production control problem usually includes some combination of inventory, allocation, and waiting-line processes. Or, again, a problem of replacement of items that fail usually involves an inventory problem, and a bidding problem may require the allocation of resources among several possible items on which bids can be placed.

The usual procedure for handling combined processes consists of "solving" them in sequence. Even with successive cyclical adjustments we know that in many cases we fail to get a true optimum. Consequently, O.R. is faced with an increasing need to combine the abstract processes and construct models involving the interaction of several of the processes discussed here. More and more scientific attention is being turned to this need.

Further, it should be noted that the five processes considered here do not cover all O.R. problem situations. But they do cover most that have been faced in practice up to this time. We can expect, however, that an increasing number of recurring processes will be revealed and subjected to mathematical analysis in the future.

Finally, the reader should not be too influenced by the name of the abstract model. Inventory models are applicable to problems of cash, working capital, and personnel. Queuing models may be applicable to the solution of certain inventory problems. Imagination is as much a key to scientific success as any other mental quality. The reader will benefit most if he reads with an open mind and an ability to perceive analogies.

SUMMARY

It has been shown that O.R. grew out of the evolution of organizations in which the management function was divided into types and levels of management. The need for scientific study of executive-type problems—those involving the interaction of functional units of the organization—and the opportunity for scientists to attack such problems provided by military management in World War II combined to produce O.R.

O.R. is perhaps still too young to be defined in any authoritative way. A tentative working definition has been provided:

> O.R. is the application of scientific methods, techniques, and tools to problems involving the operations of a system so as to provide those in control of the system with optimum solutions to the problems.

In this text emphasis is placed on man-machine systems in industrial organizations.

It has been shown that by the use of teams (whose members are drawn from different disciplines) a variety of scientific methods, techniques, and tools is made available. O.R. has begun to develop a method designed to be effective for the class of problems by which it is confronted. Its procedures can be broken into the following steps:

1. Formulating the problem.
2. Constructing a mathematical model to represent the system under study.
3. Deriving a solution from the model.
4. Testing the model and the solution derived from it.
5. Establishing controls over the solution.
6. Putting the solution to work.

Although mixed research teams provide a variety of techniques and tools on specific problems, new techniques and tools have been developed and old ones adapted for certain recurrent classes of problems involving the following five processes: inventory, allocation, waiting-time, replacement, and competitive.

Each of the phases of O.R. and classes of problems will be discussed in detail in subsequent chapters.

A number of articles on the general nature of O.R. have appeared in the literature. Most of those which appeared prior to 1954 are listed in the excellent bibliography provided in *Operations Research for Management*.[8] Some recent articles of this type are listed in the Bibliography at the end of this chapter.

We turn now to some case studies which illustrate several of the important characteristics of O.R. discussed in this chapter.

BIBLIOGRAPHY

1. Camp, Glen D., "The Science of Generalized Strategies and Tactics," *Textile Res. J.*, *XXV*, no. 7, 629–634 (July 1955).
2. Herrmann, Cyril C., and Magee, John F., "Operations Research for Management," *Harv. Busin. Rev.*, *31*, no. 4, 100–112 (July–Aug. 1953).
3. Hurni, M. L., "Observations on Operations Research," *J. Opns. Res. Soc. Am.*, *2*, no. 3, 234–248 (Aug. 1954).
4. ———, *The Purpose of Operations Research and Synthesis in Modern Business*, Management Consultation Service, General Electric Co., New York, June 24, 1955.
5. Johnson, Ellis A., "Operations Research in Industry," *Proceedings of Operations Research Conference*, Society for Advancement of Management, New York, 1954.
6. Smiddy, Harold F., and Naum, Lionel, "Evolution of a 'Science of Managing' in America," *Mgmt. Sci.*, *1*, no. 1, 1–31 (Oct. 1954).
7. Solow, Herbert, "Operations Research in Business," *Fortune*, *LIII*, no. 2, 128 ff. (Feb. 1956).
8. Trefethen, Florence N., "A History of Operations Research," in Joseph F. McCloskey and Florence N. Trefethen (eds.), *Operations Research for Management*, The Johns Hopkins Press, Baltimore, 1954.

Chapter 2

An Operations Research Study of a System as a Whole

INTRODUCTION

In the presentation of this case study emphasis is placed on the inter-relations between phases of an industrial process and the significance of these relations in research directed toward solving an executive-type problem.

Few managers or researchers would disagree in principle with the systems approach to problems. There is, however, an unfortunate dis-crepancy between principle and practice. The usual pressures on an executive generally preclude an examination of all the ramifications of his decisions. Even when time permits, however, the executive seldom has a systematic method for assuring himself that he has examined all the implications of a proposed solution to a problem.

The research methods discussed in this text (particularly in Parts II, III, and IX) are designed to provide over-all solutions to executive-type problems. The details of these methods are not considered in the presentation of this case, which is designed to illustrate the systems approach in only a general way.

This presentation, however, has another purpose. In the detailed discussions of methods, techniques, and tools which follow, it is con-venient to have a case to which to refer for illustrative purposes. Con-sequently, more detail is provided in this discussion than would be required if the purpose were only to illustrate the systems approach. Much of the detail is included in order to provide a reference point for subsequent discussions.

THE NATURE OF THE COMPANY AND THE O.R. TEAM

Let us begin with a description of the company involved. The company is known primarily for its production of a machine tool used in the manufacture of metal goods. It is the world's largest producer of this type of machine and produces more than 50 per cent of the total national output. The company also produces several other types of machines, some related and others unrelated to its major product. The selling price of the various models of the major product ranges between $10,000 and $40,000. At the time of this study the company did a total annual business of approximately $50,000,000. Employment in its two plants was about 3500. Employment was higher during the war, but even during the study (1952–1953) it was nearly at plant peak capacity.

At the initial meeting of company executives and members of Case's O.R. Group, the executives indicated that they were primarily interested in finding out whether O.R. could be applied to their operations. Although they did not want to specify a problem on which to begin, there was one in particular which concerned them. We need not consider this problem in detail; it is important in this discussion only because of the reasons for which it was *not* selected by the O.R. Group. The problem can be formulated briefly as follows.

The level of production of the machine tool was relatively constant since there was a considerable backlog of unfilled orders. The plants were operating at virtually maximum capacity. Additional orders were coming in, but in quantities less than the plants' productive capacity. Hence the backlog was shrinking. If the market were to continue as it was, the company would have caught up with the backlog in a year or so. From then on it would be overproducing the tool if it maintained its then current rate of production. One of their secondary and unrelated products was being produced at a much lower level, and sales effort was being restrained so as not to sell more than they were producing. The company felt it could increase sales of its secondary product by increased sales effort. The problem raised was: When should the company start cutting back on production of machine tools and increasing production of their secondary product, and at what rates should the cutting back and increase take place? Management asked, in effect, how to optimize overlapping production patterns and sales effort.

The O.R. team asked that this problem be deferred for the following reason. The question asked assumed that the only way of increasing production of the secondary product was by reducing production of the machine tool. That is, the question assumed that the machine tools were being manufactured with maximum efficiency, or at least that production capacity could not be effectively increased. It did not seem wise to the team to base its initial effort in the company on such a strong assumption. Indeed, it was felt that, in order to understand the assumption, the researchers would have to know much more than they did about the company's operations. Consequently, the company executives and researchers agreed that a few weeks should be devoted to orientation of the research team—that it spend this time familiarizing itself with the company and formulating an initial problem on which to begin work.

A team of three was established. It included two members of the O.R. Group of the Engineering Administration Department of Case Institute and one person from the company. The company member of the team was an expert in financial research. He served as a sort of trouble shooter on the staff of the company's treasurer, and as such dealt with a variety of complicated problems involving every phase of the company's operations. Though he had had no previous contact with O.R., his wide experience and preoccupation with *methods* of problem-solving made him an ideal member of the team.

As a matter of convenience the team was located in the treasurer's office, though it reported directly to the executive vice president of the company. The treasurer provided liaison with company personnel.

During the course of the study the team varied in size. At some stages of the study it included as many as four researchers from Case, several graduate student assistants, and up to nine additional persons from the company. Throughout the study there was frequent consultation with other members of Case's O.R. Group, other members of the faculty, and a wide variety of personnel from the company.

THE ORIENTATION PERIOD

As indicated, the initial phase of the research was one of orientation. First, a comprehensive tour of the main plant and administrative offices was arranged. The team asked to see the company's organization chart. The company was not "chart-happy" and consequently there was some difficulty in obtaining such a chart. Once it was made available and questions concerning it were asked, it was found that there was not too close a resemblance between the chart and the actual control of operations in the company. The team needed to know, first of all, the nature of the operations in which the company was involved, and second, how control over these operations was obtained and maintained.

The team decided, therefore, to study the company as an organized communication system which controls a productive process (in Chapter 4 we will determine the conceptual framework on which such a study can be based). What, then, is the ultimate source of the information that flows through the circuit? It is the customer, the user of the product. How is information concerning the customer's needs transmitted to the company? Through sales engineers. The team began its orientation, then, in the sales department. It learned how salesmen selected potential customers, what type of contact they made with customers, how they reported their activities, how orders and forecasts were prepared, etc. Then examination was made of the processing of this information through the various sections of the sales department, and the manner in which the processed information was transformed for and transmitted to the production system. The team learned further how the information came to start the flow of raw material into the production system and eventually yielded a product which was shipped to the customer. At the end of two weeks, reams of data and forms had been collected. Several days were spent extracting the essence of this complex process and recording it in a "Control and Materials Flow Chart." See Fig. 2-1. It is not necessary, for our purposes here, to explain this chart in detail, but it may be helpful to explain one part of the "circuit" in order to illustrate how such a chart greatly facilitates the understanding of the information flow in a company.

First, consider the following verbal description of a part of the information flow. The Production Planning Department receives an assembly schedule each month from the Scheduling Committee. This schedule shows the quantities and types (models) of machines to be assembled in each of the next 5 months. For each machine model scheduled, the Production Planning Department has a complete list of required parts. Further, for each part this department has on file a card which shows how many are in stock, in production, or on order from outside sources. For any one part there are four possible situations which can exist: 1. it is produced by the company and is either in stock or in production; 2. it is produced by the company and is not in stock or production; 3. it is purchased and is either in stock or on order; and 4. it is purchased and is not in stock or on order.

Let us consider here only what happens in the fourth case. For each machine model scheduled the Production Planning Department prepares a list of parts which are not in stock. This list is called a travel-

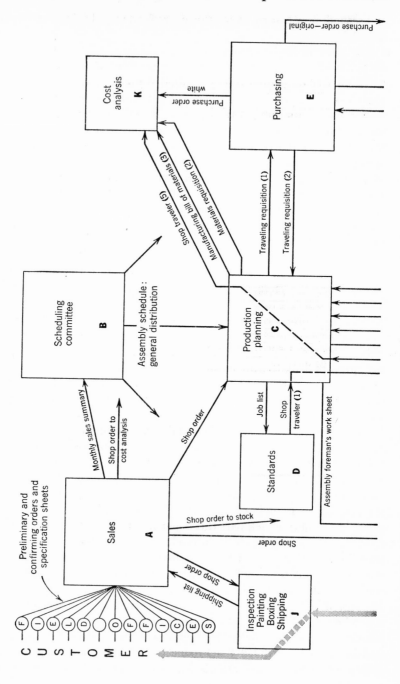

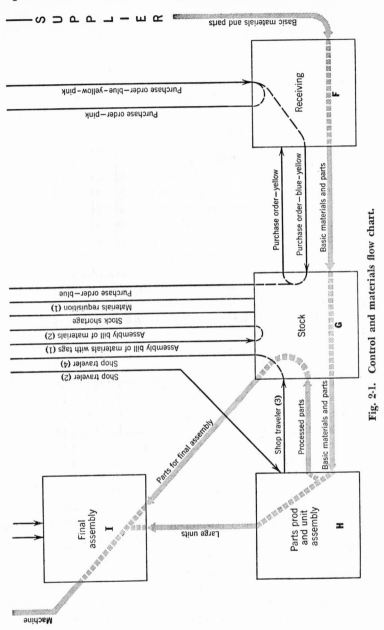

Fig. 2-1.   Control and materials flow chart.

ing requisition. It is sent to the Purchasing Department, which prepares seven copies of each order required and returns the traveling requisition to the Production Planning Department as a notice that the orders have been placed. This information is posted on the stock record cards of the parts involved. The original copy of the order is sent to the supplier. One copy goes to the Cost Analysis Department which eventually uses this and other information to determine unit production costs. Three copies are sent to the Receiving Department. The remaining two copies are placed on file in the Purchasing Department to facilitate checking of delayed deliveries.

When the Receiving Department receives the parts ordered from the supplier, it returns one copy of the order to the Purchasing Department. The Purchasing Department places its copies of the order in an inactive file. Its job is completed. The Receiving Department sends the parts along with its two remaining copies of the order to the stock room. The stock clerk receipts one copy and returns it to the Receiving Department whose job is now completed and recorded. When the parts are entered in stock the last copy of the order is sent from the stock room to the Production Planning Department. This department notes the availability of the part on that part's stock record card. The circuit is now complete.

Note how this description is represented in Fig. 2-1 in a simple manner that is relatively easy to follow. The circuits for each of the other parts-possibilities are also shown on the chart, along with other phases of the process. Not only was this study of communication and control used continuously by the team but the company's executives found it useful in discussions of organization and for orienting new employees.

In the process of collecting the information necessary for preparing the system analysis just discussed, the O.R. team began to realize that there was one problem that concerned every department. This was not surprising since the problem was that of inventory. There was general feeling in the company that inventory was too high. A few managers thought it was too low. But everyone thought about it. The O.R. team obtained records of the physical inventory taken at the end of the preceding year, and put the inventory records into table form to facilitate study. See Table 2-1. The vertical classification was by type of product, the horizontal classification by class of inventory. The inventory amounts in each cell were converted into percentages of the (approximately) $11,000,000 total value of the inventory.

Table 2-1 revealed certain things that were already known; for example, that 65% of the inventory was devoted to their major product. It also disclosed a not so obvious fact: 29% of the inventory was invested in parts in process and finished parts for the machine tool. On the basis of this fact, and the fact that an inventory problem seemed to be a good way to get into company operations, the team decided to recommend a study of the machine-tool parts inventory.

TABLE 2-1. INVENTORY BREAKDOWN IN PERCENTAGES

Class of Inventory

Product	Raw Material	Purchased Parts	Finished Units	Finished Subunits	Finished Parts	Subunits in Process	Parts in Process	Other	Total
A *	0.4	9.9		3.3	16.8	18.1	12.0	5.0	65.5
B	0.1	0.0+			0.0+		0.2	0.0+	0.3
C	0.1	0.6		0.4	2.1	2.5	1.0	0.2	6.9
D†	0.1	0.6		0.0+	2.6	2.5	2.6	0.2	8.6
E								0.2	0.2
F	0.0+	0.4	1.3	0.1	3.1	1.6	0.3	4.8	11.6
G		2.7		0.0+	0.2	0.4	0.2	3.4	6.9
Total	0.7	14.2	1.3	3.8	24.8	25.1	16.3	13.8	100.0

* The machine tool.
† The secondary product.

The team met again with the company's executives, showed and discussed the Control and Materials Flow Chart, and suggested the parts-inventory problem. The executives accepted the suggestion, and the team was "turned loose."

PLANNING PARTS PRODUCTION

Work was begun on the problem by asking company personnel what they took the parts-inventory problem to be. The usual formulation went as follows: What is the minimum parts inventory necessary to maintain our present rate of assembly and shipments? The team was dissatisfied with this formulation of the problem because it assumed that the margin of profit on sales is constant or, at any rate, if it varies the variations are not significantly related to the inventory level. If, as the team thought, the size of the inventory is related to production costs, it seemed that the size of inventory should be determined not as the least amount necessary to support a given volume of sales but as the amount which can be used to yield the greatest profit at the given sales volume. Such reasoning led the team to reformulate the problem as one of planning the production of parts in such a way as to minimize their total cost of production (including inventory costs). What is involved in the production of a part? First there are the raw materials the values of which are composed of purchase price plus freight costs. Then there is a raw-material inventory stage in which more money is invested in the materials. Next there is a planning stage in which the future of the material is determined. This planning (office setup) also involves a cost. Then the shop must be set up for producing the part. The material must be worked on, and it must wait between operations. Finally there is a finished parts inventory and a closing out of the paper work involved. On the basis of a preliminary study the team decided that raw material and in-process inventory would be little affected by changes in production planning. To simplify the problem, it was assumed that this was the case. Subsequently this assumption was checked. But more on this later.

This loose description of the production of a part had to be tightened. Such tightening was brought about by studying the current planning of parts production and by identifying and defining the pertinent variables in the process. Parts-production schedules were prepared monthly (i.e., there was a 1-month *planning period*). Not every part, however, was produced each month. Out of a total of approximately 18,000 different types of parts produced in the plant, about one-third of this number (6000) were produced each month.

It was convenient to have some time interval relative to which costs could be computed. The period of 1 year was selected. The mathematical model of the production process which was subsequently developed is general in the sense that the period used for cost computations can be set at any specified interval. The model and its development will be discussed in Chapter 7. There are three important cost variables in the model:

1. Setup and takedown cost per production run (variable cost per part).
2. Raw-material cost plus processing cost per part (fixed cost * per part).
3. Inventory carrying cost expressed as a per cent per month of the value of the part.

The meaning of at least some of these costs is far from obvious, so let us consider them one at a time.

---

* These costs are not fixed in any absolute sense but their variation is very small compared to those costs referred to as variable. As will be seen, certain raw material costs were, as a matter of fact, changed.

The Costs Involved

First let us consider the setup and takedown cost per run. The term "run" refers to all the parts which are made for a single setup of the machines used to produce them. The size of a run may vary. In other words, the run size is the number of parts produced in a continuous sequence of operations. The setup and takedown cost includes four major components:

1. *Office setup.* Before anything is done in the shop, the Production Planning Department must plan the production and the Standards Department must prepare necessary drawings and control forms.

2. *Shop setup cost.* This cost consists of the cost of actually adjusting the production equipment to perform the required operations, the cost of the scrap which is involved in making adjustments at the beginning of the run, and the cost of setting up the quality inspection procedure.

3. *Shop takedown costs.* This involves the cost of entering the finished parts in stock and performing the necessary paper work attached thereto.

4. *Office takedown.* This is the cost of the analysis performed by the Cost Analysis Section.

It is apparent that the job of estimating the value of setup and takedown cost for any specific part is not a simple one. In this case it required a good deal of work with a number of departments. This work had a good effect, for it raised an important question. The cost accounting system did not lend itself to providing values for this cost for each part. Shouldn't it be equipped to do so? The company's new comptroller used this question to reinforce his effort to convert the accounting process from one which presented passive historical data to one which provided active control data. The need for functional or operational accounting was highlighted by the team's efforts. The team was able to assist in a small way by showing how regression analysis could be used to isolate fixed and variable costs, and how statistical quality control techniques could be applied to the continuous control of these costs.

The establishment of methods for controlling, or at least detecting, changes in average values of cost variables is essential to every O.R. project. Any solution arrived at remains a solution only as long as realistic cost data are used. But costs change. Hence a procedure must be established to keep average costs constant and/or to detect changes quickly so that proper adjustments in the solution can be made. This can usually be done by statistical control methods.

Setup and takedown costs per part were then actually determined by study of the average time consumed and its cost in each of the departments involved. This study yielded the results shown in Table 2-2. It can be seen then that if the average number of production

TABLE 2-2. COST OF LABOR, BLUEPRINTS, AND PAPER

Labor:	
Production Planning Dept.	$0.87
Standards Dept.	0.20
Cost Analysis Dept.	0.38
Stock Dept.	0.10
Blueprints	0.10
Paper	0.05
Total	$1.70

runs per month is decreased there will be a decrease in production-planning costs. Hence, as pointed out earlier, the problem is not merely to minimize inventory relative to sales but also to minimize production-planning costs. These costs can be reduced by increasing the number of different parts produced per run, thereby decreasing the number of runs per year and increasing inventory. We now have a balancing problem: one factor (costs of inventory investment) weighs the scale against another factor (setup and takedown costs). This is the typical "executive-type" problem discussed in the last chapter.

By way of anticipation it was found that the setup and takedown costs are very important, and that the proper "balance" can potentially yield the company an annual reduction in parts-planning costs of approximately $40,000. This would not be a reduction in out-of-pocket costs because it was not planned to lay off planning personnel but rather to use the time thus gained to perform other tasks which could not then be done because of the shortage of personnel and space for additional personnel. The tasks to which they would be transferred would presumably yield further economies.

The second major cost category is a combination of two costs, raw material plus processing costs, which were originally treated separately. It became convenient to group them, since both are fixed costs per part. The first component is the cost of the raw material used in making the part. The second is the cost of the direct labor expended in working on the material, plus overhead. Overhead costs, which are included in the setup and takedown cost as well as in material and processing cost, were not easy to determine or allocate. A satisfactory estimate was obtained which expressed this cost as a function of man-hours of direct labor involved in the operations.

The third cost is the cost of carrying inventory. The team made a study of the costs involved in running one of the company's ware-houses. Account was taken of rent, heat and light, alarm service, wages, supervision, supplies, and depreciation. To these costs was added the cost of borrowing the capital invested in the inventory. This yielded a figure slightly more than 1% per month per dollar invested in stock. For safety's sake, in subsequent analysis a "pessimistic" figure of 2% was used as well as a 1% figure. The effect of so doing will be considered later.

Total overhead and inventory-carrying costs were, in effect, treated as costs which vary directly with changes in the number of parts produced. But these costs do have components which are fixed over certain ranges or levels of production. It was found, however, that the results eventually obtained did not significantly vary for alternative ways of allocating these costs. Consequently, the simplest way of allocating overhead and inventory-carrying costs (i.e., by hours of direct labor and dollars invested, respectively) was used.

The Planning Equation

A model of the production process was developed in which the total annual cost of production of each part was expressed as a function of the run size of that part and hence of the number of equal-size runs of the part made per year. This equation had four major cost components: 1. raw material cost, 2. production cost, 3. in-process inventory cost, and 4. finished inventory cost. Because of the brevity of the production cycle the in-process inventory cost was found to be only a small fraction of 1% of the total cost. Consequently, in-process inventory costs were not included in the equation and the resulting total annual *incremental* cost of production then became of central interest. The problem is one of finding a run size for each part which minimizes this annual cost. By use of an analytical procedure described in detail in Chapter 7, the following optimum run (or lot) size equation was developed

$$R = L \Big/ \sqrt{\frac{LPc_2}{c_1(2 - P)}}$$

The symbols in this equation have the following meanings:

R = the optimum number of parts per run
L = the number of parts required per month

P = finished inventory carrying cost expressed as a percentage of value invested in the part

c_1 = setup and takedown costs per run

c_2 = raw material plus processing cost per part

The Trial Run

When this equation was developed the team met once again with the executives of the company. The mathematics were not discussed in detail but the underlying ideas were. The meeting brought out a good deal with respect to the definition of costs. The executives decided that it would be worth trying out the model. The Production Planning Department requested that the lot-size equation be applied initially to 23 parts which they would select. No systematic sampling went into the selection of these parts. The parts were selected because they represented difficult production-planning problems.

Once the parts were selected, the team computed the total annual incremental cost of, and setup time for, producing each part using the existing scheduling practices, and also computed total annual incremental cost and setup time assuming optimum run sizes. The results indicated an amazingly large potential reduction in both costs and production time. But in order to obtain these reductions, it would be necessary to more than double the finished parts inventory. That is, by increasing run sizes and consequently by increasing the finished parts inventory, substantial reductions in time and money were indicated.

Another meeting with the executives brought agreement that the results obtained were of such a nature as to indicate the need for more systematic study of a more representative group of parts. A subassembly unit consisting of 112 parts was selected. A study was conducted to obtain an estimate of how sensitive production cost was to run size. The results indicated that the optimum planning (as compared with actual planning) would reduce incremental costs of production by 3.5 per cent, and would reduce setup time by 70%. Management considered these results significant enough to warrant further study to determine what would actually be involved in attempting to attain these potential cost and time reductions.

To some this might seem like the end of the role of research. But in fact it was in a very real sense "only the beginning" of the O.R. program. The most difficult aspects of the over-all problem appeared only when interest was concentrated on putting optimum lot-size production into effect. Indeed, this aspect of the problem is the most nearly like an executive-type problem of any we have mentioned.

Operations Research Study of a System as a Whole   33

At this point the O.R. team confronted itself with a series of questions the answering of which would assure an over-all solution to the problem of minimizing the cost of producing parts. The questions were as follows:

1. What type and quality of information is required to decrease production costs by use of the optimum-run-size (planning) equation developed, and what will be the effect of errors in this information?
2. What additional resources will be required before use can be made of the planning equation?
3. What changes in current operating procedures will have to be made before the equation can be used in production planning?
4. Can any of the operations which are affected by production quantities be changed so as to increase their effectiveness when the planning equation is in use?
5. What conditions, which were assumed in formulating the proposed planning procedure, are subject to change, and how should the procedure be modified if such changes occur?

By use of the detailed information on the system's operations (which had been gathered during the orientation period) these general questions were translated into the more specific questions which follow:

1. How much and what type of error in cost estimates will result in an increase in production cost if the planning equation is used?
2. How can the increased inventory be financed and what effect will this have on the company's credit?
3. How can the change-over to larger production runs be accomplished without creating shortages of parts during the change-over period?
4. How can high utilization of production facilities be assured when fewer but larger production runs are made each month?
5. How much additional storage space will be required and how can it be obtained?
6. How can production and processing of parts for replacement-part orders be most effectively integrated with the proposed procedure for planning production of parts for assembly?
7. Can raw-material-purchasing procedures be improved in view of the proposed changes in production of parts?
8. What can be done to minimize obsolescence of parts which will be stored in larger quantities?
9. Can assembly planning be improved in view of the proposed changes in production of parts?

10. How can the production-planning procedure be adapted to the situation (which is certain to come) when demand is not known and constant but is estimated and variable?

11. How should the actual determination of the production quantity for each part-type be made?

Before considering how these and related questions were answered, one aspect of the research findings up to this point should be noted.

It will be recalled that the problem raised at the first meeting with the executives involved increasing production of the secondary product and the cutback of production of the machine tool. The results of the first stage of the research showed a potential reduction of production time of the machine tool of approximately 150,000 man-hours per year. This time, if made available, would be sufficient to obtain the desired increase in production of the secondary product without affecting the production level of the machine tool. In effect, then, an answer to the original question was obtained by looking at the problem as a whole.

Now we turn to the second phase of the problem.

EFFECT OF POSSIBLE ERRORS ON PREDICTED COST REDUCTIONS

In the computation of economic lot sizes, setup and production cost must be estimated. These estimates were based on the costs of standard hours spent in setup and production, and were, of course, subject to error. This error could not be estimated accurately. Consequently, it was necessary to approach this problem "in reverse." The following question was asked: Could the estimated costs be so far off from the true costs that actually the present practice would be superior to the recommended policy if the true costs were known? Analysis showed that estimates of both fixed and variable costs would have to be an average of 10% less than the true value before the suggested procedure would be more costly than the current procedure. It was apparent, however, that if cost estimates were in error by this amount the company would be out of business (for lack of profit). The company could be confident, then, that they ran no risk of loss because of errors in estimation of these two costs.

What about inventory carrying costs? The same approach was taken to this question. Analysis showed that annual inventory carrying costs would have to exceed 42% of the average value of the parts carried in inventory before the recommended procedure became more costly than the current procedure. Since the company had already indicated that their most pessimistic estimate of this cost was 24%, no danger appeared in this quarter.

CAPITAL REQUIREMENTS AND CREDIT

An increase in run sizes and (consequently) in inventory requires additional capital. This requirement raised three questions: 1. How much money would be required to support the additional inventory and when would it be required? 2. At what cost could the additional capital be obtained? 3. How would the increased investment in inventory affect the company's credit? The company's representative on the team was well qualified to obtain answers to these questions. An estimate was made of the amount of money required, assuming business continued at the same level. Investigation showed that capital could be obtained at the same cost as in the past. Further, study of other companies and credit-rating procedures indicated that the company's credit was not likely to be affected by the estimated required increase in borrowed capital.

It was relatively certain at the time, however, that business would not continue at the same level, but would decrease. It was discovered that if business declined as forecasted no additional capital would be required. That is, it was determined that if the anticipated decline took place, and economic runs were scheduled, the level of inventory would remain at virtually the same level. Normally, with a decrease in business there would have been a corresponding decrease in inventory.

THE METHOD OF CONVERSION

The next major set of problems involved determining the procedure by which the shop could convert to producing larger production lots. That is, it was necessary to design a procedure for surmounting a "conversion hump." The hump occurred because the plant was operating at nearly maximum capacity, producing each month an average of 3 months' supply of each of 6000 types of parts. The proposed planning procedure required average production each month of 9 months' supply of each of 2000 types of parts. But in any month, production of 6000 different parts was required. Therefore, if 2000 were selected for production, the supply of the remaining 4000 parts would run out.

There were three possible ways of solving this problem: 1. to acquire additional personnel and equipment and thereby increase production capacity; 2. to subcontract production of some parts; and 3. to climb over the conversion hump slowly, using only available facilities. These possible plans were evaluated. Forecasts indicated that the markets would decline and consequently capital expansion would not be justified. Subcontracting costs were such that they would have involved additional production cost that would have resulted in a net loss during conversion. Consequently, a gradual conversion in the plant itself was indicated as the most feasible alternative.

This decision raised the following questions: 1. How should the conversion be accomplished? 2. How long would it take? First, it was decided to rank the models of the machine tool in terms of the likelihood of obsolescence and start the conversion on those least likely to become obsolete. Second, the potential cost reduction associated with changing from their current practices to scheduling optimum runs could be computed and the parts ranked accordingly. This ranking established a conversion priority list of parts.

To determine the amount of additional production that could be issued to the shop on any given month it was necessary to determine the amount and nature of the machine time in excess of that required for normal production. A concurrent and independent study by the Production Planning Department was directed to developing a way to use IBM equipment to "convert" a production schedule into estimated machine loadings. Since this procedure was not available at the time (but has since become available), reliance had to be placed on the planning staff to estimate the additional load that could be issued on any given month. Using this information, the O.R. team estimated that between 2 and 3 years would be required to make a complete conversion to economic lot sizes.

SHORTAGES AND STORAGE

It became apparent during the study of conversion that a production plan could not be prepared which would use all available machine time. Some machine sections would be idle part of the time while waiting for others to complete their work and send it on. The problem of scheduling machine loadings was further complicated by the fact that during the month, after the schedule was released, emergencies arose because of unforeseen shortages. High priority "shortage" orders were released to the shop and had to be superimposed on normal production. This shortage problem was a considerable one and caused great anxiety in the Production Planning Department. Through an apparently disconnected study, to be described later, the O.R. team was able to contribute to the reduction of the number of shortage orders issued to the shop. The problem of shortages became connected with that of acquiring additional storage space in this (at first) apparently disconnected study.

An increased inventory required increased storage space. The company was anxious not to rent additional storage space. Consequently, a preliminary examination of the storage of existing finished parts was made. It was apparent that little additional storage space could be obtained by revision of storage practices or by redesign of the physical layout of the storage facilities. This appeared to create a major roadblock in putting the new production plan into operation.

During the period when shortages and storage were under study, the O.R. team was asked how production of parts for repair orders could be planned. Parts were required not only for the assembly of machines but for replacement. A considerable repair order business was being "enjoyed" by the company. The practice was to add to the normal number of parts scheduled for assembly an additional number to cover possible repair orders that might be received during the period between scheduling the parts. Decision as to how many to add for repair orders was made by judgment applied to an examination of past orders.

PARTS REQUIRED FOR REPAIR

The team made a study of the distribution of repair orders for a sample of parts and uncovered two important facts: 1. The distributions of demand for parts tended to differ a good deal. 2. The variations of repair-part orders per month were considerable. A simple reorder point and reorder quantity procedure was developed. It was first necessary to classify parts by how critical they were to the operation of a machine. Class 1 consisted of those parts without which the machine cannot be operated. Class 2 was made up of those that limit, but do not prevent, use of the machine. Class 3 was composed of those that may or may not inconvenience the operator but do not limit use of the machine. With the help of those responsible for filling repair orders, acceptable risks of shortages were assigned to reflect this classification. Planning of Class 1 (essential) parts was to be performed in such a way that in only 27 out of 10,000 scheduling periods would one expect a shortage of parts in this class. For Class 2 the risk was set at 5 out of 100 scheduling periods, and for Class 3 it was set at 30 out of 100 scheduling periods. By the use of these acceptable risks and knowledge of the production cycle time of the part, it was possible to determine for each part a stock level at which parts should be reordered. Reorder quantities were to be determined by adding to assembly requirements the average monthly repair order demand for the part. That is, a special run of parts for repair would not be made, but repair requirements would be integrated into assembly requirement figures. This procedure was tested on a sample of parts. It was found that little reduction in costs would be obtained, but a very bothersome process could be made routine and the planners could thereby be relieved of considerable worry.

During this study, however, it became increasingly apparent to the team that the paper work and material handling procedure for processing repair orders had never been integrated with the main business of machine tool parts production. The team suggested, therefore, that a study of repair order processing be conducted to see if such integration was desirable and, if so, how it could be effected.

The suggestion was accepted and a special enlarged team was formed to do the job. In addition to the members of the O.R. team one representative of each section involved in the process was enlisted. A systems and procedures consultant was also employed by the company. The total team consisted of about ten people.

A flow analysis of communication in repair order processing was initiated. It was learned that one of two processes was followed, depending on whether or not all the required orders were in stock. The flow for each of these alternatives is shown in Figs. 2-2 and 2-3. These analyses suggested ways in which the flow could be simplified so as to reduce the number of form handlings and the number of pieces of paper required. But this possibility did not capture the interest of the O.R. team as much as two other aspects of the system.

First, the analysis showed that stock clerks withdrew repair parts from stock on order from the Order Department and only notified the Production Planning Department thereof after the withdrawal had been made. This withdrawal might deplete stock below the level required for that month's assembly schedule, and hence a shortage could be produced which might not be recognized until stock withdrawals were ordered for assembly purposes.

In effect, then, control of withdrawals from stock for repair orders was in the hands of the Order Department, whereas withdrawals for assembly were controlled by the Production Planning Department. This division of control was responsible in large part for the occurrence of shortages. It seemed apparent that Production Planning should be involved in the decision as to whether or not to ship repair orders and that in critical cases they should weigh the relative seriousness of delays in the filling of repair orders and assembly shortages. The current procedure implicitly weighted the seriousness of any repair order delay very high and assembly shortage very low.

Second, analysis of processing of orders for which some parts were not available showed that at the discretion of the stock clerk available parts could be withdrawn from stock, put on carts, and sent to a temporary storage area to await arrival of the other parts required for filling the order. This temporary storage ("A" storage) required a very large area. A possible substitute procedure would be to allocate these parts for shipment on the stock records maintained by the Production Planning Department and only make the stock withdrawals when all the required parts were available. Such a procedure would have two major advantages:

1. It would reduce, and eventually eliminate, "A" storage and thus make it available for finished part storage.

2. It would reduce the number of physical handlings of the repair order parts.

Out of these two considerations a new repair order process was designed. Changes began to be put into effect immediately by the various departments through the efforts of their representatives on the team. Significant effects occurred in a short time. Details had to be ironed out. To do this a subgroup was appointed which concerned itself with the detailed redesign of the system. The new repair-order-processing procedure is shown in Figs. 2-4 and 2-5. It will be seen that, by centralizing control in the Production Planning Department, not only was it possible to alleviate the shortage problem and simplify the paper work but this would then alleviate the storage problem for parts used for assembly.

Now let us return to the main line of development of the plan for producing parts for assembly.

Raw-Material Purchasing and Inventory

In evaluating the effect of the proposal on operations it was necessary to consider in what way, if any, raw-material purchasing would be affected. It was apparent that with larger production lots less frequent but larger raw-material purchases could be made. A study was instituted to determine if any price advantages would be obtained by the larger purchase quantities. Results were negative. For most raw materials the company could not take advantage of price reductions for quantity purchases because it was a relatively small consumer of these materials to start with. But it was discovered that by larger

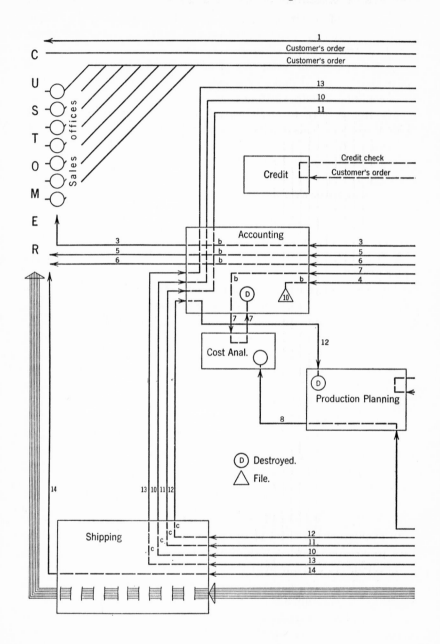

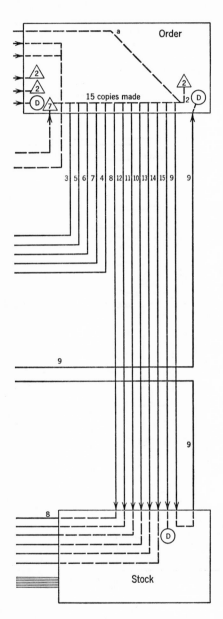

Fig. 2-2. Flow diagram of repair parts order processing in a machine tool manufacturing company when all ordered parts are available. Note that control of the process lies first with the Credit Department, second with the Stock Room. Part files are kept in Order, Stock, Production Planning, and Accounting Departments. The figure was produced by tracing the flow of numbered order forms in the plant.

100% Available:

1. Acknowledgement of order.
2. Order Dept. record.
3. Notification to branch offices.
4. Accounting Dept. record.
5. Original invoice.
6. Duplicate invoice.
7. Cost analysis.
8. Material requisition.
9. Follow-up copy.
10. Shipping Dept. copy.
11. Shipping list, Order Dept.
12. Shipping list, Production Dept.
13. Foreman's copy.
14. Packing list.
15. Request copy.
a. Held until receipt of no. 11.
b. Sent after receipt of copies 10–13.
c. Sent after shipment.

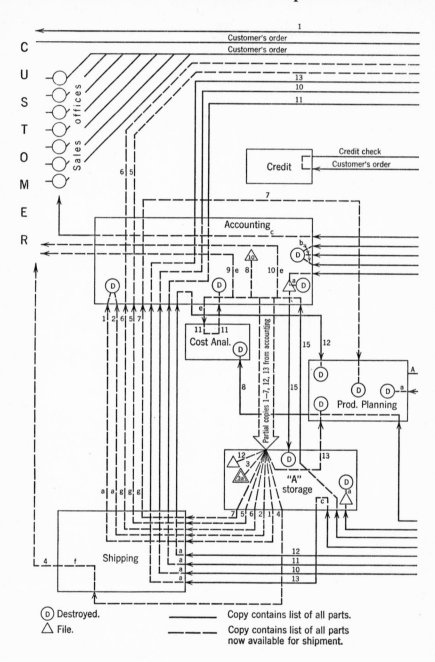

(D) Destroyed.   —————— Copy contains list of all parts.
△ File.   — — — — Copy contains list of all parts
                                                 now available for shipment.

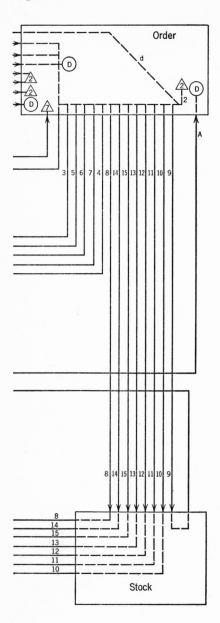

Fig. 2-3. Flow diagram of repair parts order processing in a machine tool manufacturing company when all ordered parts are *not* available. As in Fig. 2-2, the Stock Room has control of the process in this "Before" diagram, causing the communication faults described in text. Available items on partial orders are physically placed in "A" storage in this arrangement, pending availability of short parts.

Partials:

1. Packing list, Inspector's copy.
2. Packing list, Shipping copy.
3. Packing list, Stock Room copy.
4. Packing list, Customer's copy.
5. Packing list, Accounting copy.
6. Packing list, Order copy.
7. Packing list, Production copy.
8. Accounting Dept. record.
9. Original invoice.
10. Duplicate invoice.
11. Cost copy.
12. Request copy.
13. Incentive copy.
A. Promise sheet.
a. With or after final partial.
b. After receipt of no. 15.
c. After first partial.
d. After receipt of A.
e. After receipt of nos. 5, 6, 7 (dashed lines).
f. Sent with material.
g. Sent after each partial shipment.

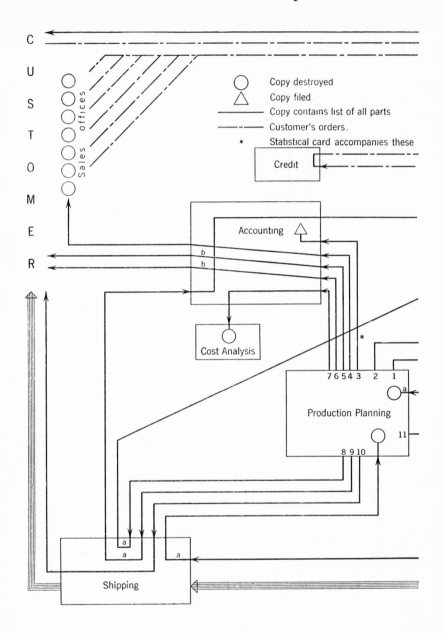

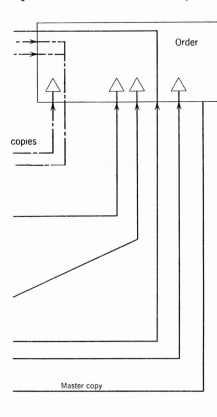

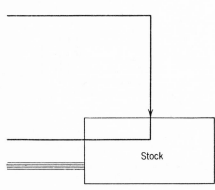

Fig. 2-4. Proposed improvement in flow diagram (see Fig. 2-2) of repair parts order processing in a machine tool manufacturing company when all ordered parts are available. In this new diagram control of the process lies first with the Credit Department, and second with Production Planning. Amount of paper work was then reduced, files concentrated in the Production Planning Department.

100% Shipment

1. Order Dept. record.
2. Acknowledgement of order.
3. Accounting Dept. record.
4. Branch office notification.
5. Invoice.
6. Duplicate invoice.
7. Cost Dept. copy.
8. Foreman's copy.
9. Shipper.
10. Packing list.
11. Stock Room order.
12. PPD Follow-up copy.
a. Sent after shipment.
b. Sent after receipt of no. 9.

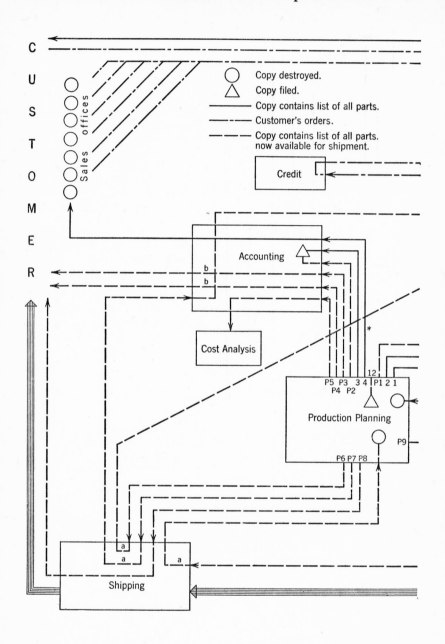

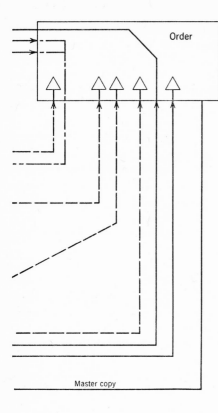

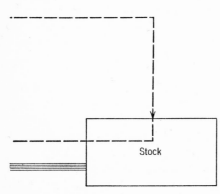

Fig. 2-5. A proposed (and installed) change in the system of Fig. 2-3 to eliminate faults evident there. Control is shifted to, and files are consolidated in, the Production Planning Department; "A" Storage is eliminated, paper work reduced. This diagram was designed using knowledge of electric control circuits.

Partials:

1. Order Dept. record.
2. Acknowledgement of order.
3. Accounting Dept. record.
4. Branch office notification.
P1. Order Dept. record.
P2. Accounting Dept. record.
P3. Original invoice.
P4. Duplicate invoice.
P5. Cost Dept. copy.
P6. Foreman's copy.
P7. Shipper.
P8. Packing list.
P9. Stock Room order.
12. PPD Follow-up copy.
a. Sent after shipment.
b. Sent after receipt of no. 9.

* *Statistical card accompanies these copies.*

purchase orders of some materials, freight costs could be considerably reduced. For example, the company rented trucks to haul large castings. A larger number of castings could be hauled at very little additional cost.

The most important result of the study of the effect of economic lot production on raw materials was the disclosure of the fact that if raw-material purchase lots were not changed, considerable reduction in raw-material inventory could be effected. This resulted from larger and less frequent withdrawals from raw-material stock. On material ordered every 6 months it was shown that average inventory could be reduced by 55%. For material ordered annually, the potential average reduction was 36%. This reduction had a supplementary value in that raw-material storage space could be reduced, and the freed space could be used for finished parts if necessary.

Obsolescence

The metal parts involved in this study do not spoil with storage but they can become obsolete because of design changes. Though this was not a very serious problem in the company the Production Planning Department was concerned with the possibility of this problem becoming more serious with an enlarged inventory. Investigation showed that the average lead time required to complete a design change was greater than 9 months, which was the duration of the proposed average production run. Consequently, a system was set up by which the Engineering Department would notify the Production Planning Department when work began which might eventually affect the design of a part. The stock record card of that part could then be tabbed to indicate that production runs of more than 3 months' requirements should not be authorized.

The Assembly Schedule

It was the practice of the company to assemble some of each machine-tool model each month. This meant that each month some parts of every type (except those used only on special attachments) were required. It would be possible, of course, to assemble each model every 2, 3, or more months. Such a change would in turn affect the pattern of withdrawal of parts from stock. Analysis showed that for parts which were used on only one model, average inventories (and hence total production costs) could be further reduced. Such reductions, however, could only be realized for a small percentage of the part-types since few parts are used on only one model. To take advantage of the small potential cost reductions the planning of assembly operations and parts production would have to be considerably complicated. The cost of this additional complexity was estimated and compared with the potential cost reduction in inventory. This resulted in the decision not to recommend any change in assembly planning or operations.

Scheduling for Variable Demand

Up to this point the study had been conducted relative to known requirements for parts used in assembly. It was only natural for the company to ask how economic lot-size computations could be used under conditions of at least partially unknown demand. The lot-size equation could be adapted for use under these conditions provided an unbiased and reliable estimate of future sales could be obtained. Studies were made to determine whether 30-day and 90-day machine sales were related to any national indices involving raw materials, related products, and general economic conditions. Although relationships were found, none would provide a reliable short-run estimate of sales.

Prior to the Korean crisis each sales office had compiled 30-day and 90-day forecasts made by individual salesmen. It was found that, of the two, the 90-day estimates were more reliable but were "biased." That is, the forecasts tended to overestimate the actual sales. By adjusting for this overestimation an unbiased forecast was obtained which had a mean deviation of about 18% from actual 90-day sales.

Market Trend Analysis

A futile effort was made to obtain a better forecast by using past sales to extract a trend which could be used to estimate future sales. The estimates obtained in this way were only half as reliable as those obtained from the salesmen's estimates. However, they were unbiased. It was found that future sales tended to deviate in a random way about the trend line. This fact suggested a method of forecasting changes in market trend.

Twelve successive 90-day sales figures (computed monthly) were plotted and a trend line was fitted by the method of least squares. The standard deviation of the 12 values about the trend line was computed. Two lines were then plotted above and below the trend line at a distance of two standard deviations. The trend line and the limits were then extended into the future. Subsequent 90-day sales were plotted each month.

If a sales figure fell outside the limits, a forecast of a change in market trend was made and a new trend and limits were computed on the basis of the last set of points which appeared to be in the new trend. If less than six points were available the computation of the new trend and limits were made anew each month until six points in a trend were obtained. The process was then continued until a point fell outside the new limits. See Fig. 2-6.

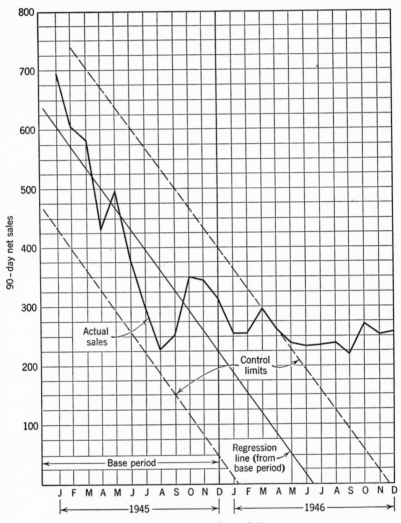

Fig. 2-6. Plotting of trend lines.

This procedure was used retrospectively over a 7-year period and every market trend change was correctly "predicted" before it would have been otherwise. On the other hand, no change was predicted which did not occur.

A member of the Sales Department suggested a modification which made use of forecasts as well as actual sales, and which expressed the limits as a percentage of the trend-line values. The trend line was plotted as already described. The forecasts (corrected for systematic

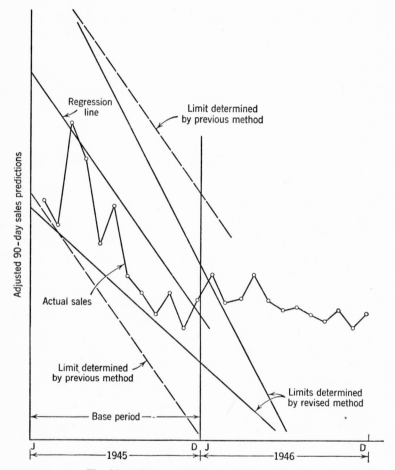

Fig. 2-7. Plotting of limits on the trend line.

overestimation) for 12 periods were then plotted and the deviation of each forecast from the trend line was determined. These deviations were expressed as percentages of the value (vertically above or below the forecast) on the trend line. The standard deviation of these percentages was computed. Then limits were plotted at three standard deviations from the trend line. The limits were not parallel to the trend line since they were plotted a fixed percentage away from the trend line. Hence they converged on the trend line as it approached zero, and diverged as it sloped upward. See Fig. 2-7. The trend and limits were projected into the future and subsequent adjusted 90-day forecasts were plotted. When a forecast fell outside the limits, a trend change was forecasted and a new trend was determined. This procedure predicted (correctly in each case) changes in trend from 2 to 5 months earlier than did the first method.

The first method of control has since been applied to another unrelated company's market (using a moving 12-month average) with equally good results. In both cases the method proved itself in current use as well as in retrospect.

Long-Run Forecasting

A study of long-run forecasting disclosed a useful relationship between one of the national indices and the company's annual sales. The question was raised as to whether annual sales could be broken into its two components, replacement and new sales. It was suspected that replacement sales have more stability than new sales and, hence, if these could be forecast separately a reliable forecast of minimum sales for the next year could be made.

Machine Replacement

Sales records did not show whether a sale involved a replacement. The O.R. team suggested a sample survey of customers to determine by interviews what percentage of sales over a series of years were for replacement of old machines. The company's executives did not feel the problem warranted the estimated survey cost. The team was asked to study the possibility of extracting the information in some way from available data.

The team began by asking the question: Why would a machine owner replace a machine? The type of machine in question does not undergo a complete breakdown; it does not "go out" like a light bulb. Its efficiency decreases and only by replacement of parts can this decrease be delayed or prevented. But, it was learned, the required amount of repair increases with time. Hence, it seemed to the team, machine replacement must occur when the owner decides that continued repair is more costly than purchase of a new machine. If this were so, it would follow that a reduction in repair rate would be an indication of an imminent replacement. This inference suggested an indirect way of studying machine replacement.

The team drew a random sample of repair part orders received in 1940, 1944, and 1948–1952 inclusive. As many as 92,000 such orders had been received in 1 year. From each order drawn the following information was recorded:

1. Year of purchase of the machine for which repair parts were ordered.
2. Dollar value of repair order.
3. Year in which order was received.

The orders received in each year were then subclassified by year of machine purchase. The total dollar volume for each subclass was then

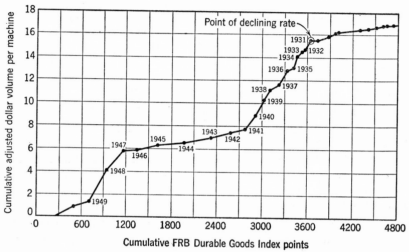

Fig. 2-8. Adjusted dollars of repair per machine by year of purchase.

computed and converted into "dollars expended per machine." This information was then plotted accumulatively as shown in Fig. 2-8. Each graph showed a year's machines for which repair order receipts declined and continued to decline. The number of years between the year sampled and the year of declining rate was determined on each of seven graphs. The results shown in Table 2-3 were obtained.

TABLE 2-3

Year Repair Order Was Placed	Number of Years Back to Drop in Repair Rate
1952	17
1951	20
1950	17
1949	19
1948	15
1944	16
1940	22

These results had little meaning until it was realized that "years to declining repair rate" was not of importance, but amount of use back to that decline was. Inquiry revealed that the Federal Reserve Board (FRB) Durable Goods Index was a good indicator of machine use. The years back to the decline in repair rate were converted into cumulative points of this index. Table 2-4 gives results obtained.

TABLE 2-4

Year Repair Order Was Placed	Cumulative FRB Durable Goods Index Points Back to Drop in Repair Rate
1952	3648
1951	3641
1950	3263
1949	3232
1948	2824
1944	2368
1940	2100

This table had two unexpected but important uses. First, it provided evidence for, and a measure of, increasing efficiency of the company's product. This was of no mere incidental value, particularly in renegotiation of sales involving defense work. Second, the observed trend when combined with a forecast of the current year's FRB index could be used to provide a priority list of years of former purchases which could guide replacement sales effort. Such a list indicates, in effect, where replacement sales are most likely to be obtained. These two results compensated, in part, for the fact that the analysis could not be used to provide an estimate (of measurable reliability and accuracy) of annual replacement business.

A number of other forecasting problems were studied, including one which revealed a close relationship between repair order business and machine sales. Such studies as these provided a firmer foundation on which larger lots of parts could be produced in the face of an uncertain future.

PRODUCTION-PLANNING OPERATIONS

The last phase of the study involved the development of a procedure by which the actual production planning could be performed. It was unrealistic to expect the production-planning clerks to use the lot-size equation. Consequently, a graphic device (a nomograph) was developed to enable them to determine economic run sizes without any computation by drawing two lines; see Fig. 2-9.

In order to use the nomograph it was necessary to have the values of setup and production costs and monthly requirements per part con-

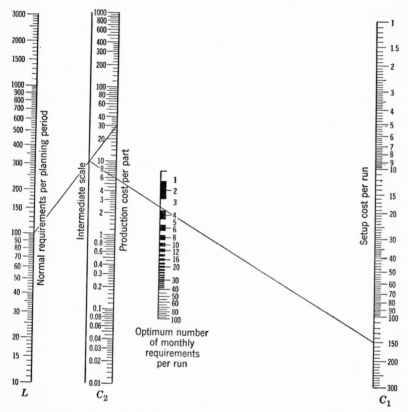

Fig. 2-9. Optimum number of monthly requirements per run. $\sqrt{(199C_1)/(LC_2)}$.
Example: $L = 100$, $C_1 = \$150$, $C_2 = \$30$. Then, optimum number of monthly requirements per run = 3.

veniently recorded. The stock record cards seemed a natural place to do this. These cards were in the process of redesign so as to adapt them for IBM use. It was possible to incorporate the information required on new stock cards. This, of course, suggested the possibility of performing the lot-size computations on IBM equipment. This was done easily, economically, and with considerable speed. The nomograph was retained, however, for checking parts which presented special problems.

CONCLUSION

In the case just presented optimization was initially obtained in a very restricted area. This optimum production-planning procedure, however, could not be put into operation until many associated problems were solved. The effect of the production-planning rule was traced through almost every function in the company. Almost every phase of the production department's activity was affected: production planning, manufacturing, stock-room procedures, and the assembly operations (through reduction of shortages). In addition, the financial, engineering, purchasing, and marketing operations were affected by the study and their activities were co-ordinated in a general over-all plan. An attempt to introduce economic production quantities without this look at the total system would either have been doomed to early failure or would have had disastrous effects on the company.

Chapter 3

Research Team Approach
to an Inspection Operation*

INTRODUCTION

One of the new factors in O.R. is the *team approach*. New and improved solutions to problems arise only when the problems are seen in a new light and when new techniques of analysis and solution are applied to them. The team approach assures O.R. of the necessary new viewpoints and problem-solving techniques. Each member of the team brings to the problem a different background and training, and each has at his command a wide variety of analytic techniques which have already proved successful in his particular field of endeavor.

In the case study which follows, it will become amply evident that the successes achieved were due almost entirely to the applications of the scientific method of investigation by a research team.

THE PROBLEM

About $4\frac{1}{2}$ years ago a large manufacturing company approached Ohio State University with a request that we initiate a research project to investigate the factors affecting visual inspection performance. The company was anxious to discover means for improving the quality and reducing the cost of the visual inspection of one of the parts which they manufactured for use in their product. The inspection task involved a 100% visual inspection of the product for flaws and defects, many so

---

*By *Loring G. Mitten,* Professor of Industrial Engineering, Ohio State University.

57

small as to be hardly visible, at a relatively high rate of speed. The large number of parts produced and inspected each year (somewhat over 2 billion) and the importance of the quality of these parts, both to the company's reputation and the satisfaction and safety of their customers, combined to create a problem of considerable magnitude and importance.

The project was accepted, and the company detailed their Director of Quality Control as project administrator. The University assembled a research team consisting of a research optometrist, a psychologist, and the author, an industrial engineer and statistician. It was agreed that the research be directed toward the discovery of those factors having a significant effect on visual inspection performance. Further, an attempt was made to arrive at some measure of the quantity and quality capabilities of inspectors.

THE FIRST PHASE

One year was spent in the University's laboratories investigating various aspects of the problem. The optometrist studied the correlation between visual inspection performance and various types and intensities of illumination, measures of keenness of eyesight among inspectors, and types of eye-movement patterns. The psychologist studied motivational problems, job satisfaction factors, and fatigue problems. The industrial engineer was concerned with the effects of various types of designs of inspection equipment and with the statistical analysis of the experimental data.

An imposing array of scientific techniques was used, ranging from physiological optics through aptitude measuring tests. The interchange of viewpoints and techniques among the three disciplines represented contributed greatly to the success of the venture. One of the most difficult problems involved in the whole study was the definition of a satisfactory measure of visual inspection performance. Those measures which had been used by the company were found to be generally unsatisfactory. Before the experiments were completed eight new methods of measuring visual inspection performance were devised. The previous lack of valid and reliable measures of performance had caused untold difficulties in earlier investigations of the inspection problem by the company and by others.

The studies showed that there were a number of factors affecting visual inspection performance, by far the most important of which was the attitude of the inspector. It was further concluded that under optimum conditions the inspection rate on this operation could be increased by 300% to 400% with a considerable improvement in the quality of the job being done.

With these results in hand, the research team and the company's co-ordinator made an in-person report to the company's top management. The company was urged to undertake a vastly expanded program of research in order to discover means for translating our findings into practical procedures for improving their inspection operations. The company's management, a very conservative group, was at first skeptical of the whole investigation, but by the close of our meeting they were highly enthusiastic and decided to proceed with the study on an even larger scale than had been recommended.

THE SECOND PHASE

As the next phase of our investigation, it was decided to undertake an intensive study of conditions and procedures in the inspection department in the plant. A variety of interesting observations resulted from this study, two of which are particularly important.

Detection of Defects

Since a number of the defects which the inspectors were supposed to detect on the surface of the part were quite minute, the company had equipped each inspection device with a magnifying lens. The logic behind this move was quite evident; when you have something very small to see, use a magnifier to make it look larger. The team's research optometrist was, however, to prove that the logical analysis of problems as complicated as this one is likely to be quite subtle. He discovered that every single inspector in the department was using the magnifying lens, not as a magnifier, but as a corrective lens. In other words, they were using the lenses, not to make the object look larger, but to relieve eyestrain. After study of the problem he was able to design a new lens which combined the effects of magnification and correction; at the same time the new lens reduced some of the eyestrain caused by the necessity for changing the eye's depth of focus as it looked from one area of the surface to another. As a result, inspection performance was improved significantly.

Worker Attitudes

The foregoing is an excellent example of the contribution which the scientist can make to the solution of operational problems. The facts so apparent to our research optometrist would probably never have been discovered by typical quality control and inspection people.

Another interesting case concerned the investigation of worker attitudes. Immediately after approval of the request for an expanded investigation, the team approached management for permission to conduct a survey of worker attitude among the personnel of the inspection department. They replied that they were not interested in worker attitudes—only in worker production. Since preliminary investigations had indicated that worker attitude was probably the primary determinant of visual inspection performance, the team persisted in its request. Management indicated that they did not wish to proceed with such a study because they felt certain that the workers would make the proposed survey an occasion for demanding higher wages. Thus, it became apparent that management's reluctance was not due to their indifference to worker attitude, but to their feeling that they knew exactly what the workers' attitudes were ("We're not being paid enough!"). Finally, management acceded to the team's request and it proceeded to conduct an attitude survey.

It should be noted at this point that attitude determination is a very tricky business, and one that should be entrusted only to competent professionals. The problem was complicated in this case by the fact that the inspection department consisted entirely of women. The O.R. team was faced, then, with the problem of getting the confidence of and determining, in as unbiased a manner as possible, the attitudes of a group of employees who management felt were antagonistic. The problem was finally solved in a manner satisfactory to all by assigning a young (and handsome) psychologist to the job of interviewing the workers. (He was the kind of young man who inspires the whispered comment among girls, "Isn't he just *too* cute.") Needless to say, with this man on the job, it was an easy task to gain the confidence of the women employees.

An analysis of the results of the interviews brought to light some most interesting facts. First, out of the 150 girls surveyed, only three even *mentioned* wages; two of these had volunteered the information they thought the job paid quite adequate wages, and only one complained that wages were too low. At the same time, 136 out of the 150 girls complained that the chairs were very uncomfortable. To say that these results were a surprise to management is a gross understatement. When they had recovered from their state of pleasant shock, they immediately had samples of a wide variety of chairs placed in the inspection department with instructions that the employees were to select the one which they liked the best. One week and $10,000 later, the entire inspection department was equipped with new chairs. It goes without saying that management and the inspection force developed a mutual admiration never before known in this company.

In this process, unfortunately, the research team had encountered a problem. The women in the inspection department felt that the young interviewer was in part responsible for obtaining the more comfortable chairs. He became a hero in their eyes. To retain one's scientific objectivity while being idolized by 150 women is a task beyond the capabilities of most human beings. Therefore, for his own good, he had to be sent back to the psychology laboratory at the University for a year; there he was given the job of watching rats run through mazes to help him get back his perspective and scientific detachment.

In addition to the complaints about the chairs, the attitude survey brought to light several other situations which, though they appeared to be trivial matters on the surface, were actually the cause of considerable employee unrest and dissatisfaction. This is an example of the way in which scientific techniques can, in the hands of experts, provide factual data on which management decisions may be based.

Training

The next phase of our investigation involved setting up a "pilot plant" in which we could carry out experiments under conditions approximating those obtaining in the plant. The team hired and undertook the training of a random sample of 12 girls. Although the inspector training program had not been slated to be a subject for investigation in this project, the necessity for training 12 new inspectors provided an opportunity to review established training procedures. Making use of the principles of the psychological theory of learning, the team was able to devise a new training program which was tested on half of the group of new inspectors. The results showed that the new procedure required only half the training time needed by the procedure then used in the plant. The new procedure was put into effect with the result that new inspectors are now productive and "earning their way" in half the time previously required.

A further and even more important result accrued from the use of the new procedure. The contract between the company and the union calls for a probationary period of a specified duration for all new employees. During this period the company has the right to discharge the employee for any reason whatsoever, but after the expiration of the probationary period the employee becomes a member of the collective bargaining unit and can be discharged only for those reasons covered by the union contract. It so happened that the old training procedure required more time than the length of the probationary period, and also it was known that performance during the training period was a very unreliable measure of "on the job" performance. Thus, it had been almost impossible for the company to weed out potentially mediocre and poor inspectors before the termination of the probationary period. The new training procedure changed this situation completely; there was sufficient time during the probationary period to complete training and to get a good evaluation of the inspector's capabilities through "on the job" measurement of performance. Thus, the company was able, over a period of time, to improve the general level of competence among inspection personnel.

Eye-Movement Patterns and Illumination

Another investigation undertaken in the pilot plant involved the study of eye-movement patterns. It is quite obvious that, if the inspector's eyes are not pointed at the spot on the surface of a part where a defect occurs, the defect will go undetected; if this occurs frequently, a poor inspection job will result. The problem was to determine exactly where the inspector's eyes were pointing. One of the research men at Ohio State University's School of Optometry helped us solve this problem by inventing a new camera which made it possible to determine, within $\frac{1}{32}$ inch, exactly where the inspector's eyes were pointing throughout the inspection task. An analysis of the eye-movement photographs showed that the average inspector was actually seeing considerably less than 100% of the surfaces of the parts which she was inspecting. This meant that, even if she recognized and removed all the parts that she *saw* had defects, she would be doing considerably less than a perfect job of inspection.

Based on scientific knowledge of the capabilities and limitations of the human eye, it was possible to devise a new inspection device and undertake a program of training the inspectors in the use of efficient eye-movement patterns, thus effectively eliminating the former difficulties.

Applying the basic laws of optics to the problem at hand, a new and improved lighting fixture was designed which, by insuring that the right amount of the right kind of light was being transmitted to the inspector's eye, allowed her to do an even more efficient job.

Varying Speed of Production

The team's investigations indicated that the difficulty of the inspection task varied with the percentage of defective parts in a batch. The team proposed that the conventional fixed-speed inspection device be equipped with a variable-speed drive, the speed to be under the control of the inspector so that she could vary the speed of the inspection operation in accord with the proportion of defective items in the batch being inspected and in accord with her own individual capabilities. There was considerable initial resistance to this idea on the part of the company. They feared that putting the control of the speed of the inspection operation in the hands of the inspector would give her an opportunity to cut down on production. Eventually, such a device was installed and tested. The result was an *increase* rather than a decrease in over-all production rate with a substantial improvement in the quality of the inspection job.

Motivation Study

Perhaps the most interesting aspect of the investigation centers around the problem of motivation. The other results which were obtained were facilitative in nature, i.e., they improved the physical and visual aspects of the inspection task to the point where the inspector could, if she *wanted to*, inspect at a much higher rate of speed and with greater accuracy. The problem was how to get the inspector to "want to."

The logical approach to the problem would be through the installation of some type of monetary incentive plan. This was the approach proposed and favored by management and such a plan was installed and studied. The improvement in the production rate was substantial, but the team was convinced from its capability studies that the inspectors were capable of achieving even higher levels of performance. The logic behind conventional incentive plans is simple and direct: more pay for more work. However, the logical analysis of this problem, as in the case of the magnifying glasses, turned out to be a little more complicated.

A review of the case histories and interview results from the experimental inspectors and those in the plant showed that only a small percentage of them depended on their wages as a primary source of support. Most of the women were either young girls just out of high school, living at home and working until they got married, or married women working to supplement their husbands' incomes. From a careful study of the value systems indicated by the data, it was concluded that extra time would be much more valuable to the inspectors than extra money. To test these conclusions a "time-off" incentive system was set up. A weekly production quota was established, and when an inspector reached the quota she could go home for the rest of the week. She received, of course, a full week's pay for her work. Under this system production increased dramatically, and a number of the girls were able to complete 5 days' work in 2 or $2\frac{1}{2}$ days. This represented almost three times the production rate normally achieved in the plant.

Investigation of the use to which the inspectors put their time off revealed that a number of new and powerful sources of motivation had been tapped. One woman, for example, wanted the additional time to spend at home with her children. The top inspector, who by far outstripped all others, was revealed to have a husband who worked on the night shift. It was deemed that no further investigation into the source of motivation in this case would be required. In short, it was found that, contrary to popular opinion, money was not the most important of the available incentives for motivating this group of workers. In their value system, time was more important than money and they were willing to work harder to get it. A detailed scientific study of the group brought this fact to light and enabled the team to use it to increase their level of performance.

The new incentive system, while extremely successful in increasing the rate of production, created another problem. The previously used checking and quality control system was not adequate to maintain the desired quality level in the outgoing product. Therefore, the team set about the task of scientifically developing a new procedure for checking and quality control. Through the use of some fairly involved statistical procedures the team was able to arrive at a scheme in which the average inspector would earn the greatest amount of time off when producing at a quantity and quality level which minimized the total cost to the company. The team was thus able to achieve that rarely attainable objective—a situation in which what was best for the worker was also best for the company.

CONCLUSION

This case study illustrates how a mixed scientific team has something new to contribute to the analysis and solution of management problems. By looking at a set of operations in many different ways an unusually wide range of controllable variables was exposed and subsequently manipulated so as to obtain considerable improvement in the inspection process. A "normal" study of inspection procedures would not have revealed such a multiplicity of "handles" to the problem.

Inspection is a procedure by which past mistakes are discovered. A more basic problem is the prevention of such mistakes. But the activity of the research team was restricted to the inspection problem by management. In the opinion of the team an O.R. study of defect prevention would have reduced the problem of inspection to very small proportions and resulted in a considerably greater payoff in lower cost and higher quality. In effect, the O.R. team was forced to suboptimize. Suboptimization is a deficiency, however, only when the researchers have the opportunity to optimize and do not take advantage of it. The restrictions imposed by management in this case were very real and the study represents an effective exploitation of the possibilities which were either left open by management or were opened as a result of the research team's efforts.

PART II

THE PROBLEM

One of the most far-reaching characteristics of the scientific approach to a practical problem is an insistence on deciding exactly what one is trying to do. . . . In how many practical affairs of the day is this essential enquiry omitted? . . . What, for instance, is Britain really trying to get out of the export drive? . . . What are Universities really training students for? . . . Such questions are admittedly difficult to answer. But it is usually possible to get somewhere near a satisfactory solution, and it is always worth trying. The method of approaching them must be two fold. On the one hand, there are certain very general considerations of value and ultimate objective . . . On the other hand, one must study what is actually being achieved as things are . . . Only by combining a criticism in broad philosophical terms with a detailed assessment of the facts can one hope to reach a sensible and practical formulation of the direction which development should take . . .[71]

There is an old saying that a problem well put is half solved. This much is obvious. What is not so obvious, however, is how to put a problem well. It has become increasingly apparent that the most productive formulation of a problem is itself a complex and technical problem. When a problem involves a system of operations—governmental, military, industrial, or commercial—it can seldom be given a complete and accurate formulation by those who face it. As a result scientists are often prone to feel that a problem is seldom what it first appears to be. The first case reported in Chapter 2 illustrates this point. The problem, as initially stated, involved the amount of production and sales effort to be put in

67

each of two product lines. The problem, as finally formulated, however, turned out to be one of increasing the efficiency of producing one of these lines.

In effect, the initial statement of a problem provided by management to an O.R. team is more apt to be a revelation of symptoms than a diagnosis. It is up to the O.R. team to provide an accurate diagnosis (i.e., formulation) of the problem with the aid, of course, of those who are involved in it. Such a diagnosis requires an intimate knowledge of the workings of the organization and its "control system." Such knowledge is seldom available in one place; organizations are generally too complex to permit individual members of it to understand its over-all operations. Consequently, the O.R. team, whether it contains company personnel or not, generally must begin with a systematic study of the organization, the way it operates, and the way these operations are controlled.

In Chapter 4, "Analysis of the Organization," we will consider some conceptual tools and procedures which are useful in analyzing an organization. More detail is presented than would be necessary if one's concern were only with a preliminary analysis of the organization. This additional detail is provided for two reasons:

1. In the initial analysis of an organization, it may become apparent that effective decision-making rules, if developed by the O.R. team, cannot be successfully applied because either *a.* the organization's communication system cannot provide the necessary information to the decision makers, or *b.* control of the area under study is broken up into decentralized segments. In either case the organization would have to be changed before any research results could be applied effectively. Such cases are not at all infrequent. An illustration of just such a situation will be presented in Chapter 4. When such a case does arise, the problem that must first be solved is a communication or control problem. The detail in Chapter 4 is directed toward equipping the reader in such cases.

2. In implementing the results of O.R., some modifications or additions to the organization's communication and control process are almost always called for. Hence, some detailed communication and control analysis is essential for putting results to work. It will be recalled that, in the case presented in Chapter 2, the storage and shortage problems were solved by changing the procedure for processing repair part orders and centralizing control for stock withdrawals. At this stage of the research, an intensive communication and control analysis was required.

In Chapter 5, we will consider a procedure for formulating the problem. It represents the author's conception of the best way to provide such a formulation. Seldom will the opportunity arise in which one can develop such a detailed formulation as is suggested. But it provides a standard toward which we believe the researchers should push their problem formulation.

One aspect of problem formulation, the weighting of objectives, requires a chapter of its own. Chapter 6 is devoted to this subject. The method of evaluating objectives presented there has other uses in research, several illustrations of which are provided in the chapter.

Chapter 4

Analysis of
the Organization

BASIC ASSUMPTIONS

During the late 1930's and the 1940's groups of physiologists, electrical engineers, mathematicians, and social scientists began to work on organizational problems. Many organizations, they found, had similar characteristics. For example, human beings seemed to suffer many faults in their nervous systems which were analogous to faults appearing in electric gun-control mechanisms. Diagrams (Fig. 4-1) which biologists and physiologists had drawn of the human nervous system even looked like electric circuit diagrams.

Groups of such scientists, working in Cambridge, Massachusetts, and elsewhere, soon saw the possibility of developing a generalized organization or control theory that would cut across scientific disciplines. Professor Norbert Wiener summarized the work of these mixed discipline groups in 1948. In his book *Cybernetics. Control and Communication in the Animal and the Machine*,[74] he said that *communication* (or information transfer) and *control* were essential processes in the functioning of an organization. Professor Wiener used information as a general concept, meaning any sign or signal which the organization could employ for the direction of its activities. The information might be an electric impulse, a chemical reaction, or a written message; very generally, anything by which an organization could guide or control its operation.

Thus, the view of Cybernetics is that *a.* organizations composed of cells in an organism, *b.* organizations composed of machines in an automatic factory or electric communication network, and *c.* organizations

69

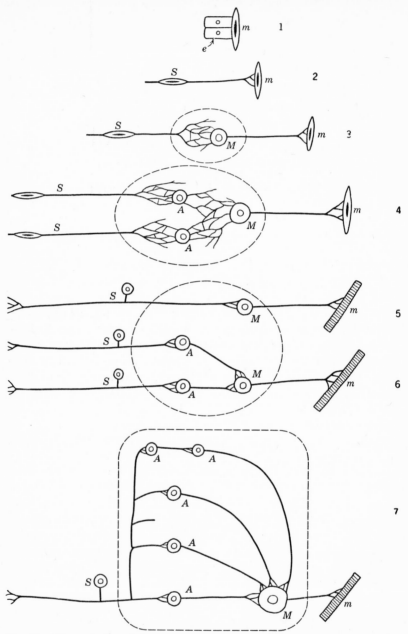

Fig. 4-1. The evolution of the nervous system. From Bayliss,[12] p. 468. Diagrams of the central nervous system drawn by physiologists look similar to electric networks drawn by electrical engineers. In general, any organization may be described as such an interconnection of parts. *Caption continued on next page.*

of human beings in social groups all follow the essential processes of communication and control in their operation.*

One can often analyze industrial or military organizations, even though they are complex, in the same communication and control terms. Such analysis can be directed toward the construction of a *communication (or control) model* * of the organization.

SOME GENERAL COMMENTS ON THE COMMUNICATION MODEL

A communication model is not mathematical; it is not used for accurate predictions or calculations. It generally takes the form of a diagram. Such a diagram enables one to bring together, from various fields of research, knowledge about organizations. The diagram and other knowledge can be used to suggest points of attack upon organizational problems, to sort relevant information about an organization from the trivial, to suggest analogies and similarities among various kinds of organizations, and to suggest, for test, solutions to organizational problems.* These hints and guides are often sorely needed by Operations Researchers, particularly at the beginning of a new project.

Since communication models have this practical importance, we will stress their use rather than give a detailed discussion of their theoretical development. The chapter is therefore divided into three parts:

* K. W. Deutsch.[32]   See also a discussion of the development of Cybernetic models in Deutsch.[28]

Continued from previous page

Diagrams of the evolution of the central nervous system.

S, Sensory neurone. A, Association neurone. M, Motor neurone. e, Epithelial cell. m, Muscle cell.

The dotted lines indicate the boundaries of the nerve centers.

1. Sponge.
2. Sea anemone.
3. Simplest form in the earthworm.
4. Intercalation of association neurones in the earthworm.
5. Exceptional, simple, reflex arc in vertebrates. Possibly existing in the case of the knee jerk.
6. Usual type in vertebrates. The cell bodies of the sensory neurones are in the dorsal root ganglia, instead of in the receptor organs, except in the olfactory organ.
7. Addition of higher centers, consisting only of association neurones, some of which are inhibitory. They form, as it were, longer and longer parallel or alternative loops between the receptor and effector organs. These loops may be followed in Fig. 4-2.

1. a simplified theoretical discussion of communication models; 2. a brief description of how to construct a communication model in practice; and 3. a discussion of the ways one can use the communication model, once it has been constructed. (References are provided at the end of the chapter for those interested in more detailed discussion of particular points.)

The communication model can be thought of as a glorified kind of fish net, spider's web, or network of nerves through which "information" passes or flows. The more formal material in later sections refers to a simple picture of this kind—in which various organizational characteristics are spoken of in terms of a communication network, of the information which passes through it, and of how both change with time.

CHARACTERISTICS OF COMMUNICATION MODELS

A model will be discussed in detail in Chapter 7. It is worth noting here, however, that a model is a miniature of, or compact representation of, an original. Usually models represent relevant points of interest in the original; these points can be combined so that the structure of the model and that of the original are similar. A set of rules may be included with a model to tell how it operates or how it can be manipulated.

The structure and points of interest used for a given model will change as the structure and points of interest in the original change. For example, if a road leading from one city to another is closed or abandoned, it may be eliminated from forthcoming editions of road maps of that area.[59]

Development of a complete communication model follows similar lines. Knowledge of three kinds is required:

1. Knowledge of a communication network which exists at a given time (a collection of relevant points of interest and their connection).

2. Knowledge of existing control processes in the network (rules of operation of the network).

3. Knowledge of how existing network and control processes change with time.

For example, the physiologist may describe a nervous system and its evolution by a series of circles and interconnecting lines (as shown in Fig. 4-1). An increased complexity of organization of the nervous system will require increased or changing interconnection of the nerve centers (as shown in Fig. 4-2). Our development of the communication model will follow just this pattern.

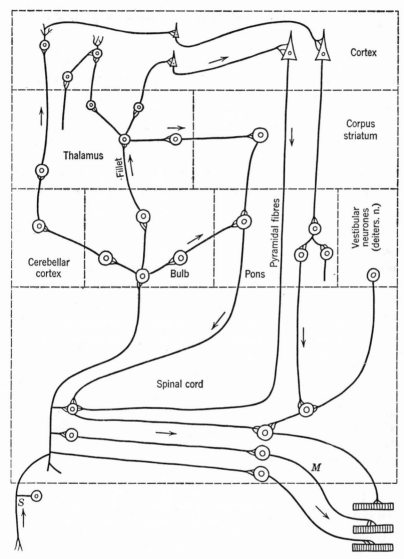

Diagram of mammalian central nervous system, according to von Monakow and Mott.

Shows the elaborate system of association neurones, arranged as parallel or alternative paths between the primary sensory neurones (S) and the final common paths (M).

Fig. 4-2. Mammalian central nervous system, according to von Monakow and Mott. From Bayliss,[12] p. 478. This is a further development of the diagrams shown in Fig. 4-1. Note the increased complexity of interconnection associated with the more refined nervous system.

THE COMMUNICATION MODEL DIAGRAM

An organization can be thought of as a group of elements (divisions in a company, operating units in a machine, people in a social group) which are in some way tied together through their communication with each other, i.e., through their letters, their phone calls, a flow of material, their division of labor, personal conversation, and the like.

If a diagram is drawn showing how communication takes place between various elements of an organization (e.g., if written material orders are traced within a manufacturing organization as they are sent from one department to another), and if the diagram also indicates communication between the organization and the outside world (e.g., if one maps the pathways through which sales orders are solicited by the company and also maps the pathways through which orders are sent back), a picture results which describes, at least in part, what the organization is doing.

The communication diagram will look—on paper—like a road map or circuit diagram similar to Fig. 4-1. Figures 2-2 through 2-5 show what happened when an analysis was made of the flow of paper work and material for a company selling repair parts for its machines. The lines represent the transmission of various pieces of paper, or information. The points (or boxes) represent places where the information is used, processed, or stored. One can get, very quickly, an idea of how complex the organization under study is just by looking at such a diagram. One can tell how the parts of the organization pictured are tied together.

The first thing to be determined about an organization is the existing structure of the communication network. The communication diagram will show this.

INTERNAL PROCESSES IN THE ORGANIZATION: HOW IT IS CONTROLLED

Organizations—companies, groups of parts in a machine, the functional elements of the human body—operate together in a communication network, but they also exhibit another characteristic: the elements of an organization operate together to reach or maintain an external goal (or its goal-image within the organization).* For the purpose of

---

* The definition of goal used by Wiener is the one meant here. For a full and important discussion, see ref. 57. Quoting from this paper: If we divide behavior into active and passive, then "Active behavior may be subdivided into two classes: purposeless (or random) and purposeful. The term purposeful is meant to denote

discussing communication models (in a simplified manner), a goal may be defined as the operating standard in use by the organization at a given time. A goal is a bench mark one aims for or tries to keep close to at a given time. For example, a shop foreman is given a production goal for the week; the accounting department will set up standard costs, etc. Such goals are fairly simple. The organization may also have more complex goals, or a whole set of simple and complex goals. The simplicity, or complexity, of the operating goal or set of goals— and the way they are used by the organization—permits one to rank organizations by their ability to handle information and "make up their own minds."

THE SIMPLE TRANSFORMATION UNIT

The elementary organization has its directions given to it continuously from an external source. It can find no goal of its own, so it

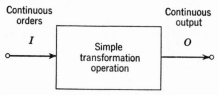

Fig. 4-3. A simple transformation unit. Continuous action is produced by a continuous series of orders. The unit has no goal of its own. An example: a gear train.

must be told what to do all the time; it cannot be left alone. Such organizations correspond to simple units of mechanical or electric trans-

---

that the act or behavior may be interpreted as directed to the attainment of a goal —i.e. to a final condition in which the behaving object reaches a definite correlation in time or space with respect to another object or event. Purposeless behavior then is that which is not interpreted as directed to a goal." The important restriction involved in this definition of goal is stated later in the paper: ". . . We have restricted the connotation of teleological behavior by applying this designation only to purposeful reactions which are controlled by the error of the reaction—i.e. by the difference between the state of the behaving object at any time and the final state interpreted as the purpose. Teleological behavior thus becomes synonymous with behavior controlled by negative feedback, and gains therefore in precision by a sufficiently restrained connotation."

Although this chapter will not discuss purposeful versus nonpurposeful behavior (or the philosophical issue of determinism versus free will), the subject was a fundamental one in the development of Cybernetics. (Understanding of this chapter may be aided by reading the original paper.[57]) The interested reader will also find elaboration of the subject in refs. 22, 34, 58, and 69.

formation (gear trains, amplifiers, etc.) that might be shown diagrammatically as in Fig. 4-3. The three fundamental processes in the link are: 1. *reception;* 2. *conduction,* processing or transformation; and 3. *output transmission* (effector action). A simple industrial transformation takes place, for instance, when a sales order is transformed into an invoice.

THE SIMPLE SORTING SYSTEM

Another elementary organization is the sorter, like a lemon grater or gravel sifter. A decision or sorting operation is built into the unit by its designer; the sorter also has to be fed continuously by an external operator. One input (say a load of gravel) can yield two or more different outputs (such as different sizes of gravel). A simple organization of this type might be diagrammed as in Fig. 4-4. It is similar to

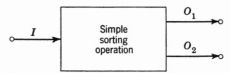

Fig. 4-4. A simple sorting unit. Two outputs are obtained from a single input. Rules for sorting (or decision) are built into the unit. The unit performs simple search and recognition operations common to more complicated processes.

Fig. 4-3 but somewhat more complex. The most familiar sorting operation in business occurs in the mail room.

Note that the sorting unit, in effect, makes a decision, the criteria for which are built into the unit. The gravel sorter must have built into it different sizes of mesh for sifting.

SIMPLE GOAL-MAINTAINING UNITS: CONTROL

The simplest type of organization which can, in some sense, control itself is characterized by its ability to monitor its own operation against an external goal. This type of unit is given one order and is left to carry that order out. An example of a purely mechanical goal-maintaining device is the governor of a steam engine (Fig. 4-5), which serves to regulate the engine's velocity under varying conditions of load. A desired velocity is set into the governor; the device seeks to maintain it.

In general, if an organization compares what it is doing with what its goal is, detects the error, if any, which exists between the two, and acts to reduce that error, then the organization *controls* its activities.

FEEDBACK NECESSARY FOR CONTROL

In order for an organization to determine if an error exists between what it is doing and what it intended to do to meet its goal, it must monitor its own activities: it must *feed back* a portion of its output for comparison with its input or standard. If the feedback tends to reduce error, rather than aggravate it, the feedback is called negative feedback—negative because it tends to oppose what the organization is doing.* The steam governor is a *negative feedback* device, and in business the constant comparison of operating costs against standard costs (in order to keep operating costs in line) is a form of negative feedback.

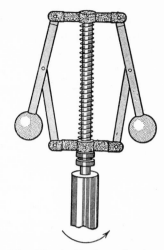

Fig. 4-5. A simple mechanical control unit, or governor, first treated by Clerk Maxwell. The governor seeks to maintain a steam-engine's velocity under changing load conditions.

One can explain the term "keeping up with the Joneses" in terms of negative feedback. The "Joneses" are what the sociologist calls a "reference group." Those of us who have such a reference group or goal (to equal the financial or social position of the Joneses) would constantly monitor our own financial and social position, detect the error or difference between our own position and the Joneses', and try to reduce the error, if possible, by appropriate action.

The nature of negative feedback is explicit if one takes an example from electrical engineering. Figure 4-6 represents a simple feedback circuit used in control devices called *servomechanisms*. Such devices can be used, for example, to actuate a radar antenna so that the position of the antenna matches the position set on a remotely located control box—in spite of wind resistance (load) at the antenna.

A certain position, or goal, can be set in the control box A, which in turn operates a motor or drive B to turn the antenna C. The actual position of the antenna, which may be different from the goal set because of, e.g., wind load, is fed back from C to A, and the error be-

---

* See Wiener's discussion of feedback, ref. 74, Chap. IV. Standard texts on electronic circuits and servomechanisms also provide discussions of feedback characteristics.

tween the position of the antenna and the goal position set is detected at A. A signal in turn is sent to motor B to reduce the error.

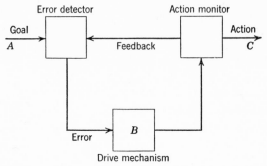

Fig. 4-6. The basic negative feedback circuit. The simplest organization which can control itself. Note the circularity of connection. A goal can be set at A, then the feedback circuit left to maintain that goal on its own. The steam governor works like this.

Mathematically, the action of the circuit is described by the following relation (refer to Fig. 4-7)

$$E_2 = E_1 \left(\frac{K}{1 - (-b)K} \right)$$

where E_1 is the input or standard set into the unit, E_2 is the output of the unit, K is the amplification factor or mechanical transformation

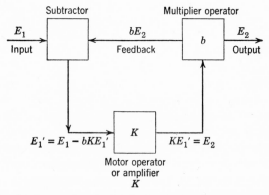

Fig. 4-7. The simple negative feedback circuit showing the mathematical relations which describe its operation.

factor of the unit, and $(-b)$ is the fraction of the unit's output E_2, used as negative feedback for error correction. In general, the greater the negative feedback, the greater the error reduction or stabilization of the unit. The unit can be arranged so that, instead of negative feedback, *positive feedback* is obtained $(+b)$. Error would then be aggravated when it occurred, oscillations would occur in the circuit's operation, etc. *Critical points for oscillation, stabilization, and error reduction are of particular interest to the control engineer, and although further discussion of feedback characteristics is beyond the scope of this chapter, the serious user of communication models should familiarize himself with feedback literature, such as that given in the bibliography.*

Control systems are in a sense circular in their operation, as can be seen from the circuit in Fig. 4-6. The feedback circuit and drive mechanism constitute a loop (or circle) of action. Systems which operate with negative feedback to maintain or reach a goal are said to be "goal-directed," and because of the circularity of action required by feedback such systems have also been called "circular causal systems."

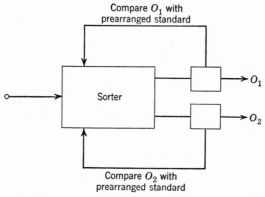

Fig. 4-8. The simple sorter with feedback applied. The output from the sorter is compared with the output desired (standard or goal) which has been built into the sorter mechanism.

The communications diagram can be studied for the presence of such circular feedback loops. This tells something about feedback and control in the organizations studied—the second point of interest. The Operations Researchers want to know, in particular, which processes are monitored, which are not; they want to obtain some idea of the efficiency of feedback loops, to determine if there is positive or negative feedback in these loops, to learn under what critical conditions negative (or positive) feedback may be useful or harmful. Scheduling and order processing systems, for example, deserve analysis with respect to stability, time lags, and feedback checks.

THE SORTER WITH FEEDBACK

If feedback can be applied to simple mechanical transformation systems (like the steam-engine governor) it is also applicable to the simple sorter. The various sorted outputs are then compared with standards for these outputs to determine if the sorter is, in fact, operating properly. The consistency and stability of the sorting operation is thereby improved. Figure 4-8 would be a diagram of such a system. The industrial inspection system of quality control, which checks various finished products against standards, sorting good and bad products into different piles, is an example of this kind of feedback sorter.

COMBINATIONS OF TRANSFORMATION AND SORTER UNITS

To obtain a more complex organization that is more versatile, various combinations of transformation and sorting units (with or without feedback) can be combined. This is roughly what happens when various parts or divisions of an organization are brought together. The most useful combination for a given job is usually not obvious, however, since the number of changes one could make in a many-part organization is inconceivably large. Furthermore, the combination of various parts may have characteristics quite different from that of the parts themselves, particularly in industrial or human organizations. Professor Wiener, who was pressed by several of his social science friends to extend his mathematical theory of Cybernetics to the area of human organization, hesitated to do so because he realized that the rapidly changing conditions of social organizations, the necessity for short-run statistics, and the interaction of observers would make precise results difficult to obtain.

In other words, as stated on p. 191 of ref. 74, in the social sciences

we have to deal with short statistical runs, nor can we be sure that a considerable part of what we observe is not an artefact of our own creation. An investigation of the stock market is likely to upset the stock market. We are too much in tune with the objects of our investigation to be good probes. In short, whether our investigations in the social sciences be statistical or dynamic—and they should participate in the nature of both —they can never be good to more than a very few decimal places, and, in short, can never furnish us with a quantity of verifiable significant information which begins to compare with that which we have learned to expect in the natural sciences. We cannot afford to neglect them; neither should we build exaggerated expectations of their possibilities. There is much which we must leave, whether we like it or not, to the unscientific, narrative method of the professional historian.

If the investigator is aware of these problems and he is looking only for fairly gross improvements in operations (as is often the case), some further discussion of complex organizations built up of the simple elements we have discussed may be helpful to the practical researcher.

THE AUTOMATIC GOAL-CHANGING UNIT

If an organization has several alternatives prepared for action, and also has the rules set up for applying one or the other of them *when external conditions change* (i.e., can *predict* the best alternative for changing conditions), it can control its own activities more effectively than can a simple feedback system. Such action requires a second-order feedback and implies that a reserve or memory of possible alternatives exists within the organization.

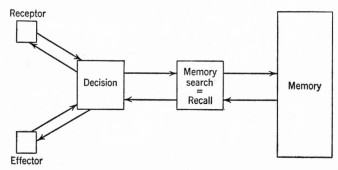

Fig. 4-9. **Feedback circuit with memory device. By adding a memory and more complicated feedback loops, an organization can have more control over its own activities. In this case a series of alternatives for action is built into the system if external conditions (detected by the receptor) change. An example is the automatic switching of a telphone exchange.**

An example of this type of organization—which can switch its standards for different courses of action—is the telephone exchange. The immediate goal of the telephone exchange is to search and find a specific number dialed by a subscriber. There may be many such numbers dialed during the day; the exchange must be prepared to receive different numbers and take different courses of action automatically for each one. (Figure 4-9 shows a simplified diagram of such a system, which is in fact a complicated sorting operation.) Another goal-changing example of similar type is the cat that chases the rat—not by following the rat's position at a given moment, but by *leading* the rat's position based on the cat's memory of how other rats ran in the past.

If an organization can control itself, particularly if it can change its goals, we call it an *autonomous* organization. The autonomy of the automatic goal-changing organization lies in its memory and ability to recall. The better the memory and the faster the recall, the more autonomous the organization is likely to be.

The storing up of information, which allows the organization to prepare various alternatives for action, is a process of *learning*. Learning may result in a reconfiguration of the internal channels of the organization, or communication network. The learning organization's structure changes with time. For example, the circuits in a telephone exchange can be expanded to include the "numbers" of more subscribers by rewiring part of the telephone exchange. Increased memory reserves generally require greater complexity of interconnection in the communication network. In terms of physiology, more memory means a greater interconnection of nerve cells. For a librarian, more memory means a greater cross referencing of index cards.

Thus, after we have found out what the existing communication and control processes in an "automatic" goal-changing organization are, we ask: How do these processes change with time? How do the inner channels of communication in the organization develop? Fall into disuse? Maintain themselves? Where is the memory of the organization located? What kind of information is put into the memory? By what manner is it stocked? What kind of information is taken out of the memory? What is the *content* of the memory; how does it change? Is the organization learning anything? Is it forgetting properly or improperly? What can it *predict* from its memory?

The operation of a system with a memory also means that certain messages have greater priority of transmission into and out of the memory than others. The possible courses of action have different priorities or *values* for application in different situations, and the researcher wants to know about these values to understand the action of the system. Again, reasoning in terms of the telephone exchange is useful. When ten telephone calls are received at once, the exchange must decide which to answer first.

THE REFLECTIVE GOAL-CHANGING UNIT

If an organization can collect information, store it in a memory, and then reflect upon or examine the contents of the memory for the purpose of formulating new courses of action, it will have reached a new level of autonomy. The mechanism that considers various goals and courses of action can be called the *consciousness* of the organization.* Reflective decision-making takes place in such third-order feedback systems. The action of the organization begins to approach what we would expect of an actual industrial or human organization. See Fig. 4-10.

To get a concrete picture of what consciousness is, imagine a person sitting back, relaxed in an overstuffed chair, speculating on what he will do next—on how he might improve his lot by completion of a certain type of research or sale of an invention, or on how his wife told him to put a new washer in the bathroom because the faucet leaks. He decides to please his wife rather than his pocketbook. He would then be using his reflective goal-changing circuits, or consciousness.

Conscious learning can be selective and take, from a wide range of external information sources, that information relevant to the organization's survival or other major goals. The consciousness may redirect the *attention* of the organization; make it *aware* of some happenings and unmindful of others. It can *initiate or cease courses of action*, based on incoming information; *investigate* network conditions in the organization; *search* the organization's memory; and *pick up deviations* between various actions and the goals which direct them—to name but a few of the activities of this third-order control center.

By taking such actions, the organization with a consciousness can direct its own *growth*. The possibility of *recognizing* valuable information received by the organization, or valuable combinations of information in the memory, permits the organization to practice *innovation*. Such abilities are highly desirable for most organizations and so, as an industrial investigator, the Operations Researcher would be interested in the consciousness of the organization (what the executives do or do not do).

Reflective goal-changing is of interest in the field of electronic computers, too. For example, computers and mechanisms which repair themselves must be conscious of their internal circuit faults. The action of such a machine "consciousness" would be like this: The consciousness circuits would become aware that other parts of the organization (e.g., parts or tubes) had broken down or been superseded by a more efficient design. The consciousness circuits would then direct replacement of the broken or outmoded parts with new or improved ones. Such action lies in the realm of possibility for computers—but industrial organizations do it every day!

The consciousness could be expected to show all the faults, in its

---

* See in particular the writings by Deutsch on growth and learning, e.g., ref. 31, Chap. 8.

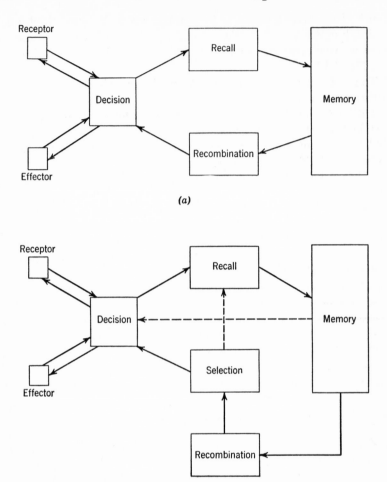

(a)

(b)

Fig. 4-10. (a) Additional memory refinements. If information in the memory can be recombined and new alternatives produced for action (by the machine or organization itself), the unit becomes more versatile and autonomous. This device makes simple predictions. (b) Additional memory refinements: development of a consciousness. If many memories can be combined, and if from the many combinations a few can be selected for further consideration, further recombination, etc., the unit will have reached a still higher level of versatility or autonomy. The dashed lines indicate comparisons of what is going on with what has happened in the past and what might occur in the future (second- and third-order predictions). In many organizations, these comparisons are poorly made.

operation, that we might find in humans or in executive groups which run organizations: delusions, faulty direction, misinterpretation of messages, lack of awareness of new opportunities, poorly defined operating goals, and the rest. Such faults are the subject of the last half of this chapter. However, another example here may be illuminating.

Consider a computer which could repair itself. It would have consciousness circuits to direct the repairs. Now if the consciousness circuits themselves were faulty and directed indiscriminate repairs to be made on the properly working machine, disaster would result. Let a drunken repairman run through a local telephone exchange and randomly unsolder relay connections, and the result would be similar. It would become virtually impossible to find all the newly created faults. The unreliability of electronic components and circuits limits the application of "self-repair" or consciousness functions in computing machines today. Similarly, executives in industrial organizations can cause disaster if they get out of commission easily.

The O.R. team should make the most use of organizational knowledge brought together by Cybernetics in the analysis of complex organizations with a memory and a consciousness. One of the functions of O.R. with its mixed discipline teams is to increase an organization's memory—by bringing in a collection of knowledge different from that of the organization's routine—and to aid its consciousness (the executives) in developing and evaluating alternatives for action.

A COMPOSITE COMMUNICATION MODEL

Figure 4-11 will serve to tie together these various ideas on communication and control in organizations. The diagram was proposed by K. W. Deutsch as a general communication model which might be used to describe complex organizations.* For the sake of discussion, it might be considered as a block diagram of a radar input gun-control mechanism which contains a memory device.

Column I of Fig. 4-11 contains circuits which operate as a simple feedback system with a fixed goal. The circuits consist of a receptor and an effector, e.g., the radar equipment for spotting planes and the gun-positioning and firing mechanisms. When a plane is picked up by the receptor device, the gun-effector devices are directed to follow the plane, or goal, and to track the position of the plane as accurately as possible.

* Figure 4-11 is adapted from K. W. Deutsch.[30] The Deutsch diagram may prove applicable to any level of social integration, including the individual.

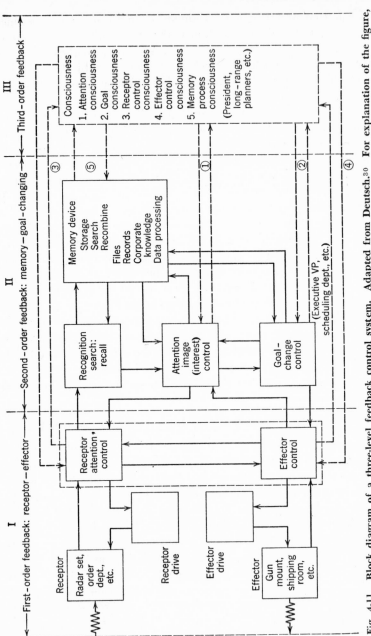

Fig. 4-11. Block diagram of a three-level feedback control system. Adapted from Deutsch.[30] For explanation of the figure, see text. Note that this diagram is a build-up of simpler units shown in Figs. 4-3 through 4-10.

The addition of memory and goal-changing circuits, located in Column II, allows the gun control to predict where the plane will be—to anticipate the plane's position rather than follow its position slavishly—and thus increases the number of hits the device can secure. Column II circuits are essentially *automatic goal-changing circuits;* the rules for changing goals are designed into the device by the communications engineer. So the action of the gun-control device can be changed (by the device itself) depending upon the type of aircraft observed, weather conditions, the predicted quality of the pilot, etc.

Column III, the consciousness, contains *reflective goal-changing circuits.* These were sketched in so the reader can see the development of the whole system, from the simple receptor and effector circuits to the complicated feedback circuits a consciousness would require. The consciousness circuits are dashed, because they are not yet part of normal electronic computers.

Again, for the sake of comparison, *analogies with industrial organizations* have been included in Fig. 4-11. Column I corresponds to the production-line–order-department combination which receives orders and fills them in a routine manner. Column II represents the domain of staff personnel, the file department, the semiautomatic or tactical goal-changing responsibilities of the executive vice-president. Column III represents the long-range planning functions of the president or the board of directors in a normal organization.

The purpose of this description of some characteristics of internal communication and control in organizations has been to give an idea of the *elaboration* that one can make on the communication diagram in order to indicate some of the analogies that can be made by using the diagram. The arrangement of receptor, effector, and processing circuits in Fig. 4-11 is also a fairly standard method of drawing communication networks. The receptor and effector circuits are to the left in the diagram, the processing circuits to the right.

Before continuing, it may be helpful to summarize what we have to work with in a communication model.

SUMMARY OF COMMUNICATION MODEL CHARACTERISTICS

The communication model should provide:

1. A map of the communication network of the organization.

2. Knowledge of the goal-maintaining or goal-directing processes of control in organization.

3. In complex goal-directed organization, some knowledge of goal-changing processes. The processes of innovation, growth, learning, the functions of memory and consciousness, and the concept of autonomy occur here.

In each of these categories, the Operations Researchers will be interested in the kind or content of information transmitted and received.

So, the complete communication model consists of a series of network pictures similar to Fig. 4-11 (in which the inner channels of the organization will change with time), plus accumulated knowledge on the processes of communication and control taken from various disciplines. This knowledge can be co-ordinated by use of the diagram.

HOW TO CONSTRUCT A MODEL DIAGRAM

The first step in the development of a communication model is to construct a communication diagram. Numerous methods have been

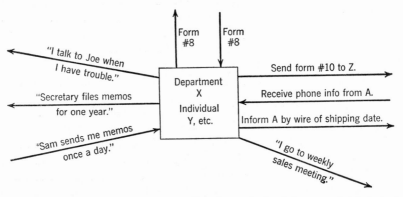

Fig. 4-12. Suggested method of recording data obtained from an interview of an element in an organization, from sampling of paper work or messages, or from direct observation of interaction in an organization. For further explanation, see text.

suggested for plotting flows of communication or interaction between individuals in groups, or between larger elements or divisions in an organization. We will outline a few of these methods, with references. At first the Operations Researcher will be more concerned with the origin and destination of communications than their subject matter.

The Interview

The object of a communication analysis is to find out who talks to whom with what effect, so asking people directly "who talks to whom" is an obvious point of attack. (From whom do you get orders? To whom do you talk most frequently? With whom do you consult when you make decisions on your job? Where does the paper work you handle come from? Where does it go?) The direction of flow is important; the researcher should note carefully the origin and destination of messages. Often inquiry about specific types of communication is more effective than a series of general questions.[52] Ask about the flow of specific types of orders such as materials, sales, etc. (For some practical interview techniques, see I. F. Marcosson.[46]) For each person interviewed, or each element in the organization examined, a set of notes should be prepared listing the forms, messages, or other important communications received by or transmitted from the person interviewed. The results for each person, department, or other element in the organization can then be shown graphically as is done in Fig. 4-12.

Direct Observation

When the organizations studied are very small or very large, the researchers may prefer direct observation to interviewing. Interviews may disrupt the communication process in small groups,* and may fail to reveal pertinent forms of communication in large groups. Observation is also a good check on the accuracy of interview responses.

Prof. Oskar Morgenstern of Princeton University cites the example of a large U.S. Navy warehouse operation he studied in Brooklyn, N.Y.† The warehouse stocked between 1 and 2 million items (about ten times more than Macy's or General Motors). The object of Morgenstern's study was to determine how these items arrived at the warehouse, and how the inventory might be controlled. Interviews indicated that most of the items arrived by train, and Morgenstern began a communication analysis of rail operations. After riding on a goat engine in the switchyards for a few days, however, he observed that although bulky items, which were the most obvious, arrived by train, the smaller items, which were more numerous and troublesome, arrived by truck. His analysis was shifted to truck operations, which, without this practical observation period, might have been neglected or not stressed sufficiently. Similarly, an actual inspection of the paper work transmitted from division to division in a large company may be

---

* Two forms of observation which have been diagrammed as in Fig. 4-12 are called *sociometry* and *interaction analysis*. A summary article on these subjects is available on pp. 562–585 in Jahoda, Deutsch, and Cook.[40] See also Chapple,[19] Bales,[7, 8] and Bavelas.[11]

† Informal Seminar discussions, Industrial Engineering 312, Columbia University, New York, Spring, 1953.

useful in finding out what is actually going on in the communication network.

Certain Types of Measurements

Just as currents and voltages are measured in electric circuits, quantitative measurements of "interaction" in social groups—and machines for obtaining such measurements—have been made in certain experimental situations.* The end result of such studies still tells us "who talked to whom." Interaction data, like interview data (Fig. 4-12), can be represented graphically.

Sampling

Sampling can be used in any of the foregoing methods of data collection to obtain, from a smaller number of observations, a picture of the communication structure to be mapped; or sampling methods can be used over a period of time to improve the accuracy of the analysis. For example, each day for a month the number of telephone calls between divisions in an organization might be sampled at the company switchboard. A sample could be taken of the flow of paper work between divisions of a company, rather than a count of all the items, to get some idea of the total number of messages passing from one division to another. (Details of sampling procedure can be found in Chapter 20.)

Difference between a Continuous and Discontinuous Pattern

A continuous flow of messages can be associated with routine operations of an organization. Such regular patterns are easy to trace through interview or sampling methods. Of equal interest, however, is the occasional "important" communication. For example, "To whom do you talk when you have trouble or emergencies in this division?" might reveal channels of communication seldom used, but of interest for many problems.

THE FINAL COMMUNICATION DIAGRAM

The communication diagram is usually drawn up in several stages. From the data collected, a series of small figures can be prepared and subsequently put together. A series of large layouts on wrapping or tracing paper will usually be required. The small drawings can be

* For example, Bales,[8] Chapple,[17] Christie, Luce, and Macy.[20] Deutsch[33] lists 14 measurements which could be made to describe organizations. Many of these measures are outlined in one form or another in this chapter.

shifted around graphically until they fit. The origin of a message can be connected with its destination by a line. The resulting diagram should look like Figs. 2-1 through 2-5, or in general like Fig. 4-12.

Time estimates (one or two men) for construction of a communication diagram (including data collection) vary from 2 weeks to 3 months, depending on the size and complexity of the organization studied.

CHECKING THE DIAGRAM

The researchers can verify, by consultation with several members of the organization under study, the accuracy of the network picture which has been drawn up. "Is this the right picture in your opinion?" . . . "Do you see any obvious faults or kinds of communication that have been left out?" are useful questions to ask. Such questions often turn up errors or omissions that may be included in an improved layout. Judgment must be used in evaluating suggestions made in confirmations of this type, however. It is necessary to check suggested "errors" to determine if they are really errors and not just faulty knowledge on the part of respondents questioned.

A USEFUL RESULT OF CHECKS ON THE COMMUNICATION DIAGRAM

It is necessary to get a point of agreement between the research consumer and research team on which future research can be based. The check does it. When future problem areas are discussed, reference can be made to the communication diagram in descriptions and explanations. Discussion will be based, at least in part, on an agreed-upon subject. Having a picture that can be pointed to, scribbled on, and drawn up in six colors is a definite advantage in this explanation process. The drawing is tangible. Often words about organization are not; they mean different things to different people. The communication diagram helps relieve some of this ambiguity.

HOW TO USE THE COMMUNICATION DIAGRAM

Methods of constructing communication diagrams can be understood best by noting the final use that will be made of the diagram. So let us look at the two main uses of the diagram for the Operations Researcher, then note some particular system faults the diagram may uncover.

Selecting or Relating Problem Areas

Many researchers feel that construction of a communication diagram leads them most successfully to special problems the organization faces.[21] The researchers may attack local area problems through the use of specialized models discussed elsewhere in this book (inventory models, queuing models, search models, etc.) and relate such problems one to another by tracing out one problem's effects, through the diagram's channels of communication, to other processes in the organization.

Studying Communication Problems Themselves

In this general view of an organization, no emergency exists. No faults are obvious. Still, we want to know if the organization is operating as effectively as it might. What improvements can be made? What meaningful problems can be formulated? What are the weak points in the system that might fail, given proper stress? Researchers often neglect communications studies unless an emergency exists, and yet—with a minimum of effort and expense—dramatic improvements frequently result from even simple communication analyses.

Take a simple commercial example: the strategy for selling Flexowriters. The Flexowriter is a modified teletype machine which operates like a typewriter and punches a coded paper tape. When a sales order is received by a company, for example, a girl can type up the order (with shipping address, stock number, and other data) on the Flexowriter. Her typing automatically punches up the paper tape. This tape can be used throughout the plant to produce bills, inventory reports, shipping manifests, and other forms automatically—formerly produced by hand—at impressive savings in time and labor.

The improvements to be made are essentially improvements in communication, and to demonstrate this fact the salesman draws up a communication diagram (like those we have discussed) of the existing organization. He also prepares a diagram in which the Flexowriter has been inserted in the system, simplifying paper-work procedures. Comparison of the two diagrams permits calculation of cost reductions expected.*

Operations Research is concerned with both of the general applications mentioned here, but since special area problems are discussed elsewhere in this book, the remainder of this chapter will be devoted to over-all communications problems in an organization.

---

* Communication or data processing analyses are even more important when large-scale computers are installed in the paper-work system. See R. G. Canning, "Data Processing System Requirements." [21]

AN OVER-ALL VIEW OF SYSTEM FAULTS

To get a general idea of what can go wrong in a communication system, look at Table 4-1, which shows numerous analogies of three organizational operations: 1. reception, 2. processing, and 3. transmission of information. Functionaries normally performing these operations, and some common faults associated with each operation, are listed.[43]

The point here is to find out what faults occur in communications systems, to note how such faults might be described in communications language, and to look for common faults in the three processes. Table 4-1 is a simplified check sheet for this purpose.

The problems of finding the cause of defectiveness and of designing the optimum organization for a given job arise at this point. The optimum organizational or communication structure for particular tasks or goals is not known, but remains a subject of intense experimental interest at this time. Thus, comparison of several fairly standard alternatives for communication patterns, usually by trial, is the method normally used to determine the best communication network for a given task. Similarly, defects found in a few standard communication and control networks can be used to suggest possible causes of and remedies for specific task-oriented or goal-directed organization faults. The processes of trouble-shooting and experimental verification are easier in the lower feedback levels of the organization, because goals are well defined, processes highly repetitive, etc.; i.e., somebody provides a production goal for the week and 1000 similar units a day are made.

AN ILLUSTRATIVE CASE

To illustrate the importance of organizational analysis we shall consider a case in which major organization deficiencies were disclosed by such an analysis. Their importance to the over-all project will be apparent.

This case involved a manufacturer whose product is heavy engines, a major component of trucks, boats, and certain types of industrial equipment. The company is a leader in its field. It has been in business for approximately 35 years and employs about 3000 persons.

The company was having increasing difficulty in meeting the delivery promises it had been forced to make in order to meet competition. As a result considerable time had been spent by supervisory personnel and management in expediting work through the various departments, including the assembly line.

TABLE 4-1. A CHART OF COMMON SYSTEM FAULTS

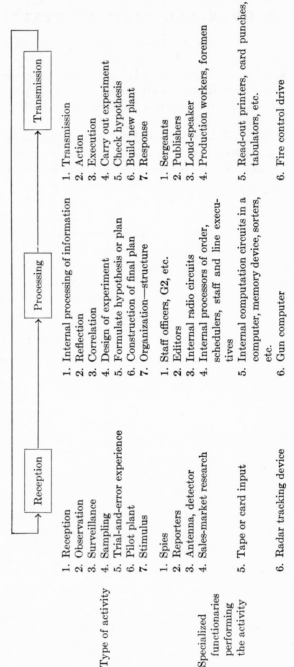

	Reception →	Processing →	Transmission
Type of activity	1. Reception	1. Internal processing of information	1. Transmission
	2. Observation	2. Reflection	2. Action
	3. Surveillance	3. Correlation	3. Execution
	4. Sampling	4. Design of experiment	4. Carry out experiment
	5. Trial-and-error experience	5. Formulate hypothesis or plan	5. Check hypothesis
	6. Pilot plant	6. Construction of final plan	6. Build new plant
	7. Stimulus	7. Organization—structure	7. Response
Specialized functionaries performing the activity	1. Spies	1. Staff officers, G2, etc.	1. Sergeants
	2. Reporters	2. Editors	2. Publishers
	3. Antenna, detector	3. Internal radio circuits	3. Loud-speaker
	4. Sales-market research	4. Internal processors of order, schedulers, staff and line executives	4. Production workers, foremen
	5. Tape or card input	5. Internal computation circuits in a computer, memory device, sorters, etc.	5. Read-out printers, card punches, tabulators, etc.
	6. Radar tracking device	6. Gun computer	6. Fire control drive

Usual faults

1. Attention improperly directed
2. Information collected in wrong form, cumbersome, etc.
3. Information collected too slowly or too fast
4. Reception insensitive or too sensitive
5. Receptor unstable
6. No receptor feedback
7. External jamming
8. Content of information changed improperly by receptor

1. Recognition faults
2. Storage inadequate, improper speed of store or search, etc.
3. Information processed too fast or too slow
4. Channels of communication missing, conflicting, overloaded, etc.
5. Change of message content improper when processed
6. Consciousness missing, inadequate, unrealistic, etc.
7. Value systems conflict, are circular, not realistic, etc.
8. Goals not set properly, are poorly defined, conflict, etc.
9. Goal locked, cannot change it regardless of incoming information
10. Poor "learning"
11. Specialized functions overlap, duplicate, etc.
12. Goal changer does not monitor processes

1. Effector improperly directed
2. Effector unstable
3. Improper effector output; does not fit environment
4. No effector feedback
5. Effector response too slow or too fast
6. Effector power insufficient or too great
7. External interference

This condition had been allowed to grow to such a degree that a substantial portion of the production became "hot" items, i.e., items requiring special priority in order to attempt to meet the delivery date quoted by the sales division. As a result of this, engine orders which had been received with adequate delivery lead time also would eventually become "hot" items, for they were continually being set further back.

Management felt that if parts inventories were adequate and balanced, then the principal cause of delay, shortages of parts, would be eliminated. With the assistance of an outside research agency, an O.R. team was formed and assigned to study this problem.

The team began with an analysis of the organization. Starting with the preparation of a sales order by a salesman, it followed the processing of information and material through delivery of the finished product to the customer. Out of the large amount of information collected, a graphic model of the communication and control process was prepared. See Fig. 4-13.

The average time associated with each phase of the process was determined. From this a total processing time was computed. This total was 50% greater than the delivery time sometimes promised. To meet even normal delivery promises, however, a considerable expenditure of money and effort was required. The paper processing and scheduling operations alone required a very large portion of normal delivery time. Therefore it became clear that the information processing and scheduling procedures would have to be changed if delivery promises were to be met.

The initial analysis of the organization had not provided the detailed information required to develop a plan for revising the processing of information and scheduling. Consequently, a more detailed analysis was made by backtracking through the entire process. Detailed graphic models of each phase of the process were prepared. This work revealed a number of specific causes of delay, the most important of which were:

1. Incomplete information on sales order.
2. Physical separation of offices in which interdependent decisions were made.
3. Decentralization of interrelated scheduling decisions.
4. Incomplete and out-of-date stock records.
5. Duplication of work.

The O.R. team then constructed a model of an organization which could perform the necessary processing and scheduling well within the

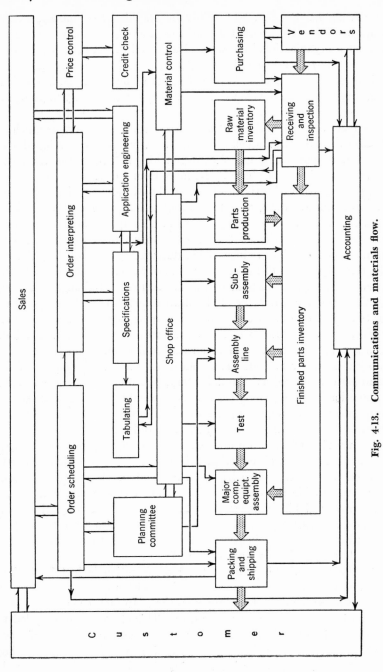

Fig. 4-13. Communications and materials flow.

time available. See Fig. 4-14. This was an "idealized" model because it did not take into account any of the practical problems associated with such organizational changes. But it did establish a standard so that subsequent study could develop a practical plan for reorganization which would come as close as possible to the "ideal." Such a practical plan was eventually developed, but only after considerably more work.

An essential aspect of this plan was the development of an effective stock-record system. The existing stock-record cards were as much as 40 days behind actual stock movement. A previously developed system of daily posting by use of card-punching machines was altered to provide records out of phase by no more than 1 day.

A consolidation of activities between the Materials and Engineering Departments was drafted. More complete information was called for from the Sales Department by means of a comprehensive order form. The physical relocation of the Specifications Group was designed to eliminate, or certainly reduce, much duplication of effort. For example, the preparation of the summary bill of material was shifted to the specifications writer instead of the draftsman. Originally this work required about one-quarter of the draftsman's time. To compensate for this effort on the part of the specifications writers, the applications engineers were put into personal contact with the specifications writers to assist in the preparation of special equipment items, so another duplication was removed. The plan called for the elimination of the planning committee and the daily build schedule was assigned to the Production Planning Department. No assembly could then be scheduled unless all the required parts were available. Data on availability of parts then came from the new stock-record cards.

By a revision in the use and method of compiling bills of material and summary bills of material, much of the paper which formerly reached the assembly line has been eliminated. It is planned eventually to provide the Shop and Inspection Departments with a machine-produced bill of materials which will indicate all major components, subassemblies, and the like. This will also serve the inspectors with a complete inspection check list and thus eliminate the specially prepared form currently in use.

At the time of this writing, the reorganization is just beginning. But while it is in process, more powerful decision-making tools are being developed for the scheduling operation. In fact, economic lot-size production of parts is well under way. This start has already led to an appropriate build-up of inventory. The number of high-priority-parts-production orders has significantly decreased and setup time has been reduced. Much needed machine time has already been made

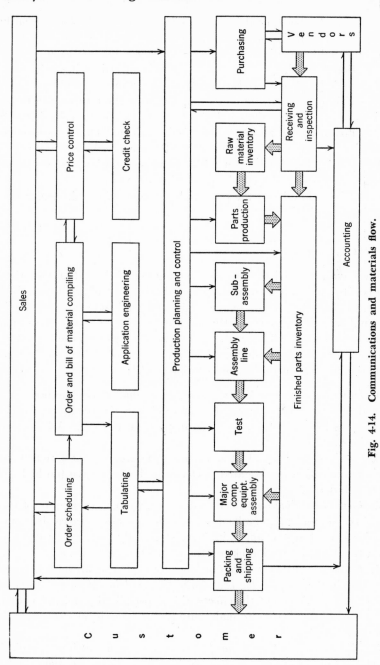

Fig. 4-14. Communications and materials flow.

available and is being used to good advantage since sales have recently increased by a significant amount.

Completed reorganization and the use of the new decision rules in production scheduling will yield considerable annual savings. The use of economic lot sizes alone is conservatively estimated to yield savings in the vicinity of $250,000. Also important to the company in terms of its long-range objectives is the fact that customer service is being and will continue to be improved. This could not have been accomplished with new decision rules alone, for they could not have been effectively implemented. But with the reorganization made possible by the organizational analysis, processing time is being and will continue to be reduced and the potential of the decision rules can be increasingly realized.

CONCLUSION

We have discussed the nature of communication models, how they are constructed and used, and indicated some of the problems raised by them. The list of uses of the model and methods for developing it was not complete but suggestive of what might be done. Attention was directed to the bibliography and footnotes for further information. This chapter can be summarized by an outline of eight steps in construction and use of the communication model:

1. *Draw a communication diagram.* Use one of the methods discussed or devise a new one. The more clearly the researcher knows what he is looking for, the cleaner diagram he will get. Ask specific questions.

2. *Check the diagram.* Is it an accurate picture? Was the right type of communication investigated? Does the diagram have too little or too much detail?

3. *Look at the diagram.* Try to discover, by inspection, any of the obvious communication faults discussed (discontinuities, excessive communication, abrupt changes in flow, etc.). By analogy or directly from the data obtained, seek out the more obscure faults.

4. *If problems of a standard type are found* (such as inventory, queuing, search, etc.), *apply the procedures discussed in subsequent chapters* of this book. Trace out the effects of the specialized problem to other parts of the organization to make sure the problem is, in fact, a standard one.

5. *If problems not of a standard type are found* (for which no standard specialized model exists), *use the communication diagram to suggest rele-*

vant variables for further study. With these relevant variables, *make a particular model to suit the case.*

6. *In particular, if the problems which are uncovered are mainly communication or control faults, use Table 4-1 to suggest relevant communication variables for further study.* Look for analogies in other disciplines. Compare the communication diagram with standard control circuits or other organizations' diagrams. Ask more specific questions. Use the check list again to suggest solutions to communication problems found, etc.

7. *Compare the proposed solutions* (obtained in the foregoing steps) *with the original communication diagram: a.* to trace out effects of local-area problem solution on other parts of the organization; *b.* to calculate estimated cost reductions, or *c.* to suggest alternate solutions not yet found.

8. *In any of these steps,* do not hesitate to use some imagination, to reason by analogy, to speculate on possible solutions. Keep a record of these speculations and trials. Test the proposed solutions, either by the development of new specialized models or through experiment. When a satisfactory solution is obtained, record the procedure. This will make it possible to recheck at a later date, or to use the information on the next research project.

BIBLIOGRAPHY

1. Adrian, E. D., *The Basic of Sensation; the Action of the Sense Organs*, W. W. Norton & Co., New York, 1928.
2. ———, *The Physical Background of Perception*, Clarendon Press, Oxford, England, 1947.
3. Alderson and Sessions Co., "Communication Analysis and Organization Planning," *Cost and Profit Outlook, VII*, no. 4 (Apr. 1954). (Alderson and Sessions Company, 1401 Walnut St., Philadelphia, Pa.)
4. Allee, W. C., *Animal Aggregations*, University of Chicago Press, Chicago, 1931.
5. ———, *The Social Life of Animals*, W. W. Norton & Co., New York, 1951.
6. Back, K. N., "The Exertion of Influence Through Social Communication," in Festinger *et al.*, *Theory and Experiment in Social Research*, Research Center for Group Dynamics, University of Michigan, Ann Arbor, 1950.
7. Bales, R. F., *Interaction Process Analysis*, Addison-Wesley Press, Cambridge, Mass., 1950.
8. ———, "The Interaction Recorder," *Hum. Relat., 1*, 456–463 (1948).
9. Barrett, E., "Cybernetics as Applied to a Study of Normal and Abnormal Adjustment Mechanisms," *J. Psychol., 30*, 11–31 (1950).
10. Barrett, E., and Post, G., "Introduction to Some Principles of Applied Cybernetics," *J. Psychol., 30*, 3–10 (1950).
11. Bavelas, A., "Communication Patterns in Task Oriented Groups," *J. Acoust. Soc. Amer., 22*, 725–730 (1950).

12. Bayliss, W. M., *Principles of General Physiology*, Longmans, Green and Co., New York, 4th ed., 1927.
13. *Bibliography on Cybernetics*, Electrical Engineering Department, Massachusetts Institute of Technology, Cambridge, 1950.
14. Bronfenbrenner, V., "The Graphic Representation of Sociometric Data," *Sociometry*, 7, 283–289 (1944).
15. Cannon, W. B., *Wisdom of the Body*, W. W. Norton & Co., New York, 1939.
16. Chapple, E. D., "Anthropological Engineering: Its Use to Administrators," *Appl. Anthrop.* (Jan.–Mar. 1943); reprinted in S. D. Hoslett (ed.), *Human Factors in Management*, Park College Press, Parksville, Mo., 1946.
17. ———, "The Interaction Chronograph: Its Evaluation and Present Application," *Personnel*, 25, 295–307 (1949).
18. ———, "How a Consultant Deals with Organizational Problems" (unpublished), Industrial Engineering Seminar 312, Columbia University, New York, Mar. 9, 1953.
19. ———, *Measuring Human Relations: An Introduction to the Study of the Interaction of Individuals*, Genet. Psychol., 22, No. 1, Feb. 1940.
20. Christie, L. S., Luce, R. D., and Macy, J., Jr., "Communication and Learning in Task-oriented Groups," Technical Report No. 231, Research Laboratory for Electronics, Massachusetts Institute of Technology, Cambridge, May 13, 1952.
21. Churchman, C. W., "Introduction," in *Proceedings of the Conference on Operations Research in Production and Inventory Control*, Case Institute of Technology, Cleveland, p. 8, Jan. 20–22, 1954.
22. Churchman, C. W., and Ackoff, R. L., "Purposive Behavior and Cybernetics," *Social Forces*, 29, 32–39 (1950).
23. Dempsey, E. W., "Homeostasis," in S. S. Stevens (ed.), *Handbook of Experimental Psychology*, John Wiley & Sons, New York, pp. 209–235, 1951.
24. Deutsch, K. W., "Communication in Self-governing Organizations" (unpublished), Industrial Engineering File No. 1589, Columbia University, New York, Spring, 1951.
25. ———, "Communication Theory and Social Science," *Amer. J. Orthopsychiat.*, 22, 469–483 (1952).
26. ———, "Higher Education and the Unity of Knowledge," in Lyman Bryson et al. (eds.), *Goals for American Education*, Conference on Science, Philosophy and Religion in their Relation to the Democratic Way of Life, Inc., New York, pp. 55–139, 1950.
27. ———, "Innovation, Entrepreneurship, and the Learning Process," in H. H. Cole and R. R. Wohl (eds.), *Change and the Entrepreneur*, Harvard University Press, Cambridge, 1949.
28. ———, "Mechanism, Organism, and Society," *Phil. Sci.*, 230–252 (July 1951).
29. ———, "Mechanism, Teleology, and Mind," *Phil. phenom. Res.*, 12, 185–222 (1951).
30. ———, "Models of Communication and Education" (unpublished), Industrial Engineering Seminar 312, Columbia University, New York, Mar. 13, 1951.
31. ———, *Nationalism and Social Communication*, Technology Press, Cambridge, and John Wiley & Sons, New York, 1953.
32. ———, "On Communication Models in the Social Sciences," *Publ. Opinion Quart.*, 16, 356–380 (1952).
33. ———, *Political Community at the International Level*, Doubleday Short Studies in Political Science, Doubleday & Co., New York, 1954.

34. Frank, L. K., "Teleological Mechanisms," *Ann. N. Y. Acad. Sci.*, *50*, 182–278 (1948).
35. Hatfield, H. S., *The Inventor and His World*, Penguin Books (Pelican Edition), New York, 1948.
36. Hebb, D. O., *The Organization of Behavior—a Neuropsychological Theory*, John Wiley & Sons, New York, 1949.
37. Hertz, D. B., *Theory and Practice of Industrial Research*, McGraw-Hill Book Co., New York, 1950.
38. Homans, G. C., "A Conceptual Scheme for the Study of Social Communication," *Amer. Sociological Rev.* (Feb. 1947).
39. Horsfall, A. B., and Arensberg, C. M., "Teamwork and Productivity in a Shoe Factory," *Hum. Organiz.* (Winter 1949).
40. Jahoda, M., Deutsch, M., and Cook, S. W., *Research Methods in Social Relations*, Part II, The Dryden Press, New York, 1952.
41. Jenkins, D., "Feedback and Group Self-Evaluation," *J. Social Issues*, *4*, 2, 50–60 (1948).
42. Lashley, K. S., "The Problem of Serial Order in Behavior," in Lloyd A. Jeffress (ed.), *Cerebral Mechanisms in Behavior*, John Wiley & Sons, New York, pp. 112–130, 1951.
43. Lasswell, H. D., "The Structure and Function of Communication in Society," in Lyman Bryson *et al.* (eds.), *The Communication of Ideas*, Harper and Brothers, New York, pp. 37–51, 1948.
44. ———, Smith, B. L., and Casey, R. D., *Propaganda, Communication, and Public Opinion*, Princeton University Press, Princeton, 1946.
45. Lazarsfeld, P. F., *Mathematical Thinking in the Social Sciences*, Free Press, Glencoe, Ill., 1954.
46. Marcosson, Isaac F., *Adventures in Interviewing*, John Lane, The Bodley Head, Ltd., London, 1920.
47. Mason, S. J., "On the Logic of Feed-back," Technical Report No. 153, Research Laboratory for Electronics, Massachusetts Institute of Technology, Cambridge, 1953.
48. Mayo, E., *The Social Problems of an Industrial Civilization*, Harvard Graduate School of Business Administration, Boston, 1945.
49. Meyer, H., "On the Heuristic Value of Scientific Models," *Phil. Sci.*, *18*, no. 4 (Oct. 1951).
50. Miller, G. A., *Language and Communication*, McGraw-Hill Book Co., 1951.
51. Morgenstern, O., *Prolegomena to a Theory of Organization*, Project RAND, RM-734, Santa Monica, 1951.
52. Nejelski, L., "Communication in Practical Affairs," in L. Bryson *et al.* (ed.), *The Communication of Ideas*, Harper and Brothers, New York, 1947.
53. Norton-Taylor, D., "Why Don't Businessmen Read Books?", *Fortune*, 116–117, (May 1954).
54. Penfield, W., and Rasmussen, T., *The Cerebral Cortex of Man*, The Macmillan Co., New York, 1950.
55. Pitts, W., and McCulloch, W. S., "How We Know Universals, the Preception of Auditory and Visual Forms," *Bull. Math. Biophys.*, *9*, 124–147 (1947).
56. Rapoport, A., and Shimbel, A., "Mathematical Biophysics, Cybernetics, and General Semantics, Etc.," *A Review of General Semantics*, *6*, 145–159 (1949).
57. Rosenblueth, A., Wiener, N., and Bigelow, W., "Behavior, Purpose, and Teleology," *Phil. Sci.*, *10*, 18–24 (1943).

58. Rosenblueth, A., and Wiener, N., "Purposeful and Non-Purposeful Behavior," *Phil. Sci.*, *17*, no. 4, 318–326 (Oct. 1950).

59. ———, "The Role of Models in Science," *Phil. Sci.*, *12*, 316–322 (1945).

60. Ruesch, J., and Bateson, G., *Communication: The Social Matrix of Psychiatry*, W. W. Norton & Co., New York, 1951.

61. ———, "Structure and Process in Social Relations," *Psychiatry*, *12*, 105–124 (1949).

62. Schneilra, T. C., "The Levels Concept in the Study of Social Organization in Animals," in Rohrer and Muzafer (eds.), *Social Psychiatry at the Crossroads*, Harper and Brothers, New York, 1951.

63. Shannon, C. E., and Weaver, W., *The Mathematical Theory of Communication*, University of Illinois Press, Urbana, 1949.

64. Simon, H. A., *Administrative Behavior*, The Macmillan Co., 1947.

65. ———, "Modern Organization Theories," *Advanced Mgmt.*, *15*, 2–4 (Oct. 1950).

66. ———, *On the Application of Servomechanism Theory in the Study of Production Control*, Project RAND, P234, Santa Monica, Aug. 15, 1951.

67. Simon, H. A., *A Study of Decision-Making Processes in Administrative Organization*, The Macmillan Co., New York, 1947.

68. Stumpers, F. L., "A Bibliography of Information Theory, Communication Theory, and Cybernetics," *Trans. I.R.E.*, PGIT-2 (Nov. 1953).

69. Taylor, R., "Purposeful and Non-Purposeful Behavior," *Phil. Sci.*, *17*, no. 4 (1950).

70. Trimmer, J. D., "Instrumentation and Cybernetics," *Sci. Monthly*, *69*, 328–331 (1949).

71. Waddington, C. H., *The Scientific Attitude*, Penguin Books, London, pp. 122–124, 1941.

72. Weber, Max, *The Theory of Social and Economic Organization*, W. Hodge, London, 1947.

73. *From Max Weber: Essays in Sociology*, translated, edited, and with an introduction by H. H. Gerth and C. Wright Mills, Oxford University Press, New York, 1946.

74. Wiener, N., *Cybernetics. Control and Communication in the Animal and the Machine*, John Wiley & Sons, New York, 1948.

75. ———, *The Human Use of Human Beings: Cybernetics and Society*, Houghton Mifflin Co., Boston, 1950.

76. ———, "Speech, Language and Learning," *J. Acoust. Soc. Amer.*, *22*, 696–697 (1950).

77. ———, "Time, Communication, and the Nervous System," in "Teleological Mechanisms," *Ann. N. Y. Acad. Sci.*, *50*, 197–219 (1948).

78. Whyte, W. H., *Is Anybody Listening?*, Simon and Schuster, New York, 1952.

Chapter 5

Formulation of

the Problem

INTRODUCTION

Research should begin with the formulation of a problem, but this step is seldom completed before the next research stage is entered. Formulating the problem is usually a sequential process. An initial formulation is completed and research proceeds, but in proceeding the problem is subjected to almost continuous and progressive reformulation and refinement. This continues until a solution is reached. In a sense, one never knows until the end of the research whether the problem was correctly formulated, and perhaps not even then.

Anxiety to get the research under way frequently leads to reduction of the time and effort devoted to formulating the problem. This is likely to be very costly. Consequently, some systematic way of formulating the problem should be a standard procedure of an O.R. team and a specific allocation of time for formulating the problem should be made.

In this chapter we shall consider an idealized procedure for problem-formulation. This procedure represents the best we know how to do at the present time, if we are subject to no restrictions whatsoever. In practice we can seldom meet this idealized standard. However, to develop a good practical procedure it is necessary to have before us a conception of the best available procedure. In addition, this idealized conception provides a procedural goal toward which we can move and thereby improve our research efforts.

The idealized procedure is a lengthy one, requiring considerable time and ingenuity. One might wonder, then, why this procedure is de-

sirable, especially in view of the fact that in many other areas of research this step is not emphasized. The answer lies in the very important and obvious fact that O.R. is research into the economics of
operations. As such it must necessarily consider the economics of its
own operations. Now the usual distinction between the practical
course of action and the ideal course of action is based on a false
notion from an economic point of view. The "practical" usually refers to an action that can be followed easily with minimum cost, effort,
and time. The "ideal" refers to an action that is costly, difficult, and
time-consuming. A moment's reflection indicates that the difference
between the ideal and the practical is not a matter of "black and white,"
but a difference lying along an economic scale. The practical is generally the less costly on a short-run basis, but is more expensive in
terms of long-run over-all objectives. The ideal, on the other hand,
usually entails greater short-run costs and is least costly and time-
consuming relative to long-run objectives.

The sound economics of the situation implies a proper balance of
the short-run and long-run objectives. Sound economics, therefore,
does not dictate either the practical or ideal solution, but does demand
that the ideal be spelled out in order to determine how close one
should come to it in the most economically designed research procedure. Only by describing the full possibilities of a research program
can one determine the economically best procedure to follow.

In the following discussion emphasis will be placed on the ideal procedure because it is so frequently overlooked. Practical considerations
will be discussed in connection with the more difficult phases of this
ideal procedure.

THE ORIENTATION PERIOD

The first period of the research, which is devoted to problem-
formulation, is called the *orientation* period. Such a period may extend from one to several months. It may terminate with the presentation of a written or oral formulation to the sponsors of the research.
This presentation may contain time and cost estimates, although these
cannot usually be very exact.

The orientation period has two important functions in addition to
formulation of the problem. As was shown in the example given in
the last chapter, the analysis made during the orientation period gives
an "outside" O.R. team an opportunity to assess the problem and the
organization before a commitment to research on a specific problem is
made. It also gives the sponsors a similar opportunity. At the end

of the orientation period, the conditions can be specified under which the research is to be conducted, and necessary administrative action can be taken to assure that these conditions are met. In effect, the orientation period is one of courtship between the O.R. team and sponsors. It is desirable to have such a period even if the team is made up exclusively of company personnel because each new O.R. problem creates new operating and administrative problems. Furthermore, such a period is required even if the research is "basic" rather than "applied," the sponsors of basic research being the scientific critics and supporters (foundations, universities, government, etc.).

THE COMPONENTS OF A PROBLEM

Before we can formulate a problem we should have some idea as to what a problem is. That is, what are the components of a problem?

First, and most obvious, is the fact that someone or some group must have the problem. This individual or group is dissatisfied with some aspect of the state of affairs and consequently wants to make a decision with regard to altering it. For this reason we shall refer to this individual or group as the *decision-maker*. Where the decision-maker controls the operations of an organized system of men and/or machines, he may also be referred to as the *policy-maker*, or *executive*. *The decision-maker is the first component of the problem.*

Second, in order for the decision-maker to have a problem he must want something other than what he has; i.e., he must have some objectives which he has not obtained to the degree he desires. *Objectives are the second component of a problem.*

Third, the decision-maker has the problem in an environment or setting that contains or lacks various resources. In the type of problem with which O.R. becomes involved, this environment is an organized system usually embracing machines as well as men. *The system, or environment, is the third component of the problem.*

Finally, a problem cannot exist unless the decision-maker has a choice from among at least two alternative courses of action or policies. *Dissatisfaction* can exist without choice, but a problem cannot. A problem always involves the question: What to do? And this question becomes a problem only when alternative courses of action are available. *Alternative courses of action are the fourth component of the problem.*

Now let us consider what should be known about each of these four components (decision-maker, objectives, system, and alternative courses of action) in order to formulate the research problem.

The Decision-Maker

First it is necessary to identify the decision-maker. In the problems with which O.R. is concerned, this involves identification of those who have the authority to initiate, terminate, and modify policies governing the organization and system under study. In some systems authority may rest in more than one individual. In any event it is essential to have an understanding of how those who share authority make decisions, particularly as a guide to the presentation of results and recommendations during and at the completion of the project.

The organization of the decision-making group should be determined. Do they make decisions in a body or in a sequence? By majority vote? If not, who has veto power and who has final authority? Is the process a formal or informal one?

The following questions may serve to direct study of the decision-making process in the problem area:

1. Who has the responsibility for making recommendations concerning modification of policies?

2. Whose approval is required and how is this approval expressed?

3. What constitutes final approval? (A majority vote in group deliberation, approval by a final authority in a sequence of reviews, etc.)

4. Does anyone have absolute veto power? If not, how can a recommendation be rejected?

5. Who has the responsibility for carrying out recommendations once they are approved?

6. Who has responsibility for evaluating the action taken?

Organization charts do not provide answers to these questions, but they may serve as useful guides in determining whom to question to get the required answers.

The Decision-Maker's Objectives

Direct questioning of decision-makers seldom reveals all their pertinent objectives relative to a problem. Such questioning provides a start but it seldom provides enough information for a complete formulation of objectives. One particularly effective way of revealing these hidden objectives is illustrated as follows. The researcher attempts to formulate a list of all possible outcomes of the project. At this stage of the problem, this list need not be accurate or complete or even realistic. The sponsor(s) should be asked what he would do if the research were to yield each of the possible outcomes listed. In many cases he will indicate that he would not act on the recommendations yielded by the research. Exploration of his reasons for refusing to accept these recommendations can reveal new objectives. In one case a policy-maker wanted to determine where to locate a new factory. Direct questioning revealed the objectives one would expect (e.g., minimize transportation cost, labor cost, etc.). But a failure to probe deeper by a method such as that just described led to a serious consequence. Results of the research strongly indicated the desirability of one particular region for the factory site. The sponsor would not act on the recommendation because he refused to have anything to do with the leader of the union (in that region) with whom he would have to negotiate. Economic considerations turned out to be secondary relative to this antipathy or desire to avoid the particular unionist involved. As a result a large part of the study had to be done over.

When studying objectives of the decision-maker we have to consider not only those objectives that the decision-maker wants to obtain to a higher degree but we must also take into account objectives already obtained that he wants to retain. An executive may want to maintain at least a specified level of employment, or he may not want to increase the amount of borrowed capital or size of a production unit. That is, an executive may have some objectives that he wants to *maintain* as well as some that he wants to *obtain*.

For example, objectives to be obtained may be: *a.* to decrease production costs; *b.* to render better customer service; and *c.* to increase a share of the market. Objectives to be retained may be: *a.* to maintain stable employment; *b.* to retain product leadership; and *c.* to preserve good relations with the community. In the problem presented in Chapter 2 (production and inventory control) there was only one objective to be attained: to reduce the total cost of production and inventory. There were many objectives to be retained, including: *a.* not to rent any additional storage space; *b.* to retain the company's credit position, and *c.* to continue assembly of machines at the same rate as was current.

The System

Most organized systems involve the following components: controllers, agents who carry out policies, instruments and materials used in so doing, outsiders who are affected by the organization's activity, and the social environment in which these components operate. Specifically, in business and industrial systems these components take the following form:

1. *Management,* which directs
2. *Men,* who control and operate
3. *Machines,* which convert

4. *Materials* into products or services made available to
5. *Consumers*, whose purchases are also sought by
6. *Competitors*.
7. *Government and the public.*

The parallel in military systems is apparent.

Management, men, machines, and materials constitute a system only by virtue of *organization*. In an organization there is a division of labor among groups each of which contributes to a sequence of operations directed toward attainment of a collective objective. To understand the organization and the resultant system one must first grasp the sequence of operations in the subgroups of the organization and the manner by which they are controlled so as to assure effectiveness relative to the organization's over-all objectives. In the preceding chapter a procedure for attaining such understanding was described.

Experience indicates that in almost every case this type of analysis is as revealing to management and other company personnel as it is to an outside O.R. team. In many cases these analyses have applications supplementary to the research which justify the expenditure of time required by the study. For example, such analyses have been used in training new employees, and in management training programs. They have been used for top-level planning in much the same way that a military general staff uses war maps. Indeed, the control and materials flow charts, as they are called, can be considered as maps of the system being manipulated. Such analyses have disclosed duplications of functions and gaps in control. In some cases they suggest other fruitful studies which can be conducted independently of the O.R. activity.

All the components referred to earlier in this section do not necessarily play an active role in an organization's operations. For example, competitors, government, and the public usually represent constraints on the system rather than active controlling agents who participate in the decision-making. For many problems it is not necessary to obtain a detailed understanding of how these constraints are imposed. In the analysis of operations given in the case presented in Chapter 2, for example, the role of competitors, government, and the public was not considered because the research was primarily concerned with the production process. If, on the other hand, the problem had come to involve price-setting, the analysis of the system would have had to be extended to include these other participants.

OBJECTIVES OF OTHER PARTICIPANTS. Once the participants in the problem other than the decision-maker have been identified, their rele-

vant interests should also be determined. Since those who carry out
the policy decisions (as well as the consumers and competitors) may be
affected by the research, an understanding of this possible effect is
essential to a complete understanding of the problem. Moreover, the
success in applying any solution suggested by the research depends on
the way it is received by the other parties. In some cases, where a
study of these parties reveals that acceptance is not likely, an educational program may have to be designed to precede the new policy.
Or again, a solution that might otherwise be acceptable might have to
be rejected because it would not be acceptable to some participants
even if preceded by an educational program. In effect, then, limitations on possible solutions emanate from the interests of these other
parties. An understanding of these interests may, in some cases, however, extend the list of possible solutions.

The techniques already discussed for uncovering objectives are applicable here as well as in the case of the decision-maker. But in general there is considerably more practical difficulty in applying them to
other participants. It is therefore frequently necessary to use other
procedures or to rely on general knowledge concerning their objectives.

In the phase of the project presented in Chapter 2 which involved
study of the processing of orders for replacement parts, a committee
was formed of those employees whose activities might be affected by
the study. Their objectives were effectively disclosed in their objections to proposed changes in the procedure. It was natural to find in
each person involved a pervasive desire to retain an important role in
the procedure. Specifically, it became clear that most objections were
based on a fear that their job security was threatened. It was also
clear that one of their important objectives was to improve company
operations if they could get credit and recognition for doing it. Once
such objectives were disclosed it was possible to take steps to assure
recognition of their contribution to the study, and to assure their security and continued importance in the processing of the orders.

Alternative Courses of Action

A number of possible alternative courses of action are ordinarily disclosed in the process of going through the earlier steps in formulating
the problem. It is very likely, however, that the list of alternatives
disclosed in this way is not exhaustive. The researchers should get as
complete a list of alternatives as possible, even to the extent of including possibilities that are not thought to be feasible.

Assurance of the relative completeness of possible courses of action
can best be obtained by an analysis of the system itself. Consider,

for example, the case of a company that provides burglar alarm services. On agreement between customer and company, an alarm system is installed which is connected to a central switchboard by the company. The company maintains crews of armed guards who are dispatched to the site on receipt of an alarm from the installation. In this case the company had been receiving a large number of false alarms. False alarms are costly to service and hence constitute a significant part of operating expenses.

The company engaged an O.R. team to study the possibility of reducing this rate. Now the company's main objective was to increase net profit, although the specific objective here was originally stated as one of reducing the alarm rate. What alternative courses of action were available to the company? An analysis of the system revealed some which were not immediately apparent.

The system begins with a sale of service to the customer. Two alternatives arise here: 1. select only customers whose type of establishment yields lower false alarm rates; 2. charge customers for service proportionately to the false alarm rate expected from the particular type of establishment.

Once the sale is completed the installation is designed and effected. Here there are a number of alternatives regarding the nature of the components of the system and the way they are combined. In effect, there are a number of alternative ways of making the installation. These alternatives can be separated into two groups, one involving the use of standard components and the other involving new components better designed to meet certain environmental conditions which cause false alarms.

Once the system is installed, false alarms are caused not only by equipment failure but also by abuse or misuse of the equipment by the subscriber. Hence another alternative is to provide more training to delinquent subscribers and/or new subscribers in the proper use of the equipment.

Since even a good installation can deteriorate with use and the passage of time, the company has inspection, maintenance, and replacement policies. Herein lies another set of alternatives regarding the timing and nature of inspections, criteria of rejection and replacement of equipment, etc.

Finally, there are alternative ways of servicing an alarm when it comes in to the central office. These alternatives involve the number and location of guards, the system of communicating with them, the possible corrective actions that can be taken by the guards, and the kind of reports they turn in on such alarms.

The derivation of a list of alternatives such as the ones given in the preceding illustration comes about by asking and answering the following questions. For each phase of the system would a change

1. in personnel affect the efficiency of the system relative to the sponsor's objectives?
2. in operations affect the efficiency of the system?
3. in the materials and/or machines affect the efficiency of the system?
4. in the environment affect the efficiency of the system?

Wherever an affirmative answer is obtained the specific alternatives at this stage can be explored.

In some cases the alternatives can be stated simply as to do A or not to do A; e.g., to produce a new product or not, or to sell to a new type of customer or not. In other cases there are many alternatives; e.g., to produce n items per run, where n can take on a wide range of values. It is important for a subsequent step in the formulation of the problem to indicate at this stage the number or range of possible alternatives.

DEVELOPING NEW COURSES OF ACTION. In some cases none of the available alternative courses of action is considered to be good enough to constitute a solution. An automobile manufacturer may not consider any existing shock absorber to be good enough for his purposes. Or a paper manufacturer may consider all available ways of inspection too costly. In such instances a new course of action is required; but since it is not available it must be developed. Such problems are *developmental*. On the other hand, problems which involve a choice from among a set of available alternatives are *evaluative*. "Developmental" and "evaluative" are extremes on a scale, the scale depending on the degree of effort required to create new alternatives. Although our concern will lie primarily with evaluative problems, an example of developmental research should be mentioned.

Suppose the army wants to develop a more effective weapon to use against a certain type of target. The O.R. team studies the available weapons and by analysis attempts to extract those characteristics on which the efficiency of the weapons depend. On the basis of this analysis they develop a conception of a new weapon whose improved efficiency can be estimated by extrapolation. The designers then study the requirements set down by the O.R. team and discover that they can only be met provided (e.g.) a certain type of sensing mechanism is put into the weapon, and that this would require a reduction of explosive materials. After this developmental research, the O.R.

team might then study ways of delivering the explosive closer to the target to compensate for its decreased lethal power. In each instance the O.R. team *evaluates* the proposed new course of action against the available alternatives.

It should be apparent that such participation of O.R. in developmental research and engineering can be of great value to industry, particularly in the development of new products and processes.

COUNTERACTIONS. Up to this point in the discussion of alternative policies or courses of action we have been concerned with those alternatives which the decision-maker has. But a certain class of actions available to the other participants (those who carry out decisions, the consumers, competitors, and public) should also be determined, i.e., the class of possible *counteractions*. A counteraction is an action which any of these participants can take which may change the effectiveness of the decision-maker's action once he takes it. These counteractions are very important, for an immediate gain to the decision-maker can be converted into a subsequent loss by such a counteraction. For example, a cut in prices may initially yield an increased sales and profit. But a greater price cut by a competitor may start a price war or force the decision-maker down to an unprofitable price level.

In many cases it is possible to uncover possible counteractions by asking the participants directly what they would do if the decision-maker were to adopt a specific policy. This is particularly the case for the operators and consumers. Competitors can seldom be approached directly. Fortunately, a history of competitive counteractions is usually available. On the basis of this history, reasonable inferences can usually be made concerning their possible counteractions.

It may be noted in passing that "counteractions" belong to the general area of prediction; not only the participants but Nature also may take a counterstep, and unless one is prepared for it the choice of action selected may be disastrous. More detailed remarks on this problem appear in Chapter 18.

Once all the possible actions and counteractions have been specified, the last step in identifying the components of the problem has been completed. The O.R. team can turn then to the second phase of problem formulation: the transformation of the decision-maker's problem into a research problem.

THE RESEARCH PROBLEM

Transformation of the decision-maker's problem into a research problem involves the following steps:

1. Editing the list of objectives obtained in the first stage of problem formulation.
2. Editing the list of alternative courses of action.
3. Defining the measure of effectiveness to be used.

Before proceeding to a detailed discussion of each of these steps, some remarks concerning the logic of decision-making (i.e., decision theory) are in order. Consider the following simplified abstract problem. Only two objectives are involved, O_1 and O_2; and only two courses of action are possible, C_1 and C_2. Now suppose we have determined the efficiency of each course of action for each objective (along a scale going from 0 to 1) and show the results in the following matrix:

	O_1	O_2
C_1	0.8	0.4
C_2	0.2	0.6

Which course of action should be selected? It is a mistake to answer either "C_1" or "C_2." The question cannot be answered without information concerning the *relative importance* of the objectives. If O_1 is much more important than O_2 it seems clear we should select C_1, but if O_2 is much more important than O_1, C_2 should be selected. How can the criterion of selection be made explicit? If we could measure the relative importance of O_1 and O_2 such a criterion could be provided. Suppose, for example, that relative importance could be measured along a scale running from 0 to 1, and that the relative importance of O_1 is 0.3, and of O_2 is 0.7. Now we can *weight* the efficiency of each course of action for each objective as follows:

	O_1	O_2	Total
C_1	$0.3 \times 0.8 = 0.24$	$0.7 \times 0.4 = 0.28$	0.52
C_2	$0.3 \times 0.2 = 0.06$	$0.7 \times 0.6 = 0.42$	0.48

The sum of the weighted efficiencies (efficiency times relative importance) of a course of action can be called its relative *effectiveness*.

Effectiveness, that is, weighted efficiency, should be the basis for selecting a course of action.

But in order to measure effectiveness one must have a measure of the importance of objectives. Such a measure is frequently difficult to supply. Consequently, some researchers are inclined to select the most important objective and to recommend that course of action which is most efficient relative to it. As can be seen in the example shown in the table just given, this could lead to an incorrect "solution" to the problem. Dropping less important objectives from consideration is not merely a convenient simplification of a problem; it is frequently a major distortion of it.

In the next chapter, a method for obtaining an approximate measure of importance of objectives is presented and illustrated.

The logic of decision-making which has been described here is quite elementary. If counteractions or uncertainties are involved a more sophisticated logic is required. (See Chapters 17 and 18 for a discussion of these complicating factors.)

Editing the Objectives and Courses of Action

The complexity of research usually depends on the number of objectives and courses of actions which must be taken into account. Consequently, it is very desirable to condense and simplify the list of objectives and alternative courses of action as much as possible before they are investigated. As yet there are no systematic procedures for doing so, but experience has yielded a few principles which are useful in performing the editing job. The next two sections consider some of these.

EDITING OBJECTIVES. The purpose of editing the objectives is to simplify and condense the list obtained in the first stage of formulating the problem. The editing procedure can be considered in three steps. The first consists of an examination of the list to determine if the attainment of any one objective is important only because it is a means to the attainment of another objective or objectives on the list. If so it may be eliminated. For example, suppose one of the objectives is "to increase the company's annual net profit," and another is to "decrease production costs." It is likely that there is interest in decreased production costs only to the extent that it leads to increased net profits. If so, "decreased production costs" can be considered as a "means," not as an objective.

Suppose the following two objectives are listed: to increase the net profit, and to increase a share of the market. The second objective may appear to be the same as the first, and it may be the same relative to certain courses of action, but not all. For example, prices can be cut to a point at which profits would decrease even though a much larger share of the market would be obtained. Now the company may say it has no interest in an increased share of the market unless it increases profit. In this case, the second objective is a means to the first and can be eliminated from the list of objectives. If, on the other hand, the company is interested in increasing its share of the market even if it results in reduced profits (within a range), then the objective should be retained on the list.

The second step of editing involves examination of each objective relative to the alternative courses of action to determine if attainment of any of the objectives would be unaffected by a choice from among the alternatives. If an objective is so unaffected, it should be eliminated from the list. For example, suppose one objective listed is "to maintain a high quality product" and the alternative courses of action involve only determination of production-lot sizes. Then, if quality is unaffected by lot size, the "quality maintenance" objective can be dropped from the list.

The third step of editing is the obvious one of combining objectives of different participants that are essentially the same. For example, both employer and employee may be interested in stable employment and both manufacturer and consumer may be interested in low price and high quality.

EDITING THE COURSES OF ACTION. The list of possible alternative actions available to the decision-maker should be examined to determine if there are reasons for eliminating any of these from further consideration. In some cases previous research may have demonstrated the impracticality of one of the alternatives. In others it may be clear that one or more courses of action will violate one or more of the restrictions placed on the research. For example, if in a problem involving the location of a plant a certain land tax rate is fixed by policy as the maximum, then locations having a higher tax rate can be eliminated from consideration.

In some cases a limitation in time or research funds makes it impractical to consider all the alternatives. Some can be eliminated on the grounds that available evidence indicates that, relative to the time and funds available, these are not fruitful areas of attack. For example, in one study the problem involved the reduction of production and inventory costs. Most of the alternatives involved phases of production. But one possibility involved a change in the distribution policies of the company. It was learned that even if this were shown to be fruitful it could not be accomplished within the time set by the company for completion of the project and implementation of the results.

Changing contracts with numerous distributors around the country would be a lengthy procedure whereas changes in internal policy could be effected in a relatively short time.

Whatever the reasons for the elimination of a course of action, they should be recorded. This permits the reasons to be re-evaluated by others and possible oversights to be brought to the attention of the team.

Defining the Measure of Effectiveness

It has been noted that measures of effectiveness consist of two component measures: 1. the importance of the objectives, and 2. the efficiency of the courses of action. In this section we shall consider how to establish the two component measures and the composite measure of effectiveness suitable to the problem.

The choice of procedure depends on the nature of the objectives. Most important in this regard is whether or not the objectives are quantitative or qualitative in nature. For example, "to increase net profit" is really a set of objectives differentiated by values along a quantitative (dollar) scale; whereas the objective "to retain family ownership of the company" is (unless reformulated) qualitative in character. Qualitative objectives are usually psychological and social and are often referred to as "intangibles" because it is so difficult to measure progress with respect to them. It is very desirable, therefore, to put objectives into quantitative terms. But it is not impossible to handle problems in which all of the objectives are qualitative in character, as will be seen later.

It is more difficult to construct measures of effectiveness where qualitative objectives are involved than where only quantitative objectives are concerned. This fact should not discourage efforts to transform qualitative objectives into quantitative ones. The history of science has repeatedly demonstrated that a property that appears in one era to require qualitative treatment is converted into quantitative terms in another era. At one time such qualitative properties as "red," "hard," "intelligent," and "communicative" were thought to be inherently qualitative. Today we know better. There is no logical or methodological reason (though there may be a practical one) why such concepts as "good will," "morale," and "responsibility" cannot be reduced to quantitative terms.

In order to understand better the steps involved in constructing a measure of effectiveness, let us consider the problems that arise in connection with the selection of one of two courses of action (C_1 and C_2) relative to two objectives: 1. increasing net profit, and 2. decreasing average service time. Suppose we knew that: a. if C_1 were used net profits would be increased by $1000 per year and average service time would be decreased by 2 days, and *b*. if C_2 were used net profits would be increased by $2000 per year and average service time would be decreased by 1 day. How would we select one of these two courses of action? To do so we need some way of "adding" the efficiencies for the two objectives relative to each course of action. One way in which this can be done is by equating a unit increase in net profit with a certain number of units of decrease in average service time. For example, if a decrease in service time of 1 day is worth $500 per year we can construct an over-all measure of effectiveness for each course of action. The effectiveness of C_1 could be represented by $1000 + 2($500), or $2000. The effectiveness of C_2 could be represented by $2000 + 1($500), or $2500. We would select C_2 under these circumstances.

The first task in constructing a measure of effectiveness, then, is to provide a method of transforming efficiencies relative to different objectives into a common measure. This requires a method of "weighting" the units in terms of which the objectives are expressed. That is, we must determine the relative values of these units. This relative value we call the *weight* of the unit of the corresponding objective.

Now, if we actually used either of these two courses of action for several years we would not expect it to yield constant results. In other words, the net profits and the decrease in service time would vary. Therefore, it is misleading to say, for example, that C_1 yields an increase of $1000 per year in net profit. It may yield many different annual increases or decreases. We should express its efficiency for the objectives in some way which reflects this possible variation.

The second problem, then, in constructing a measure of effectiveness is to devise a way of expressing efficiency (of each course of action for each objective) which takes this possible variation into account. This involves the construction of an *efficiency function*.

By combining the weights and efficiency functions for each course of action, we can obtain an *effectiveness function*. Consequently, the last problem is to construct a criterion by means of which one of the functions can be selected; i.e., to define what is meant by the "best" effectiveness function.

We shall consider each of these steps in turn, first for sets of objectives all of which are quantifiable, then for sets of objectives which contain one but not all qualitative objectives, and finally for sets consisting of only qualitative objectives.

EFFECTIVENESS FOR QUANTIFIABLE OBJECTIVES. In problems involving two or more quantifiable objectives the procedure for establishing an over-all measure of effectiveness is a very complex one. It requires certain types of information which are frequently not available. Consequently, this procedure can seldom be followed. But an explicit statement of such a procedure can provide a standard that we can try to approximate as best we can in the face of practical restrictions.

In this discussion, then, we will go through the steps required to construct the best measure of effectiveness that we know how to construct. But we will consider possible practical restrictions and how to deal with them. Before considering the steps in detail it may be helpful to enumerate them.

1. Develop a measure of efficiency relative to each objective.

2. Where the measures of efficiency obtained in step 1 differ, develop a way of transforming the measures into one common or standard measure of efficiency.

3. For each course of action and each objective determine the probability of attaining each possible level of efficiency. This is the *efficiency function* of each course of action for each objective.

4. For each course of action, "add" the efficiency functions so as to obtain a combined efficiency relative to all objectives. The result is an *effectiveness function* for each course of action relative to the entire set of objectives.

5. State the objective of the decision process in terms of maximizing or minimizing expected return, gain, or loss.

6. Construct a "return function" for each course of action. A return function expresses the expected outcome (outcome times its probability of occurrence) in terms of gains and losses.

If all the objectives in the edited list are expressed in quantitative terms (e.g., "to increase net profit," "to increase share of market," and "to decrease average service time") the following procedure can be used to weight the objectives:

1. Identify the units in terms of which each objective is defined. For example, the three objectives cited in the preceding paragraph can be expressed as:

    a. Increase net profit by x *dollars.*

    b. Increase share of market by y *per cent.*

    c. Decrease average service time by z *days.*

2. Select the most important and one other objective. Prepare a graph on which the scale defining the most important objective is the abscissa (horizontal axis) and the scale of the other objective is the

ordinate (vertical axis). Then select several values along the abscissa, determine the equivalent values along the ordinate, and plot the resulting points. Connect the points with a line, which may be straight

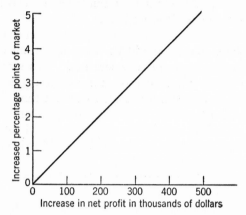

Fig. 5-1. Profit corresponding to increased percentage points of market.

or curved. Suppose, for example, each increased percentage point of the market is worth \$100,000 in net profit. Then we would get a plot as shown in Fig. 5-1. This figure permits us to transform a number of percentage points into dollars.

It may be that decreased service time becomes increasingly valuable. This might result in a plot such as is shown in Fig. 5-2.

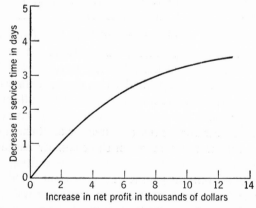

Fig. 5-2. Increase in net profit corresponding to decrease in service time.

3. Repeat step 2, comparing the units used in each of the other objectives with the one used in the most important one.

The reason for using the unit of the most important objective as a standard (i.e., as a constant abscissa) is that there is bound to be some error associated with this weighting procedure. The effect of this error is likely to be minimized by retaining the measure associated with the most important objective.

It has been argued that this error of transformation can be so serious that it is preferable to drop all but the most important objective and its measure of efficiency from consideration. This argument is not well founded. The error introduced by transforming measures of efficiency must almost of necessity be smaller than that introduced by dropping the other objectives. Such elimination is equivalent to giving the discarded courses of action zero efficiency for all the other objectives. This would generally be a very large distortion, much larger than results from the transformation.

In many cases the determination of the equivalence of units can be made by the study of past behavior. In other cases such determination must be made by reliance on judgments made by various participants. First let us consider a case in which the study of past behavior yielded a basis for such a determination.

Weighting Units by Use of Past Behavior. An electric utility company desired to reduce the cost of the "no-light" service it provided to its customers, but it was also interested in reducing the customers' waiting time for service. The cost of administering any service policy could be computed. The average waiting time for a service call could be computed for each alternative policy. Now these two measures must be added, and hence a transformation of units (dollars or time) is necessary. The question was asked as to how much a minute's waiting time is worth to the company. What dollar value has the company placed on the customers' waiting time? It was possible to determine this cost value in the following way. In the 5 years preceding the study the company had twice changed its service policy. It was possible to determine for each change the resultant loss or gain in operating costs and the resultant effect on the average customer waiting time. By combining these figures for each change it was further possible to determine how much the company had actually paid on the two occasions for decreasing the average waiting time and for increasing it. The resultant figures were consistent. This figure, then, represented the executives' valuation of customer waiting time and made possible the conversion of the time scale into a dollar scale.

It should be noted that the customers' value of waiting time is not determined by this method. But it would be possible to determine how much the average customer pays for an average minute's use of electricity.   As an alternative procedure the approximate measure of value presented in the next chapter could be used.

Weighting Units by Judgment.   If data are not available (actually or practically) for such evaluations as were described in the last section, judgment can be used as a substitute.   For example, one could merely establish by opinion how many dollars a unit of waiting time is worth. Or we could use the procedures recommended in the next chapter, by first taking roughly comparable numbers of units which define each objective.   These are weighted by the procedures described in the next chapter.   The results might look as follows:

Quantity Weighted	Weight
$1000 net profit per year	0.5
1% increase in share of market	0.3
1-day decrease in average service time	0.2

By use of these weights the units involved can be equaled.   For example, a 1% increase in share of the market would be equal to

$$(0.3/0.5)\$1000 = \$600$$

Similarly, a 1-day decrease in the average service time would be equal to

$$(0.2/0.5)\$1000 = \$400$$

Constructing an Efficiency Function.   Suppose the following results are obtained for the three illustrative objectives: An increase of 0.01% of the market is equivalent to $1.00 in net profit, and a decrease of 0.10 day of average service time is equivalent to $1.00 in net profit. Now suppose further that a course of action yields an increase in net profit of $1000, an increase of 1% in share of market, and a decrease of 1-day average service time.   Then its effectiveness could be expressed as

$$\$1000 + (1/0.01)\$1.00 + (1/0.10)\$1.00 = \$1000 + \$100 + \$10$$

$$= \$1110$$

As already indicated, there is a major shortcoming in this procedure. If the course of action were to be repeated it is highly unlikely that the same results would be obtained; i.e., net profit, increase in share of the market, and decrease of delay time would vary with repetitions of the course of action.

In order to handle the problem of varying "outputs" of a course of action, we first consider the action from the point of view of each of the objectives, and attempt to estimate the probability of success from the point of view of each objective. We then combine these results into an over-all "effectiveness" measure.

In this idealized procedure it is first necessary to construct an "efficiency function" which can be represented by a curve that describes the probability that a certain efficiency (measured on a standard scale) will be attained relative to each specific objective; see Fig. 5-3. The

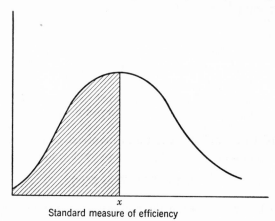

x
Standard measure of efficiency

Fig. 5-3. Efficiency function.

probability that the course of action will attain an efficiency of at most x is represented by the ratio of *the shaded area of the curve to the total area of the curve.* *

The measure of efficiency may be dollars, time, effort, per cent of job completed, or any combination of these.

There will be one efficiency function for each course of action relative to each objective. Thus, if there are three courses of action and four objectives there will be 12 (3×4) efficiency functions.

Now all the efficiency functions associated with each course of action must be combined. The mathematics involved in this combination may be very complex, but the logic is not.

Suppose, for example, we have two objectives, O_1 and O_2, and one course of action C_1, and that we want to determine the probability of gaining \$10 relative to both objectives. There are 11 different ways of obtaining such a gain (assuming gains are always in whole dollars). These are shown in Table 5-1.

* This curve is called a "probability density function" and can be represented by $f_{ij}(x)$, where i designates a specific course of action C_i, and j designates a specific objective O_j.

TABLE 5-1

Combination	Gain in Dollars Relative to O_1 of at Least	Gain in Dollars Relative to O_2 of at Least	Total Gain of at Least
1	0	10	10
2	1	9	10
3	2	8	10
4	3	7	10
5	4	6	10
6	5	5	10
7	6	4	10
8	7	3	10
9	8	2	10
10	9	1	10
11	10	0	10

There is a probability associated with each of the 11 combinations which is itself the product of the probabilities associated with each component of the combination. For example, the probability of getting the first combination, $P(0,10)$, is equal to the probability of getting $0 gain relative to O_1, $P_1(0)$, times the probability of getting $10 gain relative to O_2, $P_2(10)$; * i.e.

$$P(0,10) = P_1(0)P_2(10)$$

The total probability of exactly a $10 gain then would be

$$P(0,10) + P(1,9) + \cdots + P(10,0)$$

$$= P_1(0)P_2(10) + P_1(1)P_2(9) + \cdots + P_1(10)P_2(0)$$

The effectiveness function,† then, would express this total probability associated with any particular standard measure of efficiency.

The "Best" Effectiveness Function. Now suppose we have a 50% chance of making a dollar and a 50% chance of making nothing. Then, in this situation our *expected return* would be $0.5(\$1.00) + 0.5(0)$ = $0.50. In general, then, if there are n possible outcomes $(x_1, x_2, \cdots, x_n)$ and a probability associated with each $(p_1, p_2, \cdots, p_n)$, the expected return would be ‡

$$p_1 x_1 + p_2 x_2 + \cdots + p_n x_n = \sum_{i=1}^{n} p_i x_i$$

* Assuming that the gains relative to the objectives are not correlated.

† Mathematical details on this function are given in Note 1, Alternative 1, at the end of this chapter.

‡ Mathematical details for the continuous case are given in Note 1, Alternative 1, at the end of this chapter.

One way of choosing the best course of action would be to select that course of action whose expected return is greatest. But this is not the only principle of selection.

The expected return may have a negative value; i.e., a course of action may have an expected loss rather than gain. For example, if the standard scale used is dollars the effectiveness may appear as in Fig. 5-4.

Loss   0   Gain

Fig. 5-4. Return function.

Now it is possible to compute the expected gain and the expected loss separately. The effectiveness functions could be compared on the basis of either. The "best" function could be defined as that one which maximizes the expected gain or that one which minimizes the expected loss. Many other definitions of "best" are possible, but the three mentioned are the most commonly used. Let us consider the conditions under which each of these may be used: maximum expected return, maximum expected gain, and minimum expected loss.

If the decision-maker is confronted with the choice of a course of action which he will use repeatedly over a long period of time, he may be inclined to select that course of action which maximizes his expectations in the long run. That is, he may use the principle of maximum expected return, particularly if he is in a position occasionally to incur large short-run losses.

But the decision-maker may not be in a position to incur such losses. For example, he may have only a limited amount of capital with which to work. If he incurs a loss greater than this amount he may have to go out of business. Then his concern may be in selecting that course of action which either minimizes his expected loss or has the lowest probability of yielding a loss greater than the critical amount.

On the other hand, a decision-maker may put aside a certain amount of money for a gamble; i.e., he is prepared to lose the entire amount, but his objective is to try to make the largest possible gain. Then he would desire, in effect, to maximize his expected gain. Such is the case, for instance, of an oil company relative to exploration for oil. A budget is set up by the company for a period of several years. The job of the Production Department is to invest this money in such a way as to maximize their chance of a major oil discovery. A major oil discovery can be defined in terms of "greater than x dollars." Then that course of action can be taken which maximizes the probability of an expected gain of at least x dollars.

In general, if management policy is conservative, the criterion of the "best" effectiveness function will involve minimization of expected losses in some way. If this policy is "bullish," maximization of expected gain is likely to be more suitable. If the company is interested in the long run and has the necessary resources, maximization of expected return is likely to be most appropriate.

Determination of which of these policies is applicable is part of the analysis of the decision-maker's objectives. This policy is a type of superobjective for it is the criterion of progress in the company. It is not treated as are the other objectives in the earlier steps of problem-formulation but is "saved" for use in defining the "best" decision.

A Practical Adaptation for Quantitative Objectives. In practice the principal difficulty in following the procedure just outlined arises from the time and money required to construct an efficiency function; i.e., estimating for each course of action the probabilities associated with each possible outcome relative to each objective. It is usually much easier and more economical to estimate the average outcome since much less data are required. Consequently, the usual procedure in practice consists of the following steps:

1. (As in the standard procedure) develop a measure of efficiency relative to each objective.

2. (As in the standard procedure) transform these measures into a common measure.

3. For each course of action determine the *average* efficiency relative to each objective, and transform these into the common measure.

4. For each course of action "add" the average efficiencies relative to each objective.

5. Select that course of action with the greatest total average efficiency (or the least total inefficiency).

To illustrate this procedure let us return to the electric utility problem referred to earlier in this chapter (page 122). Two courses of action were considered in this problem: C_1, to continue to operate out of three service garages with the city divided into three corresponding service districts; and C_2, to add one service garage, employ the same number of men, and use four new service districts specified by the service department. The two objectives were O_1, to minimize operating costs; and O_2, to minimize customer waiting time. Briefly, the procedure in solving the problem went as follows:

1. The measure of efficiency for O_1 was defined as total annual service costs. The measure of efficiency for O_2 was the average waiting time per "no-light" call.

2. As described earlier, study of past decisions led to the conclusion that 1 minute's waiting time for all customers was worth approximately \$850 to the company.

3. Study of operating costs showed that C_2, as compared with C_1, would a. increase operating costs by an average of \$3247 per year, and b. decrease customer waiting time by an average of 2.1 minutes per year, which has a value of \$1832.

Therefore, C_2 would have resulted in an average annual increase of (\$3247 − \$1832), or \$1415. Hence C_1 was recommended.

A condensed description of alternative ways of obtaining a measure of effectiveness for quantitative objectives is given in Note 1 at the end of this chapter.

EFFECTIVENESS FOR A SET OF QUALITATIVE OBJECTIVES. If all the objectives in the edited list are qualitative in character, then the approximate measure of value provided in the next chapter can be used to weight them. By use of this procedure each objective will be assigned a relative value v_i, such that the sum of these values is equal to 1.

As has already been indicated, efficiency with respect to a qualitative objective can be measured in terms of the probability of successfully obtaining the objective. For example, the objective might be "to produce a lot of parts with no defects." The presence of any number of defects constitutes a failure. Hence, on any given production run the objective is either obtained or it is not. Efficiency relative to such an objective might simply be the probability of attaining it.

This measure of efficiency, however, is subject to certain restrictions. Suppose two courses of action, C_1 and C_2, have the same probability of yielding the desired objective, but one is more costly to use. Then it is obviously less efficient, if minimizing cost is also an objective. This situation can be handled in one of two ways: 1. Efficiency can be measured for each course of action relative to a specified set of restrictions regarding cost, time, etc. That is, how efficient are C_1 and C_2, if the same expenditures are made in using each? 2. "Minimization of costs" can be included as a separate objective, and the courses of action evaluated relative to this as well as the qualitative objective Here the method described in the next section would have to be used because there would be a mixture of quantitative and qualitative objectives.

Once the efficiency of each course of action for each objective is determined (E_{ij}) and the standardized value of each objective (v_j'), the effectiveness of each course of action can be expressed as

$$\sum_{j=1}^{k} E_{ij}v_j'$$

In this case the effectiveness is represented by a single value, the sum of the weighted efficiencies. Direct comparison of these values will provide a basis for a selection of the most effective course of action.

EFFECTIVENESS FOR MIXED QUANTITATIVE AND QUALITATIVE OBJECTIVES. In some cases one or more (but not all) objectives are expressed in qualitative terms (e.g., "to retain family control of the company," or "to obtain good community relations"). In such cases a modification is required in the procedures just presented.

Suppose we have the three objectives considered in the earlier example (increasing net profit, increasing share of the market, and decreasing average service time) and in addition this fourth objective: to retain family control of the company. Weights for the first three objectives can be determined as before. Suppose dollars per year is used as the standard unit. Then a dollar-per-year value must be placed on family control.

It might be possible to determine this value by study of the actual cost to the family of retaining control. But we shall assume that this is either not possible or not practical. In this case judgment must be used, but we want to obtain the judgment in such a way as to get some measure of its reliability. This can be done, in this case by obtaining participants' opinions on the three following questions:

1. How many dollars per year is family control worth?
2. How many percentage points increase in share of market per year is family control worth?
3. How many decreased days of average service time per year is family control worth?

The reliability of the replies can be checked by using the weighting factors for the units to transform all replies into dollars. If the transformed replies are not consistent some further probing will be necessary.

As indicated in the last section, in order to determine the efficiency of a course of action with respect to a qualitative objective one can measure the probability that the course of action will produce the objective. Thus, a single probability figure can represent the efficiency of a course of action for a qualitative objective. Then, for example, if family control is worth $100,000 per year, and a course of action has a probability of 0.8 of retaining family control, the expected return is $80,000. Expected return, in this case, is represented by a single value. Averages, maximums, or minimums have no meaning here.

Average expected return, maximum expected gain, minimum expected loss, or any other value can be obtained as before for the first three objectives. Then the expected return relative to the qualitative objective can be added to the total expected return determined relative to the quantitative objective. This procedure has an obvious generalization for any number and combination of qualitative and quantitative objectives.

The optimum decision procedure relative to mixed objectives can be summarized as follows:

1. Determine the total expected return relative to the quantitative objectives.

2. Determine the probability of success for each C_i relative to each of the k' qualitative objectives: P_{ij}.

3. Determine the value of each qualitative objective by equating it to a measure along the standard efficiency scale used in step 1: v_j'.

4. Determine the total expected return (R_i) for each C_i.*

WHO WEIGHTS THE OBJECTIVES

It is desirable to have each group of participants in the problem, or a representative sample from each group, do the weighting of all the objectives which are on the edited list. Now the problem is to combine the weights given by each group into a single measure of relative importance. This can be accomplished in the following way:

Let v_{ij} represent the weight given to the ith objective by the jth group of participants in the problem. Now assume that the *importance*

*

$$R_i = \sum_{j=1}^{k'} P_{ij}v_j' + \int_{-\infty}^{\infty} xg_i(x)\, dx$$

Similarly we could determine the expected gain

$$G_i = \sum_{j=1}^{k'} P_{ij}v_j' + \int_0^{\infty} xg(x)\, dx$$

where only those O_j are included whose $v_j' > 0$, and the expected loss

$$L_i = \sum_{j=1}^{k'} P_{ij}v_j' + \int_{-\infty}^0 xg(x)\, dx$$

where only those O_j are included whose $v_j' < 0$.

of each group of participants could be established. Let the importance of the *j*th group be represented by V_j. Then, if there are n groups, the composite weight of the *i*th objective would be

$$V_1 v_{i1} + V_2 v_{i2} + \cdots + V_n v_{in} = \sum_{j=1}^{n} V_j v_{ij}$$

Suppose, for example, that there are three groups of participants and that their importance is as follows: $V_1 = 0.5$, $V_2 = 0.3$, and $V_3 = 0.2$. Suppose further that they have each weighted one objective O_i, so that $v_{i1} = 0.8$, $v_{i2} = 0.3$, and $v_{i3} = 0.6$. Then the composite weight of O_i would be

$$0.5(0.8) + 0.3(0.3) + 0.2(0.6) = 0.40 + 0.09 + 0.12 = 0.61$$

Or suppose the weighting involves converting a time period into dollars and $v_{i1} = \$1000$, $v_{i2} = \$1500$, and $v_{i3} = \$1200$. Then the composite weight of O_i would be

$$0.5(1000) + 0.3(1500) + 0.2(1200) = 500 + 450 + 240 = \$1190$$

This procedure assumes that weights can be assigned to the various groups of participants who do the weighting. The principal problem here is not how to assign such weights—because the method presented in the next chapter can be used for this purpose—but who will do the weighting? The answer, unpleasant as it may be to those who try to keep values out of science, is that the Operations Research team should perform this task. The fact is that the team cannot avoid this evaluation; the only question is whether it is to face this problem consciously or unconsciously. If, for example, the team tries to "avoid" this problem by taking only the objectives of the research sponsors into account, then they are actually weighting the sponsors with a maximum value and weighting all other participants with zero value. It is preferable for the team to perform this evaluation consciously and expose and debate its results if necessary, and perhaps even modify them subsequently.

There is no doubt that a complete and satisfactory over-all weighting of objectives is an ideal. But the so-called "practical" procedure of ignoring these weights may be quite costly. Of course, even this evaluation of participant groups is very approximate; but these evaluations are not likely to result in as much of a distortion of our social values as is the complete omission of groups of participants from consideration.

SUMMARY

The procedure for formulating a problem presented in this and the preceding chapter may be summarized in the following outline:

A. Analyze the relevant operations and the communication system by which they are controlled.

1. Identify and trace each communication related to operations under study.
2. Identify each transformation of information and decision process.
3. Identify each step in the relevant operations.
4. Drop from consideration each communication or transformation which has no effect on operations (e.g., billing in production operations).
5. Group operations between control points.
6. Prepare a flow chart showing

    a. Control points and decisions made.
    b. Flow of pertinent information between control points and time consumed.
    c. Flow of materials and time of grouped operations.

B. Formulate management's problem.

1. Identify decision-makers and the decision-making procedure.
2. Determine the decision-makers' relevant objectives.
3. Identify other participants and the channels of their influence on a solution.
4. Determine objectives of the other participants.
5. Determine alternative courses of action available to decision-makers.
6. Determine counteractions available to other participants.

C. Formulate the research problem.

1. Edit and condense the relevant objectives.
2. Edit and condense the relevant courses of action.
3. Define the measure of effectiveness to be used.

    a. Define the measure of efficiency to be used relative to each objective.
    b. Weight objectives (if qualitative) or units of objectives (if quantitative).
    c. Define the criterion of best decision as some function of the sum of weighted efficiencies (e.g., maximum expected return, minimum expected loss).

Note 1.   Alternative Ways of Obtaining Measures of Effectiveness for Quantitative Objectives

For illustrative purposes assume two courses of action, C_1 and C_2, and two objectives, O_1 and O_2. Let x_{ij} represent possible values of the efficiency of C_i for O_j measured along the scale X_j.

Generalization of the following procedures to m objectives and n courses of action is straightforward.

ALTERNATIVE 1

   1.1. Apply C_1 (actually, retrospectively, or by simulation) and observe values of x_{11} and x_{12} obtained in each instance.

   1.2. Plot these in two frequency histograms, as shown in Fig. 5-5.

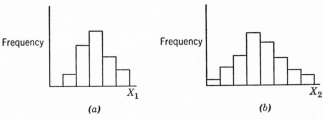

(a)   *(b)*

Fig. 5-5.   Frequency histograms.   (*a*) Efficiency of C_1 for O_1.   (*b*) Efficiency of C_1 for O_2.

   1.3. Construct a probability density function for each histogram. These are called "efficiency functions" and are represented by $f(x_{11})$ and $f(x_{12})$, as illustrated in Fig. 5-6.

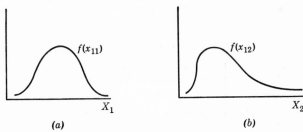

(a)   *(b)*

Fig. 5-6.   Probability density functions.   (*a*) Efficiency function of C_1 for O_1.   (*b*) Efficiency function of C_1 for O_2.

   1.4. Select one scale of efficiency as a standard and find a transformation for units along the other efficiency scale(s) into units on this standard scale. For example, if X_1 is the standard scale, find a function h such that $x_{i1} = h(x_{i2})$.

   1.5. Transform the efficiency functions for all objectives (other than the one whose scale of efficiency is used as a standard) into expressions using standard units. In this case $f(x_{12}') = f[h(x_{12})]$, where $f(x_{12}')$ is the transformed efficiency function.

1.6. Find the probability density function of $x_1 \equiv x_{11} + x_{12}'$, which is called the "effectiveness function" and is represented by $g(x_1)$ in Fig. 5-7, where

$$g(x_1) = \int_{a=-\infty}^{x} f(x_{11} = a)f(x_{12}' = x_1 - a) \, da$$

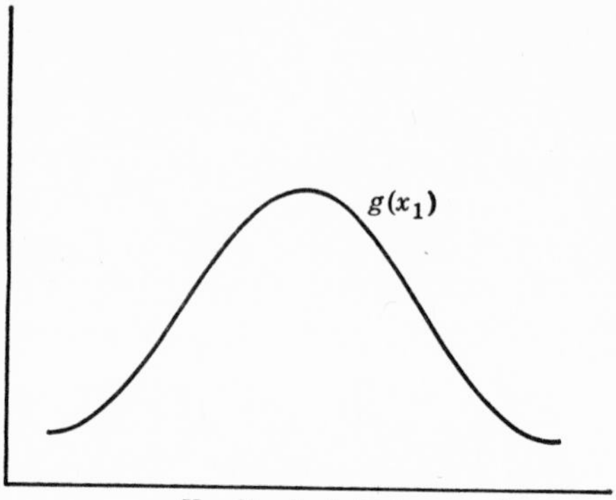

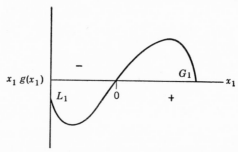

$g(x_1)$

X_1, Standard efficiency scale

Fig. 5-7.   Effectiveness function.

1.7. Then, for C_1

Expected loss $(L_1) = \int_{-\infty}^{0} x_1 g(x_1) \, dx$,   (negative)

Expected gain $(G_1) = \int_{0}^{\infty} x_1 g(x_1) \, dx_1$ (positive)

Expected return $(R_1) = G_1 + L_1 = \int_{-\infty}^{0} x_1 g(x_1) \, dx_1 + \int_{0}^{\infty} x_1 g(x_1) \, dx_1$

$$= \int_{-\infty}^{\infty} x_1 g(x_1) \, dx_1$$

These can be represented graphically in a "return function," Fig. 5-8.

$x_1 g(x_1)$

$-$

L_1 0 G_1 x_1

$+$

Fig. 5-8.   Return function.

1.8. Repeat steps 1.1 through 1.7 for C_2.
1.9. Select criterion of best decision (e.g., maximum expected return).
1.10. Select course of action which satisfies this criterion.

ALTERNATIVE 2

2.1. Transform X_2 to X_1 by getting $x_{i1} = h(x_{i2})$.

2.2. Apply C_1 and for each observed pair of values of x_{11} and x_{12} compute $x_{11} + h(x_{12})$.

2.3. Using observations of $[x_{11} + h(x_{12})]$ plot the frequency histogram as in step 1.2.

2.4. Derive the probability density function as in step 1.3. This is now the effectiveness function $g(x_1)$.

2.5. Proceed as in steps 1.7 through 1.10.

ALTERNATIVE 3, where enough data cannot be obtained to construct the probability density functions

3.1. Same as step 2.1.

3.2. Same as step 2.2.

3.3. Compute the average of observed pairs (converted and summed). This is the estimate of average effectiveness (AE).

3.4. Use the maximum average effectiveness (MAE) as the criterion of best decision.

3.5. Compute (AE) for each course of action and select one with (MAE).

BIBLIOGRAPHY

1. Ackoff, Russell L. *The Design of Social Research*, University of Chicago Press, Chicago, 1953.
2. Bross, Irwin D. J., *Design for Decision*, The Macmillan Co., New York, 1953.
3. Dewey, John, *How We Think*, D. C. Heath & Co., Boston, 1933.
4. ———, *Logic: The Theory of Inquiry*, Henry Holt & Co., New York, 1938.
5. Wilson, E. B., Jr., *An Introduction to Scientific Research*, McGraw-Hill Book Co., New York, 1952.

Chapter 6

Weighting Objectives

INTRODUCTION

In the last chapter it was shown that a completely self-conscious decision procedure in problems involving more than one objective requires a method for assigning relative values (weights) to the objectives involved. It was also shown that where quantitative objectives are involved it may be necessary to obtain weights for intervals along the scales that define the objectives (e.g., 1-day delay in delivery and 1% improvement in market position).

The necessary relative weights might be assigned in terms of dollar amounts merely by putting a certain dollar sign on every objective. This has the apparent advantages of a measure that is readily understandable, "objective," and universally used. The difficulties in the use of monetary scales are also apparent. Many objectives cannot be measured in terms of dollars. In many cases we value differently two things which can be obtained at the same cost. In other cases costs are very difficult to assign. For example, what is the true cost of an injury, a life, a failure to supply an item, a loss of "good will"? Such objectives have been miscalled "intangibles" in business operations. "Intangible" means "untouchable," and while it is true that these objectives cannot be "touched" by a dollar method of measurement, they can nevertheless be measured by other methods, one of which will be discussed in this chapter.

Further, even when an objective can be measured in monetary terms, the measure may be very difficult or costly to obtain, or its accuracy may be questionable. Thus, inventory carrying costs, sales promotional costs, and costs of distribution by product line may be very obscure in certain industries, though they are all critical for managerial decisions. In general, it is safe to say that Operations Researchers constantly face the problem of finding adequate cost and profit estimates within so-called profit-motivated enterprises.

Nevertheless, O.R. does use monetary scales in almost all its research. How does it overcome the difficulties of assigning dollar figures to objectives? Two methods are commonly used:

1. Consider first only those objectives for which a dollar figure can be objectively and accurately assigned. Construct a model of the operation in which the loss function is defined in terms of these objectives. Determine from the model the decision-rule which "optimizes" relative to the objectives. Present this decision-rule to an executive committee of the company, which evaluates the rule in terms of the "intangible" objectives and modifies it on the basis of judgment and experience.

Example: Optimization of a production process in terms of minimizing the total expected inventory carrying costs and setup costs; subsequent modification of the plan to adjust for possible instability of the labor force requirements. That is, the first plan might call for hiring a large force at the beginning of each month, and laying them off at the end of the month; the "intangible" objective of labor force stability would be introduced through judgment to modify this plan so as to equalize the force throughout the month, even though this generalization produces some increase in the total expected inventory and setup costs.

2. Set up a model in which an "intangible" objective appears, say, as a linear term. Thus, if "shortage" is taken to be an intangible, one might treat the cost of a shortage of x items in the model as a linear term C_1x. The total cost would then be written as

$$TC = C_1x + \text{Other pertinent costs}$$

Now C_1 is unknown. However, we may be able to find the minimum of TC with respect to x. For example, suppose it is possible to take the derivative of TC with respect to x, and suppose

$$d(TC)/dx = 0$$

gives a minimum. We can then compute that value of x which will yield a minimum TC and we can also compute the minimum TC. This minimum total cost will be a function of C_1 only. Now if we argue that the company has in fact been pursuing the best policy, then we can use the actual cost as an estimate of the minimum TC. Knowing this minimum, we can solve for C_1. This value of C_1 is the value the company has been assuming, whether it knows it or not, provided its past decisions have been optimum. This method of estimating values for intangibles has the disadvantage that it must assume an optimum in order to make an estimate. But the method is excellent for getting management to think quantitatively about so-called intangibles.

ILLUSTRATION OF THE METHOD

In this chapter a method is developed for estimating the relative values of a set of objectives.* The method seems to have general application. Where the measures developed herein can be applied, it may be possible to avoid the problem of "intangibles" and to assign values to all objectives along a common scale.

The method described in this chapter is also applicable to weighting outcomes, whether or not they are objectives, and to assigning relative values to objects or properties of objects and/or events. Some of these additional applications will be illustrated by case studies in the latter part of this chapter.

Both the underlying logic and the procedure are simple. To illustrate the idea, suppose we have four strips of wood of unequal length and no device for measuring length is available. Suppose further we want to determine the relative (not absolute) length of these four strips. *One* possible way of proceeding is as follows. We order the strips from the longest to the shortest. Let us call the longest A, the next B, the next C, and the shortest D. Suppose we give A a value of 100% and estimate separately for B, C, and D what percentage of A's length they represent. Suppose we get the following results. $B = 60\%$, $C = 30\%$, $D = 20\%$. Now we can put B, C, and D end to end and compare A with this combined length $(B + C + D)$. If our initial estimates were correct, $B + C + D$ is equal to 110% of A. If this comparison reveals a discrepancy, some adjustment in our original estimates will be required. Next, we compare A to $B + C$, and we would expect $B + C$ to be equal to 90% of A. This comparison would provide another check on our original estimates. Finally, in this case, we would compare B to $(C + D)$ and expect to find B to be $60/(30 + 20)$ or 120% of $(C + D)$.

* For information concerning alternative methods see Note 1 at the end of this chapter.

This procedure fundamentally consists of a systematic check on relative judgments by a process of successive comparisons. The method to be described is essentially the same as the one just recounted. Though the method is admittedly subject to some restrictions in its application (as the additivity assumptions to be given will indicate), it still has a wide range of applicability. The examples of the method that will be given depend on verbal judgments of the individual, but this restriction to oral behavior is not an essential part of the method itself. The method is applicable to actual choices or other displays of preference.

It may be helpful to precede the discussion of the technical aspect of the method by an example of how the method works. Assume that one evaluator is involved (i.e., the problem belongs to one person), and that there are four possible outcomes.

Procedure 1

1. Rank the four outcomes in order of importance. Let O_1 represent the outcome that is judged to be the most important, O_2 the next, O_3 the next, and O_4 the last.

2. Tentatively assign the value 1.00 to the most valued outcome and assign values that initially seem to reflect their relative values to the others. For example, the evaluator might assign 1.00, 0.80, 0.50, and 0.30 to O_1, O_2, O_3, and O_4 respectively. Call these tentative values v_1, v_2, v_3, and v_4 respectively. These are to be considered as first estimates of the "true" values V_1, V_2, V_3, and V_4.

3. Now make the following comparison:

$$O_1 \text{ versus } (O_2\text{-and-}O_3\text{-and-}O_4)$$

i.e., if the evaluator had the choice of obtaining O_1 or the *combination* of O_2, O_3, and O_4, which would he select? Suppose he asserts that O_1 is preferable. Then the value of v_1 should be adjusted so that

$$v_1 > v_2 + v_3 + v_4$$

For example: $v_1 = 2.00$, $v_2 = 0.80$, $v_3 = 0.50$, and $v_4 = 0.30$.

Note that the values of O_2, O_3, and O_4 have been retained.

4. Now compare O_2 versus O_3-and-O_4. Suppose O_3-and-O_4 are preferred. Then further adjustment of the values is necessary. For example: $v_1 = 2.00$, $v_2 = 0.70$, $v_3 = 0.50$, and $v_4 = 0.30$.

Now each value is consistent with all the evaluations.

5. In this case, the evaluations are completed. It may be convenient, however, to "normalize" these values by dividing each by Σv_j,

which in this case is 3.50. These standardized values are represented by v_j':

$$v_1' = 2.00/3.50 = 0.57$$
$$v_2' = 0.70/3.50 = 0.20$$
$$v_3' = 0.50/3.50 = 0.14$$
$$v_4' = 0.30/3.50 = 0.09$$

Total   1.00

Assumptions

Before formalizing the method just illustrated it may be helpful to point out some of the critical assumptions underlying this method. The first are formal assumptions:

A-1: For every outcome O_j, there corresponds a real nonnegative number V_j, to be interpreted as a measure of the true importance of O_j.

A-2: If O_j is more important than O_k, then $V_j > V_k$, and if O_j and O_k are equally important, then $V_j = V_k$.

A-3: If V_j and V_k correspond to O_j and O_k respectively, then $V_j + V_k$ corresponds to the combined outcome O_j-and-O_k.

Specifically, A-3 will fail if outcome O_1 logically implies the absence of outcome O_2. In this case, the combined outcome O_1-and-O_2 is impossible, and hence does not have the value $V_1 + V_2$. Suppose O_1 and O_2 are characterized along a scale, e.g., annual income; let $O_1 =$ an income of exactly \$20,000 a year and $O_2 =$ an annual income of exactly \$10,000 a year. But O_1-and-O_2 is impossible, and does not meaningfully have any value. Also, if the occurrence of O_1 implies the occurrence of O_2, then O_1-and-O_2 reduces to O_1, which will not in general have the value $V_1 + V_2$. Making at least \$20,000 a year implies making at least \$10,000. In this case O_1-and-O_2 reduces to making at least \$20,000 a year, and would not presumably have the same value as $V_1 + V_2$. In effect, then, the method has applicability only where the outcomes are discrete, not contradictory, and mutually independent.

A-3 is the basic additivity assumption of this method. Corollaries of this assumption are:

A-3a: If O_j is preferred to O_k, and O_k is preferred to O_l then the combined outcome O_j-and-O_k is preferred to O_l. This condition would fail if the first two outcomes were, say, "eating lobster at dinner to-night" and "eating a thick steak at dinner tonight," where the third is "eating swordfish at dinner tonight." One might not prefer a dinner which combines steak and lobster to one of only swordfish. But suitable redefining of objectives can often avoid this difficulty, for instance, by removing the restriction imposed by "tonight."

A-3*b*: The importance of the combined outcome O_j-and-O_k is equal to the importance of the combined outcome O_k-and-O_j. The order of presentation of outcomes or their grouping does not alter the preferences. For example, it is assumed that the individual will make no distinction between the combination "prestige-and-wealth" and the combination "wealth-and-prestige."

A-3*c*: If the combination O_j-and-O_k is equally preferred to O_k, then $V_j = 0$.*

The method also makes certain operational assumptions:

1. If an individual is given a range of real number values, say from 0 to 1, he can then make a first estimate of the value of each outcome along this scale which estimate provides some information about the V_j. (As indicated in the foregoing, estimates of V_j are symbolized by v_j.)

2. The method can be said to provide a basis for successive improvement of the estimates of the V_j. As we said before, the individual is subjected to two tests, each of which contributes information concerning the importance of outcomes to him. In the first test, the individual assigns *tentative* quantities to the V_j along a scale provided for him by the researcher. Next, he is presented with certain questions about combinations of outcomes, and his preferences provide additional information concerning the V_j. For example, it is assumed that his judgment on these questions is not totally influenced by his initial judgment in assigning values. That is, if he initially judged, say, $v_1 = 0.7$, $v_2 = 0.5$, and $v_3 = 0.4$, these judgments would not necessarily imply that on the second test he would say that O_1 is less preferred than the combination of O_2 and O_3. The second set of judgments has at least some potentiality for revising the first set. This assumption has actually been justified in part by data obtained from the use of the method.

Reliability and Bias

Measures of the *reliability* of the estimates can be obtained. Preliminary studies indicate that replication under controlled conditions can be approximated. But the method does not provide any estimate of the *accuracy* or *bias* of the judgments. This serious defect is shared

---

* It will be noted that, if an O_j exists satisfying the condition of A-3*c*, then this outcome has a value of zero for all methods of scaling of the kind discussed here; i.e., there is a zero-point of the scale invariant with any transformation of the V-scale. This is not true in so-called "utility" measurements discussed in refs. 12 and 14.

by all existing techniques for estimating measures of preference. At present, we do not actually have a clear and agreed-upon definition of what a "true" preference means, so that bias is in a sense not measurable. Practical use of the method may eventually suggest how bias can be estimated.

We should add that an estimate of bias could be obtained if the meaning of the V_j could be expressed in terms of certain properties (probabilities of choice) of actual choices under controlled conditions. Attempts have been made in this direction,[3] but much still remains to be done to develop procedures that can be used in research.

Formulation of the Method

The general symbolic formulation of the method of estimating the V_j is quite formidable in appearance (though not in practice).

1. Rank the outcomes in their order of value. Let O_1 represent the most valued, O_2 the next most important, $\cdots$, and O_m the least important.

2. Assign the value 1.00 to O_1 (i.e., $v_1 = 1.00$) and assign values that appear suitable to each of the other outcomes.

3. Compare O_1 versus $O_2 + O_3 + \cdots + O_m$.*

3.1. If O_1 is preferable to $O_2 + O_3 + \cdots + O_m$, adjust (if necessary) the value of v_1 so that $v_1 > v_2 + v_3 + \cdots + v_m$. In this adjustment, as in all others, attempt to keep the relative values of the adjusted group (v_2, v_3, etc.) invariant. Proceed to step 4.

3.2. If O_1 and $O_2 + O_3 + \cdots + O_m$ are equally preferred, adjust (if necessary) the value of v_1 so that $v_1 = v_2 + v_3 + \cdots + v_m$. Proceed to step 4.

3.3. If O_1 is preferred less than $O_2 + O_3 + \cdots + O_m$, adjust (if necessary) the value of v_1 so that $v_1 < v_2 + v_3 + \cdots + v_m$.

3.3.1. Compare O_1 versus $O_2 + O_3 + \cdots + O_{m-1}$.

3.3.1.1. If O_1 is preferred, adjust (if necessary) the values so that $v_1 > v_2 + v_3 + \cdots + v_{m-1}$. Proceed to step 4.

3.3.1.2. If O_1 is equally preferred, adjust (if necessary) the values so that $v_1 = v_2 + v_3 + \cdots + v_{m-1}$. Proceed to step 4.

3.3.1.3. If O_1 is preferred less, adjust (if necessary) the values so that $v_1 < v_2 + \cdots + v_3 + \cdots v_{m-1}$.

3.3.1.3.1. Compare O_1 versus $O_2 + O_3 + \cdots + O_{m-2}$, etc., until either O_1 is preferred or is equal to the rest, then proceed to step 4, or until the comparison of O_1 versus $O_2 + O_3$ is completed, then proceed to step 4.

4. Compare O_2 versus $O_3 + O_4 + \cdots + O_m$ and proceed as in step 3.

* The $+$ here designates the logical connective "and."

5. Continue until the comparison of O_{m-2} versus $O_{m-1} + O_m$ is completed.

6. Convert each v_j into a normalized value v_j', dividing it by Σv_j. Then $\Sigma v_j'$ should be equal to 1.00.

It should be noted that the resulting estimated values are relative; i.e., the deletion or addition of an outcome may affect the values obtained. Furthermore, the estimated values obtained for a set of outcomes may change over time, if the true values so change.*

The method just described is not especially suitable when there are seven or more outcomes. In such cases the method becomes cumbersome. A more suitable alternative procedure is now described. Again, we assume that this technique potentially improves the estimates. Specifically, this technique, like the previous one, may change the initial ranking of the outcomes.

Procedure 2

1. Rank the entire set of outcomes in terms of preference without assigning quantitative values.

2. Select at random one outcome from the set. Let O_s represent this (standard) outcome. Then, by random assignment subdivide the remaining set of outcomes into groups of no more than five, and preferably (though not necessarily) into groups of approximately equal size. Each outcome other than O_s should be included in one and only one group. (Alternatively, let O_s be the outcome with highest rank.)

3. Add O_s to each group and assign the value 1.00 to it ($v_s = 1.00$).

4. Use steps 1 through 5 of Procedure 1 to obtain unstandardized values for the outcomes in the groups formed in step 3 of this procedure, but in adjusting the v_j do not change the value of v_s.

5. Compare the rankings obtained from steps 2 through 4 of Procedure 2 with those obtained in step 1. If the rank orders differ, reconsider the ranking and if necessary proceed again from steps 2 to 4 of this procedure.

6. Once consistent results are obtained, normalize the values obtained in step 5 of Procedure 2 by dividing the value assigned to each objective by the sum of the values assigned to all the outcomes.

The procedure just described may be illustrated by the following example. Suppose there are ten objectives.

1. Suppose these are ranked as follows: $O_1, O_2, \cdots, O_{10}$.

* By suitable choice of the range for assigning values, the V_j scale can be transformed by any linear function with zero-intercept.

2. Suppose O_7 is selected at random.

3. The remaining outcomes may be assigned at random to three groups as follows:

(a)	(b)	(c)
O_6	O_5	O_1
O_{10}	O_9	O_3
O_2	O_4	O_8

4. O_7 is added to each group and is given the value 1.00.

5. Suppose the following unnormalized values are obtained:

(a)	(b)	(c)
$v_6 = 1.35$	$v_5 = 1.50$	$v_1 = 3.60$
$v_{10} = 0.60$	$v_9 = 0.75$	$v_3 = 3.00$
$v_2 = 2.70$	$v_4 = 1.80$	$v_8 = 0.90$
$v_7 = 1.00$	$v_7 = 1.00$	$v_7 = 1.00$

6. A comparison with step 1 shows that O_2 and O_3 have been reversed. If the original ranking were still judged correct, then the values of O_2 and/or O_3 should be readjusted in their respective groups. The steps are then carried through as before. Suppose, however, that it is decided that the computed ranking as opposed to that obtained in step 1 is correct. Then the values in step 5 are normalized (by dividing each value by 17.2) to obtain the following:

$$v_1' = 0.21 \qquad v_6' = 0.08$$

$$v_2' = 0.16 \qquad v_7' = 0.06$$

$$v_3' = 0.17 \qquad v_8' = 0.05$$

$$v_4' = 0.10 \qquad v_9' = 0.04$$

$$v_5' = 0.09 \qquad v_{10}' = 0.03$$

An assumption made in each of the illustrations is that a single individual does the evaluating. In many cases, it may be desirable to have a group do the evaluating, particularly where the decision involved is one to be made by a group. In such a case, a group vote can be taken for each comparison with the decision going to the majority. This procedure is not as cumbersome in practice as it may appear.

In some cases, it may be desirable to have each member of the group do the evaluating independently. Then the value assigned to each outcome can be an average of the values assigned to that outcome by the various members.

CASE STUDIES

Two cases are presented in which the method of this chapter was used. The first case is not an Operations Research study but it suggests a number of uses of this weighting procedure other than in formulating the problem.

Case I *

The general definition of a defect is an undesirable attribute which detracts from the salability of the product. The extent to which this detraction occurs for each of the defects under consideration cannot be quantitatively measured and is therefore determined by individual opinion on the basis of experience and industrial practice. Unfortunately, there are as many opinions concerning the relative demerits of specific defects as there are people expressing them. It is entirely possible, under these conditions, that the same lot of finished material can be either accepted or rejected depending upon the standards which are used and the individual opinions upon which these standards are founded.

There is an urgent need for a method which will enable a quantitative evaluation of varying degrees of defects to be made. The generally acceptable sampling procedures are readily obtainable for the controlled inspection of materials and justifiable conclusions can be obtained concerning their acceptability. We will now present such a method and illustrate its application.

THE RANKING METHOD. The method discussed here is a modification of the quantitative ranking method (described in the foregoing) in an effort to establish a basis for policy-making decisions. This procedure is predicated upon opinion in order to establish quantitative relationships among variables which cannot be otherwise obtained by theoretical considerations or by previous data resulting from past performance. These opinions are solicited either individually or collectively and indicate preferential merits of each variable as compared to the value of combinations of variables within the same system. The final decision is reached after continuous re-evaluations of each variable and a relative ranking established on an arbitrary scale which is consistent with each of the decisions reported during the evaluation process.

The first step in the procedure is the tentative listing of variables

* This is a portion of "A Method for Defect Evaluation" by Paul Stillson which appeared in *Industrial Quality Control*, XI, no. 1, 9–12 (July 1954), and is reproduced here with the kind permission of the author and editor.

in the order of their importance. The variable at the head of the list is arbitrarily assigned a value of 100 and the remaining variables are assigned numerical values indicating their estimated importance relative to this variable. These values are qualitative in nature and serve only as a temporary ranking for subsequent readjustment.

The individual, or group, is then requested to register an opinion as to the relative merit of the initial variable as compared to the combined effect of the second and third variables in the listing. The three possible responses to this question are: 1. the initial variable is more important than variables two and three; 2. it is less important; 3. they are equal. In the case of the first response, the value of 100 assigned to the initial factor must exceed the combined value assigned to the second and third variables which were used for this comparison. Con versely, the latter total must exceed 100 if the second response is received. Obviously, they must be equal in the event of the third response. This procedure is repeated until the initial variable has been compared with all combinations of two variables within the previous listing. Each decision is recorded and adjustments made to concur with existing and previous decisions.

In a similar manner, the second variable is compared with combinations of variables below it in the original listing. This process is continued until each variable has been evaluated and the numerical values adjusted to conform with the individual decisions.

Through continuous adjustment of the original numerical ratings, it is quite possible that the original ranking will be altered at the conclusion of the evaluation. A significant rearrangement may necessitate a revised listing and a second trial, although this should be obvious in the early stages of the procedure.

Application of Method. The inspection of finished packages in the pharmaceutical industry represents a typical operation to which this method has been applied. Both the attribute type of defect and the variable type of defect are prevalent in this inspection process and must be considered relative to their respective effects on product quality. It is recognized that these defects have varying importance as to their contribution to rejectability of the lot and must therefore be weighted accordingly. The selection of the defects is the result of the considered opinion of a responsible panel within the quality control group. In this particular case, each defect was considered an attribute and was either present or absent in the individual vials. The only limitation to the inclusion of each defect was in its definition, such that each defect could be solely responsible for lot rejection if that defect were present in a majority of the packages within a lot.

The previous standards for the acceptance or rejection of individual lots were based upon the classification of defects into two categories; namely, major and minor. An arbitrary scale was drawn in which ten minor defects, regardless of type, were equivalent to each major defect. This method of rating is commonly accepted in industrial practice. However, there was considerable disagreement among the responsible personnel concerning the foregoing equivalence rating as well as the differentiation between the two kinds of defects. Therefore, it was deemed advisable to install an acceptance standard for this operation to which all members of the panel could subscribe and in which each defect could be ranked with its respective numerical rating.

In this experiment, the panel consisted of nine men with widely varying concepts as to the relative importance of the defects under consideration. The use of group opinion in the ranking method was accomplished by accepting majority rule on each comparison and regarding the collective decision as a single response.

The defects which were included in this evaluation were specifically defined to provide for equivalent comparisons among the nine members of the panel. Decisions were made by open ballot although discussion of the specific responses was prohibited. The periodic adjustments conforming to each decision were performed in full view of the participating panel.

Experimental Results. The initial ranking of all the defects by individual members of the panel was requested along with their respective ratings. The defect at the head of the list was assigned a value of 100 and the remainder placed in a descending order with numerical values proportionate with the first defect. An average of all the values for each defect was calculated from the opinions and these ratings became the starting point of adjustment. In the general case, we may designate these defects as A through F.

The initial assessment is shown as:

Variable A	100
Variable B	60
Variable C	55
Variable D	44
Variable E	34
Variable F	27

A series of comparisons were offered to the panel in the manner described previously. With each decision the numerical values were adjusted, if necessary, until all possible combinations for comparative purposes were exhausted. A partial list of comparisons and decisions is shown in Table 6-1.

TABLE 6-1. COMPARISONS OF DEFECT COMBINATIONS

Decision Number	Comparison	Decision			Majority Decision
		Yes	No	Equal	
1	A > (B + C)	2	7	0	no
2	A > (B + D)	2	6	1	no
3	A > (B + E)	3	5	1	no
4	A > (B + F)	6	1	2	yes
5	A > (C + D)	7	2	0	yes
6	A > (C + E)	9	0	0	yes
7	A > (C + F)	9	0	0	yes
8	A > (B + C + D)	1	8	0	no
9	A > (B + C + E)	1	8	0	no
10	B > (C + D)	4	2	3	equal
11	B > (C + E)	6	1	2	yes
12	B > (C + F)	8	0	1	yes
13	B > (D + E)	9	0	0	yes
14	B > (D + F)	9	0	0	yes
15	B > (C + D + E)	2	5	2	no
16	C > (D + E)	2	7	0	no
17	C > (D + F)	1	8	0	no
18	C > (E + F)	5	2	2	yes
19	C > (D + E + F)	0	7	2	no
20	D > (E + F)	1	4	4	equal

It will be noted that the first and second decisions of the group did not necessitate any adjustment since the sum of the values representing the second and third variables was already in excess of the value for the leading variable. The third opinion poll, however, showed that the consensus was in favor of B and E over A although the original assessment was 94 versus 100 in favor of the leading variable. A necessary adjustment was then made such that the numerical ratings coincided with the majority decision. In this case, variable B was arbitrarily increased from 60 to 70. The experimenter should not be too much concerned as to the particular variable to be adjusted or the exact amount of adjustment as the adjustment itself may, in turn, be considered tentative and subject to re-evaluation by future comparisons.

The fourth decision shown in the table was evaluated by the numerical ratings using the adjusted value of B as 70 and, again, did not cause further change in the defect assessment tabulation. The next decision, the fifth, conformed with the existing ratings but began to indicate a decided trend toward the relative importance of the variables in question. The combined sum of C and D is shown in the initial rating as 99, or one unit less than the top value of 100. Yet the members of the panel voted strongly in favor of A over C and D as evidenced by the 7-to-2 majority. Therefore, future adjustment would tend to lower the values ascribed to these variables, C and D, in the event that further adjustment of the variables was necessary.

The method of adjustment was repeated as each individual decision was recorded. At each change, the resultant tabulation became the basis for further adjustment. Special mention may be made of decisions 10 and 20, as these indicate an equality between groups of variables and must be taken into consideration. In each case, the immediate adjustment conformed with all previous decisions as well as the current one.

The final ratings, based upon the procedure described, are shown as:

Variable A	100
Variable B	82
Variable C	43
Variable D	38
Variable E	24
Variable F	13

At this point, the experimenter must review all comparisons and check the majority decisions against the final ratings for conformance. Decisions 10 and 20, B versus C and D and D versus E and F, are shown as nearly equivalent as possible and still enable the other comparisons to be valid.

Discussion. The use of statistical sampling plans can now be applied to this packaging operation by assuming the leading variable to be a major defect and evaluating the succeeding variables on the basis of the aforementioned ratings. Therefore, variable B is 0.82 of a major defect, variable C is 0.43 of a major defect, etc. As a matter of record, a majority decision was obtained concerning this assumption prior to its acceptance in the inspection procedure.

If we consider a single sampling plan described in the MIL-STD-105A Tables,* it is found that for a lot size of 40,000 units and an Acceptable Quality Level of 0.65%, a maximum of seven defects is allowed in a sample of 450 prior to its rejection. However, the critical score for rejection has been set at a maximum value of 8.000 in order to avoid a range of indecision between 7.000 and 8.000. Therefore, 8.000 becomes the maximum allowable score for the inspection process on the basis of the final ratings of the defect evaluation. During the inspection, the occurrence of each defect of each type in the sample is

---

* *Military Standard, Sampling Procedures and Tables for Inspection by Attributes*, Dept. of Defense, U.S. Government Printing Office, Washington, 1950.

recorded and the total frequency of a defect is multiplied by the numerical value established for that defect. These cross products are added to obtain the total score which must not exceed the value of 8.000 in order for the entire lot to be accepted. Conversely, if the total score is greater than 8.000, the entire lot is rejected and returned for reprocessing.

It is readily apparent that a review of the inspection chart may indicate the assignable cause for rejection and suggest the type of reprocessing necessary for acceptance. In this event, the further processing is carried out on the entire lot, 100% inspection, and a second random sample of 450 taken for inspection evaluation.

An example of such an occurrence can be illustrated by a faulty capping operation in the assembly of the finished package. In this illustration, the number of units within the sample containing skewed caps was sufficiently large so that its contributory score was the cause for lot rejection. Then, the entire lot was placed on a conveyor belt and subjected to complete inspection for bad caps. The lot was then reassembled and randomly sampled for a second inspection. At that time, the sample was examined for all defects and a second total score obtained which enabled the lot to be passed.

Perhaps the most significant accomplishment of the ranking method was the establishment of a standard procedure for inspection where an arbitrary procedure had existed previously. By setting quantitative values for rejection and acceptance, the inspection procedure was taken from the realm of individual opinion and became independent of personal prejudice concerning the relative importance of each of the defects under consideration. Moreover, during the evaluation procedure, the decision-making group had occasion to examine each defect in a number of different comparisons and establish its own preferences with a greater degree of confidence.

Finally, it should be pointed out that each member of the panel expressed satisfaction with the final ranking and felt that the resultant values coincided with his own *a priori* opinion concerning the relative merits of the defects under discussion.

Case II *

The executive committee of a company wished to evaluate certain plans of action that pertained to the company's operations over the next 5 years. First of all, on the basis of preliminary study of past policy decisions the research team set up a list of what appeared to be management's 5-year objectives. The team met with the executive

* Adapted from an actual example.

committee to discuss their meaning, and suitably modify them where their meaning was not clear or where omissions seemed to occur. These objectives were:

O_1. Continuation of existing management.

O_2. Guaranteed 6% return to the owners on their original investment.

O_3. Company should be in a position to make up to 15% return on investment if market for product stayed in the range of 100% to 200% of current demand.

O_4. No firing, and reasonable promotion of key personnel of company.

O_5. Stable labor relations (as evidenced, say, by absence of strike threats and minimum hiring and firing).

O_6. Technological leadership.

O_7. Community service over and above legal requirements. (Legal requirements themselves are a necessary condition for the company's operation, and are not in this sense "objectives.")

Each objective was discussed and apparently mutual agreement on meaning was obtained. The research team felt that the additivity assumption seemed reasonably justified for this list.

Each member of the executive committee then separately followed Procedure 2 and normalized values for each of the objectives were obtained for each member. The committee then met to discuss its results, and subsequent to this discussion the members submitted a final evaluation of the objectives. In this case, each member's vote was treated equally, and v_j values for each objective were averaged. (Obviously, this procedure of voting on the objectives represents only one of a large number of possible procedures. It may be the most "democratic," since it permits discussion to modify a person's judgment, and since all voters are treated equally.)

The final results were

O_1: Security of existing management	0.25
O_2: Financial security	0.30
O_3: Financial opportunity	0.10
O_4: Key personnel	0.15
O_5: Labor stability	0.05
O_6: Technological leadership	0.05
O_7: Community service	0.10

The executive commitee was considering three possible board policies:

Policy A: Projected 200% expansion of the company's operations in 2 years, including new products and markets.

Policy B: Maintenance of present size of company, with emphasis on improvements in models of existing products.

Policy C: Maintenance of present size of company, with emphasis on replacement of less profitable products by new products.

Each policy was written out in some detail; these are only abbreviated descriptions. A committee was then formed, made up of the executive committee, product engineers, manufacturing and marketing experts, and economic advisors. This committee's task was to evaluate each policy with respect to each of the seven objectives. A composite judgment provided some number between 0 and 1, where "0" means that the policy seriously threatens the objective (probability of attainment is very small), "1" that it virtually guarantees the objective (probability very high), "0.5" that the policy has no effect on attaining the objective. Table 6-2 was obtained.

TABLE 6-2. EFFECTIVENESS OF POLICIES FOR OBJECTIVES

Objective Policy	O_1	O_2	O_3	O_4	O_5	O_6	O_7
A	0.4	0.2	0.8	0.8	0.3	0.6	0.8
B	0.9	0.9	0.2	0.3	0.8	0.4	0.3
C	0.7	0.7	0.4	0.3	0.7	0.8	0.5

In this project it was assumed that the policy which yielded the highest "expected value" would be best from the company's point of view. The expected value of policy A for all objectives was computed by multiplying the value of the objective by the effectiveness of the policy, and summing over all objectives:

Utility of policy A $= (0.4 \times 0.25) + (0.2 \times 0.30) + (0.8 \times 0.10)$

$$+ (0.8 \times 0.15) + (0.3 \times 0.05)$$

$$+ (0.6 \times 0.05) + (0.8 \times 0.10) = 0.485$$

Utility of policy B $= 0.650$

Utility of policy C $= 0.595$

Thus policy B was judged to have the highest expected value.

Note 1

A considerable amount of work has been done in the last decade in formulating formal (axiomatic) value (utility) systems. Based on a suggestion by Pareto,[11] von Neumann and Morgenstern [10] set down a set of formal conditions which, if satisfied, would provide the basis for a measure of value. Following this lead measures of value have been defined in axiomatic systems by Davidson, McKinsey, and Suppes,[5] Davidson and Suppes,[7] Suppes and Winet,[14] and others. Much of this and related work has been brought together in a recent publication, *Decision Processes*.[15] This volume and the article by Suppes and Winet [14] provide bibliographies in the value-measurement area.

The problem of deriving a measure of a social group's values from the values of the individual members is called the problem of *amalgamation*. An extensive discussion of this problem is given by Arrow.[2] The same subject is discussed by Goodman; Coombs; and Bush, Mosteller, and Thompson in *Decision Processes*.[15]

Some of the recent experimental work by economists and psychologists is summarized in an article by Edwards.[8] A critical problem in this phase of the work arises out of the difficulty of separating subjective estimates of probability and preference. The experiments of Mosteller and Nogee [9] can be interpreted as measuring value, assuming complete agreement between subjective and objective probabilities. Related methods are presented by Davidson, Siegel, and Suppes,[6] Siegel,[12] and by a number of the contributors to *Decision Processes*.[15]

BIBLIOGRAPHY

1. Ackoff, R. L., "On a Science of Ethics," *Phil. phenom. Res.*, IX, no. 4, 663–672 (June 1949).
2. Arrow, K. J., *Social Choice and Individual Values*, John Wiley & Sons, New York, 1951.
3. Churchman, C. W., and Ackoff, R. L., "An Experimental Definition of Personality," *Phil. Sci.*, *14*, no. 4, 304–332 (Oct. 1947).
4. ———, *Methods of Inquiry*, Educational Publishers, St. Louis, 1950.
5. Davidson, D., McKinsey, J. C. C., and Suppes, P., "Outlines of a Formal Theory of Value, I," Report No. 1, Stanford Value Theory Project, Feb. 1954.
6. Davidson, D., Siegel, S., and Suppes, P., "Some Experiments and Related Theory on the Measurement of Utility and Subjective Probability," Report No. 4, Stanford Value Theory Project, May 1955.
7. Davidson, D., and Suppes, P., "Finitistic Rational Choice Structures," Report No. 3, Stanford Value Theory Project, Feb. 1955.
8. Edwards, W., "The Theory of Decision Making," *Psych. Bull.*, *51*, no. 4, 380–417 (July 1954).
9. Mosteller, F., and Nogee, P., "An Experimental Measure of Utility," *J. Polit. Econ.*, *59*, no. 5, 371–404 (Oct. 1951).
10. Neumann, J. von, and Morgenstern, O., *Theory of Games and Economic Behavior*, 2nd ed., Princeton University Press, Princeton, 1947.
11. Pareto, V., *Manuel d'économie Politique*, 2nd ed., M. Giard, Paris, 1927.

12. Siegel, S., "A Behavioristic Method of Obtaining a Higher Ordered Metric Scale of Utility," Third Annual Meeting, Operations Research Society of America, New York, June 4, 1955.
13. Smith, N. M., Jr., "Comments," *J. Opns. Res. Soc. Am.*, *2*, no. 2, 181–187 (May 1954).
14. Suppes, P., and Winet, M., "An Axiomatization of Utility Based on the Notion of Utility Differences," *Mgmt. Sci.*, *I*, no. 3–4, 259–270 (Apr.–July 1955).
15. Thrall, R. M., Coombs, C. H., and Davis, R. L. (eds.), *Decision Processes*, John Wiley & Sons, New York, 1954.

PART
III

THE MODEL

The chapter comprising this part of the book discusses what a model is, what types of models there are, how to construct them, and how to use them in solving problems.

The model, it will be seen, is a representation of the system under study, a representation which lends itself to use in predicting the effect on the system's effectiveness of possible changes in the system. Of the three types of models to be considered, the iconic, analogue, and symbolic, the latter is of particular importance. By proper mathematical or logical operations, the symbolic model can be used to formulate a solution to the problem at hand. Mathematical techniques for deriving a solution, or optimizing the system, are essentially of two kinds: analytical and numerical. In certain symbolic models, there are terms or variables which cannot be evaluated exactly. In such cases, the Monte Carlo technique is applicable. Analytical, numerical, and Monte Carlo techniques are discussed and illustrated. Finally, models for certain types of recurrent systems are briefly introduced. In subsequent parts they will be discussed in more detail.

Chapter 7

Construction and Solution

of the Model

INTRODUCTION

Viewed generically, a scientific model is a *representation* of some subject of inquiry (such as objects, events, processes, systems) and is used for purposes of prediction and control. The primary function of a scientific model is *explanatory* rather than descriptive. It is intended to make possible, or to facilitate, determination of how changes in one or more aspects of the modeled entity may affect other aspects, or the whole. In the employment of models, this determination is made by manipulating the model rather than by imposing changes on the modeled entity itself.

The advantages of manipulating a model rather than an "actual" object or process are obvious, particularly obvious where changing the "actual" system is either impossible, as in astronomy, or very costly, as in complex industrial organizations.* But the importance of models to science is out of all proportion to even these obvious and massive advantages. In fact, since scientific theorizing itself becomes *identical* with model construction in some aspects, it follows that science would be as impossible in the absence of models as it would be in the absence of theory.

---

* We do not, of course, mean to suggest that all experimentation on the actual system is or should be eliminated. Testing the model is always an indispensable step in the long run, and such a test will ordinarily require some manipulation of the actual system. Moreover, some experimentation on the system is required when, as is frequently the case, there is a lack of data necessary to complete and evaluate the model or to test the model by applying it retrospectively to the past history of the actual system.

Because of this crucial character of model construction in research,* it will be fruitful to consider at some length various types of models, their important logical properties, and some of the important relationships that the types bear to each other and to modeled entities.

We shall distinguish three types of model: iconic, analogue, and symbolic. Roughly, we can say that 1. an iconic model pictorially or visually represents certain aspects of a system (as does a photograph or model airplane), 2. an analogue model employs one set of properties to represent some other set of properties which the system being studied possesses (e.g., for certain purposes, the flow of water through pipes may be taken as an analogue of the "flow" of electricity in wires), and 3. a symbolic model is one which employs symbols to *designate* properties of the system under study (by means of a mathematical equation or set of such equations).

As has been indicated, these are rough characterizations. Actually, a complete and precise description of each type and, particularly, of the relationships which hold among the types would lead to a quite complex discussion involving considerations of symbolic logic and formal semantics. For present purposes, it will be convenient to by-pass some of the complicated problems which such considerations will bring in, and concentrate instead on features of just the rough characterization we have given—remembering always that there is a good deal more to be said about the subject of models than can be covered in this chapter.

It will have been noticed that the three types of models mentioned represent a progression in several respects. The iconic model is usually the simplest to conceive and the most specific and concrete. Its function is generally descriptive rather than explanatory, i.e., it seldom reveals causal relationships. Accordingly, it cannot easily be used to determine or predict what effects many important changes on the actual system might have. The symbolic model is usually the most difficult to conceive and the most general and abstract. Its function is more often explanatory than descriptive. Accordingly, it is ordinarily well suited to the prediction or determination of effects of changes on the actual system. Analogues fall between iconic and symbolic models in both respects.

* In established branches of science, such as physics and chemistry, many conventionally accepted models are available (such as models of the atom). Several prototype models have already been developed which are applicable to specific classes of problems attacked by O.R., too. (These will be surveyed later in this chapter.)

Iconic Models

An iconic model "looks like" what it represents. Many photographs, paintings, and sculptures are iconic models of persons, objects, or scenes. The toy automobile is an iconic model of a "real" automobile. A globe is an iconic model of the earth. Astronomy has produced iconic models of parts of the solar system, and physics has produced what, until recently, purported to be iconic models of the molecule and atom. In general, a representation is an iconic model to the extent that its properties are the same as those possessed by what it represents. These properties, however, are usually subjected to a metric transformation; i.e., they are usually scaled up or down. In a globe, for example, the diameter of the earth is scaled down, but the globe has approximately the same shape as the earth and the relative sizes of continents, seas, etc., are approximately correct. A model of an atom, on the other hand, is scaled up so as to make it visible to the naked eye. Transformation of the scale of the properties represented makes for economy and facility of use. Under ordinary conditions we can work more easily with a model of a building, the earth, an atom, or a production system than we can with the modeled entity itself. A pilot plant, for example, which is a scaled-down iconic model of a full-scale factory, can be manipulated more easily than can the factory itself.

Iconic models are particularly well suited for representing either static or dynamic things at a specific moment of time. For example, a photograph or a flow plan can provide a good "picture" of the plant. But iconic models are generally difficult to use to represent dynamic situations, such as the operations of a factory. For this reason they are not well adapted for use in studying the effect of changes in a process or system. It is possible, of course, to construct a small working model of a factory. But this would usually be too costly to construct and to modify as required in efforts to study possible improvements in the system.

An iconic model, however much it resembles the "original," is still like the other types of model in so far as it usually differs from that which it represents in that it does not have all the properties of what is represented. Only those properties are represented which are essential for the purpose which the model is to serve. Part of the economy in the use of any model in science lies in this selectivity. Properties not pertinent to an investigation need not be included in the model. This is true even in nonscientific studies. Models of automobiles used in the study of a parking problem need not have upholstery or motors

in them.   Likewise, for some purposes, a globe or map does not have to
show relief (i.e., elevation).

Analogues

In constructing a model of most objects, events, processes, or systems, it is not always convenient to reproduce all the pertinent properties even if they are scaled down or up.   For example, we cannot conveniently reproduce the geological structure of the earth in a globe.
But we can easily represent various types of geological formations by
different colors.   If we do so, we are making a convenient substitution
of one property (color) for another (geological structure) according to
some transformation rules.   In maps, for example, where such transformations are common, the rules for so doing are usually given in the
legend.   The map's legend may tell that a solid line represents a hard-
surfaced road or that a broken line represents an improved road.   To
the extent that a model represents one set of properties by another set
of properties, that model is an *analogue*.

Graphs are very simple analogues.   In graphs we use distance to
represent such properties as time, number, per cent, age, weight, and
many other properties.

A graph, like other analogues, is frequently well suited for representing quantitative relationships between properties of classes of things.
Graphs enable us to predict how a change in one property will affect
another property.

By transforming properties into analogous properties we can frequently increase our ability to make changes.   Usually it is simpler to
change an analogue than to change an iconic model, and, compared
with iconic models, not as many changes are generally required to get
the same results.   For example, contour lines on a map are an analogue
model of the rise and fall of the terrain.   It is easier to change the contour lines of a 2-dimensional map than to change the relief (iconic
model) on a 3-dimensional one.

The analogue is successful in representing dynamic situations, that
is, processes or systems.   We often can construct a device whose operations are analogous to those of a production line in a factory.   We can
change the sales demand by suitable modification of inputs to the device.   This would be difficult to accomplish if we had used an iconic
model, such as a scaled-down working model of a machine shop.

Another related advantage of an analogue over an iconic model is
that, with fewer modifications, the analogue can usually be made to
represent many different processes of the same type.   Thus an analogue
model is more general than an iconic model.

An excellent example is the analogue of the control and materials flow which is shown in Fig. 2-1. A small-scale (iconic) model of the plant could not be used effectively to study the effect of certain changes in the communication system. An analogue, such as a flow chart, is quite simple and effective for this purpose.

Symbolic Models

In a symbolic model, the components of what is represented and their interrelationship are given by symbols. The symbols employed are generally mathematical or logical in character. To illustrate the construction of a symbolic model of a very simple process, let us consider the inventory process in the problem discussed in Chapter 2. Monthly production of monthly requirements can be represented by the following graphic analogue:

Input *	1 1 1 1 1 1 1 1 1 1 1
Stock level *	↓0↓0↓0↓0↓0↓0↓0↓0↓0↓0↓
	↓ ↓ ↓ ↓ ↓ ↓ ↓ ↓ ↓ ↓ ↓
Output *	1 1 1 1 1 1 1 1 1 1 1

From this we can determine that the average inventory is equal to zero. If 2 months' supply are made every other month, we get the following analogue:

$$
\begin{array}{cccccc}
2 & 2 & 2 & 2 & 2 & 2 \\
\end{array}
$$

↓1 0↓1 0↓1 0↓1 0↓1 0↓1 0

↓ ↓ ↓ ↓ ↓ ↓ ↓ ↓ ↓ ↓ ↓
1 1 1 1 1 1 1 1 1 1 1

From this we can determine that the average inventory is equivalent to $\frac{1}{2}$ of a month's requirement. We could proceed in this manner and conceive and draw a separate representation for each production quantity that could be scheduled. But it is much simpler to represent the process symbolically.

Let x = the number of months' requirements made per run. Then the *average* number of months' supply in inventory can be represented by the following simple symbolic expression

$$\left(\frac{x-1}{2}\right)$$

* Number of monthly requirements.

In many cases the analogue is cumbersome because the study of a change takes time. For example, the use of an analogue computer to study the effect of sales changes on a production process may take many runs. But if the system can be represented by a mathematical equation (as was done in Chapter 2), the effect of changes can be derived in a few steps of a mathematical deduction. Accordingly, in this and later chapters, we will be primarily concerned with symbolic models. However, it should be kept in mind that problems can and do arise for which analogues are more efficient, for instance, when the system involved is so complex that the amount of work required to construct a symbolic model is prohibitive.

CONSTRUCTING THE MODEL

It will be recalled that the formulation of the problem required an analysis of the system showing the principal phases of the system under study and the way the system could be controlled. A diagram which does this (such as the flow chart shown in Fig. 2-1) is either an iconic model or analogue. In effect, then, the first stage in model construction is performed during the formulation of the problem. But subsequent to this system analysis, the alternative policies to be evaluated are made explicit and a measure of effectiveness is defined. Hence, the next step is to construct a model in which the effectiveness of the system can be expressed as a function of the values of the variables which define the system. Certain of these variables can be changed by executive decisions (the run size in the case presented in Chapter 2), while others cannot (consumer demand). Those which can be so changed are called "control" variables. The control variables are those aspects of the system, values of which are used to define the alternative courses of action being considered.

Briefly, the role of the symbolic model in O.R. can itself be described by the use of symbols as follows:

Let E represent the measure of effectiveness to be used. Let X_i represent the aspects of the system (variables) which can be controlled by management decision, and let Y_j represent the uncontrollable aspects of the system. Then, in model construction, we attempt to formulate one or more equations of the form

$$E = f(X_i, Y_j)$$

The extraction of a solution from such a model consists of determining those values of the control variables X_i for which the measure of effectiveness is maximized.

There may, of course, be as few as one control variable (e.g., number of runs per year in an economic lot-size equation). Furthermore, in some cases it is convenient to use a measure of *in*effectiveness rather than effectiveness (e.g., expected cost rather than expected profit) and the solution consists of minimizing this measure.

Components of the System

We can begin to construct a symbolic model of the system by itemizing all the components of the system which contribute to the effectiveness or ineffectiveness of the operation of the system. If "total expected cost" is used as a measure of effectiveness (such as was done in the case presented in Chapter 2), we can begin by examining the iconic model or analogue of the system prepared in the formulation of the problem. We can extract the operations and materials which involve a cost. Such an initial list might look as follows:

1. Production costs.
   a. Purchase price of raw material.
   b. Freight charges on raw material.
   c. Receiving and stock entry of raw material.
   d. Raw-material inventory.
   e. Production planning (office setup).
   f. Shop setup.
   g. Processing.
   h. In-process inventory.
   i. Shop takedown and stock entry.
   j. Office takedown.
   k. Finished part inventory.
2. Marketing costs.
3. Overhead costs.

Pertinence of Components

Once a complete list of the components of the system is compiled, the next step is to determine whether or not each of these components should be taken into account. This is done for each component listed by determining whether or not this component is affected by the choice of a course of action from among alternatives. Frequently one or more of the components (e.g., fixed costs) are independent of the choice from among the alternative courses of action being considered in the study. If the problem is to determine the most economic production quantities, then we may not have to consider the marketing costs since they may not be affected by the lot-size determination. If marketing costs are dropped from consideration, then it must be remembered that "total cost" must be replaced by a new incremental cost such as "total cost of production." In many cases, although a component is affected by the decision in question, the effect may be very small relative to the sum of the effects on the other components. In the case discussed in Chapter 2, in-process inventory cost was dropped because its contribution to total production cost was negligible.

At this stage in the development of the model, it may not be clear whether or not the effect of a component is significant, though it may appear to be. It may be assumed that the effect is negligible and the component can temporarily be dropped from consideration. But the assumption should be checked when the information and research tools are available for so doing.

In some cases the system is not understood well enough to provide assurance that the variables listed are pertinent. Then it may be desirable either to test for pertinence experimentally or by statistical analysis of available data. That is, we may want to determine by experiment or analysis of available data whether or not the variables listed have anything to do with the effectiveness of the system. We may need to explore, make guesses and check them, and find out "why" the system operates as it does. Which factors, in short, produce the effects observed? Which can be manipulated to produce the effects desired?

The methods of *designed experimentation* (discussed in Part IX) are often useful in this type of exploratory investigation. For example, when the so-called important factors associated with "false alarms" in a (previously referred to) national burglar alarm network were investigated, little was known about the "causes" of these system failures. A series of electric circuits installed in retail stores, warehouses, factories, etc., were supposed to transmit signals over telephone cables to a central office to indicate the presence of intruders in the protected premises after closing time. Photoelectric cells, relays, and other devices were used as detectors. In an excessive number of cases, however, signals were received which alerted the company police when no intruder, in fact, could be found. Birds, cats, loose windows, and various environmental factors were suggested as possible "causes" of these false alarms. A list of approximately 100 factors was compiled. By survey methods and designed experimentation, unimportant factors were eliminated, leaving a list of only a very few environmental factors which were pertinent.

Combining and Dividing the Components

It may be convenient to group certain components of the system. For example, the purchase price, freight cost, and receiving cost of raw material can be combined into a "raw-material acquisition cost." This acquisition cost may not be affected by lot sizes. But, even if this is the case, this cost cannot be dropped from consideration because it contributes to the cost of production and, in turn, the finished inventory cost depends on the money invested in the product. Hence, to compute the cost of money as a part of inventory cost, the raw-material cost must be taken into account. Such indirect effects on the measure of effectiveness should not be overlooked.

Substituting Symbols

For each component remaining on the modified list it is necessary to determine whether its value is *fixed* or *variable*. If a component is variable, we should find those aspects of the system which affect its value. For example, processing cost is usually composed of

1. the number of units processed, and
2. the cost of processing a unit.

Or again, finished inventory cost depends on

1. the number of units in inventory,
2. the time in inventory, and
3. the inventory holding cost per unit.

Once such a breakdown has been made for each variable component in the modified component list, it is convenient to assign a symbol to each subcomponent.

In the example given in Chapter 2, the following list of symbols was derived by the procedure just described:

c_1 = average setup and takedown cost per run

c_2 = average raw material plus processing cost per part

P = average finished-part–inventory-carrying cost per month expressed as a fraction of the money invested in the product

L = the normal number of parts required per month

R = the number of equal-size runs per year

K = expected total relevant cost of producing the parts required for 1 year. ("Relevant" refers to the omission of in-process inventory costs)

The last symbol represents the measure of effectiveness that was employed.

In some cases, we can begin to construct a single equation which expresses the effectiveness of the process or system as a function of the various components which have been symbolized. In other cases a set of equations will be required. To illustrate the procedure, we will consider a simple case in which only one equation is required. For this purpose, let us return to the case presented in Chapter 2 and see how the first (tentative) symbolic model of the production system was constructed.

Illustration of Symbolic Model Construction *

The symbols listed in the preceding section will be used together with the following symbols which are added as a matter of convenience:

$$N = 12L/R = \text{the number of parts per run (where 12 arises as the}$$
$$\text{number of months in a year)}$$

$$K_R = K/R = \text{expected total relevant cost per run}$$

The total relevant cost per run is the sum of three components: the setup and takedown cost, the manufacturing and material cost, and the inventory cost on the investment. (Changes in in-process inventory cost were assumed to be negligible and so were not included in the total relevant cost.) The equation was constructed by the following steps:

Average setup cost per run $= c_1$ (1)

Average manufacturing and material cost per run $= Nc_2$ (2)

Average inventory cost on the investment:

$$\left(\frac{c_1}{N} + c_2\right) = \text{Average investment per part up to the finished}$$
$$\text{inventory phase} \quad (3a)$$

$$P\left(\frac{c_1}{N} + c_2\right) = \text{Average inventory carrying cost per part per}$$
$$\text{month} \quad (3b)$$

$$N/L = \text{Number of months' requirements per run} \quad (3c)$$

---

* The development of economic lot-size equations under the condition of known demand dates back at least to the work of F. W. Harris in 1915. Only recently have economists, statisticians, and operations researchers extended this work to cover variable lead time demand. (See Part IV.) Many models such as the one developed here for illustrative purposes can be found in the literature; see refs. 2, 4, 9, 12, 14–17, 19, and 25.

It was then necessary to determine the amount in inventory after a run. This can be approached by a graphic analogue as was done earlier in the chapter. It will be recalled that, in this case, we assumed that parts were withdrawn monthly for assembly and, furthermore, that parts were completed just at the time of this withdrawal for assembly.*

Accordingly, if 1 month's supply is made at a time, we get the following picture:

$$
\begin{array}{ll}
\text{Input} & 1\ \ 1\ \ 1 \\
\text{Inventory} & \downarrow 0 \downarrow 0 \downarrow 0 \\
 & \downarrow\ \ \downarrow\ \ \downarrow \\
\text{Output} & 1\ \ 1\ \ 1
\end{array}
$$

If a 2 months' supply is produced at a time, we get:

$$
\begin{array}{ll}
\text{Input} & 2\ \ \ \ \ 2\ \ \ \ \ 2 \\
\text{Inventory} & \downarrow 1\ \ 0 \downarrow 1\ \ 0 \downarrow \\
 & \downarrow\ \downarrow\ \downarrow\ \downarrow\ \downarrow \\
\text{Output} & 1\ \ 1\ \ 1\ \ 1\ \ 1
\end{array}
$$

If a 4 months' supply is produced at a time, we get:

$$
\begin{array}{ll}
\text{Input} & 4\ \ \ \ \ \ \ \ \ \ \ \ 4 \\
\text{Inventory} & \downarrow 3\ \ 2\ \ 1\ \ 0 \downarrow \\
 & \downarrow\ \downarrow\ \downarrow\ \downarrow\ \downarrow \\
\text{Output} & 1\ \ 1\ \ 1\ \ 1\ \ 1
\end{array}
$$

From these diagrams we can see that if an x months' supply is made at a time, the total number of month-supply inventories per run is equal to

$$(x - 1) + (x - 2) + \cdots + 1$$

This is algebraically equivalent to

$$\frac{x(x - 1)}{2}$$

---

* That is, our model assumes both discrete insertions to stock and discrete withdrawals from stock, with these withdrawals commencing immediately as each insertion to stock occurs. Interestingly enough, the resulting symbolic model is also valid for continuous insertions to and continuous withdrawals from stock. A third model, that of discrete insertions to stock and continuous withdrawals from stock, yields a numerically similar equation which appears in many of the references cited earlier in this section.

But the number of month-supplies made per run is N/L. That is, $x = N/L$. Then

$$\left(\frac{N}{2L}\right)\left(\frac{N}{L} - 1\right) = \text{Number of month-supply in-}$$
$$\text{ventories per run *} \qquad (3d)$$

$$L\frac{N}{2L}\left(\frac{N}{L} - 1\right) = \frac{N}{2}\left(\frac{N}{L} - 1\right) = \text{Number of part-month in-}$$
$$\text{ventories per run} \qquad (3e)$$

$$\frac{N}{2}\left(\frac{N}{L} - 1\right)P\left(\frac{c_1}{N} + c_2\right) = \text{Average total inventory}$$
$$\text{carrying cost per run} \qquad (3f)$$

Therefore, the expected total relevant cost per run is

$$K_R = c_1 + Nc_2 + \frac{N}{2}\left(\frac{N}{L} - 1\right)P\left(\frac{c_1}{N} + c_2\right)$$
$$= c_1 + Nc_2 + \frac{Pc_1}{2}\left(\frac{N}{L} - 1\right) + \frac{NPc_2}{2}\left(\frac{N}{L} - 1\right) \qquad (4a)$$

Or, since $N = 12L/R$

$$K_R = c_1 + \frac{12L}{R}c_2 + \frac{Pc_1}{2}\left(\frac{12}{R} - 1\right) + \frac{12LPc_2}{2R}\left(\frac{12}{R} - 1\right) \qquad (4b)$$

Now

$$K = RK_R = \text{Expected total relevant cost per year} \qquad (5a)$$

Therefore

$$K = Rc_1 + 12Lc_2 + \frac{Pc_1 R}{2}\left(\frac{12}{R} - 1\right) + \frac{Pc_2 12L}{2}\left(\frac{12}{R} - 1\right) \qquad (5b)$$

Finally

$$K = Rc_1 + 12Lc_2 + \frac{Pc_1 R}{2}\left(\frac{12}{R} - 1\right) + 6Pc_2 L\left(\frac{12}{R} - 1\right) \qquad (5c)$$

Equation $5c$ is a mathematical model of a very simple and highly restricted production-inventory system expressed in terms of an expected total incremental annual cost of production. This model would be considerably complicated if demand were variable and production lead time had to be taken into account. More realistic inventory models will be considered in Part IV. However, *the point here, of course, has not been to develop a general model of production and inventory processes but, rather, to illustrate the method by which a symbolic model is constructed.*

---

* Equation $3d$ holds exactly only if N/L is an integer; otherwise it provides only an approximation, but a good one.

FROM MODEL TO SOLUTION

The model is an instrument which helps us to evaluate alternative policies efficiently. The selection of a procedure for deriving a solution to the problem from the model depends on the characteristics of the model. These procedures can be classified into two types: analytic and numerical. Analytic procedures are essentially deductive in character, whereas numerical procedures (variations of trial and error) are essentially inductive in character. In some cases, neither of these procedures can be applied until a term in the equation has been evaluated by what is called the Monte Carlo technique. Analytic, numerical, and Monte Carlo techniques are each considered in turn.

In proceeding from the model to the solution, the reader should bear in mind the fact that the policy which appears to be best in terms of the model may not be the best in actuality. For one thing, the model may not represent reality accurately. For example, some relevant variable may not be included. Or the value (such as K) which is minimized in the solution may not be the best measure of effectiveness relative to the objectives of the research program (e.g., minimizing production time may be twice as important as minimizing production costs). Thus, when we refer to "solutions," we refer to solutions *relative to the model*, and not necessarily relative to the real system that is represented by the model.

Analytic Solutions

Regarding the model already presented which culminated in eq. 5c, we might ask how many parts should be made per production run, i.e., what is the most economic lot size?

Examination of eq. 5c shows that this problem can be translated into the question: what value of R (the number of equal-size runs per year) will minimize K (the expected total annual relevant cost)?

We can provide a solution to this question in at least two ways. A graphical solution can be obtained by plotting the value of K obtained for various values of R, and selecting that value of R for which K is minimum. Or, a general solution can be obtained by the use of elementary differential calculus. This would give us the value of R, expressed as a function of the other variables, which minimizes the value of K. We can determine this value of R by finding the most economic run size.

First, the derivative of K (eq. 5c) with respect to R is taken

$$\frac{dK}{dR} = c_1 - \frac{Pc_1}{2} - \frac{72LPc_2}{R^2} \tag{6a}$$

Set this equal to zero

$$c_1 - \frac{Pc_1}{2} - \frac{72LPc_2}{R^2} = 0 \tag{6b}$$

Then

$$R^2 = \frac{72LPc_2}{(c_1 - Pc_1/2)} = \frac{144LPc_2}{c_1(2 - P)} \tag{6c}$$

or

$$R = \sqrt{\frac{144LPc_2}{c_1(2 - P)}} = \text{most economic number of runs per year} \tag{6d}$$

i.e., the value of R which minimizes K, provided

$$\frac{d^2K}{dR^2} > 0 \tag{6e}$$

But

$$\frac{d^2K}{dR^2} = 144LPc_2R^{-3} = \frac{144LPc_2}{R^3} > 0 \tag{6f}$$

Finally then, since $N = 12L/R$, the most economic run size N_0 is given by

$$N_0 = 12L \div \sqrt{\frac{12^2LPc_2}{c_1(2 - P)}} = 12L \div 12 \sqrt{\frac{LPc_2}{c_1(2 - P)}}$$

$$= L \div \sqrt{\frac{LPc_2}{c_1(2 - P)}}$$

i.e.,

$$N_0 = \sqrt{\frac{Lc_1}{c_2}\frac{(2 - P)}{P}} \tag{6g}$$

In effect, eq. 6g specifies symbolically the best course of action relative to planning production lot sizes under the conditions represented by the model.

As the nature of the model changes, so will the kind of mathematics required to derive a solution. In the solution just derived, all that was required was elementary differential calculus and algebra. Suppose the model contained two control variables instead of one. This would be the case, for example, in a chemical process where two products are being scheduled which are not separated in the production process until after they have gone through some production steps together. The cost equation constructed in such a case would take the form

$$K = f(X_1, X_2, Y_1, Y_2, \cdots, Y_n)$$

where X_1 and X_2 are the control variables, and Y_j $(j = 1, 2, \cdots, n)$

represent the uncontrollable factors. To derive a solution from a model of this form, we would first take the (partial) derivative of K with respect to X_1 $(\partial K/\partial X_1)$ and then the (partial) derivative of K with respect to X_2 $(\partial K/\partial X_2)$. We then set each of the resulting equations equal to zero and solve these two equations for X_1 and X_2.*

This procedure, involving partial differentiation and the solution of a system of simultaneous equations, is applicable to models containing any number of control variables. But the computations become increasingly complex with an increase in the number of control variables. In many such cases, however, computing machines can be used to advantage.

A different type of mathematical complexity is introduced into the model if the system represented is restricted in some way. For example, suppose that in the production-inventory problem discussed in the foregoing and in Chapter 2, it is necessary to take machine capacity into account. To avoid scheduling more than can be produced, we will have to include, as part of the model, an inequation † which states that the total time scheduled on a certain machine section cannot exceed the amount of time available. Such an inequation might take the following form

$$n_A t_A + n_B t_B + \cdots + n_K t_K \leqq T \tag{7}$$

where T is the total time available in the machine section, n_A is the number of part A scheduled, t_A is the time required in that machine section to process one unit of part A, etc.

To take such a restriction into account in deriving a solution from the model, it is necessary to use the technique of Lagrangian multipliers or some variation thereof. Models of this type and their solution are discussed in Chapter 10.

In many cases it is more convenient to represent the system under study by a set of equations rather than by just one equation. For example, suppose we have two supply points (sources) A and B, with quantities of material Q_A and Q_B available. Further, suppose there are two places (destinations), 1 and 2, requiring this material in quantities R_1 and R_2, where $R_1 + R_2 \leqq Q_A + Q_B$. Finally, unit shipping costs from A to 1 (C_{A1}), A to 2 (C_{A2}), B to 1 (C_{B1}), and B to 2 (C_{B2})

---

* Setting the partial derivatives equal to zero is just a necessary condition. Necessary and sufficient conditions for a maximum or minimum value of a function of two variables can be found in standard advanced calculus books.

† An inequation results from restrictions expressed in the form "less than," "more than," "at most," "at least," etc. Symbolically, "less than" is denoted by $<$, "less than or equal" is denoted by $\leqq$, "more than" by $>$, and "more than or equal" by $\geqq$.

vary. The problem is to ship supplies from sources A and B to destinations 1 and 2 so as to minimize total shipping costs.

Representation of the system just described is not difficult if we use a set of equations and inequations. Let N_{A1} represent the number of units to be shipped from A to 1, etc. Then, the total shipping cost K can be expressed as follows

$$K = N_{A1}C_{A1} + N_{A2}C_{A2} + N_{B1}C_{B1} + N_{B2}C_{B2} \tag{8}$$

But we know that

$$
\begin{aligned}
N_{A1} + N_{A2} &\leq Q_A \\
N_{B1} + N_{B2} &\leq Q_B \\
N_{A1} + N_{B1} &= R_1 \\
N_{A2} + N_{B2} &= R_2
\end{aligned}
\tag{9}
$$

This situation can be represented by the matrix shown in Table 7-1.

TABLE 7-1

Source	Amt. Avail. at Source	Destination 1	Destination 2	Total Shipped from Source
A	Q_A	N_{A1}	N_{A2}	$\leq Q_A$
B	Q_B	N_{B1}	N_{B2}	$\leq Q_B$
Total required at destination		R_1	R_2	

The problem can be stated in terms of this matrix as follows: find the values of N_{A1}, N_{A2}, N_{B1}, and N_{B2} which minimize K, the total shipping cost, subject to the restrictions expressed in the equations and inequations given in the foregoing. The solution to such a problem may involve the use of matrix algebra. Models of this kind and their solution will be discussed in Part V. Although it is possible to solve such a problem analytically by mathematical deduction, it is frequently more convenient to do so by trial and error or a variation thereof (iterative procedures), which will be discussed in the next section.

Models can take on a variety of mathematical forms and consequently may require many different types of mathematical analysis for deriving a solution. Therefore, the derivation of solutions may require a high order of mathematical competence. But the formulation of a model does not necessarily require all the skills required to solve it. For this reason, an O.R. team does not need to contain only mathematicians; but, for this reason also, the availability of mathematical skills is essential for effective work.

Numerical Solutions

Numerical techniques of deriving a solution from a model consist essentially of substituting numbers for the symbols in the model and finding which set of substituted numbers yield the maximum effectiveness. For example, we can determine the optimum value of the control variable(s) in a symbolic (mathematical) model by trying every possible substitution of values for the control variable(s) and by computing the effectiveness associated with each substitution. Then, we can select that set of values which yields the highest measure of effectiveness. This procedure, however, is likely to be lengthy, tedious, and costly even if electronic computers are used. It is not usually necessary, however, to try every possible substitution of values, for it is usually possible to design a procedure in which subsequent substitutions tend to yield improvements over the previous ones. When further substitutions do not significantly improve over previous tries, the process is stopped. Thus we can converge on a solution with fewer steps than are required by exhaustive trial and error. Such a procedure of what may be thought of as progressive trial and error is called *iteration*.

As an example of an iterative procedure, let us consider the following very simple model that can be represented by a matrix and one inequation. Suppose a salesman has two accounts, A and B, from each of which he obtains an amount of business that depends on the amount of time he spends with each. But the salesman has only 6 hours available for these two customers. How should he spend his time so as to maximize the business obtained?

We can express the responsiveness of each customer to sales time in tabular form. (See Table 7-2). For sales-response functions of the

TABLE 7-2

Time Spent per Customer	Customer A		Customer B	
	Expected Return	Incremental Increase	Expected Return	Incremental Increase
1	$ 8	$8	$12	$12
2	14	6	21	9
3	18	4	28	7
4	20	2	34	6
5	21	1	38	4
6	21	0	41	3
7	21	0	42	1
8	21	0	42	0

type given in this table (parabolic or quadratic functions), the following iterative procedure can be used.

1. We start by allocating an equal amount of the available time to each customer; i.e., 3 hours to each. The total return would be \$18 + \$28, or \$46.

2. We determine for which account an additional hour would yield the larger *increase* in return. This is B, with a possible increase of \$34 − \$28, or \$6.

3. We compare the gain computed in step 2 with the loss associated with reducing by 1 hour the time spent with A. This is \$18 − \$14, or \$4.

4. Since the loss is less than the gain (\$4 < \$6), we reallocate time as follows: 2 hours to A and 4 hours to B, with an associated total return of \$48.

5. We continue until a further net gain is not possible. In this case, no further gain is possible. An increase of 1 hour with A or B would result in a \$4 increase, whereas a decrease of 1 hour with A or B would result in a \$6 decrease. In either case, then, there would be a net loss of \$2.

The optimum allocation in this case,* then, is 2 hours to A and 4 hours to B.

A more technical illustration of iteration is given in Note 1 at the end of this chapter. Various more complex iterative procedures for solving more realistic types of problems will be discussed in Part V.

The Monte Carlo Technique

In constructing a model of a system, it is desirable to use variables whose values can be obtained without too much difficulty. However, some of the expressions in the model which are built up out of even very simple variables may themselves become very complex. This is particularly true if probability concepts are involved.

For example, consider a new product which contains two parts that eventually fail. These might be a vacuum tube and a condenser. From past tests we know the probability of failure of each item as a function of time in use; i.e., we know what is called the "life curve" of each of the items. What we want to know, however, is the life curve of the product which contains both of these elements. Put another way, if $f(t)$ represents the life curve of one of the parts, and $g(t)$ represents the life curve of the other, then the life curve of the products is a function

* This solution could have been obtained by inspection of Table 7-2. However, the point here has not been to solve this, or any other, problem but, rather, to illustrate another iterative procedure.

of these two life curves, say $h[f(t), g(t)]$, or simply $h(t)$. If a term such as this appears in a model of a system we cannot derive a solution from the model either analytically or iteratively until it has been evaluated. That is, assuming functions $f(t)$ and $g(t)$ are known, function $h(t)$ must be made explicit before a solution can be derived.

Now, in some cases $h(t)$ can be derived by mathematical analysis, for example, when $f(t)$ and $g(t)$ are normal probability density functions. In other instances, however, it is not possible or practical to evaluate such a function by mathematical analysis. This is true, for example, in certain of the key terms appearing in queuing and replacement models (see Parts VI and VII). But fortunately, such expressions can be evaluated approximately by the Monte Carlo technique. That is, the Monte Carlo technique is a procedure by which we can obtain approximate evaluations of mathematical expressions which are built up of one or more probability distribution functions; such expressions are quite common in the models used in O.R. This procedure, then, when combined with analytical or iterative procedures makes it possible to derive a solution to a problem modeled by an equation containing terms of the type under discussion.

The Monte Carlo technique consists of a new use of an old procedure. The old procedure is "unrestricted random sampling" (selecting items from a population in such a way that each item in the population has an equal probability of being selected). This "new" twist consists of using random sampling to play a game with nature or a man-made system in which an experiment is simulated. In essence, the Monte Carlo technique consists of simulating an experiment to determine some probabilistic property of a population of objects or events by the use of random sampling applied to the components of the objects or events. This rather abstract statement can be clarified both by illustration and an understanding of the development of the method.

Just as the discovery of the laws of gravity are attributed in legend to Newton's observation of a falling apple, so the discovery of the Monte Carlo technique goes back to a legendary mathematician observing the perambulation of a saturated drunk. Each of the drunk's steps was supposed to have an equal probability of going in any direction. The mathematician wondered how many steps the drunkard would have to take, on the average, to get a specified distance away from his starting point. This was called the problem of a *random walk.* An application of random sampling called *"stochastic sampling"* was developed to solve this problem, but the method was found to have wide practical applications, and was subsequently given the more colorful name, the *Monte Carlo* technique.

TABLE 7-3. Random Numbers

09 73 25 33	76 53 01 35 86	34 67 35 48 76	80 95 90 90 17	39 29 27 49
54 20 48 05	64 89 47 42 96	24 80 52 40 37	20 63 61 04 02	00 82 29 16
42 26 89 53	19 64 50 93 03	23 20 90 25 60	15 95 33 47 64	35 08 03 36
01 90 25 29	09 37 67 07 15	38 31 13 11 65	88 67 67 43 97	04 43 62 76
80 79 99 70	80 15 73 61 47	64 03 23 66 53	98 95 11 68 77	12 17 17 68
06 57 47 17	34 07 27 68 50	36 69 73 61 70	65 81 33 98 85	11 19 92 91
06 01 08 05	45 57 18 24 06	35 30 34 26 14	86 79 90 74 39	23 40 30 97
26 97 76 02	02 05 16 56 92	68 66 57 48 18	73 05 38 52 47	18 62 38 85
57 33 21 35	05 32 54 70 48	90 55 35 75 48	28 46 82 87 09	82 49 12 56
79 64 57 53	03 52 96 47 78	35 80 83 42 82	60 93 52 03 44	35 27 38 84
52 01 77 67	14 90 56 86 07	22 10 94 05 58	60 97 09 34 33	50 50 07 39
80 50 54 31	39 80 82 77 32	50 72 56 82 48	29 40 52 42 01	52 77 56 78
45 29 96 34	06 28 89 80 83	13 74 67 00 78	18 47 54 06 10	68 71 17 78
68 34 02 00	86 50 75 84 01	36 76 66 79 51	90 36 47 64 93	29 60 91 01
59 46 73 48	87 51 76 49 69	91 82 60 89 28	93 78 56 13 68	23 47 83 41
48 11 76 74	17 46 85 09 50	58 04 77 69 74	73 03 95 71 86	40 21 81 65
12 43 56 35	17 72 70 80 15	45 31 82 23 74	21 11 57 82 53	14 38 55 37
35 09 98 17	77 40 27 72 14	43 23 60 02 10	45 52 16 42 37	96 28 60 26
91 62 68 03	66 25 22 91 48	36 93 68 72 03	76 62 11 39 90	94 40 05 64
89 32 05 05	14 22 56 85 14	46 42 75 67 88	96 29 77 88 22	54 38 21 45
49 91 45 23	68 47 92 76 86	46 16 28 35 54	94 75 08 99 23	37 08 92 00
33 69 45 98	26 94 03 68 58	70 29 73 41 35	53 14 03 33 40	42 05 08 23
10 48 19 49	85 15 74 79 54	32 97 92 65 75	57 60 04 08 81	22 22 20 64
55 07 37 42	11 10 00 20 40	12 86 07 46 97	96 64 48 94 39	28 70 72 58
60 64 93 29	16 50 53 44 84	40 21 95 25 63	43 65 17 70 82	07 20 73 17
19 69 04 46	26 45 74 77 74	51 92 43 37 29	65 39 45 95 93	42 58 26 05
47 44 52 66	95 27 07 99 53	59 36 78 38 48	82 39 61 01 18	33 21 15 94
55 72 85 73	67 89 75 43 87	54 62 24 44 31	91 19 04 25 92	92 92 74 59
48 11 62 13	97 34 40 87 21	16 86 84 87 67	02 07 11 20 59	25 70 14 66
52 37 83 17	73 20 88 98 37	68 93 59 14 16	26 25 22 96 63	05 52 28 25
49 35 24 94	75 24 63 38 24	45 86 25 10 25	61 96 27 93 35	65 33 71 24
54 99 76 54	64 05 18 81 59	96 11 96 38 96	54 69 28 23 91	23 28 72 95
96 31 53 07	26 89 80 93 54	33 35 13 54 62	77 97 45 00 24	90 10 33 93
80 80 83 91	45 42 72 68 42	83 60 94 97 00	13 02 12 48 92	78 56 52 01
05 88 52 36	01 39 09 22 86	77 28 14 40 77	93 91 08 36 47	70 61 74 29
17 90 02 97	87 37 92 52 41	05 56 70 70 07	86 74 31 71 57	85 39 41 18
23 46 14 06	20 11 74 52 04	15 95 66 00 00	18 74 39 24 23	97 11 89 63
56 54 14 30	01 75 87 53 79	40 41 92 15 85	66 67 43 68 06	84 96 28 52
15 51 49 38	19 47 60 72 46	43 66 79 45 43	59 04 79 00 33	20 82 66 85
86 43 19 94	36 16 81 08 51	34 88 88 15 53	01 54 03 54 56	05 01 45 11
08 62 48 26	45 24 02 84 04	44 99 90 88 96	39 09 47 34 07	35 44 13 18
18 51 62 32	41 94 15 09 49	89 43 54 85 81	88 69 54 19 94	37 54 87 30
95 10 04 06	96 38 27 07 74	20 15 12 33 87	25 01 62 52 98	94 62 46 11

Let us consider the problem of the "random walk." Suppose a drunkard is leaning against a lamppost in the middle of a large paved city square. He decides to walk, going nowhere in particular. As we observe him, he might take a few steps in one direction, then some more steps in another direction, etc., in an unpredictable, or *random*, manner. The problem is to determine how far he will be from the lamppost after n irregular zigzag phases of his walk. That is, what is the drunkard's *most probable* distance from the lamppost after n steps?

How can such a probable distance be estimated without observing a large number of drunkards in similar circumstances? An extended number of observations would be impossible or impractical to make. However, since the one drunkard moves at random, we may simulate patterns of his walk by means of a table of random numbers (See Table 7-3),* and thereby approximate the actual physical situation. From a large number of these simulated trials, we are then able to estimate the probable distance for any n irregular zigzag phases.

To illustrate how the Monte Carlo technique can be applied to the problem of the "random walk," let us obtain an estimate of the probable distance traveled after five steps of equal size (i.e., $n = 5$). To do this, let us refer to Table 7-3 which is a 2-digit random number table. Also, let us use the following symbolism:

1. The lamppost is represented by the origin of the X and Y axis. See Fig. 7-1.
2. The first digit of the 2-digit random number selected from the table represents one unit of X, positive if even or zero, negative if odd.
3. The second digit of the same 2-digit random number selected represents one unit of Y, positive if even or zero, and negative if odd.
4. (x_n, y_n) represents the position of the drunk at the end of the nth phase.
5. d_n equals the distance of the drunk from the lamppost at the end of the nth phase; that is, $d_n^2 = x_n^2 + y_n^2$.

If we "start at random," selecting the 2-digit number, say, in column 10 and row 6 of Table 7-3, and then read down, we obtain the following five numbers: 36, 35, 68, 90, and 35. These numbers may then be arranged and the drunkard's moves obtained as shown in Table 7-4. The points (x_n, y_n) may also be plotted as in Fig. 7-1.

* For a discussion of the nature of these tables see Chap. IV of ref. 1. For a complete table see ref. 21. This latter work also contains a bibliography of tables and works on this subject.

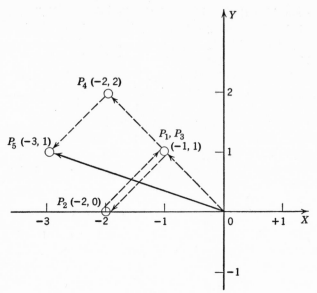

Fig. 7-1. Plotting of points (x_n, y_n).

TABLE 7-4

Phase n	First Digit	Second Digit	Point Location (x_n, y_n)
1	3	6	$(-1, 1)$
2	3	5	$(-2, 0)$
3	6	8	$(-1, 1)$
4	9	0	$(-2, 2)$
5	3	5	$(-3, 1)$

In this example, then, *one* estimate is that the drunkard will be 3.16 units from the lamppost at the end of the 5th phase. This is obtained as follows:

$$d_5^2 = x_5^2 + y_5^2$$

$$d_5^2 = 9 + 1$$

$$d_5 = \sqrt{10} = 3.16$$

This procedure must then be repeated for different random numbers in the table so that we obtain a group of estimates of the desired distance. The estimates in this group can then be averaged to yield an average estimated distance from the lamppost. In general, our estimates will improve as we increase the number of such samples.

More generally, from many such simulated trials, we may estimate the probability of the drunkard's being a specified distance from the lamppost for any number n of irregular zigzag phases.

As a point of interest and as a basis for the reader comparing his own Monte Carlo solutions, it might be pointed out that, for this example, an analytic solution is obtainable and is given by

$$d_n = a\sqrt{n}$$

i.e., the most probable distance of the drunkard from the lamppost, *after a large number of irregular phases of his walk*, is equal to the average length a of each straight track he walks, times the square root of the number n of phases of his walk.

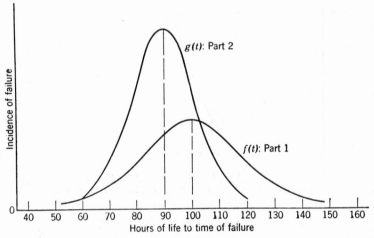

Fig. 7-2. Life curves.

With this example of the use of the Monte Carlo technique in mind, let us return to the problem with which discussion of the Monte Carlo technique opened, namely: determination of the life curve of a product containing two parts whose life curves are known. Let us assume that both of the parts have life curves which are normal, the first $f(t)$, having a mean of 100 hours with a standard deviation of 20 hours, and the second, $g(t)$, having a mean of 90 hours and a standard deviation of 10 hours. These two curves are shown in Fig. 7-2.

The life characteristics of the components can also be shown as cumulative life curves. See Fig. 7-3.

In the assembly of the product, one from each class of parts will be selected at random. By use of the Monte Carlo method we can select these parts at random and observe the resulting life spans of the product. However, before doing so, a word should first be said as to how a random selection of items from a normal population can be made.* Since *a.* items must be selected in such a way that each has an equal probability of being selected and *b.* there are more items with life spans in one interval (say, 95 to 105) than in other intervals (say, 75 to 85), the procedure must be such that the probability of selecting an item in any interval along the time scale is equal to the proportion of items falling in that interval. This means that we cannot take a random

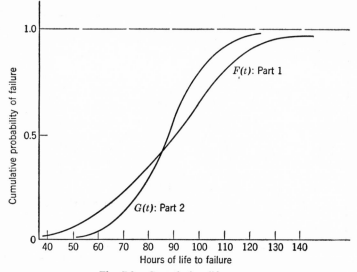

Fig. 7-3. Cumulative life curves.

sample of values along the abscissa (horizontal axis) of either Fig. 7-2 or Fig. 7-3, because, if we did, we would have the same probability of drawing an item with a life span between 95 to 105 as between 75 to 85. Consequently, we must select values at random along the ordinate (vertical scale). For cumulative life curves (as in Fig. 7-3), this is done as follows:

The distance from the base of the ordinate to the highest value reached on the life curve of each part can be divided into, say, 100 equal spaces. Then, by use of a table of random numbers (such as Table 7-3), values along the ordinate (probability scale) can be selected. As each value is selected, a horizontal line is drawn to the curve. Then, a line is drawn through this point of intersection perpendicular to the

* Since the two parts in this example each follow normal distributions, our discussion will refer to normal distributions. However, the method for obtaining a random selection is general and applies to any distribution.

TABLE 7-5. RANDOM NORMAL NUMBERS *

$$\mu = 0, \sigma = 1$$

	(1)	(2)	(3)	(4)	(5)	(6)	(7)
1	0.464	0.137	2.455	−0.323	−0.068	0.296	−0.288
2	0.060	−2.526	−0.531	−1.940	0.543	−1.558	0.187
3	1.486	−0.354	−0.634	0.697	0.926	1.375	0.785
4	1.022	−0.472	1.279	3.521	0.571	−1.851	0.194
5	1.394	−0.555	0.046	0.321	2.945	1.974	−0.258
6	0.906	−0.513	−0.525	0.595	0.881	−0.934	1.579
7	1.179	−1.055	0.007	0.769	0.971	0.712	1.090
8	−1.501	−0.488	−0.162	−0.136	1.033	0.203	0.448
9	−0.690	0.756	−1.618	−0.445	−0.511	−2.051	−0.457
10	1.372	0.225	0.378	0.761	0.181	−0.736	0.960
11	−0.482	1.677	−0.057	−1.229	−0.486	0.856	−0.491
12	−1.376	−0.150	1.356	−0.561	−0.256	0.212	0.219
13	−1.010	0.598	−0.918	1.598	0.065	0.415	−0.169
14	−0.005	−0.899	0.012	−0.725	1.147	−0.121	−0.096
15	1.393	−1.163	−0.911	1.231	−0.199	−0.246	1.239
16	−1.787	−0.261	1.237	1.046	−0.508	−1.630	−0.146
17	−0.105	−0.357	−1.384	0.360	−0.992	−0.116	−1.698
18	−1.339	1.827	−0.959	0.424	0.969	−1.141	−1.041
19	1.041	0.535	0.731	1.377	0.983	−1.330	1.620
20	0.279	−2.056	0.717	−0.873	−1.096	−1.396	1.047
21	−1.805	−2.008	−1.633	0.542	0.250	0.166	0.032
22	−1.186	1.180	1.114	0.882	1.265	−0.202	0.151
23	0.658	−1.141	1.151	−1.210	−0.927	0.425	0.290
24	−0.439	0.358	−1.939	0.891	−0.227	0.602	0.973
25	1.398	−0.230	0.385	−0.649	−0.577	0.237	−0.289
26	0.199	0.208	−1.083	−0.219	−0.291	1.221	1.119
27	0.159	0.272	−0.313	0.084	−2.828	−0.439	−0.792
28	2.273	0.606	0.606	−0.747	0.247	1.291	0.063
29	0.041	−0.307	0.121	0.790	−0.584	0.541	0.484
30	−1.132	−2.098	0.921	0.145	0.446	−2.661	1.045
31	0.768	0.079	−1.473	0.034	−2.127	0.665	0.084
32	0.375	−1.658	−0.851	0.234	−0.656	0.340	−0.086
33	−0.513	−0.344	0.210	−0.736	1.041	0.008	0.427
34	0.292	−0.521	1.266	−1.206	−0.899	0.110	−0.528
35	1.026	2.990	−0.574	−0.491	−1.114	1.297	−1.433
36	−1.334	1.278	−0.568	−0.109	−0.515	−0.566	2.923
37	−0.287	−0.144	−0.254	0.574	−0.451	−1.181	−1.190
38	0.161	−0.886	−0.921	−0.509	1.410	−0.518	0.192
39	−1.346	0.193	−1.202	0.394	−1.045	0.843	0.942
40	1.250	−0.199	−0.288	1.810	1.378	0.584	1.216

* This table is reproduced in part from a table of the RAND Corporation.

base. See Fig. 7-4. The value is read on the base where this perpendicular intersects it. For example, suppose the number 0.55 is read
from the random number table. Figure 7-4 then shows how the value
88 hours is obtained for a given probability curve.

Repeating this procedure, we can then obtain a random selection
from the given normal population. This rather tedious procedure is
not necessary, however, since it has been done already in great detail,

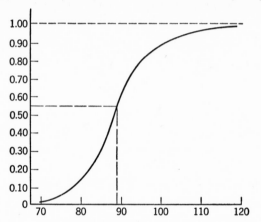

Fig. 7-4. Random selection from normal distribution.

and the results have been put into convenient tables of random normal numbers such as Table 7-5. Table 7-5 can be used very easily to
determine the life curve of the product in question. We then proceed
by preparing a table of the form shown in Table 7-6.

TABLE 7-6. Data for Constructing Life Curve of a Product

Part 1		Part 2		Life of Product
(1)	(2)	(3)	(4)	(5)
Random Normal Number	Life of Part $100 + 20$ (1)	Random Normal Number	Life of Part $90 + 10$ (3)	Smallest Value Appearing in (2) and (4)
0.464	109.28	0.137	91.37	91.37
0.060	101.20	−2.526	64.74	64.74
1.486	129.72	−0.354	86.46	86.46
1.022	120.44	−0.472	85.28	85.28
1.394	127.88	−0.555	84.45	84.45
0.906	118.12	−0.513	84.87	84.87
1.179	123.58	−1.055	79.45	79.45
−1.501	69.98	−0.488	85.12	69.98
−0.690	86.20	0.756	97.56	86.20
1.372	127.44	0.225	92.25	92.25

In columns (1) and (3) we simply list values taken from the table of random normal numbers. We can start anywhere in any column. In this case, the first two columns of Table 7-5 were selected, starting at the top. The values taken from the table are in units of standard deviations. Consequently, they must be converted to hours. This is done by multiplying the value taken from the table by the appropriate standard deviation (20 for Part 1 and 10 for Part 2) and adding the value so obtained to the appropriate mean (100 for Part 1 and 90 for Part 2). Then the time of the first failure is noted in column (5). The data in column (5) can then be used to construct a life curve for the product.

In most practical situations, we would want many more than ten "observations" since a more reliable life curve can be fitted to a larger number of observations. The greater the desired accuracy of evaluation of the term in question, the larger the sample must be. (For details on sample size and resulting accuracy see Part IX). Here we are only illustrating the procedure. Furthermore, it should be noted that in most cases where the Monte Carlo technique can be applied, the procedure lends itself to the use of high-speed electronic computers.

Suppose that when the data were collected on the life of the two parts, it had not been possible to obtain a good fit of a life curve. The Monte Carlo technique could be applied to the raw data themselves without resorting to the life curve. Each observation obtained for each part could have been numbered consecutively. Then, by use of a table of random numbers (such as Table 7-3), an observed life span of each part could be chosen. These would then be used in columns (2) and (4) in Table 7-6 instead of those derived from the table of random normal numbers.

Once the expression in the model has been evaluated by the Monte Carlo technique, a solution of the model can be obtained either by iteration or analysis. The combination of the use of Monte Carlo technique with analytic and numerical procedures for solving models will be illustrated in later discussions of queuing and replacement models (Parts VI and VII).

Finally, it should be noted that in some equations all the terms are such that the Monte Carlo techniques can (or need to) be used to evaluate them. In such cases, then, this method is a way of evaluating the equation as well as terms in it. For more detailed discussion of this and other phases of the method see refs. 7, 10, 11, 13, 20, and 23.

MODELS ASSOCIATED WITH RECURRENT TYPES OF PROBLEMS

As might be suspected, there are certain types of problems which frequently arise in industry and government. Considerable work has been done in the formulation of models for such problems. Although the various models which have been formulated can seldom be applied without modification, the required modification is frequently minor, and hence considerable time can be saved if one is familiar with them. Parts IV through VIII are devoted to a presentation of these models and the analysis which has produced them. In a sense, familiarity with these models, and experience in using them and appropriately modifying them to meet specific situations, form an important part of Operations Research training. Here we survey briefly the processes and related problems for which prototype models have been developed. The reader should note in each case the "balancing" of at least two conflicting aspects of the system. This balancing characterizes all the models for executive-type problems. Five classes of problems are considered: inventory, allocation, waiting-line, replacement, and competitive.

Inventory Problems

All inventory problems have certain general characteristics. First, there is the fact that, as inventory increases, the cost of holding goods also increases, but the cost arising from an inability to fill orders (the shortage cost) decreases. Consequently, one aspect of the inventory problem is to find an inventory level which minimizes the sum of the expected holding and shortage costs. However, in many cases, such as the one discussed earlier in this chapter, inventory costs and production costs are not independent, and hence the two must be considered jointly. The larger the production lot is, the less the production costs are because setup cost per unit is reduced. But the larger the production lot, the larger the inventory holding cost. On the other hand, the smaller the production lot, the less is the inventory holding cost, but the greater is the unit production cost. A production-inventory model, then, expresses the total cost of production in terms of setup costs, material and processing costs, inventory holding costs, and shortage costs. Another cost that must frequently be taken into account is that arising from changes in the level of production (e.g., costs of hiring and layoff). Purchasing-inventory models differ primarily in that purchase price is substituted for material and processing costs and this price is affected by quantity discounts; i.e., its value changes in steps (discretely).

Inventory problems fall into three classes: 1. The time of production or purchase is fixed at regular intervals and the quantity to be produced or purchased is to be determined. 2. The production or purchase quantity is fixed and the time of production or purchase is to be determined. 3. Both the time of production or purchase and the quantity are to be determined. In situations where demand is constant (as in the case presented in Chapter 2), these problems become identical. They are distinct only if demand varies.

Symbolic models have been constructed for a variety of production- and purchase-inventory systems; those for which there is either a known or variable demand, others where the demand is either discrete or continuous, and those where the lead time required to get goods (once an order is placed) is either virtually instantaneous or consumes an amount of time which must be taken into account. Part IV is concerned with these models.

Allocation Problems

Allocation problems arise when there are a number of activities (jobs or tasks) to be performed and the available resources (supplies or facilities) are not sufficient for performing each activity in the best possible way. These problems are divisible into three types:

1. Both the required activities and available resources are specified. The problem is to allocate the resources to the activities in such a way as to either maximize some measure of effectiveness (e.g., expected profit) or minimize some measure of ineffectiveness (e.g., expected cost or time).

2. Only the available resources are specified. The problem is to determine what mixture of activities, if performed with the available resources, will either maximize some measure of effectiveness or minimize some measure of ineffectiveness.

3. Only the required activities are specified. The problem is to determine what mixture of resources, if applied to these activities, will either maximize some measure of effectiveness or minimize some measure of ineffectiveness.

Examples of these three types of problems are the following:

1. Production requirements are set. Facilities of a certain plant are available. There are alternative ways of producing each of the required products. Facilities do not permit each product to be produced in the best possible way. How should production be allocated to the facilities so as to fill the requirements at the lowest possible cost?

2. A plant with a specified capacity for producing various products is available. What mix of products should be made so as to assure maximum return on production effort?

3. An airline's flight schedule is specified for a given month. How many flight crews based where will minimize operating costs?

Linear programming and related techniques can be applied in certain cases in obtaining solutions to allocation problems. These techniques, the models, and case studies will be discussed in Chapters 11, 12, and 13.

Waiting-Line Problems

There is a large class of processes which involve waiting lines, such as depositors at a bank, customers at a cafeteria, incoming planes at an airfield, and goods in process in a machine shop. Such processes have the following characteristics. Things requiring work or service flow to service facilities in a certain pattern. There may be an accumulation of work at the facilities, in which case the objects requiring work or service form a waiting line. This waiting may involve a cost of in-process inventory, delay in shipments, irritation of customers, etc. On the other hand, there may be excessive gaps between arrivals of things requiring work or service, so that facilities are idle for part of the time. This idle time also involves a cost.

Two types of recurrent problems arise out of these conditions: 1. The arrivals are random and not subject to control. The problem is to determine the optimum amount of facilities. 2. Facilities are fixed. The problem is to determine the optimum schedule of the flow of work to the available facilities. Queuing theory, which is applicable to the first class of problems, is discussed and illustrated in Chapters 14 and 15. The second class of problems is referred to as "line-balancing" or "line-loading" problems. Models for and solutions to problems of this latter type involve "combinatorial analysis." The appropriate models and some exact and approximate solutions are discussed in Chapter 16.

Combined Inventory-Allocation-Queuing Problems

Many problems require the use of more than one type of model. For example, complete production and control involves each of the three types of problems discussed in the preceding three sections of this chapter.

In some cases, complete control of production involves answering the following questions:

1. How much of each product should be made? That is, what production lot sizes should be planned? We may refer to this as the pro-

duction *planning* problem, for which various production-inventory and economic lot-size models are available.

2. To what facilities should the required production be allocated and/or from what materials should the products be made? This is the *allocation* problem, for which *allocation* or *programming* models are available.

3. In what sequence and when should the production lots be started? This is the *scheduling* problem, for which queuing or waiting-line models are available.

The answers to these three questions are not independent. For example, we may first obtain an optimum answer to the planning problem, and then, relative to this optimum, obtain a best allocation; then, relative to this best allocation we may obtain an optimum schedule. But the final result may not be an over-all optimum. That is, sequential optimizing for each of the three problems does not necessarily yield an over-all optimum. Indeed, the resulting plan, program, and schedule may be impossible to realize. For example, it may not be possible to produce (and hence program) all the products in economic lots, for the required production facilities may be greater than those which are actually available. Or, again, a program may be such that it cannot be scheduled so as to be accomplished in the required time. In general, at the present time we have no way of simultaneously optimizing these three interdependent decisions. We either have to use approximations to an over-all optimum or we have to proceed by sequential optimization (really, suboptimization). In sequential optimization we can review each optimum in light of the one subsequently obtained, and by gradually making necessary adjustments we can converge near an over-all optimum.

Replacement and Maintenance Problems

Replacement and maintenance are essentially the same processes. The difference lies in what the researcher considers an operating unit to be. For example, we can consider the replacement of a truck's tire to be truck maintenance or replacement of a truck to be fleet maintenance. Maintenance, then, is the process of replacing components. In this and subsequent discussions only the term "replacement" is used but it should be interpreted to include maintenance as well.

Replacement problems are divisible into two classes: those involving a unit whose efficiency decreases with use (i.e., items that degenerate) and those involving units which have relatively constant efficiency until they fail or die. Turret lathes are examples of degenerating units and light bulbs are examples of nondegenerating units.

In dealing with the replacement of degenerating units, one must balance the additional cost of new equipment against increases in efficiency resulting from the new equipment. This balance changes, depending on the efficiency of the old equipment (and, hence, usually on its age) and on the improvement provided by new equipment.

Replacement problems involving nondegenerating units generally have the following characteristics. Equipment or facilities break down at various times. Each breakdown can be remedied as it occurs by replacement or repair of the faulty unit. There is a certain cost associated with each individual correction (replacement or repair). On the other hand, before any unit fails, each unit can be replaced or have preventative maintenance performed on it. Because of the quantity of work involved, the unit correction cost usually goes down in group replacement, but the total number of unit corrections required goes up. In between the two extremes (unit replacement after each failure versus group replacement before any failures) are many possible alternatives, each defined by the time at which group replacement is performed. Associated with each intermediate time is an expected number of individual replacements. The problem, then, is to select a time for group replacement which minimizes the sum of the expected costs due to each type of replacement.

Replacement models and applications are discussed in Chapter 17.

Competitive Problems

A competitive situation, in general, is one in which 1. two parties or groups are in conflict relative to a set of their respective objectives, and 2. these parties or groups co-operate relative to either an objective (or set of objectives) they share in common or an objective (or set of objectives) of a third party or group served by the competitors. A 2-person game such as chess is a competitive situation. The opponents are in conflict relative to their respective objectives of winning the game. That is, an increase in the probability of A's obtaining his objective necessarily implies a decrease in the probability of B's obtaining his objective. But A and B may co-operate relative to a common objective, such as recreation. In industrial competition the competitors may be in conflict relative to obtaining sales but they may be co-operative relative to the consumer's interests in price and quality. If the consumer is not thus served we will have conflict, not competition. Competitors may, by coalition, transfer themselves into a co-operative rather than a competitive relationship.

The theory of games, like communications theory (see Chapter 4), has yielded mathematical models which deal with such idealized competitive situations, but these models have not as yet found many industrial applications. In the few cases where these models are said to have been applied, industrial security is involved and, hence, the details (and even some of the broad aspects) of the applications have not been made public. Nevertheless, the theory of games provides a useful conceptual framework which can be used more widely at present than the associated mathematical theory.

Most games analyzed in the theory of games are relatively simple compared with industrial competition. In most games the rules can be explicitly stated. In many games the possible moves or sequences of moves can be enumerated, and the consequences of each can be specified. This information, supplemented by further information concerning the opponents' probable behavior, can be used to develop a strategy for playing the game. Von Neumann and Morgenstern, in their *Theory of Games and Economic Behavior*,[18] have shown how, for some games, a "best" strategy can be selected.

Most industrial and military competition seldom can be put into game-theoretical form because of the complexity of these situations and the lack of pertinent information concerning outcomes of strategies and possible actions of the opposition. Nevertheless the conceptualization of the theory of games can be fruitfully applied in some such cases. For example, it may be possible to determine what the most effective countermeasures (strategy) of an opponent may be. Then, if we can select a strategy which assures a gain even though the opponent selects his best strategy, we are assured of at least this minimum gain. The success of such an approach obviously depends on our ability to determine the best possible strategy the opponent can select. This type of approach has been used with considerable success by O.R. teams in military problems.

One particular recurrent type of competitive situation involves bidding, such as bidding for contracts, concessions, rights, and licenses. The essential conflict in a bidding situation is that as bids are increased the chance of winning increases but expected profits (resulting from winning) decrease. On the other hand, if bids are decreased the chance of winning decreases but profits increase. The problem, then, is to get a "best" balance between chances of winning and profits. Recently developed bidding models are applicable in this area.

Chapter 18 deals with the theory of games and Chapter 19 with bidding models.

CONCLUSION

This chapter has considered ways in which a model can be used to evaluate possible changes in a process. It would be harmful to leave the impression that this relationship (of the model as process-evaluator) is unidirectional. In practice, when the process is studied and the results of the study are utilized, information continuously becomes available to the researchers, information which can be used to evaluate the model. For example, the model may be used to predict certain costs that will be incurred if certain policies are followed. Once the policies are followed, the actual costs incurred may vary from those predicted. This might indicate the incompleteness of the model and, hence, provide a basis for its re-evaluation. Consequently, the model and the process can be used to evaluate each other, and should be so used. As we learn more about the process, it is only natural that modifications in the model should be introduced. This has been the case in the development of models in every branch of science. No model is ever perfect, because our knowledge of that which is modeled is always less than complete. The procedure for checking or testing the model will be discussed in Chapters 20 and 21.

The perennial question of researchers is where to begin the research. Some believe that data should be collected before any model is constructed, lest the model prejudice the researcher and cause him to twist the data to his own liking. Others believe that we do not know what data to collect until a model is constructed. A more sophisticated attitude recognizes a continuous interplay between data collection and correction, and model construction-reconstruction. A discussion of the history of thought on the nature of this interplay is given elsewhere.[5, 6]

It should also be re-emphasized that a solution extracted from a model is not necessarily a solution to the problem. For example, an economic-lot-size equation will provide an "optimum" lot size only as long as, say, the setup cost is known accurately and stays constant. This cost is not likely to stay constant for any length of time. Consequently, controls should be designed to check the values of the variables in the model so that recomputation can be made when a change has occurred. The subject of control itself will be considered in more detail in Chapter 21.

The importance of these controls cannot be overemphasized. It is common knowledge that the characteristics of industrial and governmental processes change significantly over relatively short periods of time. We must act on this awareness by designing into the solution of the problem methods for determining when the solution ceases to be a solution, and how a new solution can be obtained.

Note 1. An Illustration of Iteration

To illustrate iterative procedures, let us briefly describe one which is referred to as *Newton's method for solving equations* and which is to be found in standard calculus texts. It is an iterative procedure for determining, within any desired degree of accuracy, the roots of an algebraic equation. The method is based on the fact that, for a short distance, the tangent to a smooth curve forms almost a continuation of the curve.

Newton's method may be formulated as follows: Let $f(X) = 0$ be the equation under consideration. A root of this equation is the abscissa of a point at which the curve $Y = f(X)$ crosses the X axis.

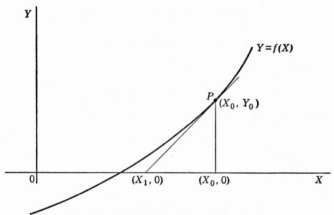

Fig. 7-5. Figure for Newton's method.

We start with a trial "solution," say X_0 (see Fig. 7-5). This value X_0 determines a point P on the curve whose co-ordinates are (X_0, Y_0). The tangent to the curve at P is then drawn and will intersect the X-axis at $(X_1, 0)$. If the curve and the tangent are nearly coincident over the range (X_0, X_1), the value X_1 will be an approximate root of the equation. Furthermore, using the fact that the slope of the tangent at P is given by $f'(X_0)$, namely the derivative of $f(X)$ evaluated at $X = X_0$, we obtain the relationship

$$X_1 = X_0 - \frac{f(X_0)}{f'(X_0)} \tag{10}$$

If necessary, the procedure may be repeated as many times as necessary where, in general

$$X_{n+1} = X_n - \frac{f(X_n)}{f'(X_n)} \tag{11}$$

Whether and how fast the process will converge depends on the function $f(X)$ and the initial value X_0. Conditions favorable to convergence are evidently that $f(X_0)$ be small and $f'(X_0)$ be large.

To illustrate Newton's method, let us suppose that

$$f(X) = X^3 - 3X^2 + 4X - 2$$

While there are many devices which can be used to locate integers between or at which roots will lie, let us arbitrarily take $X_0 = 2$ as our trial "solution." *

Now

$$f'(X) = 3X^2 - 6X + 4$$

so that

$$f(2) = 8 - 12 + 8 - 2 = 2$$

$$f'(2) = 12 - 12 + 4 = 4$$

Hence, using eq. 11, we obtain

$$X_1 = 2 - \tfrac{2}{4} = 1.5$$

Continuing in this manner

$$f(1.5) = (\tfrac{3}{2})^3 - 3(\tfrac{3}{2})^2 + 4(\tfrac{3}{2}) - 2 = \tfrac{5}{8}$$

and $$f'(1.5) = 3(\tfrac{3}{2})^2 - 6(\tfrac{3}{2}) + 4 = \tfrac{7}{4}$$

so that

$$X_2 = 1.5 - \tfrac{5}{14} = 1.143$$

Continuing once more, we obtain:

$$f(1.143) = 0.147$$

$$f'(1.143) = 1.060$$

so that

$$X_3 = 1.143 - \frac{0.147}{1.060} = 1.004$$

We could continue in this manner, measuring at each stage of the iterative procedure the value of $f(X_i)$ to indicate how quickly we are converging to a solution [obviously, at a point of solution X^*, $f(X^*) = 0$], and, hence, obtain this solution within any prescribed degree of accuracy.

* For the particular $f(X)$ chosen, $X = 1$ is obviously a solution, and is that which we wish to approximate by Newton's method. The deviation from the value $X = 1$ will, of course, measure the degree of accuracy of this approximation.

BIBLIOGRAPHY

1. Ackoff, R. L., *The Design of Social Research*, University of Chicago Press, Chicago, 1953.
2. Alford, L. P., and Bangs, J. R., *Production Handbook*, Ronald Press, New York, pp. 99–106, 1944.
3. Arrow, K. J., "Mathematical Models in the Social Sciences," in Daniel Lerner and H. D. Laswell (eds.), *The Policy Sciences*, Stanford University Press, Stanford, 1951.
4. Avery, F. B., "Economic Manufacturing Quantity," *Industr. Mgmt.*, *63*, no. 3, 169–170, 189 (Mar. 1922).
5. Churchman, C. West, *Theory of Experimental Inference*, The Macmillan Co., New York, 1948.
6. ———, and Ackoff, R. L., *Methods of Inquiry*, Educational Publishers, St. Louis, 1950.
7. Curtiss, J. H., "Sampling Methods Applied to Differential and Difference Equations," in *Seminar on Scientific Computation*, International Business Machines Corp., New York.
8. Dewey, John, *Logic: The Theory of Inquiry*, Henry Holt & Co., New York, 1938.
9. Grant, Eugene L., *Principles of Engineering Economy*, Ronald Press, New York, pp. 263–268, 272–273, 1938.
10. Kahn, H., *Applications of Monte Carlo*, Project RAND, RM-1237-AEC, Santa Monica, Apr. 19, 1954.
11. ———, and Marshall, A. W., "Methods of Reducing Sample Size in Monte Carlo Computations," *J. Opns. Res. Soc. Am.*, *1*, no. 5, 263–278 (Nov. 1953).
12. Kimball, D. A., *Industrial Economics*, McGraw-Hill Book Co., New York, pp. 283–287, 1929.
13. King, Gilbert W., "The Monte Carlo Method as a Natural Mode of Expression in Operations Research, *J. Opns. Res. Soc. Am.*, *1*, no. 2, 46–51 (Feb. 1953).
14. Koepke, C. A., *Plant Production Control*, John Wiley & Sons, New York, pp. 379–387, 1941.
15. Lehoczky, P. N., "Lower Costs by Economic Lot Sizes," *Mfg. Inds.*, *16*, no. 4, 299–300 (Aug. 1928).
16. Littlefield, P. H., *The Determination of the Economic Size of Production Orders*, Massachusetts Institute of Technology, Cambridge, Course XV, Thesis No. 3, 1924.
17. Mellen, G. H., "Practical Lot Quantity Formula," *Mgmt. & Adm.*, *9*, no. 6, 565–566 (June 1925), and *10*, no. 3, 155 (Sept. 1925).
18. Neumann, J. von and Morgenstern, O., *Theory of Games and Economic Behavior*, Princeton University Press, Princeton, 2nd ed., 1947.
19. Raymond, F. E., *Quantity and Economy in Manufacture*, McGraw-Hill Book Co., New York, 1931.
20. Rich, R. P., "Simulation as an Aid to Model Building," *J. Opns. Res. Soc. Am.*, *3*, no. 1, 15–19 (Feb. 1955).
21. The RAND Corporation, *A Million Random Digits*, The Free Press, Glencoe, 1955.
22. Thrall, R. M., Coombs, C. H., and Davis, R. L., eds., *Decision Processes*, John Wiley & Sons, New York, 1954.

23. U. S. Dept. of Commerce, National Bureau of Standards, *Monte Carlo Method*, Applied Mathematics Seminar 12, June 11, 1951.
24. Wilson, E. Bright, Jr., *An Introduction to Scientific Research*, McGraw-Hill Book Co., New York, 1952.
25. Younger, J., and Gesechelin, J., *Work Routing, Scheduling, and Dispatching in Production*, Ronald Press, New York, 3rd ed., pp. 52–57, 1947.

PART
IV

INVENTORY MODELS

More O.R. has been directed toward inventory control than toward any other problem area in business and industry. Applications to military inventory problems are becoming increasingly numerous as well. For this reason there are more models available for this class of problems than for any other.

As far back as 1915 an economic-lot-size equation was developed by F. W. Harris which minimized the sum of inventory-carrying and setup costs where demand was known and constant. Industrial engineers, economists, and mathematicians added to this work so that by 1950 a considerable literature existed. The developments up to about 1952 have been summarized and augmented by Whitin.[33] Most of the techniques and tools currently used by O.R. in the inventory control area, however, have been developed in the last few years.* This recent development began with the attempt to provide procedures which are applicable in situations in which demand is not known with certainty but can only be estimated.

One problem that arises when uncertainty of demand is taken into account is that of providing a buffer stock to protect against shortages. Research on this problem was fruit-

* A simplified version of this work has been presented by Laderman, Littauer, and Weiss.[20]

fully conducted by Fry,[15] Eisenhart,[13] Arrow, Harris, and Marschak,[2] and Tompkins [28, 29] among others. Whitin [33] has considered the interaction between lot-size considerations and buffer stocks. Dvoretzky, Kiefer, and Wolfowitz [11, 12] showed the conditions under which optimum inventory levels can be found. As Whitin [33] has stated,

> The analysis of Arrow, Harris and Marschak constituted a considerable extension of the previous results. A year later the results of Dvoretzky, Kiefer and Wolfowitz appeared, these results being by far the most advanced from the standpoint of elegance, generality, and the use of high-powered mathematics. Their articles were generalized to include consideration of delivery time lags as a probability distribution, simultaneous demands for several items, interdependence of demand in the various time periods, and cases where the probability distribution of demand is not completely known (pp. 35–36).

In contrast with this very general approach the models given in Chapter 8 are suited to specific inventory situations. The models presented progress from very simple situations to more complex ones. The presentation emphasizes the *method* of model construction and discloses, among other results, the fundamental dependence of an optimal planning procedure on the ratio of inventory-carrying cost to the cost of a shortage. Mathematical details of the derivation of solutions from these models are given in the notes at the end of the chapter.

Some other very useful specific models have been developed for application to a hierarchy of storage points by Berman and Clark.[8] These models apply, for example, where a central warehouse supplies a number of field warehouses which in turn supply distributors.

The effect of quantity discounts on purchase quantities has been investigated by Whitin.[33] A generalized technique applicable to a series of quantity discounts under restricted conditions is given and illustrated in Chapter 9.

In Chapter 10 consideration is given to the imposition of restrictions resulting from limited facilities, time, or money. It explains how such restrictions can be incorporated into inventory models and how optimum decision rules can be derived. Since the procedure of deriving solutions from models which incorporate such restrictions is not a common one, the mathematical details are provided in the body of the chapter. A higher degree of mathematical sophistication is required for their understanding than for the material in Chapters 8 and 9.

The text presented in the three chapters of this part applies to the so-called static inventory problem. Work has also been done on the dynamic problem in which one is concerned with the effect of a decision in the current period on subsequent periods. Several types of approach to the dynamic problem have been taken.

One type of approach uses the servomechanism concept. It consists essentially of utilizing some form of feedback to adjust production or purchases to changing demand. One feasible servoprocedure has been developed and applied at Carnegie Institute of Technology.[19, 26] This procedure makes use of Norbert Wiener's autocorrelation methods. A related method has been developed by Vassian,[30] a method which minimizes the variance of the inventory balance under specified conditions and which, unlike the Carnegie approach, uses discrete distributions of demand and inventory. In two industrial O.R. projects done at Case Institute of Technology [1, 16] use was made of the statistical control chart as the feedback device.

In the dynamic approach to inventory problems the cost associated with changes in the level of production is taken into account. The available techniques are designed to set a total production level which minimizes the sum of inventory carrying cost, setup cost, shortage cost, and this change-over cost. As yet, however, no way of simultaneously optimizing the total production quantity and the individual item-order quantities is available.

Charnes, Cooper, and Farr [9] have applied linear programming (a technique to be discussed in Part V) to setting over-all production levels where there are significant seasonal fluctuations in demand and where demand is assumed to be known. Through the development of a new technique, "Dynamic Programming," Bellman [3–5, 7] has made it theoretically and computationally feasible to approach the dynamic inventory problem with the calculus of variations. Bellman, Glicksberg, and Gross [6] have applied this method to deriving optimal inventory policies of various types for a range of assumptions concerning operating conditions. At Carnegie a matrix method, "Quadratic Programming," [18] has been developed and applied to setting over-all production levels where the cost functions have a quadratic form.

Two recent summaries of inventory theory have been provided by Whitin [32] and Simon and Holt.[27]

Before turning to inventory models and their solution it should be emphasized that no one of the models developed here or in other places is likely to be applicable *in toto* in any specific situation. But it should be possible for the researcher to make the necessary modifications if he understands how such models are developed, i.e., the methodology of model construction.

Chapter 8

Elementary

Inventory Models

INTRODUCTION

The purpose of this chapter is to introduce the kind of analysis that yields symbolic models of inventory processes. No effort is made here to develop one general model to cover a wide variety of problems. Instead, we shall consider a sequence of relatively simple inventory problems and specific models which are applicable to them. Generality is sacrificed for practicality since easy-to-apply tools are the product of this elementary approach. Furthermore, applications rather than derivations are emphasized.

The general class of problems to be considered involves decisions concerning inventory levels. These decisions can be classified as follows:

1. The time at which orders for goods are to be placed is fixed and the quantity to be ordered must be determined.
2. Both order quantity and order time must be determined.

The research problem is to find ways of optimizing such decisions. An optimum decision, in this discussion, is one which minimizes the sum of the costs associated with inventory. These costs are of three types:

1. Cost of obtaining goods, through purchasing or manufacturing (the "setup" cost). This is a fixed cost per lot and, hence, a variable cost per unit.
2. Cost of holding a unit in inventory. This involves such contrib-

199

utory costs as the cost of money spent in producing the part, storage, handling, obsolescence, damage, insurance, and taxes.

3. Cost of shortage. This is the cost associated with either a delay in meeting demand or the inability to meet it at all.

These costs may remain constant or may vary as a function of time (for example, the cost associated with a delivery delay during one season may be greater than the cost associated with a delay during some other season); and/or they may vary as a function of the number of units involved (for instance, storage cost per unit may vary with the number of units stored).

In addition to cost variables, two other major classes of variables are involved in general inventory problems: *demand* variables and *order* variables.

Demand Variables. Demand may be either known or unknown. If known it may be constant or variable per unit time. The quantities of goods required may be values along either a discrete scale (e.g., number of automobiles) or a continuous scale (e.g., number of gallons of oil).

TABLE 8-1. CLASSIFICATION OF CHARACTERISTICS OF
INVENTORY PROBLEMS

1. Purchase or manufacturing cost per unit

2. Stock-holding cost per unit time   a. Constant
                                            b. Variable

3. Shortage cost

4. Demand | A. Known | a. Constant
           | | b. Variable
           | B. Estimated

5. Quantities required | A. Discrete units
                       | B. Continuous quantities

6. Distribution of withdrawals | A. Continuous | a. Constant rate
   over time | B. Discontinuous | b. Variable rate

7. Reorder lead time | A. Virtually zero
                     | B. Positive

8. Reorder cycle time | A. Known | a. Constant
                      | B. Estimated | b. Variable

9. Input quantities | A. Discrete | a. Constant
                    | B. Continuous | b. Variable

10. Distribution of inputs | A. Continuous | a. Constant rate
    over time | B. Discontinuous | b. Discontinuous rate

In addition, the withdrawal of goods from stock may be discontinuous in time (such as the sale of ice cream in a ball park) or continuous (the sale of ice cream at a soda fountain located in a large airport). Finally, the rate of withdrawal may be constant or variable.

Order Variables. The order lead time (i.e., the elapsed time between placing an order and acquisition of the goods ordered) may be either virtually instantaneous (e.g., in ordering milk at a grocery store) or of significant duration. The times at which orders can be placed may either be fixed or variable. The delivery of goods to stock may be in quantities which are either discrete or continuous, and either constant or variable. Finally, arrivals may be either continuous or discontinuous and at either a constant or variable rate.

Many other types of variation are possible, but even those enumerated yield several thousand classes of inventory problems. The characteristics enumerated are shown in Table 8-1 in such a way as to facilitate identification of the problem type.

Models for only a few problem types will be considered here. But an understanding of the method used in solving these will facilitate the development of solutions for other types.

The following is a list of symbols which are used throughout the discussion of Inventory Models I through VI:

q = input, or quantity ordered

q_i = input which occurs at the beginning of the ith time interval

q_0 = optimum order quantity

r = requirements per time interval

r_i = requirements for the ith time interval

S_i = inventory level at beginning of ith interval

s_i = inventory level at end of ith interval. Note: $s_i = S_i - r_i$, and $S_i = s_{i-1} + q_i$

S_0 = optimum inventory level at the beginning of a time interval

t = an interval of time

t_s = interval between placing orders—in units of time

t_{s0} = optimum interval between placing orders

T = period for which a policy is being established

R = total requirement for period T

C_1 = holding cost per unit of goods for a unit of time

C_2 = shortage cost per unit of goods for a specified period

C_s = setup cost per production run

TEC = total expected relevant cost. (In this chapter TEC is sometimes called the total expected cost. Actually, inasmuch as such costs as the price of the item are not affected by the size of run and, hence, are not included in Models I through VI, we really mean total expected *relevant* costs)

TEC_0 = minimum (optimum) total expected relevant cost

$P(r)$ = probability of requiring r units, where r is a discrete variable

$f(r)$ = probability density function of r, where r is a continuous variable

$P(r \leq S)$ = probability of requiring S units or less than S units, where r is a discrete variable

$F(r)$ = cumulative probability function of r, where r is a continuous variable

$F(S) = \int_0^S f(r)\,dr$ = probability of requiring S or less units, where r is a continuous variable

MODEL I

Consider a manufacturer who has to supply R units at a constant rate to his customers during time T. Hence, demand is fixed and known. No shortages are to be permitted; consequently, the cost of a shortage is infinite (i.e., $C_2 = \infty$). The variable costs associated with the manufacturing process are

C_1 = the cost of holding one unit in inventory for a unit of time

C_s = the setup cost per production run

The manufacturer's problem is to determine:

1. How often he should make a production run.
2. How many units should be made per run.

Cost Equation and Analytic Solution

The situation just described can be represented graphically as is done in Fig. 8-1.

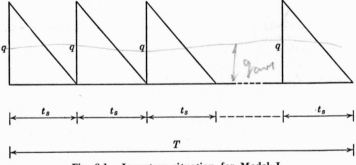

Fig. 8-1. Inventory situation for Model I.

Let q represent the run size, t_s the interval of time between runs, and R the total requirement for the planning period T. Then

$$\frac{R}{q} = \text{the number of runs during time } T$$

Hence

$$t_s = \frac{T}{R/q} = \frac{Tq}{R}$$

$y = \frac{Rt}{T}$

If the interval t_s begins with q units in stock and ends with none, then

$$\frac{q}{2} = \text{average inventory during } t_s$$

$$\frac{q}{2}C_1 t_s = \text{inventory costs during } t_s$$

The total expected relevant cost per run, then, will consist of these inventory costs plus the setup cost C_s: $(q/2)C_1 t_s + C_s$. Finally, the *TEC* over time T will be the cost per run times the number of runs during time T

$$TEC = \left(\frac{q}{2}C_1 t_s + C_s\right)\frac{R}{q}$$

Substituting, for t_s, the equivalent expression just given, we get

$$TEC = \left(\frac{q}{2}C_1 \frac{Tq}{R} + C_s\right)\frac{R}{q}$$

i.e.,

$$TEC = \frac{C_1 T q}{2} + \frac{C_s R}{q} \tag{1}$$

Examining eq. 1, we can see that the two right-hand terms represent total inventory costs and total setup costs respectively. The first of these terms increases with the increase in the run size, but the second decreases. The solution of this inventory problem, then, consists of finding that value of q (the run size), say q_0, for which the sum of these two costs is minimum. See Fig. 8-2.

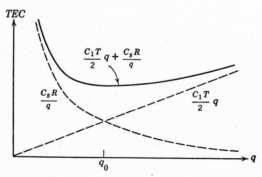

Fig. 8-2. Solving for q_0, Model I.

A solution can be derived analytically by the use of elementary differential calculus. This is done in Note 1 at the end of this chapter. The optimum value of q, denoted by q_0, is found to be

$$q_0 = \sqrt{2 \frac{R}{T} \frac{C_s}{C_1}} \qquad (2)$$

The corresponding optimum t_s and minimum TEC are

$$t_{s0} = \sqrt{2 \frac{T}{R} \frac{C_s}{C_1}} \qquad (3)$$

$$TEC_0 = \sqrt{2RTC_1C_s} \qquad (4)$$

Example I

A manufacturer has to supply his customer with 24,000 units of his product per year. This demand is fixed and known. Since the unit is used by the customer in an assembly-line operation, and the customer has no storage space for the units, the manufacturer must ship a day's supply each day. If the manufacturer fails to supply the required units, he will lose the account and probably his business. Hence, the cost of a shortage is assumed to be infinite, and, consequently, none will be tolerated. The inventory holding cost amounts to $0.10 per unit per month, and the setup cost per run is $350.

The problem is to find the optimum run size q_0, the corresponding optimum scheduling period t_{s0}, and minimum total expected relevant yearly cost TEC_0. In this case, then,

$$T = 12 \text{ months}$$

$$R = 24{,}000 \text{ units}$$

$$C_1 = \$0.10 \text{ per month}$$

$$C_s = \$350 \text{ per production run}$$

Substituting in eqs. 2, 3, and 4, we obtain the following solution

$$q_0 = \sqrt{2 \frac{24{,}000}{12} \frac{350}{0.10}} = 3740 \text{ units per run}$$

$$t_{s0} = \sqrt{2 \frac{12}{24{,}000} \frac{350}{0.10}} = 1.87 \text{ months} = 8.1 \text{ weeks between runs}$$

$$TEC_0 = \sqrt{2(24{,}000)(12)(0.10)(350)} = \$4490 \text{ per year}$$

MODEL II

This problem type is similar to the one discussed under Model I except that we shall now assume that shortages may be allowed to occur (i.e., the cost of a shortage is not infinite).

Cost Equation and Analytic Solution

This inventory situation can be represented graphically as is done in Fig. 8-3, where S is the inventory level at the beginning of each interval.

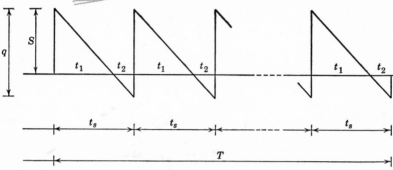

Fig. 8-3. Inventory situation for Model II.

Using a simple geometrical relationship (i.e., similar triangles), we observe that

$$t_1 = \frac{S}{q} t_s$$

$$t_2 = \frac{q - S}{q} t_s$$

The average number of units in inventory during t_1 is $S/2$. Therefore

$$\frac{S}{2} C_1 t_1 = \text{the average inventory cost during } t_1$$

Similarly, the average number of units short during t_2 is $(q - S)/2$. Therefore

$$\frac{q - S}{2} C_2 t_2 = \text{the average shortage cost during } t_2$$

Hence, the total expected cost during T is expressed as follows

$$TEC(q, S) = \left(\frac{S}{2} C_1 t_1 + \frac{q - S}{2} C_2 t_2 + C_s \right) \frac{R}{q}$$

Substituting the values of t_1 and t_2 obtained in the foregoing, we get

$$TEC(q, S) = \left(\frac{S}{2} C_1 \frac{S}{q} t_s + \frac{q - S}{2} C_2 \frac{q - S}{q} t_s + C_s\right) \frac{R}{q}$$

$$= \left(\frac{S^2}{2q} C_1 t_s + \frac{(q - S)^2}{2q} C_2 t_s + C_s\right) \frac{R}{q}$$

Substituting the value of t_s obtained under Model I (i.e., $t_s = Tq/R$), and simplifying, we get

$$TEC(q, S) = \frac{S^2 C_1 T}{2q} + \frac{(q - S)^2 C_2 T}{2q} + \frac{C_s R}{q} \tag{5}$$

From eq. 5 the optimum values of q and S can be derived, as is done in Note 2 at the end of this chapter. The results are

$$q_0 = \sqrt{2 \frac{R}{T} \frac{C_s}{C_1}} \sqrt{\frac{C_1 + C_2}{C_2}} \tag{6}$$

$$S_0 = \sqrt{2 \frac{R}{T} \frac{C_s}{C_1}} \sqrt{\frac{C_2}{C_1 + C_2}} \tag{7}$$

The corresponding values of t_s and TEC are

$$t_{s0} = \sqrt{2 \frac{T}{R} \frac{C_s}{C_1}} \sqrt{\frac{C_1 + C_2}{C_2}} \tag{8}$$

$$TEC_0 = \sqrt{2RTC_1C_s} \sqrt{\frac{C_2}{C_1 + C_2}} \tag{9}$$

If we compare the results of Model II with those of Model I we note:

1. Equations 2, 3, and 4 can be derived by letting C_2 become infinitely large in eqs. 6, 8, and 9. This result is not surprising since Model I is a special case of Model II.

2. If $C_2 \neq \infty$, then

$$\sqrt{2RTC_1C_s} \sqrt{\frac{C_2}{C_1 + C_2}} < \sqrt{2RTC_1C_s}$$

Hence, the total expected costs associated with decisions based on Model II are smaller than those based on Model I.

Example II

Let us consider the same situation as was given in the example under Model I except that we now have a shortage cost C_2 of \$0.20 per unit per month.

Substituting in eqs. 6 through 9, we obtain

$$q_0 = \sqrt{2 \frac{24{,}000}{12} \frac{350}{0.10}} \sqrt{\frac{0.10 + 0.20}{0.20}} = 4578 \text{ units per run}$$

$$S_0 = \sqrt{2 \frac{24{,}000}{12} \frac{350}{0.10}} \sqrt{\frac{0.20}{0.10 + 0.20}} = 3056 \text{ units}$$

$$t_{s0} = \sqrt{2 \frac{12}{24{,}000} \frac{350}{0.10}} \sqrt{\frac{0.10 + 0.20}{0.20}} = 2.29 \text{ months} = 9.9 \text{ weeks}$$

$$TEC_0 = \sqrt{2(24{,}000)(12)(0.10)(350)} \sqrt{\frac{0.20}{0.10 + 0.20}} = \$3667$$

Furthermore, using optimum policy, the expected number of shortages at the end of each scheduling period would be $4578 - 3056$, or 1522 units.

MODEL III

The problem type to be considered here introduces, in addition to a finite cost of shortage (as in Model II), the following concepts.*

Estimated variable demands and input.

Discrete units.

Discontinuous distribution over time of withdrawals and input at a discontinuous rate.

Known and constant reorder cycle time.

Example III

An electric power company is about to order a new generator for its plant. One of the essential parts of the generator is very complicated and expensive and would be impractical to order except with the order of the generator. Each of these parts is uniquely built for a particular generator and may not be used on any other. The com-

---

* In this model and in Model VI, we do not take into consideration the cost of carrying inventory of parts until they are used. Rather, in this elementary inventory situation we are balancing the cost of having excess parts that are *never* used against the cost of being short of parts when needed.

pany wants to know how many spare parts should be incorporated in the order for each generator.

The following information is available: The cost of the part (when ordered with the generator) is $500. If a spare part is needed (because of the failure of the part in use) and is not available, the whole generator becomes useless. The cost of the down time of the generator, plus having the part made to order, is $10,000. A study of the behavior of similar parts in similar generators yields the information shown in Table 8-2 based on 100 generators.

TABLE 8-2

No. of Spare Parts Required	No. of Generators Requiring Indicated No. of Spare Parts	Estimated Probability of Occurrence of Indicated No. of Failures
0	90	0.90
1	5	0.05
2	2	0.02
3	1	0.01
4	1	0.01
5	1	0.01
6 or more	0	0.00

Cost Equation

The cost equation (i.e., symbolic model) for this type of problem may be developed as follows. For any quantity in stock S, suppose r units are used. Then for a specified period of time, the cost associated with having S units in stock is either:

1. $(S - r)C_1$, where $r \leqq S$ (i.e., where the number of units used is less than or equal to the number of units in stock); or

2. $(r - S)C_2$, where $r > S$ (i.e., where the number of units required is greater than the number of units in stock).

But we do not know beforehand what the value of r will be. However, there is a probability of occurrence associated with each value of r, i.e., $P(r)$. Then the expected cost associated with a particular value of r is either

$$P(r)(S - r)C_1, \text{ where } r < S; \text{ or}$$

$$P(r)(r - S)C_2, \text{ where } r > S.$$

If $r = S$, then the expected cost is equal to zero.

To get the total expected cost, we must sum over all the expected costs, i.e., the costs associated with each possible value of r. The total expected cost TEC associated with a stock level of S units is then given by the following equation

$$TEC(S) = C_1 \sum_{r=0}^{S} P(r)(S - r) + C_2 \sum_{r=S+1}^{\infty} P(r)(r - S) \quad (10)$$

Solution by Enumeration

We can apply eq. 10 to Example III and compute the total expected cost associated with any of the reasonable stock levels (i.e., from 0 to 5, since the failure data indicate that there is no probability of more than five failures). In the example, we shall assume that the cost of not using a part is simply its purchase cost inasmuch as holding costs are negligible. Therefore, $C_1 = \$500$. The cost of a shortage C_2 is assumed to be \$10,000, and consists of the cost of the resulting down time plus custom production of the part.

Applying eq. 10 to each stock level, we obtain the following TEC's

$$TEC(S = 5) = \$500[0.90(5 - 0) + 0.05(5 - 1) + 0.02(5 - 2)$$
$$+ 0.01(5 - 3) + 0.01(5 - 4) + 0.01(5 - 5)] = \$2395$$

$$TEC(S = 4) = \$500[0.90(4 - 0) + 0.05(4 - 1) + 0.02(4 - 2)$$
$$+ 0.01(4 - 3) + 0.01(4 - 4)] + \$10,000[0.01(5 - 4)]$$
$$= \$2000$$

$$TEC(S = 3) = \$500[0.90(3 - 0) + 0.05(3 - 1) + 0.02(3 - 2)$$
$$+ 0.01(3 - 3)] + \$10,000[0.01(5 - 3) + 0.01(4 - 3)]$$
$$= \$1710$$

$$TEC(S = 2) = \$500[0.90(2 - 0) + 0.05(2 - 1) + 0.02(2 - 2)]$$
$$+ \$10,000[0.01(5 - 2) + 0.01(4 - 2) + 0.01(3 - 2)]$$
$$= \$1525$$

$$TEC(S = 1) = \$500[0.90(1 - 0) + 0.05(1 - 1)] + \$10,000[0.01(5 - 1)$$
$$+ 0.01(4 - 1) + 0.01(3 - 1) + 0.02(2 - 1)] = \$1550$$

$$TEC(S = 0) = \$10,000[0.01(5 - 0) + 0.01(4 - 0) + 0.01(3 - 0)$$
$$+ 0.02(2 - 0) + 0.05(1 - 0)] = \$2100$$

This comparison indicates that the optimum stock level is two parts.

Analytic Solution

It is possible to obtain an analytic solution to the problem of determining the value of S which minimizes the total expected cost. The derivation of an analytic solution is given in Note 3 at the end of this chapter. The result is as follows: The value of S which minimizes the TEC is that value S_0 which satisfies the condition

$$P(r \leqq S_0 - 1) < \frac{C_2}{C_1 + C_2} < P(r \leqq S_0) \qquad (11)$$

This inequation can be used to solve Example III in the following way:

1. Reformulate the data given in the example as shown in Table 8-3.

TABLE 8-3

S	r	$P(r)$	$P(r \leqq S)$
0	0	0.900	0.900
1	1	0.050	0.950
2	2	0.020	0.970
3	3	0.010	0.980
4	4	0.010	0.990
5	5	0.010	1.000
6 or more		0.000	1.000
		1.000	

2. Compute the value of $C_2/(C_1 + C_2)$, which in this case is \$10,000/(\$500 + \$10,000) = 0.952.

3. Find that value of S from the table in step 1 which satisfies the inequality

$$P(r \leqq S - 1) < 0.952 < P(r \leqq S)$$

In this case, the relevant value of S is 2, since

$$P(r \leqq 1) < 0.952 < P(r \leqq 2)$$

i.e.,

$$0.950 < 0.952 < 0.970$$

Then S_0 (the optimum inventory level) is 2.

It should be noted, in passing, that if there is an S_0 such that

$$P(r \leqq S_0) = C_2/(C_1 + C_2)$$

then there are two optimums, S_0 and $S_0 + 1$. Additionally, if

$$P(r \leqq S_0 - 1) = C_2/(C_1 + C_2)$$

then there will be two optimums, namely, $S_0 - 1$ and S_0. The two equality conditions are, however, equivalent.

To summarize:

1. From the data, prepare a table showing $P(r)$ and $P(r \leqq S)$ for each reasonable value of r.

2. Compute $C_2/(C_1 + C_2)$.

3. Find the value of S which satisfies the inequality (or corresponding equalities)

$$P(r \leqq S - 1) < \frac{C_2}{C_1 + C_2} < P(r \leqq S)$$

ESTIMATING COST OF A SHORTAGE. The analytic solution to this problem can be used to determine what range of values a decision-maker actually places on a shortage. Suppose, for example, that in the foregoing illustration we did not know the cost of a shortage but did know that the decision-maker's policy was to maintain a stock level of three parts. We can now ask for what values of C_2 does $S_0 = 3$? The question can be answered as follows

$$P(r \leqq S_0 - 1) < \frac{C_2}{C_1 + C_2} < P(r \leqq S_0)$$

Substituting

$$P(r \leqq 2) < \frac{C_2}{\$500 + C_2} < P(r \leqq 3)$$

$$0.970 < \frac{C_2}{\$500 + C_2} < 0.980$$

The minimum value of C_2 is determined by letting

$$\frac{C_2}{\$500 + C_2} = 0.970$$

Then

$$C_2 = \frac{(0.970)(\$500)}{(1 - 0.970)} = \$16,167$$

The maximum value of C_2 is determined by letting

$$\frac{C_2}{\$500 + C_2} = 0.980$$

from which

$$C_2 = \frac{(0.980)(\$500)}{(1 - 0.980)} = \$24,500$$

Therefore, $16,167 $\leq C_2 \leq$ $24,500. The answer, then, is that the decision-maker places on C_2 a value between $16,167 and $24,500.

MODEL IV

This problem type is the same as that given in the last section except for the fact that the stock levels are now assumed to be continuous (rather than discrete) quantities. Hence the probability of an order within the range r_1 to r_2 is expressed by the integral $\int_{r_1}^{r_2} f(r)\ dr$, and the probability of an order being less than or equal to a value S is *

$$\int_0^S f(r)\ dr = F(S)$$

Cost Equation

The cost equation for this type of problem is similar to the one derived for the problem under Model III. $P(r)$ is replaced in eq. 10 by $f(r)\ dr$, and the summation is replaced by an integral. Then

$$TEC(S) = C_1 \int_0^S (S - r)f(r)\ dr + C_2 \int_S^\infty (r - S)f(r)\ dr \qquad (12)$$

In this case, an analytic solution shows (see Note 4) that the total expected cost is minimum for that value of S which satisfies the following condition

$$F(S) \equiv \int_0^S f(r)\ dr = \frac{C_2}{C_1 + C_2} \qquad \qquad (13)$$

Example IV

A baking company sells one of its types of cake by weight. If the product is not sold on the day it is baked, it can only be sold at a loss of 15¢ per pound. But there is an unlimited market for 1-day-old cake. The cost of holding a pound of cake in stock for one day, then, is 15¢. On the other hand, the company makes a profit of 95¢ on every pound of cake sold on the day it is baked. Thus the cost of a shortage is 95¢ per pound. Past daily orders form a triangular distribution as shown in Fig. 8-4.

In this case, the probability density function of r is

$$f(r) = 0.02 - 0.0002r$$

The problem is to determine how many pounds of cake the company should bake daily.

---

* Negative orders (i.e., returns) are not considered here.

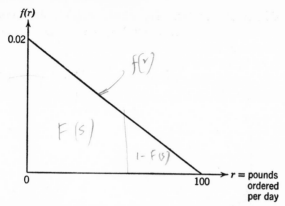

Fig. 8-4. Distribution of daily orders for baking company, **Example IV.**

SOLUTION. In this case $C_1 = 15¢$ and $C_2 = 95¢$. Then

$$\frac{C_2}{C_1 + C_2} = \frac{95}{15 + 95} = 0.8636$$

To find the optimum order quantity q_0, we must find a stock level S which satisfies the condition

$$F(S) = \frac{C_2}{C_1 + C_2} = 0.8636; \text{ i.e., } \int_0^S f(r)\, dr = 0.8636$$

This can be done as follows

$$\int_0^S f(r)\, dr = \int_0^S (0.02 - 0.0002r)\, dr = \left(0.02r - \frac{0.0002r^2}{2}\right)_0^S = 0.8636$$

$$0.02S - 0.0001S^2 = 0.8636$$

Therefore

$$S = 100 \pm 36.93$$

Consequently, there are two solutions:

1. $q_1 = 100 + 36.93 = 136.93$ pounds
2. $q_2 = 100 - 36.93 = 63.07$ pounds

The first solution is not applicable since the given probability distribution for r is not applicable over 100 pounds. Therefore, the second solution is used.

In this particular case, since $f(r)$ is a straight line, the same result could have been obtained from simple geometric considerations instead

of the use of integral calculus. The graph of $f(r)$ is also shown in Fig.
8-5. The area under $f(r)$ is 1. We wish to find S such that the area
under $f(r)$ between O and S (the trapezoid $OCDE$) is 0.8636. The area
of the trapezoid is the sum of the areas of the rectangle A and the triangle B in the figure. Since we wish it to be 0.8636, we put area $A +$
area $B = 0.8636$.

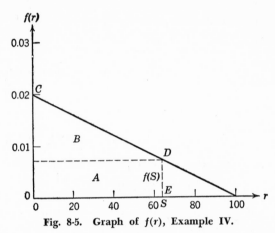

Fig. 8-5. Graph of $f(r)$, Example IV.

Now the area of A is $Sf(S)$, and the area of B is $\frac{1}{2}S[0.02 - f(S)]$.
Substituting, we get

$$S[f(S)] + \tfrac{1}{2}S[0.02 - f(S)] = 0.8636$$

i.e.

$$S(0.02 - 0.0002S) + \tfrac{1}{2}S(0.02 - 0.02 + 0.0002S) = 0.8636$$

or

$$0.02S - 0.0001S^2 = 0.8636$$

so that

$$S = 100 \pm 36.93$$

Interpretation of Optimum S

The equation $F(S) = C_2/(C_1 + C_2)$ can be written as $C_2/C_1 =$
$[F(S)]/[1 - F(S)]$ and, accordingly, has a very interesting interpretation. That is, under the optimum conditions, the ratio of the probability of demand being less than the optimum inventory level to the
probability of its being greater is equal to the ratio of the unit shortage
cost to the unit holding cost.

MODEL V

This problem type is similar to the previous one with one important exception, the reorder lead time in this case is significant. That is, the time between placing an order and delivery of the goods ordered must be taken into account.

Example V

A shop owner places orders daily for goods which will be delivered 7 days later (i.e., the reorder lead time is 7 days). On a certain day, the owner has 10 pounds in stock. Furthermore, on the 6 previous days, he has already placed orders for the delivery of 2, 4, 1, 10, 11, and 5 pounds, in that order, over each of the next 6 days. To facilitate computations, we shall assume conditions similar to those in the last example, namely

$$C_1 = 15\cent; C_2 = 95\cent$$

and the distribution of requirements over a 7-day period (R') is

$$f(R') = 0.02 - 0.0002R'$$

The problem is: How many pounds should be ordered for the 7th day hence; i.e., what should be the value of q_7?

Cost Equation and Analytic Solution

First let us enumerate the characteristics of the situation which are known:

k = the number of order cycle periods in the order lead time

s_0 = the stock level at the end of the period preceding placing of the order

$q_1, q_2, \cdots, q_{k-1}$ = quantities already ordered and due to arrive on the 1st, 2nd, $\cdots$, and $k - $ 1st days

$f(R') = f\left(\sum_{i=1}^{k} r_i\right)$, where R' is the requirement over the order lead time (in this case, 7 days).

The problem is to determine the value of q_k which will minimize the total expected cost of the kth order cycle period.

We will construct a cost equation covering the order lead time; i.e., covering the kth order cycle period. The reason for this is that the total expected cost for the period from 1 to $k - $ 1 is already determined since orders for $q_1, q_2, \cdots, q_{k-1}$ have already been placed. Therefore, minimization of the total expected cost from 1 to k is equivalent to minimizing the total expected cost for the kth period.

The stock at the end of the kth period can be expressed as follows

$$s_k = s_0 + \sum_{i=1}^{k-1} q_i + q_k - \sum_{i=1}^{k} r_i$$

Let

$$S' = s_0 + \sum_{i=1}^{k-1} q_i + q_k$$

$$R' = \sum_{i=1}^{k} r_i$$

Substituting S' for S and R' for R in eq. 12, we get

$$TEC(S') = C_1 \int_0^{S'} (S' - R')f(R') \, dR' + C_2 \int_{S'}^{\infty} (R' - S')f(R') \, dR' \quad (14)$$

Since eq. 14 is essentially the same as eq. 12, we see from eq. 13 that the optimum value of S' is that value which satisfies the equation

$$F(S_0') = \frac{C_2}{C_1 + C_2} \qquad (15)$$

Once the optimum value of S' (i.e., S_0') is determined, we can determine the optimum value of q_k from the following

$$q_{k0} = S_0' - (s_0 + \sum_{i=1}^{k-1} q_i) \qquad (16)$$

The detailed justification of this solution is given in Note 5 at the end of this chapter.

Solution to Example V

First, we must determine the optimum value of S'. This is the value that satisfies the condition

$$F(S') = \frac{C_2}{C_1 + C_2} = \frac{95}{15 + 95} = 0.8636$$

Then, using the distribution $f(R') = 0.02 - 0.0002R'$, we determine the value of S' by solving

$$F(S') = \int_0^{S'} (0.02 - 0.0002R') \, dR' = 0.8636$$

Earlier in this chapter it was shown that the solution is given by $S' = 63.07$ or 63 pounds.

Since

$$S' = s_0 + \sum_{i=1}^{6} q_i + q_7$$

we can solve for the optimum value of q_7 *ordered*

$$63 = 10 + (2 + 4 + 1 + 10 + 11 + 5) + q_7$$

$$q_7 = 63 - 10 - 33 = 20 \text{ pounds}$$

The optimum order quantity, then, is 20 pounds.

MODEL VI

This problem type is similar to that considered under Model III except that withdrawals from stock are continuous. It is assumed in this case that the withdrawal rate is virtually constant. The type of situation considered can be represented graphically as in Fig. 8-6.

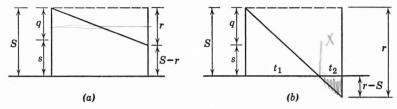

Fig. 8-6. Illustration for Model VI.

Figure 8-6a occurs when $r \leqq S$. Figure 8-6b results when $r > S$, i.e., when demand exceeds stock. The region below the horizontal axis represents shortages.

Example VI

A manufacturer wants to know what is the optimum stock level of a certain part used in filling orders which come in at a relatively con-

TABLE 8-4

No. of Units Required per Month	Probability of Occurrence
0	0.1
1	0.2
2	0.2
3	0.3
4	0.1
5	0.1
6 or more	0.0

stant rate but not a constant size. Delivery of these parts to him is virtually immediate. He regularly places his orders for these parts at the beginning of each month. Study of demand reveals that the probabilities shown in Table 8-4 are associated with various requirements per month. Finally, the cost of holding a unit in stock 1 month is $1.00, and the cost of a unit shortage per month is $20.00.

Cost Equation and Analytic Solution

First let us consider the cost associated with the situation shown in Fig. 8-6a, where, for a given value of r, the average number of units in stock over the order cycle period is

$$\tfrac{1}{2}[S + (S - r)] = S - \frac{r}{2}$$

Therefore, since $P(r)$ is the probability of requiring r discrete units, the expected cost associated with holding this number of units in stock over the period is $C_1 P(r)[S - (r/2)]$. The total expected cost associated with Fig. 8-6a is obtained by summing over all values of $r \leq S$, i.e.,

$$C_1 \sum_0^S P(r)[S - (r/2)].$$

Now consider Fig. 8-6b, where $r > S$. First we will take into account that portion of the period during which there are no shortages. The portion of the period for which this is true is $t_1/(t_1 + t_2)$, which by use of similar triangle relationships we note is equal to S/r. The average amount stocked is $S/2$. Then the holding cost for each r during this portion of the period is

$$C_1 \left(\frac{S}{2}\right)\left(\frac{S}{r}\right) = C_1 \left(\frac{S^2}{2r}\right)$$

The portion of the period during which there are shortages is $(r - S)/r$. The average amount short is $(r - S)/2$. Then, for each r, the shortage cost is

$$C_2 \left(\frac{r - S}{r}\right)\left(\frac{r - S}{2}\right) = C_2 \frac{(r - S)^2}{2r}$$

Combining these components, we get the following cost equation

$$TEC(S) = C_1 \sum_{r=0}^S P(r) \left(S - \frac{r}{2}\right) + C_1 \sum_{r=S+1}^\infty P(r) \frac{S^2}{2r}$$

$$+ C_2 \sum_{r=S+1}^\infty P(r) \frac{(r - S)^2}{2r} \quad (17)$$

By use of the method described in Note 6 at the end of this chapter, we can determine that the optimum value of S is that which satisfies the following condition

$$\left[P[r \leq (S-1)] + \left(S - \frac{1}{2}\right) \sum_{S}^{\infty} \frac{P(r)}{r} \right] < \frac{C_2}{C_1 + C_2}$$

$$< \left[P(r \leq S) + \left(S + \frac{1}{2}\right) \sum_{S+1}^{\infty} \frac{P(r)}{r} \right] \quad (18)$$

For purposes of simplification let us represent eq. 18 as follows:

$$L(S-1) < \frac{C_2}{C_1 + C_2} < L(S) \quad (19)$$

Solution to Example

To facilitate computation it will be convenient to prepare a work form such as is shown in Table 8-5. Next we compute

$$\frac{C_2}{C_1 + C_2} = \frac{20}{1 + 20} = \frac{20}{21} = 0.9524 \quad \checkmark$$

TABLE 8-5. WORK FORM

S	r	$P(r)$	$\dfrac{P(r)}{r}$	$\sum_{S+1}^{\infty} \dfrac{P(r)}{r}$	$\left(S + \dfrac{1}{2}\right) \sum_{S+1}^{\infty} \dfrac{P(r)}{r}$	$P(r \leq S)$	$L(S) = P(r \leq S) + \left(S + \dfrac{1}{2}\right) \sum_{S+1}^{\infty} \dfrac{(Pr)}{r}$
0	0	0.1	∞	0.445	0.2225	0.1 $\checkmark$	0.3225
1	1	0.2	0.200	0.245	0.3675	0.3	0.6675
2	2	0.2	0.100	0.145	0.3625	0.5	0.8625
3	3	0.3	0.100	0.045	0.1575	0.8	0.9575
4	4	0.1	0.025	0.020	0.0900	0.9	0.9900
5	5	0.1	0.020	0.000	0.0000	1.0	1.0000
>5	>5	0.0	0.000	0.000	0.0000	1.0	1.0000

From Table 8-5, we now select that value of S which satisfies the condition

$$L(S-1) < \frac{C_2}{C_1 + C_2} < L(S)$$

$S = 3$ satisfies this condition since

$$0.8625 < 0.9524 < 0.9575 \quad \checkmark$$

The total expected cost associated with a stock level of three units can be computed by use of cost eq. 17

$$TEC(3) = \$1[(0.1)(3) + (0.2)(2.5) + (0.2)(2.0) + (0.3)(1.5)] +$$
$$\$1[(0.1)(\tfrac{9}{8}) + (0.1)(\tfrac{9}{10})] + \$20[(0.1)(\tfrac{1}{8}) + (0.1)(\tfrac{4}{10})]$$
$$= 1.65 + 0.2025 + 1.05 = \$2.9025 \quad \checkmark$$

Case Study Employing Model VI

Up to this point the examples have been very simple, and perhaps unrealistic. It may be helpful, therefore, to illustrate the use of one of the models in a real case. This will be done using Model VI.

The company involved in this case manufactures a part used extensively in machines, particularly in automobiles, airplanes, tractors, etc. It is a relatively small part which is sold at low cost. The manufacturing process is divided into two stages. In the first, the raw material is shaped, surfaced with an alloy, and milled. In the second, the parts are stamped out and finished. The reasons for the two stages are: a. the parts are produced in many sizes and types, and b. many of the sizes and types are made from the same strips. Therefore, there is considerably less variety in the first manufacturing stage than there is in the second. The second phase is the more costly and lengthy. Delays in the second stage of manufacture can be very expensive to the company. Consequently, inventories of the prepared strips are maintained so that when an order is received there need be no delay owing to the unavailability of the required strip. Because of the high costs (in loss of business) associated with delivery delays the company's policy was to maintain in inventory at the end of the first stage of the process a quantity sufficient to cover 95% of the demands that could be expected during the period between production runs of the strip. Study showed that this was equivalent, in this case, to assigning to the shortage cost a value 19 times as great as that assigned to the holding cost.* The problem was to determine both the frequency with which production runs of the strip should be made and the quantity to be run. Because of practical considerations it is desirable to run a particular strip once every 1, 2, 3, or more months, but not, say, every $2\frac{1}{2}$ or $5\frac{1}{4}$ weeks.

To simplify computation and thereby better expose the method employed, simplified data will be used. First, the costs are as follows:

$$C_1 = \$100$$
$$C_2 = 19C_1 = \$1,900$$
$$C_s = \$350$$

Assume that the distribution of monthly requirements is as shown in Table 8-6.

---

* While the mathematics are not shown here, they are quite similar to those derived for Model IV. That is, the condition $C_2 = 19C_1$ follows immediately from $C_2/(C_1 + C_2) = 0.95$.

TABLE 8-6

Demand per Month	Probability of Occurrence
r	$P(r)$
0	0.1
1	0.2
2	0.4
3	0.2
4	0.1
5 or more	0.0

Let us determine the optimum amount of strip to make if the policy is to produce monthly. We begin by preparing a table with the necessary data and computations; see Table 8-7.

TABLE 8-7

S	r	$P(r)$	$\dfrac{P(r)}{r}$	$\displaystyle\sum_{S+1}^{\infty}\dfrac{P(r)}{r}$	$\left(S+\dfrac{1}{2}\right)\displaystyle\sum_{S+1}^{\infty}\dfrac{P(r)}{r}$	$P(r \leq S)$	$L(S)$
0	0	0.1	∞	0.492	0.246	0.1	0.346
1	1	0.2	0.200	0.292	0.438	0.3	0.738
2	2	0.4	0.200	0.092	0.230	0.7	0.930
3	3	0.2	0.067	0.025	0.088	0.9	0.988
4	4	0.1	0.025	0.000	0.000	1.0	1.000

Next, we compute

$$\frac{C_2}{C_1 + C_2} = \frac{(19)(100)}{100 + (19)(100)} = \frac{1900}{2000} = 0.95 \quad \checkmark$$

Then, using Table 8-7, we select that value of S which satisfies the condition

$$L(S-1) < \frac{C_2}{C_1 + C_2} < L(S)$$

$S = 3$ satisfies this condition, since

$$0.930 < 0.95 < 0.988 \quad \checkmark$$

The total expected inventory cost per month associated with $S = 3$ is found by using eq. 17

$$TEC(S = 3) = \$100[(0.1)(3) + (0.2)(2.5) + (0.4)(2.0) + (0.2)(1.5)]$$
$$+ \$100[(0.1)(\tfrac{9}{8})] + \$1900[(0.1)(\tfrac{1}{8})]$$
$$= \$100(1.9) + \$100(0.1125) + \$1900(0.0125)$$
$$= \$190 + \$11.25 + \$23.75 = \$225.00$$

To obtain the total relevant cost of production * we must add the cost of a setup

$$\$225 + \$350 = \$575$$

The optimum total annual cost for a run each month, then, would be $(12)(\$575) = \$6900$.

Now we want to determine the optimum annual cost associated with a policy of making a run every 2 months. First, it is necessary to obtain a distribution of requirements over a 2-month period. The probability of obtaining zero requirements over a 2-month period is $(0.1)(0.1) = 0.01$, i.e., the product of the probabilities of requiring zero units each month. Similarly, we can compute (where P_2 = the probability associated with a 2-month period and P_1 = the probability associated with a 1-month period) †

$$P_2(1) = P_1(0)P_1(1) + P_1(1)P_1(0) = (0.2)(0.1) + (0.1)(0.2) = 0.04$$

$$P_2(2) = P_1(0)P_1(2) + P_1(1)P_1(1) + P_1(2)P_1(0) = (0.1)(0.4) +$$
$$(0.2)(0.2) + (0.4)(0.1) = 0.12$$

$$P_2(3) = P_1(0)P_1(3) + P_1(1)P_1(2) + P_1(2)P_1(1) + P_1(3)P_1(0) =$$
$$(0.1)(0.2) + (0.2)(0.4) + (0.4)(0.2) + (0.2)(0.1) = 0.20$$

$$P_2(4) = P_1(0)P_1(4) + P_1(1)P_1(3) + P_1(2)P_1(2) + P_1(3)P_1(1) +$$
$$P_1(4)P_1(0) = (0.1)(0.1) + (0.2)(0.2) + (0.4)(0.4) +$$
$$(0.2)(0.2) + (0.1)(0.1) = 0.26$$

$$P_2(5) = P_1(1)P_1(4) + P_1(2)P_1(3) + P_1(3)P_1(2) + P_1(4)P_1(1) =$$
$$(0.2)(0.1) + (0.4)(0.2) + (0.2)(0.4) + (0.1)(0.2) = 0.20$$

$$P_2(6) = P_1(2)P_1(4) + P_1(3)P_1(3) + P_1(4)P_1(2) = (0.4)(0.1) +$$
$$(0.2)(0.2) + (0.1)(0.4) = 0.12$$

$$P_2(7) = P_1(3)P_1(4) + P_1(4)P_1(3) = (0.2)(0.1) + (0.1)(0.2) = 0.04$$

$$P_2(8) = P_1(4)P_1(4) = (0.1)(0.1) = 0.01$$

As before, we prepare the form shown in Table 8-8. Then the optimum value of S is 5 since

$$0.932 < 0.95 < 0.979$$

---

* Note that the manufacturing cost (exclusive of setup) of the product is the same regardless of the size of run. Hence, it is not included in the total relevant cost of production.

† This procedure assumes that the distribution of requirements is the same for each month.

TABLE 8-8

S	r	$P(r)$	$\dfrac{P(r)}{r}$	$\sum\limits_{s+1}^{\infty}\dfrac{P(r)}{r}$	$\left(S+\dfrac{1}{2}\right)\sum\limits_{s+1}^{\infty}\dfrac{P(r)}{r}$	$P(r \le S)$	$L(S)$
0	0	0.01		0.299	0.150	0.01	0.160
1	1	0.04	0.040	0.259	0.389	0.05	0.439
2	2	0.12	0.060	0.199	0.498	0.17	0.668
3	3	0.20	0.067	0.132	0.462	0.37	0.832
4	4	0.26	0.065	0.067	0.302	0.63	0.932
5	5	0.20	0.040	0.027	0.149	0.83	0.979
6	6	0.12	0.020	0.007	0.046	0.95	0.996
7	7	0.04	0.006	0.001	0.008	0.99	0.998
8	8	0.01	0.001	0.000	0.000	1.00	1.000

Therefore, the optimum total annual cost associated with a policy of making a run every 2 months is

$6\{\$350 + \$200[(0.01)(5) + (0.04)(4.5) + (0.12)(4.0)$

$+ (0.20)(3.5) + (0.26)(3.0) + (0.20)(2.5)]$

$+ \$200[(0.12)(\tfrac{25}{12}) + (0.04)(\tfrac{25}{14}) + (0.01)(\tfrac{25}{16})]$

$+ \$3800[(0.12)(\tfrac{1}{12}) + (0.04)(\tfrac{4}{14}) + (0.01)(\tfrac{9}{16})]\}$

$\qquad = 6\{\$350 + \$200[2.69] + \$200[0.337] + \$3800[0.027]\}$

$\qquad = 6(\$1058)$

$\qquad = \$6348$

Computations can be made now for a policy of producing every 3 months. The result (which can be verified by the reader) would be a minimum total annual cost of $7109.

We can summarize the results as follows:

Scheduling Period in Months	Minimum Total Annual Costs in Dollars
1	6900
2	6348
3	7109

Further computations for longer scheduling periods would reveal, in this case, rising annual costs. It is clear, then, that enough units should be produced every *other* month so that the initial inventory consists of five units.

Note 1

In this note, we determine that value of q, denoted by q_0, which minimizes the total expected cost $TEC(q)$, where

$$TEC(q) = \tfrac{1}{2}C_1 Tq + C_s R/q$$

Proceeding by the use of calculus,

$$\frac{dTEC}{dq} = \frac{1}{2}C_1 T - C_s R/q^2$$

so that, setting this derivative equal to zero, we get *

$$q_0 = \sqrt{\frac{2RC_s}{TC_1}}$$

Therefore

$$t_{s0} = \frac{Tq_0}{R} = \frac{T}{R}\sqrt{2\frac{RC_s}{TC_1}} = \sqrt{2\frac{T}{R}\frac{C_s}{C_1}}$$

$$(TEC)_0 = \frac{C_1 T}{2}q_0 + C_s R/q_0$$

$$= \frac{C_1 T}{2}\sqrt{2\frac{R}{T}\frac{C_s}{C_1}} + C_s R\bigg/\sqrt{2\frac{R}{T}\frac{C_s}{C_1}}$$

i.e.

$$(TEC)_0 = \sqrt{2RTC_1 C_s}$$

(Note that for optimum q *in this model*, the cost of carrying inventories is equal to the cost of the setups.)

Note 2

In this note, we determine the values of q and S which minimize the total expected cost where

$$TEC(q, S) = \frac{S^2 C_1 T}{2q} + \frac{(q - S)^2 C_2 T}{2q} + \frac{C_s R}{q} \qquad (20)$$

* Since, for $q = q_0$, $d^2(TEC)/dq^2 = 2C_s R/q^3 > 0$, then $q = q_0$ will give a minimum TEC.

Proceeding by the use of calculus, we get

$$\frac{\partial TEC}{\partial S} = \frac{SC_1 T}{q} - \frac{(q - S)C_2 T}{q}$$

$$\frac{\partial TEC}{\partial q} = -\frac{S^2 C_1 T}{2q^2} + \frac{4q(q - S) - 2(q - S)^2}{4q^2} C_2 T - \frac{C_s R}{q^2}$$

Setting these partial derivatives equal to zero * and simplifying, we obtain

$$S = q \frac{C_2}{C_1 + C_2}$$

$$q^2 C_2 - (C_1 + C_2)S^2 = \frac{2C_s R}{T} \tag{21}$$

Solving this system of equations for S and q, we then obtain

$$q_0 = \sqrt{2 \frac{R}{T} \frac{C_s}{C_1}} \sqrt{\frac{C_1 + C_2}{C_2}} \tag{22}$$

$$S_0 = \sqrt{2 \frac{R}{T} \frac{C_s}{C_1}} \sqrt{\frac{C_2}{C_1 + C_2}} \tag{23}$$

Hence

$$t_{s0} = \frac{T q_0}{R} = \sqrt{2 \frac{T}{R} \frac{C_s}{C_1}} \sqrt{\frac{C_1 + C_2}{C_2}} \tag{24}$$

To solve for $(TEC)_0$, we note that

$$\frac{S_0^2}{q_0} = q_0 \left(\frac{C_2}{C_1 + C_2} \right)^2$$

so that, substituting from eqs. 23 and 24 into eq. 20, and simplifying, we obtain

$$(TEC)_0 = \sqrt{2RTC_1 C_s} \sqrt{\frac{C_2}{C_1 + C_2}} \tag{25}$$

Note that, for (optimum) q_0 and S_0, the cost of carrying inventory is again equal to the cost of the setups. Furthermore, note that the ratio of the cost of carrying surplus to the cost of "carrying" a shortage is inversely proportional to the unit costs of surplus and shortage.

* Setting these partial derivatives equal to zero is necessary, but not sufficient, for extremal values. Necessary and sufficient conditions for maximal and minimal values may be found on p. 281 of Pipes.[24]

Note 3

In this note, we determine the value of S which minimizes the total expected costs TEC, where

$$TEC(S) = C_1 \sum_{r=0}^{S} (S - r)P(r) + C_2 \sum_{r=S+1}^{\infty} (r - S)P(r) \qquad (26)$$

We first substitute $(S + 1)$ for S in eq. 26, obtaining

$$TEC(S + 1) = C_1 \sum_{r=0}^{S+1} (S + 1 - r)P(r) + C_2 \sum_{r=S+2}^{\infty} (r - S - 1)P(r)$$

$$= C_1 \sum_{0}^{S} (S + 1 - r)P(r) + C_1[(S + 1)$$

$$- (S + 1)]P(S + 1) + C_2 \sum_{S+1}^{\infty} (r - S - 1)P(r)$$

$$- C_2[(S + 1) - (S + 1)]P(S + 1)$$

$$= C_1 \sum_{0}^{S} (S - r)P(r) + C_1 \sum_{0}^{S} P(r)$$

$$+ C_2 \sum_{S+1}^{\infty} (r - S)P(r) - C_2 \sum_{S+1}^{\infty} P(r)$$

Or, since

$$\sum_{0}^{\infty} P(r) = 1$$

i.e.

$$\sum_{S+1}^{\infty} P(r) = 1 - \sum_{0}^{S} P(r)$$

we have

$$TEC(S + 1) = TEC(S) + (C_1 + C_2)P(r \leqq S) - C_2 \qquad (27)$$

Similarly,

$$TEC(S - 1) = TEC(S) - (C_1 + C_2)P(r \leqq S - 1) + C_2 \qquad (28)$$

Consider, now, S_0 such that

$$(C_1 + C_2)P(r \leqq S_0) - C_2 > 0$$

$$-(C_1 + C_2)P(r \leqq S_0 - 1) + C_2 > 0 \qquad (29)$$

For any integer S' larger than S_0 and for any integer S'' smaller than

S_0, inequations 29 would hold since $P(r \leqq S_0)$ is nondecreasing for increasing S_0. Hence, if inequations 29 hold *

$$TEC(S'') > TEC(S_0) \text{ for } S'' < S_0$$

and

$$TEC(S') > TEC(S_0) \text{ for } S' > S_0$$

We have thus found the value of S which minimizes the total expected cost; namely, S_0 satisfying inequalities 29. These inequalities may be rearranged to give

$$P(r \leqq S_0 - 1) < \frac{C_2}{C_1 + C_2} < P(r \leqq S_0) \tag{30}$$

It should be noted that if S_0 is such that

$$P(r \leqq S_0 - 1) < \frac{C_2}{C_1 + C_2} = P(r \leqq S_0)$$

then eq. 27 leads to

$$TEC(S_0 + 1) = TEC(S_0)$$

In this case, the optimum value of S is either S_0 or $S_0 + 1$.

Finally, if S_0 is such that †

$$P(r \leqq S_0 - 1) = \frac{C_2}{C_1 + C_2} < P(r \leqq S_0)$$

eq. 28 leads to

$$TEC(S_0 - 1) = TEC(S_0)$$

so that the optimum value of S is either $S_0 - 1$ or S_0.

Note 4

In this note, we determine the value of S which minimizes the total expected cost TEC, where

$$TEC(S) = C_1 \int_0^S (S - r)f(r) \, dr + C_2 \int_S^\infty (r - S)f(r) \, dr \tag{31}$$

Now, if

$$g(x) = \int_{h(x)}^{k(x)} f(x, y) \, dy$$

---

* This shows that S_0 is an absolute minimum point rather than just a relative (or local) minimum point.

† It should be noted that these two exceptional cases are equivalent.

then

$$\frac{dg(x)}{dx} = \int_{h(x)}^{k(x)} \frac{\partial f(x, y)}{\partial x} \, dy + f[x, k(x)] \frac{dk(x)}{dx} - f[x, h(x)] \frac{dh(x)}{dx} \quad (32)$$

Thus, from eq. 31, it follows that

$$\frac{d(TEC)}{dS} = C_1 \int_0^S f(r) \, dr - C_2 \int_S^\infty f(r) \, dr$$

$$= C_1 F(S) - C_2[1 - F(S)] \quad (33)$$

$$= (C_1 + C_2)F(S) - C_2$$

TEC will have a relative extreme (maximum or minimum) at S_0 if

$$\frac{d(TEC)}{dS}\bigg|_{S=S_0} = 0$$

Therefore, from eq. 33, we have as a necessary condition for an extreme value

$$(C_1 + C_2)F(S_0) - C_2 = 0$$

Therefore

$$F(S_0) = \frac{C_2}{C_1 + C_2} \quad (34)$$

Furthermore

$$\frac{d^2 TEC}{dS^2}\bigg|_{S=S_0} = C_1 f(S_0) + C_2 f(S_0) = (C_1 + C_2)f(S_0)$$

Since C_1 and C_2 are not both zero, and since $f(S) \geqq 0$, then

$$\frac{d^2 TEC}{dS^2}\bigg|_{S=S_0} \geqq 0$$

If the inequality holds, then S_0 gives the minimum. If the equality holds, then $f(S_0) = 0$. But $f(r)$ is a continuous function and $f(r) \geqq 0$. Therefore, if $f(S_0) = 0$, then $f(r)$ has a minimum at S_0, namely zero. It follows that $TEC(S)$ has a minimum at $S = S_0$. Therefore, $S = S_0$ satisfying $F(S_0) = C_2/(C_1 + C_2)$ gives a minimum of $TEC(S)$.

Note 5

In this note we give the detailed justification to the solution of Model V.

Now

$$s_1 = s_0 + q_1 - r_1$$

$$s_2 = s_1 + q_2 - r_2 = s_0 + (q_1 + q_2) - (r_1 + r_2)$$

$$s_3 = s_2 + q_3 - r_3 = s_0 + (q_1 + q_2 + q_3) - (r_1 + r_2 + r_3)$$

.

.

.

$$s_k = s_{k-1} + q_k - r_k$$

Therefore

$$s_k = s_0 + (q_1 + q_2 + \cdots + q_k) - (r_1 + r_2 + \cdots + r_k)$$

i.e.

$$s_k = s_0 + \sum_{i=1}^{k-1} q_i + q_k - \sum_{i=1}^{k} r_i \quad \checkmark$$

Let

$$S' = s_0 + \sum_{i=1}^{k-1} q_i + q_k$$

$$R' = \sum_{i=1}^{k} r_i \qquad \text{const.}$$

Therefore, $dS' = dq_k$. Furthermore, from the foregoing, we see that

$$s_k > 0 \quad \text{when} \quad R' < S'$$

$$s_k < 0 \quad \text{when} \quad R' > S'$$

Hence, since

$$TEC(S') = C_1 \int_0^{S'} (S' - R')f(R') \, dR' + C_2 \int_{S'}^{\infty} (R' - S')f(R') \, dR'$$

we obtain

$$TEC(q_k) = C_1 \int_0^{S'} (S' - R')f(R') \, dR' + C_2 \int_{S'}^{\infty} (R' - S')f(R') \, dR'$$

Taking the first derivative

$$\frac{d(TEC)}{dq_k} = \frac{d(TEC)}{dS'} \frac{dS'}{dq_k} = C_1 F(S') - C_2[1 - F(S')]$$

Setting this expression equal to zero then yields

$$F(S_0') = \frac{C_2}{C_1 + C_2}$$

Finally, then, from S_0' we obtain q_{k0}

$$q_{k0} = S_0' - s_0 - \sum_{i=1}^{k-1} q_i$$

Note 6

In this note, we determine the value of S which minimizes the total expected cost TEC, where

$$TEC(S) = C_1 \sum_0^S \left(S - \frac{r}{2}\right) P(r) + C_1 \sum_{S+1}^{\infty} \frac{S^2}{2r} P(r)$$
$$+ C_2 \sum_{S+1}^{\infty} \frac{(r - S)^2}{2r} P(r) \quad (35)$$

Substituting $(S + 1)$ for S in eq. 35 yields

$$TEC(S + 1) = C_1 \sum_0^{S+1} \left(S + 1 - \frac{r}{2}\right) P(r) + C_1 \sum_{S+2}^{\infty} \frac{(S + 1)^2}{2r} P(r)$$
$$+ C_2 \sum_{S+2}^{\infty} \frac{(r - S - 1)^2}{2r} P(r) \quad (36)$$

Now

$$C_1 \sum_0^{S+1} \left(S + 1 - \frac{r}{2}\right) P(r) = C_1 \sum_0^S \left(S + 1 - \frac{r}{2}\right) P(r)$$
$$+ C_1 \left(S + 1 - \frac{S + 1}{2}\right) P(S + 1)$$
$$= C_1 \sum_0^S \left(S - \frac{r}{2}\right) P(r) + C_1 \sum_0^S P(r)$$
$$+ C_1 \left(\frac{S + 1}{2}\right) P(S + 1)$$

Similarly

$$C_1 \sum_{S+2}^{\infty} \frac{(S + 1)^2}{2r} P(r) = C_1 \sum_{S+1}^{\infty} \frac{S^2}{2r} P(r) + C_1 S \sum_{S+1}^{\infty} \frac{P(r)}{r}$$
$$+ \frac{C_1}{2} \sum_{S+1}^{\infty} \frac{P(r)}{r} - C_1 \frac{S + 1}{2} P(S + 1)$$

$$C_2 \sum_{S+2}^{\infty} \frac{(r-S-1)^2}{2r} P(r) = C_2 \sum_{S+1}^{\infty} \frac{(r-S)^2}{2r} P(r) - C_2 \sum_{S+1}^{\infty} P(r)$$

$$+ SC_2 \sum_{S+1}^{\infty} \frac{P(r)}{r} + \frac{1}{2} C_2 \sum_{S+1}^{\infty} \frac{P(r)}{r}$$

Therefore, from eqs. 35 and 36, it follows that

$$TEC(S+1) = TEC(S)$$

$$+ (C_1 + C_2) \left[P(r \leqq S) + \left(S + \frac{1}{2} \right) \sum_{S+1}^{\infty} \frac{P(r)}{r} \right] - C_2 \quad (37)$$

Next, let

$$L(S) = P(r \leqq S) + \left(S + \frac{1}{2} \right) \sum_{S+1}^{\infty} \frac{P(r)}{r} \quad (38)$$

then, from eq. 37

$$TEC(S+1) = TEC(S) + (C_1 + C_2)L(S) - C_2 \quad (39)$$

Similarly, substituting $(S-1)$ for S in eq. 39, we obtain

$$TEC(S-1) = TEC(S) - (C_1 + C_2)L(S-1) + C_2 \quad (40)$$

Now, $L(S)$ is a nondecreasing function of S. This can be proved as follows:

$$L(S+1) = P(r \leqq S+1) + \left(S + 1 + \frac{1}{2} \right) \sum_{S+2}^{\infty} \frac{P(r)}{r}$$

$$= P(r \leqq S) + P(S+1) + \left(S + \frac{1}{2} \right) \sum_{S+1}^{\infty} \frac{P(r)}{r}$$

$$- \frac{(S + \frac{1}{2})}{(S+1)} P(S+1) + \sum_{S+1}^{\infty} \frac{P(r)}{r} - \frac{P(S+1)}{S+1}$$

$$= L(S) - \frac{1}{2} \frac{P(S+1)}{S+1} + \sum_{S+1}^{\infty} \frac{P(r)}{r}$$

i.e.

$$L(S+1) = L(S) + \sum_{S+2}^{\infty} \frac{P(r)}{r} + \frac{1}{2} \frac{P(S+1)}{S+1}$$

whence, since

$$\sum_{S+2}^{\infty} \frac{P(r)}{r} + \frac{1}{2} \frac{P(S+1)}{S+1} \geqq 0$$

we have

$$L(S+1) \geqq L(S) \quad (41)$$

Consider, now, S_0 such that

$$(C_1 + C_2)L(S_0) - C_2 > 0$$
$$-(C_1 + C_2)L(S_0 - 1) + C_2 > 0 \tag{42}$$

For any $S' > S_0$ and $S'' < S_0$, inequations 42 hold since $L(S)$ is non-decreasing. Hence

$$TEC(S'') > TEC(S_0), \quad S'' < S_0$$
$$TEC(S') > TEC(S_0), \quad S' > S_0$$

Therefore, the value of S which minimizes the total expected cost is that value S_0 which satisfies inequation 42 or, by rearrangement, the inequalities

$$L(S_0 - 1) < \frac{C_2}{C_1 + C_2} < L(S_0) \tag{43}$$

where

$$L(S) = P(r \le S) + \left(S + \frac{1}{2}\right) \sum_{S+1}^{\infty} \frac{P(r)}{r}$$

Finally, it should be noted, as in Note 3, that

$$\frac{C_2}{C_1 + C_2} = L(S_0)$$

implies that either S_0 or $(S_0 + 1)$ is optimum while, equivalently,

$$\frac{C_2}{C_1 + C_2} = L(S_0 - 1)$$

implies that either $(S_0 - 1)$ or S_0 is optimum.

BIBLIOGRAPHY

1. Ackoff, R. L., "Production and Inventory Control in a Chemical Process," *J. Opns. Res. Soc. Am., 3,* no. 3, 319–338 (Aug. 1955).
2. Arrow, K., Harris, T., and Marschak, J., "Optimal Inventory Policy," *Econometrica, 19,* no. 3, 250–272 (July 1951).
3. Bellman, R., "Some Applications of the Theory of Dynamic Programming," *J. Opns. Res. Soc. Am., 2,* no. 3, 275–288 (Aug. 1954).
4. ———, "Some Problems in the Theory of Dynamic Programming," *Econometrica, 22,* no. 1, 37–48 (Jan. 1954).
5. ———, "The Theory of Dynamic Programming," *Bull. Amer. math. Soc.,* no. 6, 503–516 (Nov. 1954).
6. Bellman, R., Glicksberg, I., and Gross, O., "On the Optimal Inventory Equation," *Mgmt. Sci., 2,* no. 1, 83–104 (Oct. 1955).

7. Bellman, R., Glicksberg, I., and Gross, O., "The Theory of Dynamic Programming as Applied to a Smoothing Problem," *J. Soc. Ind. Appl. Math.*, *2*, no. 2, 82–88 (June 1954).

8. Berman, E. B., and Clark, A. J., "An Optimal Inventory Policy for a Military Organization," RAND Report D-647, Mar. 30, 1955.

9. Charnes, A., Cooper, W. W., and Farr, D., "Linear Programming and Profit Preference Scheduling for a Manufacturing Firm," *J. Opns. Res. Soc. Am.*, *1*, no. 3, 114–129 (May 1953).

10. Dannerstedt, G., "Production Scheduling for an Arbitrary Number of Periods Given the Sales Forecast in the Form of a Probability Distribution," *J. Opns. Res. Soc. Am.*, *3*, no. 3, 300–318 (Aug. 1955).

11. Dvoretzky, A., Kiefer, J., and Wolfowitz, J., "On the Optimal Character of the (*A, S*) Policy in Inventory Theory," *Econometrica*, *21*, no. 4, 586–596 (Oct. 1953).

12. ———, "The Inventory Problem," *Econometrica*, *20*, no. 2, 187–222 (Apr. 1952) and no. 3, 450–466 (July 1952).

13. Eisenhart, C., *Some Inventory Problems*, National Bureau of Standards, Techniques of Statistical Inference, A2-2C, Lecture 1, Jan. 6, 1948 (hectographed notes).

14. Feeney, G. J., "A Basis for Strategic Decisions on Inventory Control Operations," *Mgmt. Sci.*, *2*, no. 1, 69–82 (Oct. 1955).

15. Fry, T. C., *Probability and Its Engineering Uses*, D. Van Nostrand and Co., New York, 1928 (see in particular pp. 229–232).

16. Hare, V. C., and Hugli, W. C., "Applications of Operations Research to Production Scheduling and Inventory Control, II," *Proceedings of the Conference on "What is Operations Research Accomplishing in Industry?"*, Case Institute of Technology, Cleveland, 1955.

17. Hoffman, A. J., and Jacobs, W., "Smooth Patterns of Production," *Mgmt. Sci.*, *1*, no. 1, 92–95 (Oct. 1954).

18. Holt, C. C., Modigliani, F., and Simon, H. A., "A Linear Decision Rule for Production and Employment Scheduling," *Mgmt. Sci.*, *2*, no. 1, 1–30 (Oct. 1955).

19. Holt, C. C., and Simon, H. A., "Optimal Decision Rules for Production and Inventory Control," *Proceedings of the Conference on Production and Inventory Control*, Case Institute of Technology, Cleveland, 1954.

20. Laderman, J., Littauer, S. B., and Weiss, L., "The Inventory Problem," *J. Amer. statist. Ass.*, *48*, no. 264, 717–732 (Dec. 1953).

21. Magee, J. F., "Production Scheduling to Meet a Sales Forecast," *Notes from M.I.T. Summer Course on Operations Research*, Cambridge, 134–138, 1953.

22 ———, "Studies in Operations Research I: Application of Linear Programming to Production Scheduling," Arthur D. Little Inc., Cambridge, Mass. (unpublished).

23. ———, "Guides to Inventory Policy. No. 1. Functions and Lot Size," *Harv. Busin. Rev.*, *34*, no. 1, 49–60 (Jan.–Feb. 1956).

24. Pipes, Louis A., *Applied Mathematics for Engineers and Physicists*, McGraw-Hill Book Co., New York, 1946.

25. Raymond, F. E., *Quantity and Economy in Manufacture*, McGraw-Hill Book Co., New York, 1931.

26. Simon, H. A., "On the Application of Servomechanism Theory in the Study of Production Control," *Econometrica*, *20*, no. 2, 247–268 (Apr. 1952).

27. ———, and Holt, C. C., "The Control of Inventory and Production Rates—A Survey," *J. Opns. Res. Soc. Am.*, *2*, no. 3, 289–301 (Aug. 1954).

28. Tompkins, C. B., "Determination of a Safety Allowance," Logistics Papers, Engineering Research Associates, Issue no. 2, Appendix I to Bimonthly Progress Report No. 18.

29. ———, "Lead Time and Optimal Allowances—an Extreme Example," Conference on Mathematical Problems in Logistics, George Washington University, Appendix I to Quarterly Progress Report No. I, Dec. 1949–Feb. 1950.

30. Vassian, H. J., "Application of Discrete Variable Servo Theory to Inventory Control," *J. Opns. Res. Soc. Am.*, *3*, no. 3, 272–282 (Aug. 1955).

31. Whitin, T. M., "Inventory Control and Price Theory," *Mgmt. Sci.*, *2*, no. 1, 61–68 (Oct. 1955).

32. ———, "Inventory Control Research: A Survey," *Mgmt. Sci.*, *1*, no. 1, 32–40 (Oct. 1954).

33. ———, *The Theory of Inventory Management*, Princeton University Press, Princeton, 1953.

Chapter 9

Inventory Models
with Price Breaks

In this chapter, we consider a class of inventory problems in which the unit manufacturing or purchase cost is variable. This situation is quite typical for purchased parts which are subject to quantity discounts. While it is possible to develop this generalization of the inventory problem for each of the models considered in Chapter 8, we will exhibit this generalization only with respect to Model I of Chapter 8, this model being the one most frequently used as a point of departure.

To paraphrase the problem of Model I (Chapter 8), consider a manufacturer who has to purchase or supply R units at a constant rate during time T. Hence, demand is both fixed and known. No shortages are to be permitted; consequently, the cost of a shortage is infinite (i.e., using the notation of Chapter 8, $C_2 = \infty$). The variable costs associated with the manufacturing or purchasing process can be designated by *

k_1 = cost per unit of manufacturing or purchasing
P = monthly holding cost expressed as a decimal fraction of the value of the unit
C_s = setup cost per production run or, when for purchased parts, the setup cost associated with the procurement of the purchased items

* In Chapter 8, since the unit manufacturing or purchase cost was assumed to be constant, we did not need to consider this cost directly. Rather, we needed only to consider the *holding charges* associated with this cost. This was done when computing C_1 in Chapter 8. Now, however, since the manufacturing or purchase cost is variable, it must be considered directly, hence the need for introducing new symbols at this time.

TEK = total expected cost
TEK_0 = minimum (optimum) total expected cost

As in Chapter 8, we let

T = the period of time for which a policy is being established
R = total requirement for period T
t_s = interval between placing orders
t_{s0} = optimum interval between placing orders
q = input, or quantity ordered
q_0 = optimum order quantity (i.e., Economic Lot Size or Economic Purchase Quantity)

Since a variable unit cost of manufacturing or purchase is most appropriate for purchased parts (because of quantity discounts), we shall hereafter refer only to purchased parts. This is done, without any loss in generality, in order to facilitate the discussion which follows.

The problem, then, can be stated as one of determining:

1. How often should parts be purchased.
2. How many units should be purchased at any one time.

It might also be mentioned at this time that the procurement setup cost, denoted by C_s, need not be limited to just those elements associated with setting a purchase order in motion. Also possibly affected by the purchase quantity is the receiving cost, cost of receiving inspection, etc. Where these costs are affected by the purchase quantity, a "setup" cost should be determined and included in establishing C_s.

BASIC COST EQUATIONS

For any *one* value of the unit purchase cost k_1, the situation just described can be represented graphically as was done in Fig. 8-1. Furthermore, as in Chapter 8,

R/q = the number of runs during time T

$$t_s = \frac{T}{R/q} = Tq/R$$

$\frac{1}{2}q$ = average inventory during the interval t_s

Therefore, for each run (or procurement), the number of part-month inventories will be given by

$$\tfrac{1}{2}qt_s = \tfrac{1}{2}q(Tq/R) = \tfrac{1}{2}Tq^2/R$$

while the number of lot-month inventories will be given by

$$(\tfrac{1}{2}qt_s)/q = \tfrac{1}{2}Tq/R$$

The component costs for each run will then be given by

C_s = the procurement setup cost

qk_1 = the purchasing cost of q items, where the unit purchase cost is given by k_1

$C_s\left(\dfrac{Tq}{2R}\right)P$ = the cost, associated with the setup, of inventory for period t_s

$qk_1\left(\dfrac{Tq}{2R}\right)P$ = the cost, associated with the purchase, of inventory for period t_s

Therefore, the total cost for the period t_s is given by

$$C_s + qk_1 + C_s\frac{Tq}{2R}P + qk_1\frac{Tq}{2R}P$$

so that the total cost *for the entire period T* is given by

$$TEK = \left(C_s + qk_1 + C_s\frac{Tq}{2R}P + qk_1\frac{Tq}{2R}P\right)\frac{R}{q}$$

i.e.

$$TEK = \frac{C_s R}{q} + k_1 R + \frac{C_s TP}{2} + k_1\frac{TP}{2}q \qquad (1)$$

The minimum TEK can then be obtained by taking the first derivative of TEK with respect to the variable q and setting the resulting expression equal to zero

$$\frac{d(TEK)}{dq} = -\frac{C_s R}{q^2} + \frac{1}{2}k_1 TP$$

Therefore, setting $d(TEK)/dq = 0$, we obtain *

$$q_0 = \sqrt{\frac{C_s R}{k_1 T}\frac{2}{P}} \qquad (2)$$

* Comparing eq. 2 with eq. 2 of Chapter 8 (Model I) shows that the essential part of the cost of holding one unit in inventory is the purchase cost, here given by k_1. A little reflection will show that this is so; i.e., the holding cost resulting from the setup is constant regardless of the lot size.

Substituting into eq. 1 gives for the optimum *total* cost, TEK_0, associated with a unit purchase cost of k_1

$$TEK_0 = \frac{C_sR}{\sqrt{(2C_sR)/(k_1TP)}} + k_1R + \frac{C_sTP}{2} + k_1\frac{TP}{2}\sqrt{\frac{2C_sR}{k_1TP}}$$

$$= \sqrt{\frac{k_1TPC_sR}{2}} + k_1R + \frac{1}{2}C_sTP + \sqrt{\frac{k_1TPC_sR}{2}}$$

i.e.

$$TEK_0 = \sqrt{2k_1TPC_sR} + k_1R + \frac{1}{2}C_sTP \qquad (3)$$

Now let us consider a first generalization to the case where the purchase cost is subject to one price break.

PURCHASE-INVENTORY MODEL WITH ONE PRICE BREAK

In this section, we consider a typical purchasing situation where one quantity discount applies. Such a situation may be represented as follows:

Range	Quantity	Unit Purchase Price *
R_1	$1 \leqq q_1 < b$	k_{11}
R_2	$q_2 \geqq b$	k_{12}

where b is that quantity at and beyond which the quantity discount applies. Thus, for any purchase quantity, q_1, in range R_1, the total expected cost TEK_1 will be given by

$$TEK_1 = \frac{C_sR}{q_1} + k_{11}R + \frac{C_sTP}{2} + k_{11}\frac{TP}{2}q_1 \qquad (4)$$

and, similarly, for any purchase quantity, q_2, in range R_2, the total expected cost TEK_2 will be given by

$$TEK_2 = \frac{C_sR}{q_2} + k_{12}R + \frac{C_sTP}{2} + k_{12}\frac{TP}{2}q_2 \qquad (5)$$

The situation may be represented graphically as follows. First, if we neglect, for the moment, the terms $(k_1R + \frac{1}{2}C_sTP)$ in the expression for TEK, we obtain Fig. 9-1. (The complete graphical representation is given in Fig. 9-4.) Now, since $k_{12} < k_{11}$

$$(k_{12}R + \tfrac{1}{2}C_sTP) < (k_{11}R + \tfrac{1}{2}C_sTP)$$

* Here, $k_{12} < k_{11}$.

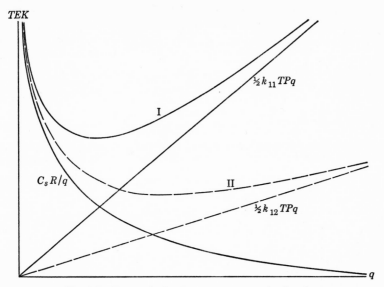

Fig. 9-1. Economic lot-size curves: one price break.

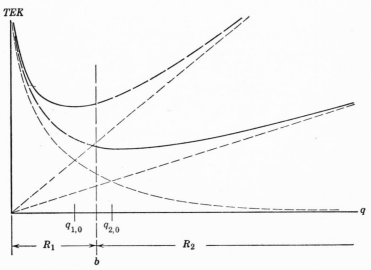

Fig. 9-2. Economic lot-size curve, $q_{2,0} \geqq b$.

Furthermore, from Fig. 9-1 (and also from eqs. 4 and 5), it is clear that the minimum cost for curve II (corresponding to k_{12}) is less than the minimum cost for curve I (corresponding to k_{11}).* Hence, if we let $q_{1,0}$ and $q_{2,0}$ denote the respective values of q_1 and q_2 which yield minimum costs, we can derive the following decision rules:

1. Compute $q_{2,0}$. If $q_{2,0} \geqq b$ (as in Fig. 9-2), then the previous discussion applies and the optimum lot size is $q_{2,0}$. ✓

2. If $q_{2,0} < b$ (as in Fig. 9-3), then the quantity discount no longer applies to the purchase quantity $q_{2,0}$. Furthermore, since the mini-

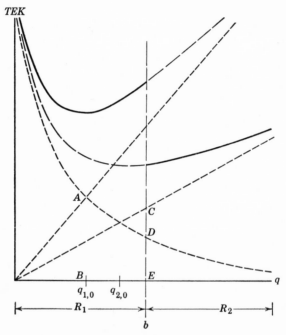

Fig. 9-3.   Economic lot-size curve, $q_{2,0} < b$.

mum cost occurs at a point for which the abscissa is *less* than b, i.e., at $q_{2,0} < b$, the total expected cost will be monotonic increasing over the entire price range R_2, and the least cost for range R_2 will occur at $q = b$. Hence, to determine the optimum purchase quantity, we need only compare the *total* expected cost for lot size $q = q_{1,0}$ with that for lot size $q = b$. These cost equations follow from eq. 1 and are given by

* In general, for n price breaks, the following inequalities hold: $q_{1,0} < q_{2,0} < \cdots < q_{n,0}$. They follow immediately by considering eq. 3 and $k_{1,n} < k_{1,n-1} < \cdots < k_{11}$.

$$TEK_0(q_{1,0}) = \frac{C_sR}{q_{1,0}} + k_{11}R + \frac{C_sTP}{2} + k_{11}\frac{TP}{2}q_{1,0} \qquad (1a)$$

$$TEK(b) = \frac{C_sR}{b} + k_{12}R + \frac{C_sTP}{2} + k_{12}\frac{TP}{2}b \qquad (1b)$$

Comparing $TEK(b)$ with $TEK_0(q_{1,0})$, term by term, shows that, since $q_{1,0} < b$ and $k_{12} < k_{11}$

$$\left(\frac{C_sR}{b} + k_{12}R + \frac{C_sTP}{2}\right) < \left(\frac{C_sR}{q_{1,0}} + k_{11}R + \frac{1}{2}C_sTP\right)$$

However, $\frac{1}{2}k_{12}TPb$ may, or may not, be less than the corresponding term $\frac{1}{2}k_{11}TPq_{1,0}$. Hence, we must compare the total costs as indicated in the foregoing.

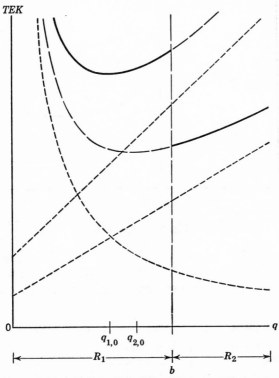

Fig. 9-4. Economic lot-size curve, $q_0 = b$.

Referring to Fig. 9-3, we see that we are adding $(k_{11}R + \frac{1}{2}C_sTP)$ to $2\overline{AB}$ and comparing this value with $[(k_{12}R + \frac{1}{2}C_sTP) + \overline{CE} + \overline{DE}]$. See Fig. 9-4.

We now illustrate the use of these decision rules by means of three examples.

Example I

A manufacturer of engines is required to purchase 2400 castings per year. This requirement is assumed here to be fixed and known. These

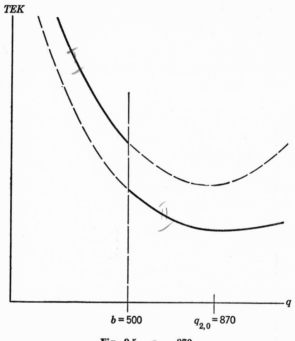

Fig. 9-5. $q_0 = 870$.

castings are subject to quantity discounts; i.e., the manufacturer is given a lower price for quantity purchases within certain ranges. The problem is to determine the optimum purchase quantity q_0. For this example, we are given:

$T = 12$ months
$R = 2400$ units
$P = 0.02$
$C_s = \$350$ per procurement (includes cost of obtaining bids, etc.)
$b = 500$
$k_{11} = \$10.00 \ (1 \leqq q_1 < 500)$
$k_{12} = \$9.25 \ (q_2 \geqq 500)$

We compute $q_{2,0}$ as given by eq. 2 and obtain

$$q_{2,0} = \sqrt{\frac{350(2400)(2)}{(9.25)(12)(0.02)}} = 870$$

Since $q_{2,0} = 870$ is greater than $b = 500$, i.e., since $q_{2,0} = 870$ is within the range $q_2 \geqq 500$, then the optimum purchase quantity will be $q_0 = 870$. This situation is represented by Fig. 9-5.

Example II

A different situation arises than for Example I when the procurement setup cost is only \$100; i.e., when $C_s = \$100$. Here,

$$q_{2,0} = \sqrt{\frac{(100)(2400)(2)}{(9.25)(12)(0.02)}} = 465$$

Since $q_{2,0} = 465 < 500$, we must also compute $q_{1,0}$

$$q_{1,0} = \sqrt{\frac{(100)(2400)(2)}{(10)(12)(0.02)}} = 447$$

Then, we must compare $TEK(447)$ with $TEK(500)$; i.e., we compare the optimum cost relative to unit price k_{11} (in this case, for $q_{1,0} = 447$) with the cost of procuring the least quantity which will entitle us to the price break (in this case, $b = 500$). The expressions for $TEK(b)$ and TEK_0 are given by eqs. 1 and 3 respectively.

$$TEK_0(447) = \sqrt{2(10)(12)(0.02)(100)(2400)} + 10(2400)$$
$$+ \tfrac{1}{2}(100)(12)(0.02)$$

Thus $TEK_0(447) = \$25,085$.

$$TEK(500) = \frac{100(2400)}{500} + (9.25)(2400) + \frac{1}{2}(100)(12)(0.02)$$
$$+ \frac{1}{2}(9.25)(12)(0.02)(500)$$

Thus $TEK(500) = \$23,247$.

Therefore, since, in this example, $TEK(500) < TEK_0(447)$, the optimum purchase quantity is determined by the price break; i.e., $q_0 = 500$. This situation is shown in Fig. 9-6.

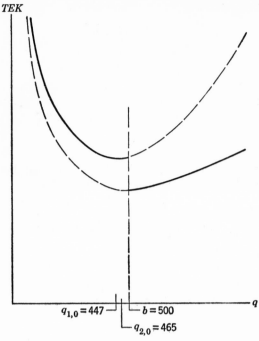

Fig. 9-6. $q_0 = 500.$

Example III

In this example let us assume that we have the conditions of Example II, *except* that the price break does not occur until $q = 3000$. Here, as before

$$q_{2,0} = 465 < 3000$$

Therefore, we must next compute $q_{1,0}$ which, as previously determined, is equal to 447. Also, from before

$$TEK_0(447) = \$25,085$$

We compare $TEK_0(447)$ with $TEK(3000)$

$$TEK(3000) = \frac{100(2400)}{3000} + (9.25)(2400) + \frac{1}{2}(100)(12)(0.02)$$

$$+ \frac{1}{2}(9.25)(12)(0.02)(3000)$$

i.e., $TEK(3000) = \$25,622.$

Here, $TEK(3000) > TEK_0(447)$. Therefore, the optimum purchase quantity is now $q_0 = 447$. This situation is represented in Fig. 9-7.

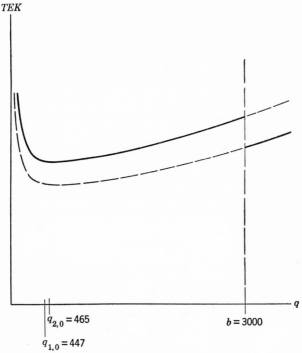

Fig. 9-7. $q_0 = 447$.

PURCHASE-INVENTORY MODELS WITH TWO PRICE BREAKS

In this section we generalize one step further by considering a purchasing situation where two quantity discounts apply. Such a situation may be represented as follows:

Range	Quantity	Unit Purchase Price
R_1	$1 \leqq q_1 < b_1$	k_{11}
R_2	$b_1 \leqq q_2 < b_2$	k_{12}
R_3	$q_3 \geqq b_2$	k_{13}

where b_1 and b_2 are those quantities which determine the price breaks.

For this situation, essentially the same general discussion holds as in the previous situation. This results in the following decision rules:

1. Compute $q_{3,0}$. If $q_{3,0} \geqq b_2$, then the optimum purchase quantity is $q_{3,0}$.

2. If $q_{3,0} < b_2$, then compute $q_{2,0}$. Since $q_{3,0} < b_2$, then $q_{2,0} < b_2$.[*] Accordingly, either $q_{2,0} < b_1$ or $b_1 \leqq q_{2,0} < b_2$. If $q_{3,0} < b_2$ *and* $b_1 \leqq q_{2,0} < b_2$, then proceed as in the case of only one price break; i.e., compare $TEK_0(q_{2,0})$ and $TEK(b_2)$ to determine the optimum purchase quantity.

3. If $q_{3,0} < b_2$ *and* $q_{2,0} < b_1$, then compute $q_{1,0}$ which, of necessity, will now satisfy the inequality $q_{1,0} < b_1$. In this situation, compare $TEK_0(q_{1,0})$ with $TEK(b_1)$ and $TEK(b_2)$ to determine the optimum purchase quantity.

These decision rules will now be illustrated by means of five examples. The reader should note that these examples represent, one by one, the five possible situations which could result for the purchasing problem with two price breaks. The data for these five examples are given in Table 9-1 and represent a price structure which allows for two price breaks.

TABLE 9-1

Symbol[†]	Units	Example IV	Example V	Example VI	Example VII	Example VIII
T	months	12	12	12	12	12
R	pieces	2400	2400	2400	2400	2400
C_s	dollars	\$350.00	\$100.00	\$100.00	\$100.00	\$100.00
P	—	0.02	0.02	0.02	0.02	0.02
k_{11}	dollars	\$10.00	\$10.00	\$10.00	\$10.00	\$10.00
b_1	pieces	500	500	400	500	3000
k_{12}	dollars	\$9.25	\$9.25	\$9.25	\$9.25	\$9.25
b_2	pieces	750	750	3000	1500	5000
k_{13}	dollars	\$8.75	\$8.75	\$8.75	\$9.00	\$8.75

† These symbols are defined at the beginning of this chapter.

Example IV

Computing $q_{3,0}$, we obtain

$$q_{3,0} = \sqrt{\frac{(350)(2400)(2)}{(8.75)(12)(0.02)}} = 894 > 750$$

so that the optimum purchase quantity is $q_0 = 894$. This situation is illustrated in Fig. 9-8.

* It should be noted that $q_{1,0} < q_{2,0} < q_{3,0} < \cdots < q_{n,0}$.

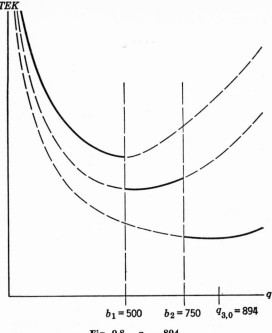

Fig. 9-8. $q_0 = 894$.

Example V

Computing $q_{3,0}$, we obtain

$$q_{3,0} = \sqrt{\frac{100(2400)(2)}{(8.75)(12)(0.02)}} = 478$$

Since $q_{3,0} = 478 < 750$, we next compute * $q_{2,0}$. This has already been done in Example II, namely

$$q_{2,0} = 465$$

Since $q_{2,0} = 465 < 500$, we next compute $q_{1,0}$ which, also from Example II, is given by

$$q_{1,0} = 447$$

* The reader should note that since $q_{n-1,0} < q_{n,0}$, $q_{2,0}$ will, in this case, be less than 478. Then, since $478 < 500$, we need not actually calculate $q_{2,0}$ since its value is inadmissible here as a solution.

We now need to compare $TEK_0(447)$ with $TEK(500)$ and $TEK(750)$. From Example II we have

$$TEK_0(447) = \$25{,}085$$

$$TEK(500) = \$23{,}247$$

Furthermore, from eq. 1 we have

$$TEK(750) = \$22{,}119.50$$

Therefore, since $TEK(750) < TEK(500) < TEK_0(447)$, the economic purchase quantity for this example is $q_0 = 750$. This situation is represented in Fig. 9-9.

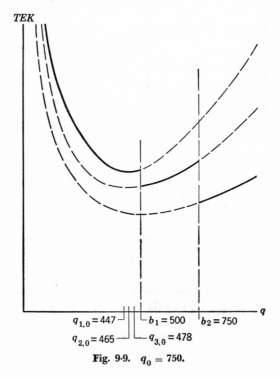

Fig. 9-9. $q_0 = 750.$

Example VI

As in Example V

$$q_{3,0} = 478$$

$$q_{2,0} = 465$$

Since $q_{2,0} = 465$ falls within the range $R_2(400, 3000)$, we need not calculate $q_{1,0}$. Rather, we need only compare $TEK_0(465)$ with $TEK(3000)$.

$$TEK(3000) = \$24{,}242$$

Furthermore

$$TEK_0(465) = \$23{,}244$$

Therefore, in this case, the most economic purchase quantity is $q_0 = 465$. This situation is shown in Fig. 9-10.

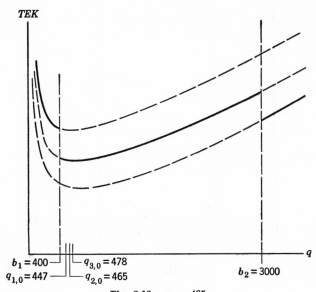

Fig. 9-10. $q_0 = 465$.

Example VII

Here

$$q_{3,0} = \sqrt{\frac{(100)(2400)(2)}{(9)(12)(0.02)}} = 471 < 1500$$

From Example II

$$q_{2,0} = 465 < 500$$

$$q_{1,0} = 447$$

Comparing $TEK(1500)$, $TEK(500)$, and $TEK_0(447)$ yields

$$TEK(1500) = \$23{,}392$$

From Example II

$$TEK(500) = \$23{,}247$$

$$TEK_0(447) = \$25{,}085$$

Hence, here, the optimum purchase quantity is $q_0 = 500$. This situation is represented in Fig. 9-11.

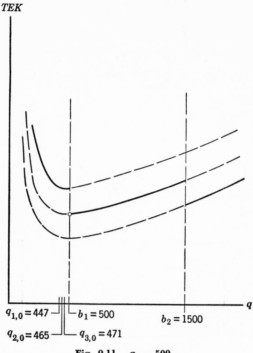

Fig. 9-11. $q_0 = 500$.

Example VIII

As in Example V

$$q_{3,0} = 478$$

$$q_{2,0} = 465$$

$$q_{1,0} = 447$$

Hence, here we must compare $TEK_0(447)$, $TEK(3000)$, and $TEK(5000)$. From Example II, we have

$$TEK_0(447) = \$25,085$$

For $q = 3000$ at \$9.25 each, we have

$$TEK(3000) = \$25,622$$

Furthermore

$$TEK(5000) = \$26,310$$

Therefore, comparing $TEK_0(447)$, $TEK(3000)$, and $TEK(5000)$, we see that the most economic purchase quantity is $q_0 = 447$. This situation is illustrated in Fig. 9-12.

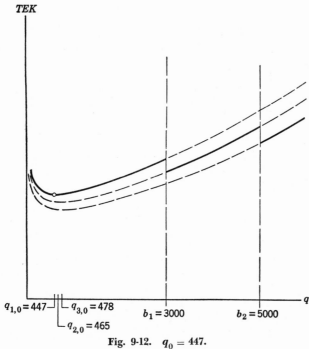

Fig. 9-12. $q_0 = 447$.

PURCHASE-INVENTORY MODELS WITH MORE THAN TWO PRICE BREAKS

Having exhibited and illustrated decision rules for determining most economic purchase quantities when the unit purchase cost is subject to either one or two price breaks, we can now readily generalize these decision rules to treat a purchasing situation for any number of price breaks.

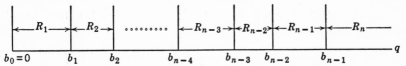

Fig. 9-13. Figure for general decision rule: $n - 1$ price breaks.

Let us denote the price ranges by $R_1, R_2, \cdots, R_n$; the price break quantities which determine these ranges by $b_1, b_2, \cdots, b_{n-1}$; and the economic purchase quantities for each price by $q_{1,0}$, $q_{2,0}$, $\cdots$, $q_{n,0}$. See Fig. 9-13. Then the following general decision rules apply:

1. Compute $q_{n,0}$. If $q_{n,0} \geqq b_{n-1}$, then the optimum purchase quantity is $q_{n,0}$.

2. If $q_{n,0} < b_{n-1}$, compute $q_{n-1,0}$. If $q_{n-1,0} \geqq b_{n-2}$ (i.e., $b_{n-2} \leqq q_{n-1,0} < b_{n-1}$), then proceed as in the case of one price break; i.e., compare $TEK_0(q_{n-1,0})$ with $TEK(b_{n-1})$ to determine the optimum purchase quantity.

3. If $q_{n-1,0} < b_{n-2}$, then compute $q_{n-2,0}$. If $q_{n-2,0} \geqq b_{n-3}$, then proceed as in the case of two price breaks; i.e., compare $TEK_0(q_{n-2,0})$ with $TEK(b_{n-2})$ and $TEK(b_{n-1})$ to determine the optimum purchase quantity.

4. If $q_{n-2,0} < b_{n-3}$, then compute $q_{n-3,0}$. If $q_{n-3,0} \geqq b_{n-4}$, then compare $TEK_0(q_{n-3,0})$ with $TEK(b_{n-3})$, $TEK(b_{n-2})$, and $TEK(b_{n-1})$.

5. Continue in this manner until $q_{n-j,0} \geqq b_{n-(j+1)}$, $[0 \leqq j \leqq n - 1]$,* and then compare $TEK_0(q_{n-j,0})$ with

$$TEK(b_{n-j}), \ TEK(b_{n-j+1}), \ \cdots, \ TEK(b_{n-1})$$

This procedure involves a finite number of steps—in fact, *at most n,* where n denotes the number of price ranges.

APPLICATION OF PRICE-BREAK INVENTORY MODELS

The price-break inventory model just presented was modified and employed by the company described in Chapter 4, namely, a manufacturer of heavy engines located in a small midwestern city.

Many of the parts needed for these engines are purchased from outside vendors. These purchased parts may be divided into two categories:

1. Those parts for which a vendor discount price schedule already exists.

2. Those parts (such as new parts) for which no vendor discount schedule exists as yet.

Parts in the second category are usually submitted to prospective vendors for bids. Bids are then prepared by the vendors and prices are quoted, based either on price breaks determined by the vendor or, as in many instances, on price breaks requested by the purchaser.

* We define $b_0 = 0$.

The use of price-break inventory models for purchasing parts of the first category is readily apparent. For those parts in the second category, an additional gain results when the purchase-inventory model is first used to predetermine appropriate price-break levels. This may be illustrated by means of Example IV above.

In Example IV, it was seen that the economic purchase quantity is equal to 894 units. Since this quantity lies in the price range of 750 units or greater, the unit cost is $8.75. It is reasonable to assume that requesting a price break at 894 units would result in a quotation less than $8.75.

If, for example, one obtained a vendor quotation of $8.50 for 894 units or more, the total expected cost would be given by

$$TEK(894 @ \$8.50) = \left[350 + 894(8.50) + 350 \frac{(12)(894)}{2(2400)}(0.02) \right.$$

$$\left. + 894(8.50) \frac{(12)(894)}{(2)(2400)}(0.02) \right] \frac{2400}{894}$$

i.e.

$$TEK(894 @ \$8.50) = \$22,293.50$$

Similarly, the total expected cost for 894 units at $8.75 yields

$$TEK(894 @ \$8.75) = \$22,920$$

Therefore, the savings to be obtained by requesting the new price break will be $627.*

It should be noted that this procedure yields only an approximate "best" answer. For, if one computes the economic purchasing quantity (for Example IV) based on a unit price of $8.50 ($q \geq 894$), one obtains

$$q_0 = \sqrt{\frac{(350)(2400)(2)}{(8.50)(12)(0.02)}} = 907$$

However, the difference in total cost between the optimum value and the approximate "best" answer is usually extremely small. In fact, returning to our example, this difference is given by

$$TEK(q = 894 @ \$8.50) - TEK(q_0 = 907 @ \$8.50)$$

$$= \$22,293.50 - \$22,293 = \$0.50$$

a truly insignificant amount.

---

* Note that, in addition to the immediately evident savings of 894 ($8.75 − $8.50) = $223.50, additional savings are obtained through lower costs of inventory.

Conceptually, one can always converge to an over-all optimum answer by a step-by-step procedure which considers further price breaks. Thus, again returning to our example, a "better" answer might result from obtaining a new quotation based upon a price break at 907 units. However, as here in this example, one would soon reach a point of impracticality, where the cost of calculating further refinements * is greater than the refinements to be achieved.

* This includes the cost of obtaining prices based on new price ranges.

Chapter 10

Inventory Models
with Restrictions

INTRODUCTION

In Chapter 8 a set of models was developed for controlling inventory in situations where it was not necessary to consider any restrictions on production facilities, storage facilities, time, or money. When such restrictions are introduced in situations involving more than one product, it is necessary to allocate the limited available resources among the products. Consequently, the model should enable us to determine how much of each item to produce (or purchase) under the specified restrictions. Such models are "mixed" in the sense that they involve allocation (or programming) as well as planning decisions. This chapter, then, provides a transition to Chapter 11 which considers more complex but "pure" allocation problems.

FIXED ASSETS

Allocation, as previous discussion (Chapter 7) disclosed, involves assigning materials, machines, men, and/or other facilities (such as space) to jobs to be done. These materials, machines, men, and other facilities are "assets" to the organization because their use involves potential profit. If it is relatively difficult to dispose of these assets they are referred to as "fixed." But it should be realized that the difference between "fixed" assets and "fluid" assets (e.g., inventory of finished goods) is relative, referring to the difficulty in profitably "unloading" them.

Fixed assets are a large portion of the assets of modern industrial establishments. The expense of acquiring these assets is usually charged (by depreciation or amortization) against income over a period of years and, in each year, the expense is charged to the cost of production of each product made. However, the usual accounting convention of allocating fixed costs should not be permitted to influence the allocation of the *use* of these assets. Rather, the use of the assets should be allocated in a way that maximizes the profits of the company.

The cost of fixed assets on hand is of an historical nature and cannot be changed by any action taken now. However, these assets have a value to the extent that they contribute to profit. Determination of this value is of importance in deciding upon the acquisition of additional fixed assets. In this chapter, the evaluation and optimum allocation of fixed assets will be illustrated by the determination of economic lot sizes under conditions of: 1. no limitation on fixed assets, 2. limitation on one asset, and 3. limitation on two assets, in that order. Calculation of minimum production costs and of the value of fixed assets will be shown in each case.

In the case study presented in Chapter 2 and in the development of the related economic lot-size equation developed in Chapter 7 we considered an optimization problem independently of fixed assets. We shall begin this discussion of allocating fixed assets by constructing a model very similar to the one presented earlier except that the cost equation simultaneously involves two parts, and withdrawals are assumed to be uniformly continuous. Subsequently, we shall consider the allocation of fixed assets.

Optimizing Lot Sizes: No Consideration of Fixed Assets

A company produces two products, X_1 and X_2, for which the demand is both known and constant. It is necessary to produce these in discrete lots, rather than continuously, and it is desired to operate at minimum total cost. The costs to the company are: 1. the direct material and labor costs for the products, 2. setup (and takedown) costs for each lot, and 3. inventory carrying costs. Following the method outlined in Chapter 7, we can derive the total cost as a function of the lot size of each product.

Let

L_i = monthly sales of product i (assumed to be known and constant)

C_{i1} = setup cost for a lot of product i

C_{i2} = raw material and direct labor cost per unit of product i

N_i = number of units of product i in each lot

P = monthly inventory holding charges expressed as a decimal fraction of the value of inventory

The production cost for a lot of product i is the sum of setup costs and direct costs $C_{i1} + N_i C_{i2}$. Assuming that sales are made at a uniform rate, a lot will last N_i/L_i months. For example, if 300 units are sold per month, a lot of 200 will last $\frac{200}{300}$ or $\frac{2}{3}$ of a month, while a lot of 600 will last $\frac{600}{300}$ or 2 months. Consequently, there will be L_i/N_i lots per month on the average. If lots last $\frac{2}{3}$ month, there will be produced $\frac{3}{2}$ or $1\frac{1}{2}$ lots per month on the average. If lots last 2 months, $\frac{1}{2}$ lot will be produced per month on the average.

Hence the sum of the monthly setup and direct costs will be given by

$$\frac{L_i}{N_i}(C_{i1} + N_i C_{i2}), \qquad \text{i.e., } \frac{L_i C_{i1}}{N_i} + L_i C_{i2}$$

Inventory carrying charges are principally insurance, taxes, and interest on the value of the investment in inventory. (Let us assume at this stage that storage costs are part of fixed expense.) The value of investment in inventory is given by the product of the average number of units in inventory and the investment per unit. Since we have assumed that sales (i.e., withdrawals from inventory) are made uniformly over each period, the inventory of product i will go from a maximum of N_i, the lot size, to a minimum of 0 (see Fig. 10-1). The

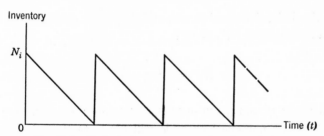

Fig. 10-1. Units in inventory as a function of time.

average level of inventory will be $N_i/2$. The value per unit of inventory will be $(C_{i1}/N_i) + C_{i2}$, or the average setup cost per unit plus the direct costs.

Hence we may write the average value of inventory of product i as

$$\frac{N_i}{2}\left(\frac{C_{i1}}{N_i} + C_{i2}\right), \qquad \text{i.e., } \frac{C_{i1} + N_i C_{i2}}{2}$$

From the accounting point of view, it may be necessary to include a share of the overhead in the inventory value. However, this overhead figure is not a function of lot size and so may be disregarded in this formulation.

If we express monthly inventory carrying charges as a percentage P of average inventory value, we can complete the expression for the cost of product i per month. That is

$$K_i = \frac{L_i C_{i1}}{N_i} + L_i C_{i2} + P\frac{C_{i1} + N_i C_{i2}}{2} \tag{1}$$

Therefore, the total cost for all products, excluding fixed charges, is given by

$$K = \sum_i K_i = \sum_i \frac{L_i C_{i1}}{N_i} + \sum_i L_i C_{i2} + \frac{P}{2}\sum_i N_i C_{i2} + \frac{P}{2}\sum_i C_{i1} \tag{2}$$

We may assume that all costs are included either in the fixed costs, setup costs, direct costs, or carrying charges. Our object is to find values of N_i which minimize this total cost or, equivalently, which minimize K. In order to use the methods of differential calculus, we shall assume that the N_i's can vary continuously. Then, from eq. 2, we obtain

$$\frac{\partial K}{\partial N_i} = \frac{-L_i C_{i1}}{N_i^2} + \frac{PC_{i2}}{2} \quad \text{for all } N_i \tag{3}$$

Setting the derivative equal to zero and solving for optimum N_i, which we shall designate by N_i^*, gives †

$$N_i^* = \sqrt{\frac{2L_i C_{i1}}{PC_{i2}}} \tag{4}$$

as the value of N_i which will yield the minimum total cost.

The following numerical example will illustrate the calculation of the N_i^*'s. Assume we know the following for the two products X_1 and X_2:

Product	L_i	C_{i1}	C_{i2}
X_1	200	$100	$12
X_2	400	$ 25	$ 7

† Given a function $f(X_1, X_2, \cdots, X_n)$, the conditions that the first partial derivatives vanish are only necessary (but not sufficient) for a maximum or minimum value. However, in this case, it can easily be shown that the value of N_i^* given in eq. 4 yields a minimum value.

and $P = 0.005$.   Then

$$N_1{}^* = \sqrt{\frac{(2)(200)(100)}{0.005(12)}} = \sqrt{\frac{(400)(100)}{0.060}} = \frac{200}{\sqrt{0.060}} = 816$$

$$N_2{}^* = \sqrt{\frac{(2)(400)(25)}{0.005(7)}} = \sqrt{\frac{(400)(100)}{0.070}} = \frac{200}{\sqrt{0.070}} = 756$$

We may chart the costs of production of each of these products as a function of the lot size, showing the relation of the minimum cost to the costs of other lot sizes.   This is done in Fig. 10-2.

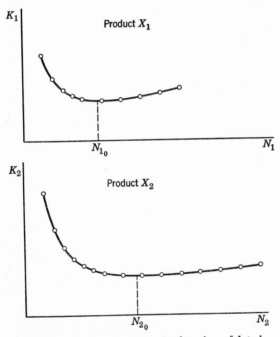

Fig. 10-2.   Production costs as a function of lot size.

The total cost for the company using the economic (optimal) lot sizes is, for products X_1 and X_2

$$K = \frac{(200)(100)}{816} + \frac{(400)(25)}{756} + (200)(12) + (400)(7)$$

$$+ \frac{0.005}{2}[(816)(12) + (756)(7)] + \frac{0.005}{2}(100 + 25)$$

$$= \$5275.76 \text{ (unrestricted)}$$

We can plot the optimal lot sizes on a 2-dimensional chart as shown in Fig. 10-3, in which point P is the pair of lot sizes 816 and 756 that minimize total cost. The closed curves around P connect pairs of lot-size points which yield equal costs. These "iso-cost" lines represent higher and higher costs as one goes farther and farther from P.

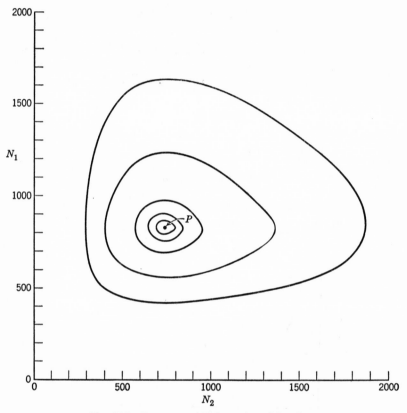

Fig. 10-3. Iso-cost curves for pairs of lot sizes.

Economic Lot Sizes Subject to a Linear Restriction

Suppose that the lot sizes that minimize cost are not achievable because of the limited availability of some fixed asset. For example, let us assume that warehouse space is limited. As we noted earlier, the average inventory level of each product equals half the lot size. Thus, if one unit of product i requires W_i cubic feet of space, the average space occupied by product i is $\frac{1}{2}W_iN_i$. Thus, the average total space required will be $\frac{1}{2}\sum_i W_iN_i$.

As a practical matter, there are many cases where the space cannot be completely utilized. Hence more space than $\frac{1}{2}\Sigma W_i N_i$ is actually required. In fact, if products are stored in bins or tanks where each product has a set of bins or tanks reserved for its storage only, the required space will be $\sum_i W_i N_i$. However, for this example we shall use $\frac{1}{2} \sum_i W_i N_i$ as the space requirement. Later, it will be seen that, with minor changes, the results obtained also apply to other storage situations. That is, if S is the total available space (excluding aisles, etc.) we require that $\sum_i (W_i N_i/2) \leq S$.

To illustrate, if we let

$$W_1 = 5 \text{ cubic feet}$$

$$W_2 = 35 \text{ cubic feet}$$

$$S = 14{,}000 \text{ cubic feet}$$

in our earlier example for products X_1 and X_2, then we require that

$$5\frac{N_1}{2} + 35\frac{N_2}{2} \leq 14{,}000$$

or, equivalently, that

$$5N_1 + 35N_2 \leq 28{,}000$$

This inequality, together with the requirement that lot sizes be non-negative, is illustrated by the shaded area in Fig. 10-4. The boundaries of the area are the equations

$$N_1 = 0, \qquad N_2 = 0, \qquad \text{and} \qquad 5N_1 + 35N_2 = 28{,}000$$

Point P (756, 816) lies outside the shaded area since

$$\frac{(5)(816)}{2} + \frac{(35)(756)}{2} = 15{,}270 > 14{,}000$$

Therefore, we must find a new point *in* the area which represents lot sizes that minimize total cost subject to the given restriction on warehouse space. We proceed as follows: *

---

* What follows is essentially an adaptation of the technique of Lagrangian multipliers and was suggested by an unpublished paper of Beckmann.[1] An alternate procedure is given in Klein.[3]

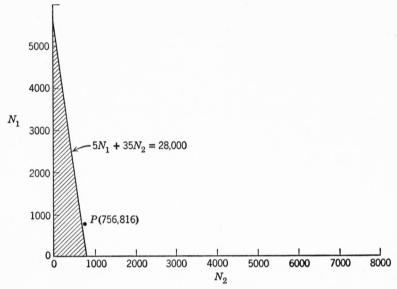

Fig. 10-4. Pairs of lot sizes that satisfy warehouse restrictions.

Define a quantity λ such that †

$$\lambda < 0 \quad \text{when} \quad S - \tfrac{1}{2}\Sigma W_i N_i = 0$$
$$\lambda = 0 \quad \text{when} \quad S - \tfrac{1}{2}\Sigma W_i N_i > 0 \tag{5}$$

Then, $\lambda(S - \tfrac{1}{2}\Sigma W_i N_i)$ is identically equal to zero. Hence it may be added to cost eq. 2 without changing the value of K.

Therefore

$$K = \Sigma \frac{L_i C_{i1}}{N_i} + \Sigma L_i C_{i2} + \frac{P}{2}\Sigma C_{i1} + \frac{P}{2}\Sigma N_i C_{i2} + \lambda\left(S - \frac{1}{2}\Sigma W_i N_i\right)$$

$$\tag{6}$$

While K has not changed in value, the partial derivative of K with respect to N_i has changed to

$$\frac{\partial K}{\partial N_i} = \frac{-L_i C_{i1}}{N_i^2} + \frac{PC_{i2}}{2} - \frac{\lambda W_i}{2} \quad \text{for each } N_i \tag{7}$$

Setting the derivative equal to zero and solving for optimum N_i, we obtain

$$N_i^* = \sqrt{\frac{2L_i C_{i1}}{PC_{i2} - \lambda W_i}} \tag{8}$$

† Note that $S - \tfrac{1}{2}W_i N_i < 0$ is not admissible and, hence, need not be considered.

For each product, the quantities L_i, C_{i1}, C_{i2}, W_i, and P are known, but λ is still unknown. However, for any arbitrarily assigned value of λ, N_i and, hence, $\frac{1}{2}\Sigma W_i N_i$ (the average total storage space required) can be calculated. If $\frac{1}{2}\Sigma W_i N_i$ exceeds S, then the lot sizes are too large. In this case, decrease λ repeatedly and recompute until $\frac{1}{2}\Sigma W_i N_i = S$ has been obtained. If $\frac{1}{2}\Sigma W_i N_i$ is less than S for all negative λ, set λ equal to zero. The resulting N_i's will allow the smallest possible total costs for the company with existing warehouse space S.

If we assume that space may be rented at \$$D$ per cubic foot † per month, we may form the cost equation to include rental for storage space

$$K = \Sigma \frac{L_i C_{i1}}{N_i} + \Sigma L_i C_{i2} + \frac{P}{2} \Sigma C_{i1} + \frac{P}{2} \Sigma N_i C_{i2} + D\Sigma \frac{1}{2} W_i N_i \quad (9)$$

Then

$$\frac{\partial K}{\partial N_i} = \frac{-L_i C_{i1}}{N_i{}^2} + \frac{P}{2} C_{i2} + \frac{DW_i}{2}$$

$$N_i{}^* = \sqrt{\frac{2L_i C_{i1}}{PC_{i2} + DW_i}} \quad (10)$$

Comparing eqs. 8 and 10, we see that $-\lambda$ is the rental value or imputed rent of the owned warehouse space S. Thus, if $-\lambda$ is greater than D, it would profit the company to rent additional warehouse space.

TABLE 10-1 ‡

λ	$N_1{}^*$	$N_2{}^*$	$\frac{1}{2}(5N_1 + 35N_2)$
-0.0000	816	756	15,270.0
-0.0001	813	721	14,650.0
-0.0002	810	690	14,100.0
-0.0003	806	663	13,617.5
-0.0005	800	617	12,797.5
-0.0007	794	580	12,135.0
-0.0010	784	535	11,322.5

‡ The $N_i{}^*$ were computed by use of eq. 8.

To determine N_1 and N_2 for our example, we will take successive values of λ until the space requirement is down to 14,000 cubic feet. This is shown in Table 10-1. We see in Table 10-1 that space requirements are down to the available 14,000 cubic feet when λ is about

† The rental \$$D$ per cubic foot is not included in P. P includes interest, personal property taxes, insurance, and anything else which is proportional to the value of inventory. D is space cost per cubic foot and includes rent, heat, light, etc.

−0.0002. The economic lot sizes for this value of λ are 810 and 690 for products X_1 and X_2 respectively.

Using these economic lot sizes, we may calculate the monthly cost for the company as follows

$$K = \left[\frac{(200)(100)}{810} + \frac{(400)(25)}{690}\right] + [(200)(12) + (400)(7)]$$

$$+ \frac{0.005}{2}[(810)(12) + (690)(7)] + \frac{0.005}{2}(100 + 25)$$

$$= (24.69 + 14.49) + (5200) + 36.69$$

$$= \$5275.87 \text{ (restricted by warehouse space)}$$

The increase in cost over the unrestricted case (where $K = \$5275.76$) is virtually negligible since the available space is nearly as much as that required in the unrestricted case. Hence in this example lot sizes are very near to the unrestricted optimum lot sizes.

This example illustrates a method for finding optimum lot sizes when the variables are restricted. It further shows that the imputed rent of the available warehouse space is $0.0002 per cubic foot per month. It would not be worth while renting additional space to permit operation with unrestricted economic lot sizes unless the rental was less than the value of $-\lambda$, in this case, less than $0.0002 per cubic foot.

While inventory was restricted in this example in terms of space occupied, identical treatment would be used on problems in which inventory value, number of units, or any other linear function of lot sizes was limited.

Economic Lot Sizes Subject to Nonlinear Restriction

Warehouse space limitations, as described in the preceding section, are a linear restriction on the lot sizes. The line representing this restriction, as shown in Fig. 10-4, restricts lot sizes to the shaded area. Another common restriction on lot sizes is the availability of machine time. In addition to the actual cost of setup, a certain amount of time is required for setups during which production is stopped. Frequent setups consume more time, leaving less time for production. Obviously, smaller lots require more frequent setups than do larger lots.

Hence, the time required for setups can be expressed as a function of the lot sizes. Using our earlier notation, the average number of setups per month for product X_i will be given by L_i/N_i.

Let t_i = time required to set up for product X_i. Then the expected total time required each month for setups is given by $\Sigma[(L_i t_i)/N_i]$. Thus, if T is the time available for setups (after allowing time for production of L_i units of each product), we require that

$$T - \sum \frac{L_i t_i}{N_i} \geq 0$$

Suppose that, to continue our example, we are given

$$t_1 = 40 \text{ hours (for product } X_1)$$

$$t_2 = 10 \text{ hours (for product } X_2)$$

$$T = 14 \text{ hours (total available setup time)}$$

Then

$$14 - \left[\frac{(200)(40)}{N_1} + \frac{(400)(10)}{N_2} \right] \geq 0$$

i.e.

$$\frac{8000}{N_1} + \frac{4000}{N_2} \leq 14$$

expresses the time limitation as a (nonlinear) function of the lot sizes.* This restriction is shown graphically in Fig. 10-5. The shaded area in Fig. 10-5 covers the combination of lot sizes N_1 and N_2, such that the time restriction is satisfied. Again we find that P lies outside the shaded area. Neglecting the warehouse restriction considered earlier, we wish to find lot sizes in the shaded area that minimize cost. We proceed as follows:

Define the quantity μ such that

$$\mu < 0 \quad \text{when} \quad T - \Sigma \frac{L_i t_i}{N_i} = 0$$

$$\mu = 0 \quad \text{when} \quad T - \Sigma \frac{L_i t_i}{N_i} > 0$$

(11)

Thus $\mu\{T - \Sigma[(L_i t_i)/N_i]\}$ is always zero and may be added to the

* The reader should note that a very simple change of variables would render this function linear. However, later in this chapter, we shall consider simultaneously the (linear) restriction due to space and the (nonlinear) restriction due to setup time. Since both restrictions cannot simultaneously be linear in the same variables, no linearizing transformation is made here.

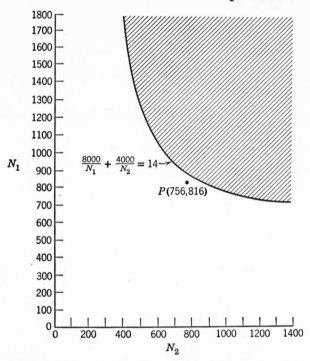

$$\frac{8000}{N_1} + \frac{4000}{N_2} = 14$$

$P(756,816)$

Fig. 10-5. Pairs of lot sizes that satisfy setup time limitation.

cost equation without changing the value. Therefore, proceeding as before

$$K = \Sigma \frac{L_i C_{i1}}{N_i} + \Sigma L_i C_{i2} + \frac{P}{2} \left(\Sigma C_{i1} + \Sigma N_i C_{i2} \right) + \mu \left(T - \Sigma \frac{L_i t_i}{N_i} \right) \quad (12)$$

K is minimized by finding (partial) derivatives with respect to the N_i and equating the derivatives to zero.†

Therefore,
$$\frac{\partial K}{\partial N_i} = \frac{-L_i C_{i1}}{N_i{}^2} + \frac{P}{2} C_{i2} + \mu \frac{L_i t_i}{N_i{}^2}$$

$$N_i{}^* = \sqrt{\frac{2 L_i (C_{i1} - \mu t_i)}{P C_{i2}}} \qquad \text{for each } i \qquad (13)$$

For each product L_i, t_i, C_{i1}, C_{i2}, and P are known and it is necessary

† Again, it should be made clear that these conditions are necessary but not sufficient. However, here, too, eq. 13 yields a minimum.

to find the value of μ for which $\{T - \Sigma[(L_i t_i)/N_i]\} = 0.$† In this example, we will find N_1^*, N_2^*, and $[(L_1 t_1)/N_1 + (L_2 t_2)/N_2]$ for successive values of μ. These are given in Table 10-2. We notice that

TABLE 10-2 ‡

μ	N_1^*	N_2^*	$\dfrac{8000}{N_1} + \dfrac{4000}{N_2} = $ Total Setup Time
0	816	756	$9.80 + 5.29 = 15.09$
-0.1	832	769	$9.62 + 5.20 = 14.82$
-0.2	848	784	$9.43 + 5.10 = 14.53$
-0.3	864	798	$9.26 + 5.01 = 14.27$
-0.4	879	814	$9.10 + 4.91 = 14.01$
-0.5	894	826	$8.94 + 4.84 = 13.78$

‡ The N_i^* were computed by use of eq. 13.

the total setup time is reduced to 14 hours by taking $\mu = -0.4$ (approximately). The economic lot sizes for this value of μ are 879 and 814 for products X_1 and X_2, respectively.

Costs for the company with these lot sizes are

$$K = \left[\frac{(200)(100)}{879} + \frac{(400)(25)}{814} \right] + [(200)(12) + (400)(7)]$$

$$+ \frac{0.005}{2} [(879)(12) + (814)(7) + 100 + 25]$$

$$= (22.75 + 12.29) + (5200) + 0.0025(16,371)$$

$$= \$5275.97$$

Again, the increase in cost is relatively small for the same reasons as in the previous case.

Economic Lot Sizes Subject to Two Restrictions

Now assume that the warehouse restriction and the setup time restriction previously cited must both be satisfied. Under the warehouse restriction, both lot sizes were reduced from the unrestricted optimum, and consequently setups were increased in number and setup time requirements were thereby increased. Similarly, adjusting only to the setup time restriction increased lot sizes and thereby increased

† Here, too, if $\{T - \Sigma[(L_i t_i)/N_i]\} > 0$ for *all* negative values of μ, then we set μ equal to zero.

space requirements. We now require that lot sizes change in such a way that warehouse space and setup time requirements are *both* reduced. Only the shaded region in Fig. 10-6 contains pairs of values of N_1 and N_2 which satisfy both requirements.

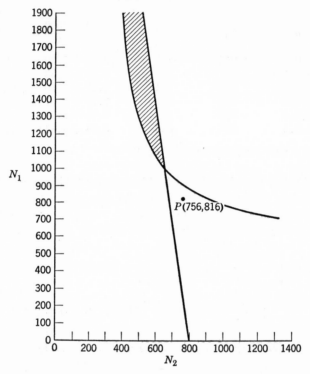

Fig. 10-6. **Pairs of lot sizes that satisfy warehouse space and setup time restrictions.**

It should be pointed out that there need not always be a solution to this problem; i.e., there need not always be an intersection of the two curves as in Fig. 10-6. A company may find that increased demand for their products increases the time required for production, thereby decreasing the time available for setups. This situation is shown by a shift of the curve to the right in Fig. 10-7. As a result of the decrease in available time, longer runs are necessary to cut down on setups but longer runs involve increased inventories. Hence the demand cannot be met without additional equipment *or* the possibility of an increase in inventory. This latter may mean more space or merely authorization to increase the investment in inventory.

In our numerical example, we can construct the cost equation as before, with two "zero-valued" terms added. Therefore

$$K = \Sigma \frac{L_i C_{i1}}{N_i} + \Sigma L_i C_{i2} + \frac{P}{2} (\Sigma N_i C_{i2} + \Sigma C_{i1})$$

$$+ \lambda \left(S - \Sigma \frac{W_i N_i}{2} \right) + \mu \left(T - \Sigma \frac{L_i t_i}{N_i} \right) \quad (14)$$

Taking the partial derivatives, equating them to zero, and solving for the N_i, we obtain

$$N_i{}^* = \sqrt{\frac{2L_i(C_{i1} - \mu t_i)}{PC_{i2} - \lambda W_i}} \quad (15)$$

Using this equation, we can calculate $N_1{}^*$ and $N_2{}^*$ for many values of μ and λ. These are shown in Tables 10-3 and 10-4. These pairs of lot

TABLE 10-3. ECONOMIC LOT SIZES ($N_1{}^*$) FOR PRODUCT X_1 FOR SPECIFIED VALUES OF μ AND λ

$-\lambda$ / $-\mu$	0.000	0.001	0.002	0.003	0.004	0.005	0.006
0	816	784	756	730	707	686	667
1	966	928	894	864	837	812	789
2	1095	1052	1014	980	949	920	894
3	1211	1164	1121	1083	1049	1017	989
4	1317	1265	1219	1178	1140	1106	1075
5	1414	1359	1309	1265	1225	1188	1155
6	1506	1446	1394	1346	1304	1265	1229

TABLE 10-4. ECONOMIC LOT SIZES ($N_2{}^*$) FOR PRODUCT X_2 FOR SPECIFIED VALUES OF μ AND λ

$-\lambda$ / $-\mu$	0.000	0.001	0.002	0.003	0.004	0.005	0.006
0	756	535	436	378	338	309	286
1	894	632	516	447	400	365	338
2	1014	717	586	507	454	414	383
3	1121	793	647	561	501	458	424
4	1219	862	704	609	545	498	461
5	1309	926	756	655	586	535	495
6	1394	986	805	697	623	569	527

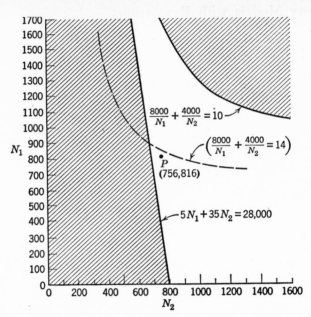

Fig. 10-7. Illustration of case with nonexistent solution for two restrictions.

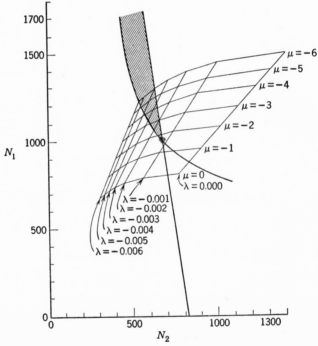

Fig. 10.8. Pairs of lot sizes for specified values of μ and λ.

sizes are plotted in Fig. 10-8. For any of the points of intersection in Fig. 10-8, follow the line to the right to read the value of μ and follow the line down to read the value of λ. The shaded area on Fig. 10-8 contains the pairs of lot sizes which satisfy both restrictions. We can see from the chart that we cannot get a point in the shaded area if $\mu = 0$ or if $\lambda = 0$. Hence both must be negative, and so

$$T - \Sigma \frac{L_i t_i}{N_i} = 0$$

$$S - \Sigma \frac{W_i N_i}{2} = 0$$

These conditions are met at the intersection of the two boundary lines. From Fig. 10-8, we may observe that this intersection takes place at about $N_1 = 1015$, $N_2 = 655$.

Checking our results, we see that these lot sizes require

$$\frac{1015}{2} \times 5 + \frac{655}{2} \times 35 = 14{,}000 \text{ cubic feet}$$

of warehouse space. Furthermore, the setup time required is

$$\frac{8000}{1015} + \frac{4000}{655} = 7.88 + 6.11 = 13.99 \text{ hours}$$

Hence, the lot sizes that minimize cost and still satisfy the restrictions on available warehouse space and machine time are

$$N_1{}^* = 1015$$

$$N_2{}^* = 655$$

From the cost equation, we can find the average monthly cost using these lot sizes. That is

$$K = \frac{200 \times 100}{1015} + \frac{400 \times 25}{655} + (200 \times 12 + 400 \times 7)$$

$$+ \frac{0.005}{2} (1015 \times 12 + 655 \times 7 + 125)$$

$$= 19.70 + 15.27 + 5200 + 42.23$$

$$= \$5277.20$$

From the values of N_1^* and N_2^*, we can calculate the implicit values of λ and μ from eq. 15. We have

$$(1015)^2 = \frac{2 \times 200(100 - \mu \times 40)}{0.005 \times 12 - 5\lambda}$$

$$(655)^2 = \frac{2 \times 400(25 - \mu \times 10)}{0.005 \times 7 - 35\lambda}$$

or

$$(1015)^2(0.060 - 5\lambda) = 40{,}000 - 16{,}000\mu$$

$$(655)^2(0.035 - 35\lambda) = 20{,}000 - 8{,}000\mu$$

Solving these two equations for μ and λ, we have

$$\lambda = -0.001278$$

$$\mu = -1.77576$$

It may be seen in Fig. 10-8 that the values of λ and μ lie between -0.001 and -0.002, and -1 and -2 respectively. These calculated values lie within those limits.

We may summarize the results of the four examples in Table 10-5

TABLE 10-5. Summary of Four Examples

Conditions	N_1^*	N_2^*	K	λ	μ	$\frac{1}{2}\Sigma N_i W_i$	$\Sigma \frac{L_i t_i}{N_i}$
Unrestricted	816	756	\$5275.76	0	0	15,270	15.09
Warehouse restriction	810	690	\$5275.87	−0.0002	0	14,100	15.67
Machine time restriction	879	814	\$5275.97	0	−0.40	16,443	14.02
Both restrictions	1015	655	\$5277.20	−0.0013	−1.78	14,000	13.99

and make certain observations on the effect of the restrictions on lot sizes, costs, and the value of the assets.

1. Compared to the unrestricted condition, the warehouse restriction lowers both lot sizes, while the machine time restriction raises both lot sizes. The combined restriction raises one and lowers the other lot size.

2. Each restriction increases costs independently and both restrictions taken together further increase costs.

3. The value of the assets (warehouse and machinery) is greater when both restrictions must be satisfied than when only one restriction must be satisfied.

It is interesting to note that we have considered a case where neither asset was sufficient to permit us to use the unrestricted optimum lot sizes. It was possible to find a solution without acquiring additional warehouse space or machinery and the cost of the restricted solution is not very different from the unrestricted minimum cost. Finally, the implicit value of warehouse space is 0.13¢ per cubic foot per month and the implicit value of machine time is $1.78 per hour per month. These values may be used to evaluate the policy of acquiring either additional space and/or additional machinery.

Several theoretical problems implicit in the method of this chapter become very serious when the number of restrictions or the number of commodities increases. One such problem is the very existence of a solution. It was shown earlier that no solution exists for certain values of the restrictions. Specifically it was shown that warehouse space and machine time may both be so limited that no combination of lot sizes exists which will produce the required output and meet both restrictions (see Fig. 10-7).

Given the existence of a solution, a second theoretical problem is the construction of an efficient method for finding the optimum solution. The trial-and-error method used in the chapter may be improved by some procedure which dictates each new trial on the basis of the results of the previous trial.

One method that may prove to be of value is described in an article by Crockett and Chernoff.[2] The articles by Beckmann,[1] Kuhn and Tucker,[4] and Slater [5] are concerned with necessary and sufficient conditions for an optimum solution. These conditions may provide the key to improved methods of calculating solutions.

The difficult theoretical problems to be solved do not detract from the usefulness of the method of this chapter in the many practical problems that can be characterized with very few restrictions.

BIBLIOGRAPHY

1. Beckmann, Martin, "A Lagrangian Multiplier Rule in Linear Activity Analysis and Some of Its Applications," Cowles Commission Discussion Paper: Economics no. 2054 (unpublished) Nov. 5, 1942.
2. Crockett, Jean Bronfenbrenner, and Chernoff, Herman, "Gradient Methods of Maximization," *Pac. J. Math. 5* (1955).

3. Klein, Bertram, "Direct Use of Extremal Principles in Solving Certain Optimizing Problems Involving Inequalities," *J. Oper. Res. Soc. Amer.*, *3*, no. 2, 168–175 (May 1955).
4. Kuhn, H. W., and Tucker, A. W., "Nonlinear Programming," in Jerzy Neyman (ed.), *Second Berkeley Symposium on Mathematical Statistics and Probability*, University of California Press, Berkeley, pp. 481–492, 1951.
5. Slater, Morton, "Lagrange Multipliers Revisited," Cowles Commission Discussion Paper: Mathematics no. 403 (unpublished) Nov. 7, 1950.

PART V

ALLOCATION MODELS

Allocation models are used to solve a class of problems which arise when (*a*) there are a number of activities to be performed and there are alternative ways of doing them, and (*b*) resources or facilities are not available for performing each activity in the most effective way. The problem, then, is to combine activities and resources in such a way as to maximize over-all effectiveness. These problems are divisible into two types:

1. An amount of work to be done is specified. Certain resources are available; i.e., a fixed capacity and/or material for doing the job is available and, hence, constitutes a restriction or limitation. The problem is to use these limited facilities and/or materials to accomplish the required work in the most economical manner.

2. The facilities and/or materials which are to be used are considered to be fixed. The problem is to determine what work, if performed, will yield the maximum return on use of the facilities and/or materials.

The tool which has come to be most closely associated with allocation problems is linear programming and such related procedures as activity analysis and mathematical programming.

The major contribution to what Orden [36] has called the "basic science development" of these methods has been made by T. C. Koopmans and his colleagues of the Cowles Commission.[28, 29]   Closely related developments include those in interindustry economics, starting with the work of Leontief.

With the development of the simplex technique for solving linear programs by Dantzig,[12] the door was opened for feasible applications of the tool.   Charnes and Lemke [2, 6] modified the technique to control computational errors due to "round-off."   Dantzig and others [11, 14-16] have subsequently developed a generalized, or "revised," simplex technique to treat nonconvergent (or "degenerate") cases.   Mention should be made of the useful introductory exposition of the simplex technique published by Charnes, Cooper, and Henderson.[4]   The simplex technique is discussed in Chapter 11.

An important subclass of allocation processes consists of situations in which requirements and resources are expressed in terms of only one kind of unit (e.g., freight cars or tons of steel).   The transportation technique, which is sufficient to solve this subclass of problems (where the restriction of linearity holds), was developed by Hitchcock [27] in 1941 and, later, independently by Koopmans [30] in 1947.   Very recently Dwyer [18] has developed a new technique for solving the Hitchcock transportation problem, a technique which makes use of a method for reducing matrices.   Dwyer's technique reduces the computational work considerably as compared to that developed by Hitchcock and Koopmans.   Ford and Fulkerson [21] have recently published a procedure based on flow theory for solving the transportation problem.   This procedure also simplifies the computations required of the older techniques.   Vidale [39] offers a graphical solution to the transportation problem where the requirements are perfectly matched by the available capacity.   The transportation technique is discussed in Chapter 11.

The "dual" theorem of linear programming was first developed by Gale, Kuhn, and Tucker [23] with supplementary contributions being made by Rubin, von Neumann, Orden, and Dantzig.   This theorem asserts that to every maximization problem in linear programming there corresponds a specific symmetric problem of minimization involving the same data as the original problem.   It has facilitated the solution of several practical problems and has enabled mathematicians to solve problems in other mathematical areas which, at first glance, seem unrelated.   For example, Hoffman used the duality theorem to prove a theorem of Dilworth in topology dealing with partially ordered sets.   Fulkerson and Dantzig [22] have applied the theorem to determine the maximal capacities of networks.   The dual theorem is discussed briefly in Appendix 11C.

The assignment problem is another special case of the linear programming problem, one in which each required activity needs one (and only one) exclusive resource or facility. Although research on this problem, and variations thereof, have dated back to as early as the work of König in 1916, no great interest was aroused in this area until the fairly recent work of Votaw and Orden,[40] Flood,[19] Kuhn,[31] and others. Kuhn's work is based on some ideas in matrix theory developed by Egerváry in 1931. Flood [20] found some short cuts to the Kuhn-Egerváry method which have been published and others which are forthcoming. The assignment problem is discussed in Chapter 12.

Computational programs have been developed for solving simplex, transportation, and assignment problems on IBM equipment. Charnes and Cooper have developed and employed a number of devices that take advantage of the special properties of a given matrix and permit resolution of large-scale systems. Dantzig [13] has developed short-cut computational methods for solving a class of systems whose matrices are "block-triangular."

Charnes and Lemke [7] have broken the linearity restriction of linear programming. They have developed an "extended simplex method" to obtain solutions, within an arbitrary degree of approximation, to problems involving certain nonlinear functions (nonlinear separable convex polynomials).

A great amount of effort has been devoted to the application of linear programming techniques to the solution of industrial and military problems. Chapter 13 discusses the highlights of several case studies in which linear programming techniques were applied.

Chapter 11

Linear Programming

INTRODUCTION

Linear programming refers to techniques for solving a general class of optimization problems dealing with the interaction of many variables subject to certain restraining conditions. In solving these problems, objectives such as profits, costs, quantities produced, or other measures of effectiveness are to be obtained in the best possible, or optimal, fashion subject to certain restraining conditions. These restraining conditions, in turn, may arise from a variety of sources, such as government, marketing, business production, storage, raw material, or legal restrictions.

For example, certain steel products may be obtained in a steel mill by various combinations of raw materials and hot-rolling, cold-rolling, annealing, normalizing, and slitting operations. To be able to reach an optimal programming decision, all possible combinations (and even permutations) of these operations and materials must be considered simultaneously. Here, profit (or cost * or amounts) might be the objective which is to be optimized, and the restrictions imposed on the processes could include, for example:

1. Capacity limitations of each operational facility.
2. Minimum amounts required for each product.

* In many (if not most) cases, there is a great difference between programs which maximize profits as opposed to minimizing costs. Only if the product quantities are fixed or if the sales prices are directly proportional to the costs will the two programs be the same.

3. Production requirements, both as to quality and quantity.
4. Delivery requirements.
5. Limitations on the availability of operating fuels.
6. Limitations on the availability of raw materials.

SOLUTION OF LINEAR PROGRAMMING PROBLEMS

General techniques for treating problems involving large and complicated arrays of interacting variables have long been known in mathematics. Some of these techniques, e.g., those dealing with systems of simultaneous equations, were originally developed by mathematicians and have subsequently found widespread applications in such fields as economics, engineering, physics, biology, and statistics. Furthermore, their range of application has been greatly extended by the many recent developments in the field of computing equipment, especially with respect to high-speed electronic computers. In the case of linear programming, the restrictions are usually stated in such terms as "not more than," "not less than," "at least," and "at most," and, accordingly, are usually represented by inequalities or systems of inequalities. For this reason, the techniques applicable to systems of equations are generally inadequate for handling linear programming problems.*

Fortunately, however, iterative techniques of solving systems of simultaneous inequations and, in turn, choosing from a set of solutions the best possible or optimal one(s) in terms of a given objective have been developed within the past few years. Among these techniques the most important ones are those known as the *transportation technique* and the *simplex technique*. Before discussing any of these techniques, however, the types of problems which can be treated by their use will be described and a few illustrations cited.

---

* One technique for solving a class of optimization problems in which restrictions appear in the form of inequalities has already been discussed in Chapter 10, namely a modified Lagrangian multiplier technique. The usual Lagrangian multiplier technique is not applicable to the problems discussed in this chapter since, for example, it does not guarantee the nonnegativity of the solution variables. The modified Lagrangian multiplier technique of Chapter 10 is practical only for small-scale problems. The techniques to be presented here are excellent for large-scale problems and also guarantee the nonnegativity of the solution variables, but are generally applicable only to *linear* problems, i.e., ones in which the optimizing function is linear and the restrictions are given as linear equalities or inequalities.

WHEN CAN LINEAR PROGRAMMING BE USED?

Generally speaking, linear programming can be used for optimization problems in which the following conditions are satisfied:

1. There must exist an objective, such as profit, cost, or quantities, which is to be optimized and which can be expressed as, or represented by, a *linear* function.*

2. There must be restrictions on the amount or extent of attainment of the objective and these restrictions must be expressible as, or representable by, a system of linear equalities or inequalities.

For example, if one were to maximize the profit associated with the manufacture of a given class of products subject to capacity limitations on the producing machines, one would first have to obtain the following data:

1. Profit per part as produced on each machine.

2. Production time per part for each machine.

3. Total hours available on each machine for the production of the given class of products.

4. Amounts of each product which may (or must) be produced.

With these data, one would then have to express the total profit as a linear function and express the machine capacity limitations as a system of linear inequalities. If this use of linear functions and linear inequalities is realistic, then one can proceed to apply linear programming techniques.

Examples of Linear Programming Problems

PROBLEM I. The earliest problems in programming were transportation problems where, for example, it was desired to minimize the cost of shipping a homogeneous product manufactured in, say, n mills, each in a different geographical location, and shipped to consumers at m different destinations. Freight and storage rates, as well as delivery commitments on consumer orders, were all given.

---

* The linearity assumption is inherent in the techniques to be discussed in this chapter and simply means that, for example, it costs ten times as much to produce ten items as it does to produce one, that it takes ten times as much production time for these ten items as compared to one item, etc. If this assumption cannot realistically be made, or if the functions cannot be linearized by a suitable transformation of variables, then the techniques of linear programming will not be applicable. It should be added, however, that research has already been conducted both for the case where the objective function is piecewise linear and for nonlinear programming, especially where the functions are quadratic in nature.

A variation of this problem will presently be stated and solved in order to illustrate how one of the techniques of linear programming may be applied to this general class of problems.

PROBLEM II.   A second problem deals with the blending of aviation gases.[5] Here, specifications and prices of selected grades of commercial aviation gasoline are given in terms of minimal octane ratings, maximal vapor pressures, and maximum permitted concentrations of tetraethyl lead.   Prices and chemical properties relevant to output ratings are also given, as well as upper limits on the capacities of input materials which can be used to produce the various grades of gasoline. The problem is to combine the inputs in the production of the outputs in such a way that: *a.* maximum receipts will be obtained, and *b.* need for additional storage capacity will be avoided.

PROBLEM III.[24]   It is required to procure a given total quantity of each of a number of related items from producers.   The items are related in the sense that they can be produced by the same contractor and his capacity to produce any one item is dependent on how much his production facilities are strained by the production of the other items in the contract.   Because of a contractor's limited capacity, more production on one item results in reduced production on another. The contractor is permitted to submit bids on any or all items specified in the invitation.   The bidder must state:

a. The price per unit of each item for which a bid is made.

b. The maximum and minimum quantity of each item which he can deliver.

c. The maximum and minimum size of total contract which he is willing to accept.   This type of information can be expressed in various ways as:

Type 1: The maximum (and minimum) total dollar value of the contract.

Type 2: The maximum (and minimum) total number of units of all items.

Type 3: A certain percentage (not more than 100%) of each item capacity expressed in *b* is acceptable provided that the sum of such percentages does not exceed 100.   There is an implication here that the stated limitations on the individual item are proportional to the ease of production.

Type 4: Bid is made and capacity stated on a number of items, but only one item may be chosen in awarding contract.

The problem, then, is to award the contracts to the various bidders so that the following conditions are satisfied:

a. The cost of the whole procurement over all items must be minimum.

b. The number of units of each item made by all contractors must be at least as great as the total number required.

OTHER PROBLEMS. A fourth problem will also be stated presently to illustrate the second of the two techniques of linear programming to be discussed. Other problems which have been solved by linear programming deal with areas such as:

1. Personnel assignment.[37]
2. Optimum crop rotation plan.[26]
3. Allocating manufactured products.[1,9]
4. Optimal bombing patterns.
5. Design of weapons systems.
6. Optimal purchasing policy.

THE TRANSPORTATION TECHNIQUE

In order to be able to discuss linear programming from a practical point of view and, at the same time, avoid highly mathematical aspects of the techniques, the analytic techniques of solving linear programming problems will be presented by means of specific examples. The first technique to be discussed is the *transportation technique* * and, appropriately, will be illustrated by means of a railroad transportation problem dealing with the effective distribution of empty freight cars. The problem has been deliberately simplified because of space limitations, and, furthermore, is such that the results can be obtained directly by inspection, thus offering a check on the results obtained by using the analytic method.

The problem is that of moving empty freight cars from "excess" origins to "deficiency" destinations in such a manner that the total cost of the required movement is a minimum, subject, of course, to any restrictions which might be imposed by practical considerations.

Tables 11-1 and 11-2 exhibit the physical program requirements (i.e., the given conditions of the problem) and the unit (per freight car) shipping costs.

Table 11-1 states that origins S_1, S_2, and S_3 have surpluses of 9, 4, and 8 empty freight cars respectively, while destinations D_1, D_2, D_3, D_4, and D_5 are in need of 3, 5, 4, 6, and 3 empties respectively. (For simplicity, it has been assumed that the problem is self-contained, i.e.,

---

* The transportation technique is applicable to that subclass of linear programming problems in which the requirements and resources are expressed in terms of only one kind of unit.

TABLE 11-1. Physical Program Requirements

Origins \ Destinations	D_1	D_2	D_3	D_4	D_5	Surpluses
S_1	X_{11}	X_{12}	X_{13}	X_{14}	X_{15}	9
S_2	X_{21}	X_{22}	X_{23}	X_{24}	X_{25}	4
S_3	X_{31}	X_{32}	X_{33}	X_{34}	X_{35}	8
Deficiencies	3	5	4	6	3	21

that the number of excess cars is equal to the number of deficiencies.)*

Table 11-2 lists the unit costs C_{ij}† of sending an empty freight car from the ith origin to the jth destination. (In keeping with accepted mathematical practice, i denotes the row and j the column). Thus

TABLE 11-2. Unit Shipping Costs

Origins \ Destinations	D_1	D_2	D_3	D_4	D_5
S_1	C_{11} -10	C_{12} -20	C_{13} -5	C_{14} -9	C_{15} -10
S_2	C_{21} -2	C_{22} -10	C_{23} -8	C_{24} -30	C_{25} -6
S_3	C_{31} -1	C_{32} -20	C_{33} -7	C_{34} -10	C_{35} -4

* This need not have been the case since a problem can be made self-contained through the introduction of dummy origins or destinations. (See Chap. 9 in ref. 38.)
† Minus signs are used for the costs since they represent negative profits.

the problem is to obtain values of the X_{ij} ($i = 1, 2, 3; j = 1, 2, 3, 4, 5$) of Table 11-1 such that they: 1. satisfy the given stipulated movement requirements, and 2. minimize the total cost of so doing.*

Obtaining a First Feasible Solution

The first step in using the transportation technique is to exhibit a *feasible* solution, namely one which satisfies the movement requirements. (If a feasible solution also minimizes the total cost, it is then called an *optimal feasible* or, in this case, a *minimal feasible* solution). This can easily be done by applying a technique which has been developed by Dantzig [10] and which Charnes and Cooper [8] refer to as *"the northwest corner rule."*

The northwest corner rule may be stated as follows:

1. Start in the northwest corner of the requirements table (Table 11-1) and compare the amount available at S_1 with the amount required at D_1.

    a. If $D_1 < S_1$, i.e., if the amount needed at D_1 is less than the number of units available at S_1, set X_{11} equal to D_1 and proceed to cell X_{12} (i.e., proceed horizontally).

    b. If $D_1 = S_1$, set X_{11} equal to D_1 and proceed to cell X_{22} (i.e., proceed diagonally).

    c. If $D_1 > S_1$, set X_{11} equal to S_1 and proceed to X_{21} (i.e., proceed vertically).

2. Continue in this manner, step by step, away from the northwest corner until, finally, a value is reached in the southeast corner.

Thus, in the present example (see Table 11-3), one proceeds as follows:

1. Set X_{11} equal to 3, namely, the smaller of the amount available at S_1 (9) and that needed at D_1 (3), and

2. Proceed to X_{12} (rule *a*). Compare the number of units still available at S_1 (namely 6) with the amount required at D_2 (5) and, accordingly, let $X_{12} = 5$.

3. Proceed to X_{13} (rule *a*) where, here, there is but one unit left at S_1 while four units are required at D_3. Thus set $X_{13} = 1$ and then

4. Proceed to X_{23} (rule *c*). Here $X_{23} = 3$.

5. Continuing, $X_{24} = 1$, $X_{34} = 5$, and, finally, in the southeast corner, $X_{35} = 3$.

---

* The notation "X_{ij} ($i = 1, 2, 3; j = 1, 2, 3, 4, 5$)" refers to the 15 possible X_{ij}'s which arise by assigning to i the values 1, 2, or 3 and to j the values 1, 2, 3, 4, or 5. These 15 X_{ij}'s are exhibited in Table 11-1.

The feasible solution obtained by this northwest corner rule is shown in Table 11-3 by the circled values of the X_{ij}. That this set of values is a feasible solution is easily verified by checking the respective row and column requirements. The corresponding total cost of this solu-

TABLE 11-3. First Feasible Solution

Origins \ Destinations	D_1	D_2	D_3	D_4	D_5	Total surpluses
S_1	③	⑤	①			9
S_2			③	①		4
S_3	✓			⑤	③	8
Total deficiencies	3	5	4	6	3	21

tion is obtained by multiplying each circled X_{ij} in Table 11-3 by its corresponding C_{ij} in Table 11-2 and summing the products. That is *

$$\text{Total cost} = \sum_{j=1}^{5} \sum_{i=1}^{3} C_{ij}X_{ij} = \sum_{i=1}^{3} \sum_{j=1}^{5} C_{ij}X_{ij}$$

The total cost associated with the first feasible solution is computed as follows

$$\text{T.C.} = X_{11}C_{11} + X_{12}C_{12} + X_{13}C_{13} + X_{23}C_{23} + X_{24}C_{24} + X_{34}C_{34}$$
$$+ X_{35}C_{35}$$
$$= (3)(-10) + (5)(-20) + (1)(-5) + (3)(-8) + (1)(-30)$$
$$+ (5)(-10) + (3)(-4)$$
$$= -\$251 \text{ (minus sign means "cost" rather than "profit")}$$

Evaluation of Alternative Possibilities

Now that one has a feasible program and has determined its corresponding total cost, how does one know whether or not this program

---

* Note that for any cell in which no circled number appears the corresponding X_{ij} is equal to zero.

is optimal? To be able to determine whether a feasible program is optimal, it is necessary to "evaluate" alternative possibilities; i.e., one must evaluate the opportunity costs associated with *not* using the cells which do not contain circled numbers. Such an evaluation is illustrated by means of the program given in Table 11-3 and is exhibited in Table 11-4 (noncircled numbers only). This evaluation is obtained as follows: *

1. For any cell in which no circled number appears, describe a *path* in this manner: Locate the nearest circled-number cell in the same *row* which is such that another circled value lies in the same *column*.

TABLE 11-4. FIRST FEASIBLE SOLUTION (WITH EVALUATIONS): C = 251

Origins \ Destinations	D_1	D_2	D_3	D_4	D_5	Total
S_1	③	⑤	①	-18	-11	9
S_2	-11	-13	③	①	-18	4
S_3	8	17	19	⑤	③	8
Total	3	5	4	6	3	21

Thus, in Table 11-4, if one starts with cell S_3D_1 (row 3, column 1), the value ⑤ at S_3D_4 (row 3, column 4) satisfies this requirement; i.e., it is the closest circled-number cell in the third row which has another circled value, ① at S_2D_4, in the same column (column 4). (Note that the circled number ③ in position S_3D_5 fails to meet this requirement.)

2. Make the horizontal and, then, vertical moves so indicated. That is, in the example, move from S_3D_1 to S_3D_4 to S_2D_4 (see Table 11-4).

3. Having made the prescribed horizontal and vertical moves, repeat the procedure outlined in steps 1 and 2. For the example, this

* For an alternative method of evaluation of these cells, see Appendix 11A.

now gives cells S_2D_3 and S_1D_3 respectively; accordingly, one moves from ① at S_2D_4 to ① at S_1D_3 by way of ③ at S_2D_3.

4. Continue in this manner, moving from one circled number to another by, first, a horizontal move and, then, a vertical move until, by only a horizontal move, that column is reached in which the cell being evaluated is located. (The fewest steps possible should be used in this circumambulatory procedure). Thus, to continue the example, this step is from ① at S_1D_3 to ③ at S_1D_1.

5. Finally, move to the cell being evaluated (here, S_3D_1). This completes the path necessary to evaluate the given cell. (Note: For the purposes of evaluation, the path ends, rather than starts, with the cell being evaluated.)

6. Form the sum, with alternate plus and minus signs, of the unit costs associated with the cells being traversed (these unit costs are given in Table 11-2). This is the (noncircled) evaluation to be entered into the appropriate cell in Table 11-4. Thus, for the example, one has for the evaluation of cell S_3D_1:

Path (Table 11-4)	S_3D_4	S_2D_4	S_2D_3	S_1D_3	S_1D_1	S_3D_1
Unit cost (Table 11-2)	-10	-30	-8	-5	-10	-1
Evaluation (S_3D_1)	$+ (-10) - (-30) + (-8) - (-5) + (-10) - (-1) = +8$					

Accordingly, one enters $+8$ in cell S_3D_1 of Table 11-4.

7. Repeat the procedure outlined until all cells not containing circled numbers are evaluated.

Iterative Procedure Toward an Optimum Solution

Having completed the evaluation, one can now determine whether or not an optimal solution has been achieved. *If the noncircled numbers (the evaluations) are all nonnegative, then an optimum has been achieved.* If one or more noncircled numbers are negative, then further improvement with respect to the objective function is possible * (e.g., the negative numbers in S_1D_4, S_2D_2, etc., in Table 11-4).

This improvement is obtained by an iterative procedure in which

---

* At this stage, it should be quite apparent that one must be careful to circle the values of X_{ij} obtained in a feasible solution in order to distinguish them from the "evaluation" numbers which are also in the same table.

one proceeds as follows: 1. Of the one or more negative values which appear, select the most negative one,* e.g., $-N$. 2. Retrace the path used to obtain this most negative value. 3. Select those circled values which were preceded by a *plus* sign in the alternation between plus and minus and, of these, choose the one with the *smallest* value * written in its circle, e.g., m. 4. One is now ready to form a new table, wherein one replaces the most negative value, $-N$, by this smallest value, m. 5. Circle the number m and then enter all the *other* circles (except the one which contained the value m in the previous program) in their previous cells, but *without* any numbers inside.†

TABLE 11-5a

Origins \ Destinations	D_1	D_2	D_3	D_4	D_5	Total
S_1	◯	◯	◯	①		9
S_2			◯			4
S_3				◯	◯	8
Total	3	5	4	6	3	21

Thus, in Table 11-4 the most negative number ‡ is -18 and appears in both cells S_1D_4 and S_2D_5 (i.e., $-N = -18$). For such ties, one may arbitrarily select either of the cells containing this most negative number. Here, cell S_1D_4 is chosen. Retracing the path used to obtain the "-18" value in cell S_1D_4, one obtains, symbolically, $+S_1D_3$, $-S_2D_3$, $+S_2D_4$. Of those preceded by a plus sign, namely S_1D_3 and

---

* If there is more than one such value, any one of these may be selected arbitrarily.

† *The improvement in cost from one program to the next will then be equal to mN.*

‡ In practice, one need not select the most negative number. It is permissible, and sometimes advantageous, to select the *first* negative number which appears. Since the improvement from one program to the next is given by mN, a study of Table 11-4 shows that selections of S_2D_1, S_2D_2, S_2D_5, or S_1D_5 would have resulted in improvements of 33, 39, 18, and 11 respectively, as compared with the improvement of 18 resulting from the selection of S_1D_4. Another alternative is to examine all products, mN, and select that negative numbered cell which results in the greatest improvement, in this case, S_2D_5.

S_2D_4, both have the circled value ① in their cells. Consequently, either one of these may be chosen as the circled value to be moved. In this case, cell S_2D_4 is arbitrarily chosen. The circled value ① is

TABLE 11-5*b*.   SECOND FEASIBLE SOLUTION: $C = 233$

Origins \ Destinations	D_1	D_2	D_3	D_4	D_5	Total
S_1	③	⑤	⓪	①	7	9
S_2	-11	$\boxed{-13}$	④	18	0	4
S_3	-10	-1	1	⑤	③	8
Total	3	5	4	6	3	21

TABLE 11-6.   THIRD FEASIBLE SOLUTION: $C = 181$

Origins \ Destinations	D_1	D_2	D_3	D_4	D_5	Total
S_1	③	①	④	①	7	9
S_2	2	④	13	31	13	4
S_3	$\boxed{-10}$	-1	1	⑤	③	8
Total	3	5	4	6	3	21

then entered into cell S_1D_4 (see Table 11-5*a*), i.e., that cell where $\boxed{-18}$ appeared in Table 11-4.* The other circles (without numbers) are then entered in the same positions as before (see Table 11-5*a*).

---

* Therefore, the improvement over the program given in Table 11-4 will be $1 \times 18 = 18$ cost units. That is, the next program (Table 11-5*b*) will cost $251 - 18 = 233$ cost units.

A new feasible solution is obtained by filling in the circles according to the given surplus-deficiency (input-output) specifications. This solution is given by the circled values in Table 11-5*b*. The program is then evaluated, as before, and negative (noncircled) numbers still

TABLE 11-7. FOURTH FEASIBLE SOLUTION: $C = 151$

Origins \ Destinations	D_1	D_2	D_3	D_4	D_5	Total
S_1	10	①	④	④	7	9
S_2	12	④	13	31	13	4
S_3	③	⌐−1⌐	1	②	③	8
Total	3	5	4	6	3	21

TABLE 11-8. OPTIMUM FEASIBLE SOLUTION: $C = 150$

Origins \ Destinations	D_1	D_2	D_3	D_4	D_5	Total
S_1	10	1	④	⑤	7	9
S_2	11	④	12	30	12	4
S_3	③	①	1	①	③	8
Total	3	5	4	6	3	21

appear. Accordingly, the process is successively repeated (Tables 11-6, 11-7, and 11-8) until, finally, in Table 11-8 the evaluation of the corresponding program given therein results in all (noncircled) numbers being nonnegative. Here, then, an optimal feasible solution, or program, has been reached.

Thus the optimal set of movement orders which makes the total cost of movement of the empty freight cars a minimum is given in Table 11-8. Furthermore, this minimum total cost is $150 as compared with $251 for the original feasible (but obviously nonoptimal) program.

Alternate Optimal Programs

In closing the discussion of the transportation technique, it might be well to add that in many problems (contrary to the one just discussed) alternate optimal programs may exist. If any of the evaluation numbers in the optimum tableau are zero, then alternate optimal tableaux exist. These alternate optimal solutions are obtained by essentially the same procedure as that which was just given. The only variation is that the zeros (if any) which appear in the optimal feasible solutions are now treated in exactly the same manner as were the negative values.*

TABLE 11-9.   UNIT COST MATRIX

Origins \ Destinations	D_1	D_2	D_3	D_4	D_5	Total
S_1	-2	-1	-4	-3	0	5
S_2	$+1$	-3	-5	-2	-1	7
S_3	-1	-4	-3	-2	-1	6
Total	2	2	5	4	5	18

Furthermore, given such alternate optimal programs, say $\{P_1\}$, $\{P_2\}$, $\cdots$, $\{P_n\}$, where $\{P_n\}$ refers to the set of X_{ij} which form the nth optimal program, then †

$$\{P_{n+1}\} = a_1\{P_1\} + a_2\{P_2\} + \cdots + a_n\{P_n\}$$

* Alternate optimal programs are important in that they provide the programmer with a wider selection of "best" choices and offer him the opportunity to consider secondary objectives as well.

† This equation simply states that, first, every element of a matrix is multiplied by the corresponding constant, and that, second, corresponding elements are then added to form a new matrix which, incidentally, will contain the same number of rows and columns as the old ones.

Linear Programming

is also an optimal program * *provided* the a_i are nonnegative constants such that

$$\sum_{i=1}^{n} a_i = a_1 + a_2 + a_3 + \cdots + a_n = 1$$

For example, the cost minimization problem represented by Table 11-9 has two optimum programs, namely those given in Tables 11-10 and 11-11. Table 11-11 is obtained from Table 11-10 (and vice versa)

TABLE 11-10. OPTIMUM PROGRAM FOR TABLE 11-9

Origins \ Destinations	D_1	D_2	D_3	D_4	D_5	Total
S_1	4	②	2	2	③	5
S_2	②	1	2	③	②	7
S_3	2	2	⑤	①	0	6
Total	2	2	5	4	5	18

TABLE 11-11. ALTERNATE OPTIMUM PROGRAM FOR TABLE 11-9

Origins \ Destinations	D_1	D_2	D_3	D_4	D_5	Total
S_1	4	②	2	2	③	5
S_2	②	1	2	④	①	7
S_3	2	2	⑤	0	①	6
Total	2	2	5	4	5	18

* The former optimal programs are called *basic* optimal programs while those just obtained by using the a_i's are called *derived* optimal programs.

by treating the zero in cell S_3D_5 of Table 11-10 (or cell S_3D_4 of Table 11-11) as the "most negative number" and proceeding as before.

An infinite number of *derived* optimal programs can now be obtained by forming what are called *"convex linear combinations"* of the two *basic* optimum programs. Thus, if we select two positive fractions whose sum is unity, e.g., $\frac{1}{4}$ and $\frac{3}{4}$, we can obtain a new optimal program by multiplying every element of the first program by $\frac{1}{4}$ and every element of the second program by $\frac{3}{4}$ and then adding corresponding cells.

TABLE 11-11a

$\frac{1}{4}$ Table 11-10 =

Origins ╲ Destinations	D_1	D_2	D_3	D_4	D_5	Total
S_1		$\left(\frac{1}{2}\right)$			$\left(\frac{3}{4}\right)$	5
S_2	$\left(\frac{1}{2}\right)$			$\left(\frac{3}{4}\right)$	$\left(\frac{1}{2}\right)$	7
S_3			$\left(\frac{5}{4}\right)$	$\left(\frac{1}{4}\right)$		6
Total	2	2	5	4	5	18

TABLE 11-11b

$\frac{3}{4}$ Table 11-11 =

Origins ╲ Destinations	D_1	D_2	D_3	D_4	D_5	Total
S_1		$\left(\frac{3}{2}\right)$			$\left(\frac{9}{4}\right)$	5
S_2	$\left(\frac{3}{2}\right)$			(3)	$\left(\frac{3}{4}\right)$	7
S_3			$\left(\frac{15}{4}\right)$		$\left(\frac{3}{4}\right)$	6
Total	2	2	5	4	5	18

This yields the derived optimum program of Table 11-12 and is obtained as shown in Tables 11-11a and b. Similarly, other optimum programs could be derived for other nonnegative fractions whose sum is equal to 1.*

TABLE 11-12. A Derived Optimum Program:
$\frac{1}{4}$ Table 11-10 + $\frac{3}{4}$ Table 11-11

Origins \ Destinations	D_1	D_2	D_3	D_4	D_5	Total
S_1		②			③	5
S_2	②			③¾	⑤⁄₄	7
S_3			⑤	①⁄₄	③⁄₄	6
Total	2	2	5	4	5	18

Observations on the Transportation Technique

Although the exposition just given treats only a (linear) minimization problem, it should be obvious that the transportation technique is equally applicable to (linear) maximization problems. The only difference in solving maximization problems lies in the preparation of the "profit" matrix. Whereas in the minimization problem all costs are entered with a negative sign, here all profits (or whatever units are involved in the maximization problem) are entered without any modification of signs. Once the initial datum matrix is obtained, one proceeds to the solution exactly as previously outlined and illustrated.

Secondly, it should be noted that many variations exist on the transportation technique. One such variation is discussed in Appendix 11A. Other variations have already been cited in the text. A further variation that may decrease the number of iterations involves a re-

---

* It should be noted that, in general, derived optimal programs will involve fractional answers. Obviously, these programs are for use only where nonintegral answers are realistic.

arrangement of the cost matrix; using the problem cited in Tables 11-1 and 11-2, this may be illustrated as follows:

1. Form a new matrix in which the first row and first column correspond to the cell yielding the least cost. In the example, this is S_3D_1. Enter the totals of 8 for S_3 and 3 for D_1 in the new matrix. Place the smallest of these two numbers in that cell, S_3D_1.

	D_1					Totals
S_3	3					8
Totals	3					

2. This satisfies the requirement for D_1, but still leaves 5 units available at S_3. Hence, select the next least unit cost which involves S_3. In our example, this is -4 in cell S_3D_5. Therefore, list D_5 in the second column and enter the corresponding total (requirement) of 3. Comparing the requirement of 3 units at D_5 with the remaining availability of 5 units at S_3, we assign 3 units to cell S_3D_5.

	D_1	D_5				Totals
S_3	3	3				8
Totals	3	3				

3. Since 2 units are still available at S_3, select the third highest cost, namely -7 in S_3D_3. Enter D_3 in the third column along with its total requirement of 4 units. Comparing the requirement of 4 units

	D_1	D_5	D_3			Totals
S_3	3	3	2			8
Totals	3	3	4			

at D_3 with the remaining availability of 2 $(8-3-3)$ units at S_3, we assign 2 units to cell S_3D_3, thereby using all available units at S_3 but leaving 2 units still to be assigned to D_3.

4. Comparing the costs associated with D_3 $(C_{13} = -5$ and $C_{23} = -8)$, we select S_1 as the entry for the second row and, with it, enter the availability at S_1, namely 9.

	D_1	D_5	D_3			Totals
S_3	3	3	2			8
S_1						9
Totals	3	3	4			

Comparing this availability at S_1 (i.e., 9) with the remaining requirement at D_3 (i.e., $2 = 4 - 2$), we enter 2 units in cell S_1D_3, thereby satisfying the requirement at D_3.

5. Proceeding in this fashion, the following matrix is obtained:

	D_1	D_5	D_3	D_4	D_2	Totals
S_3	3	3	2			8
S_1			2	6	1	9
S_2					4	4
Totals	3	3	4	6	5	21

The cost for this initial feasible solution is given by

$$3(-1) + 3(-4) + 2(-7) + 2(-5) + 6(-9) + 1(-20) + 4(-10)$$

i.e., neglecting the minus sign which indicates cost,

$$\text{T.C.} = \$153$$

as compared with the first feasible solution of \$251 obtained by the Northwest Corner Rule (and with the optimum solution of \$150). Such a reshuffling of the cost matrix * generally leads to a better (i.e., lower cost or higher profit) first feasible solution so that the optimum solution is usually reached after a smaller number of alterations.

Finally,† it might be well to observe that the transportation technique: 1. can be used to determine opportunity costs associated with deviations from indicated optimal programs, and 2. does not require any complex mathematics; rather, it requires only addition, subtraction, and multiplication. This means that clerical assistance can readily be employed in solving problems of a much larger scope and, consequently, it is to be expected that the transportation technique will be increasingly applied to problems in many disciplines and fields of endeavor.

---

* The reader should note that this first feasible solution costing \$153 could have been obtained without reshuffling the matrix. One simply starts in the cell of lowest cost (here, S_3D_1) and proceeds accordingly.

† For further reading on the transportation technique, including a discussion of so-called degenerate cases, the reader is referred to ref. 8. The mathematical derivation of the transportation technique is given in ref. 29, Chap. 23.

GENERAL LINEAR PROGRAMMING PROBLEM

In the first part of this chapter, a member of a class of optimization problems was solved by the transportation technique. In this part, the general linear programming problem will be considered and, with it, a general technique of arriving at optimal solutions, or programs,* for these problems will be presented. The technique referred to was formulated only recently by G. B. Dantzig [10] and is called the *simplex technique*.†

Briefly, the simplex technique is one which is applicable to problems of optimizing a linear function subject to restrictions which are in the form of linear inequalities. As in the case of the transportation technique, the simplex technique will be presented by means of a specific example. Before proceeding to this example, however, some pertinent symbols and concepts will be discussed.

Mathematical Symbols and Notations

First of all, it might be well to illustrate the difference between an *equation* and an *inequation*. An equation, such as $y = 2x$, represents,

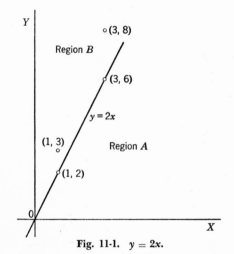

Fig. 11-1. $y = 2x$.

geometrically, a straight line of "slope" 2; see Fig. 11-1. It is a simple and concise way of saying, "We have a relationship between two

---

* The direct result is an optimal *allocation*, not an optimal schedule.

† The mathematical derivation of the simplex technique will not be discussed here. It can be found in ref. 29, Chap. 21.

variables, x and y, such that, given any value of x, the value of y is twice as large." Furthermore, any point whose abscissa x and ordinate y satisfy this *linear* relationship, $y = 2x$, will lie on this line. For example, the point whose (rectangular Cartesian) co-ordinates are given by $x = 1$, $y = 2$ [written as (1,2)] and the point (3,6) are points lying on this line and, hence, are *solutions* of the given equation.*
Conversely, any point, such as (1,3) and (3,8), which does not lie on the given straight line does not satisfy the corresponding equation or functional relationship.

An inequation is represented by one of four different symbols, depending on the desired interpretation. These symbols are $<$, $>$, $\leq$ or $\leqq$, and $\geq$ or $\geqq$. $<$ indicates that the value of the variable on the left is less than the value of the variable on the right. Thus, $y < 2x$ means that, for any given value of x, y will be *less than* twice that given value of x. This inequation is satisfied by any point which lies within region A of Fig. 11-1; i.e., the co-ordinates of any point (x,y) in region A (*not* including the boundary line $y = 2x$) are such that its ordinate y is less than two times the value of its abscissa x. Similarly, $y > 2x$ implies that, for any given value of x, y assumes a value *greater than* two times that of x. This is represented geometrically by all points in region B (*not* including the line $y = 2x$).

Still more general are the other notations, $\leq$ and $\geq$. $\leq$, or equivalently $\leqq$, means that the value of the variable on the left is *less than or equal to* the value of the variable on the right. Thus, $y \leq 2x$ means that for a given value of x, y is less than or equal to two times that value of x. Another way of saying this is that the value y is *at most* equal to two times the value of x. Geometrically, this inequation, $y \leq 2x$, is represented by any and all points in region A *and* on the straight line $y = 2x$. Finally, $y \geq 2x$, or equivalently $y \geqq 2x$, means that the value of y is *greater than or equal to* two times the value of x and is represented geometrically by any and all points in region B and on the straight line $y = 2x$.

Hence, the inequalities $y \leq 2x$ and $y \geq 2x$ also preserve the equality $y = 2x$ in that any solution of the latter is automatically a solution of either (and both) of the former. Conversely, however, a solution of, say, $y \geq 2x$, need not be a solution of $y = 2x$. Thus, while points (1,6) and (3,8) (and infinitely many others) are solutions of $y \geq 2x$, they are *not* solutions of $y = 2x$. See Fig. 11-1.

---

* When one speaks of the point (x,y), one really means the point whose co-ordinates are x and y, where in a rectangular Cartesian co-ordinate system, for example, the first named is the abscissa and the latter is the ordinate.

As another example, consider the system of three inequations

$$x - 5 \geq 0$$

$$y - 2 \geq 0$$

$$-6x - 8y + 120 \geq 0$$

Geometrically, the solutions to this system of inequations are represented by the (closed) set of points lying on and in the triangle ABC of Fig. 11-2. That is, there exists an infinite number of solutions to

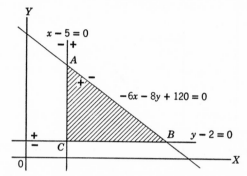

Fig. 11-2. Region bounded by three straight lines.

this system of inequations. On the other hand, the corresponding system of equations

$$x - 5 = 0$$

$$y - 2 = 0$$

$$-6x - 8y + 120 = 0$$

has *no* solutions. (In order for a solution to exist, all three straight lines would have to intersect in a common point such as do the three lines of Fig. 11-3.)

Thus, by means of the foregoing examples, it is easily seen that an equation (or system of equations) is much more restrictive than a corresponding inequation (or system of inequations).* Conversely, it is seen that the inequation permits a much greater freedom in that solutions of the equation, if any, are but a special subset of all the solutions of the inequation. This difference is very important in many problems of business and industry. These problems will usually con-

---

* From this point forth, inequalities will refer only to the symbols $\leq$ and $\geq$. No more mention will be made of $<$ and $>$.

tain restrictions such as, "The variation in size must be *no greater than* 0.002 inch from the specification," ". . . produce at least *as much as* . . . ," "deliver these amounts *within* the specified time period," ". . . cost *no more than* . . . ," and the like. These restrictions are inequations; i.e., they set upper or lower bounds, not exact bounds. Any improper interpretation of these restrictions, either in the literary or mathematical formulation of the problem, which transforms a system of inequalities into a system of equalities immediately removes

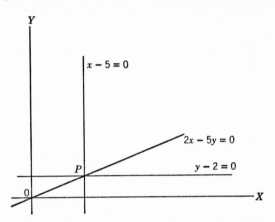

Fig. 11-3. Solution of three linear equations as point of intersection.

vast areas of possible solutions and, as indicated in the second example just given, might even lead to failure to determine any solution whatsoever, even though one or more properly exist. Furthermore, even if one is able to determine a so-called optimal solution for the system of equalities, there may exist many solutions of the true system (of inequalities) which are better in terms of optimizing the given objective. On the other hand, in contrast to equalities, systems of inequalities will admit optimal solutions which do not lie on the line as well as any which do lie on the line. Consequently, it is important that one always determine the true restrictional relationships in order to avoid misleading and costly results.

Another symbol which will be used is the summation symbol Σ. If one has an expression such as

$$X_1 + X_2 + X_3 + X_4 + X_5 + X_6 + X_7$$

this may, first of all, be shortened by use of intermediate dots, as follows

$$X_1 + X_2 + \cdots + X_7$$

However, a still more compact "shorthand" is given by $\sum\limits_{j=1}^{7} X_j$ where

$$\sum_{j=1}^{7} X_j = X_1 + X_2 + \cdots + X_7$$

This symbol, the Greek letter capital sigma, is especially convenient for denoting infinite series. For example, the infinite series

$$1 + \tfrac{1}{2} + \tfrac{1}{4} + \tfrac{1}{8} + \tfrac{1}{16} + \tfrac{1}{32} + \cdots$$

(which, incidentally, adds up to the value 2) can be written more compactly as

$$\sum_{n=0}^{\infty} \frac{1}{2^n}$$

Finally, double subscripts will also be used, such as X_{ij}. The use of double subscripts arises quite naturally from one's desire and need to be able to locate and refer to numbers (or *elements*) in a rectangular chart (or *matrix*) in a simple manner. Thus, if one considers the matrix

Column Row	C_1	C_2	C_3	C_4
R_1	1	2	4	7
R_2	-3	6	1	0
R_3	-2	-1	0	3

then X_{12} refers to the element which lies in the first row and second column, namely 2. More generally, for any rectangular matrix, the matrix itself will be denoted by $\{X_{ij}\}$ and X_{ij} will refer to the particular element in the ith row and the jth column of the matrix.

With these mathematical notations in mind, let us now return to the general problem of solving systems of simultaneous equations or inequations and, in turn, selecting from among the alternative solutions the best (optimal) one(s) in terms of the stated objective. In particular, let us now see how the second of the two techniques, namely the simplex technique, is designed to handle the general linear programming problem.

THE SIMPLEX TECHNIQUE

To illustrate the simplex technique, let us consider the following relatively simple example: A manufacturer wishes to maximize the profits associated with producing two products, R and S. Products R and S are manufactured by a 2-stage process in which all initial operations are performed in machine center I and all final operations may be performed in either machine center IIA or in machine center * IIB. Machine centers IIA and IIB are different from each other in the sense that, in general, for any given product they yield different unit rates and different unit profits. For this example, let us also assume that a certain amount of overtime has been made available in machine center IIA for the manufacture of products R and S. Since the use of overtime results in changes (decreases) in unit profits (but not in unit rates), let us denote separately, by machine center IIAA, any overtime use of machine center IIA.

The unit times required to manufacture products R and S, the hours available in each machine center, and the unit profits are given in Table 11-13. Also, to simplify the discussion which follows, in this

TABLE 11-13

Operation	Machine Center	Product R			Product S			Hours Available
		R_1	R_2	R_3	S_1	S_2	S_3	
1	I	0.01	0.01	0.01	0.03	0.03	0.03	850
	IIA	0.02			0.05			700
2	IIAA		0.02			0.05		100
	IIB			0.03			0.08	900
Profit per part (in dollars)		0.40	0.28	0.32	0.72	0.64	0.60	

table R_1, R_2, and R_3 are introduced to denote the three possible combinations for producing R, and similarly, S_1, S_2, and S_3 are defined for product S.

To repeat, then, the problem is to determine how much of each product should be made through the use of each possible combination of machine centers so as to maximize the total profits, keeping in mind the prescribed limitations on the capacities of the machine centers.†

* Here a machine center means a group of machines, not necessarily of the same make, but such as may be logically grouped for the problem and analysis which follows.

† The assumption here is that one can sell all that one can produce. This is a simplification which may be removed very easily by imposing additional restrictions in the form of maximum permissible quantities of each product.

Let us now rephrase the problem in mathematical form. If X_1, X_2, X_3, X_4, X_5, X_6 denote the amounts to be made of products R_1, R_2, R_3, S_1, S_2, S_3 respectively, then the total profit Z will be given by (see Table 11-13)

$$Z = 0.40X_1 + 0.28X_2 + 0.32X_3 + 0.72X_4 + 0.64X_5 + 0.60X_6 \quad (1)$$

Furthermore, the restrictions to the problem will be given by

$$0.01X_1 + 0.01X_2 + 0.01X_3 + 0.03X_4 + 0.03X_5 + 0.03X_6 \leqq 850$$
$$0.02X_1 + 0.05X_4 \leqq 700$$
$$0.02X_2 + 0.05X_5 \leqq 100 \quad (2)$$
$$0.03X_3 + 0.08X_6 \leqq 900$$

(These restrictions simply state that the sum of the times required to manufacture products R and S in each machine center must not exceed the total time available in that machine center.)

The problem may now be restated as follows: * Determine the values of $X_j \geqq 0$ (where $j = 1, 2, \cdots, 6$) which <u>maximize</u>

$$Z = 0.40X_1 + 0.28X_2 + 0.32X_3 + 0.72X_4 + 0.64X_5 + 0.60X_6 \quad (1)$$

subject to the restrictions

$$0.01X_1 + 0.01X_2 + 0.01X_3 + 0.03X_4 + 0.03X_5 + 0.03X_6 \leqq 850$$
$$0.02X_1 + 0.05X_4 \leqq 700$$
$$0.02X_2 + 0.05X_5 \leqq 100 \quad (2)$$
$$0.03X_3 + 0.08X_6 \leqq 900$$

Next, to proceed toward a simplex technique solution, the system of *inequations* 2 is reduced to an equivalent system of *equations* by introducing new <u>*nonnegative*</u> variables X_7, X_8, X_9, X_{10} so that

$$0.01X_1 + 0.01X_2 + 0.01X_3 + 0.03X_4$$
$$+ 0.03X_5 + 0.03X_6 + X_7 = 850$$
$$0.02X_1 + 0.05X_4 + X_8 = 700 \quad (3)$$
$$0.02X_2 + 0.05X_5 + X_9 = 100$$
$$0.03X_3 + 0.08X_6 + X_{10} = 900$$

---

* The restrictions $X_j \geqq 0$, $j = 1, 2, \cdots, 6$ arise from the fact that, since the manufacturing process is irreversible, one must preclude the appearance of negative values for these variables.

These new variables, X_7, X_8, X_9, and X_{10}, are variously called "disposal activities," "pseudo variables," or "slack variables." In this problem, it can be seen that *positive* values of these slack variables represent underutilization of capacity in machine centers I, IIA, IIAA, and IIB respectively.

To complete the transformation of the present set of equations (1 and 3) into the standard form used in the simplex technique, and also to achieve a much desired compactness, a final set of transformations is now made. Suppose that one were to rearrange eqs. 3 so that corresponding X_j's appear in the same column. Then, treating all blanks as zeros, one would have for X_1, for example, the column of coefficients: 0.01, 0.02, 0, 0, reading from top to bottom. The final set of transformations is that which lets the symbol P_j denote the column of coefficients of X_j $(j = 1, 2, \cdots, 10)$, and P_0 denote the right-hand column of numbers in the system of eqs. 3.*

Furthermore, the P_j's (and P_0) are such that multiplication of P_j (or P_0) by a real number means that each component of the column is to be multiplied by that real number. Thus, referring back to the coefficients of X_1

$$X_1 P_1 = X_1 \begin{pmatrix} 0.01 \\ 0.02 \\ 0 \\ 0 \end{pmatrix} = \begin{pmatrix} 0.01X_1 \\ 0.02X_1 \\ 0 \\ 0 \end{pmatrix} \tag{4}$$

Finally, if P_1 and P_2 are two such "vectors," then

$$X_1 P_1 + X_2 P_2 = X_2 P_2 + X_1 P_1 \tag{5}$$

Our linear programming problem may now be restated using the symbols P_j as follows: Determine the values of a set of nonnegative X_j (where $j = 1, 2, \cdots, 10$) which maximize the linear form (functional) †

$$Z = 0.40X_1 + 0.28X_2 + 0.32X_3 + 0.72X_4 + 0.64X_5$$
$$+ 0.60X_6 + 0 \cdot X_7 + 0 \cdot X_8 + 0 \cdot X_9 + 0 \cdot X_{10} \tag{1a}$$

subject to the restrictions

$$\sum_{j=1}^{10} X_j P_j = P_0 \tag{3a}$$

---

* That is, the P_j's and P_0 are *vectors* in, for this problem, a 4-dimensional space, the dimensionality of the space being determined by the number of restrictions to the problem.

† Here, we are assuming a zero profit or cost associated with each slack variable X_7, X_8, X_9, and X_{10}.

With the statement of the problem in this form, we are now ready to carry out its solution by means of the simplex technique.* The first step consists of exhibiting the column vectors P_j in a systematic form. This is done in Table 11-14 by means of eqs. 3, all blank spaces in the table representing zeros.

TABLE 11-14

P_1	P_2	P_3	P_4	P_5	P_6	P_7	P_8	P_9	P_{10}	P_0
0.01	0.01	0.01	0.03	0.03	0.03	1				850
0.02			0.05				1			700
	0.02			0.05				1		100
		0.03			0.08				1	900

It should be noted that eqs. 3 can be generated simply by multiplying each coefficient in any P_j column by the corresponding X_j and then reading across the rows. (The heavy vertical line shows where to place the equal signs.) Also, the square submatrix formed by $\{P_7, P_8, P_9, P_{10}\}$ which consists of elements which are equal to 1 on the main diagonal and which are everywhere else equal to zero is of special importance. This matrix is called the *unit* or *identity* matrix. The set of vectors which form the identity matrix are, in turn, said to be a *unit basis* of the particular space of interest, which is, in this problem, a 4-dimensional space.†

For the simplex calculational procedure which follows, these columns are now rearranged as shown in Table 11-15a. Then, a column labeled "Basis" is inserted to the left of the P_0 column and, in this column,

* Actually, by means of the *dual* theorem of linear programming, one has a choice of two problems to solve instead of just one. This is because every linear programming problem has a dual problem such that one involves maximizing a linear function, say Z, and the other involves minimizing a linear function, say g, and $Z_{max} = g_{min}$. For further discussion of the dual problem of linear programming, see Appendix 11C, and also refs. 4 and 29.

† The basis vectors are linearly independent vectors in terms of which every point in the n-dimensional (here, $n = 4$) space may be uniquely expressed and in terms of which a solution (or solutions) will be stated.

TABLE 11-15a

c_i \ c_j							0.40	0.28	0.32	0.72	0.64	0.60
	Basis	P_0	P_7	P_8	P_9	P_{10}	P_1	P_2	P_3	P_4	P_5	P_6
	P_7	850	1				0.01	0.01	0.01	0.03	0.03	0.03
	P_8	700		1			0.02	0.02		[0.05]	0.05	
	P_9	100			1							
	P_{10}	900				1			0.03			0.08
	Z_j											
	$Z_j - C_j$						−0.40	−0.28	−0.32	−0.72*	−0.64	−0.60

TABLE 11-15b

c_i \ c_j							0.40	0.28	0.32	0.72	0.64	0.60
	Basis	P_0	P_7	P_8	P_9	P_{10}	P_1	P_2	P_3	P_4	P_5	P_6
	P_7	430	1	−0.6			−0.002	0.01	0.01		0.03	0.03
0.72	P_4	14,000		20			0.4	0.02		1		
	P_9	100			1							
	P_{10}	900				1			0.03		[0.05]	0.08
	Z_j	10,080		14.4			0.288					
	$Z_j - C_j$	10,080		14.4			−0.112	−0.28	−0.32		−0.64*	−0.60

TABLE 11-15c

C_i \ C_j							0.40	0.28	0.32	0.72	0.64	0.60
	Basis	P_0	P_7	P_8	P_9	P_{10}	P_1	P_2	P_3	P_4	P_5	P_6
0.72	P_7	370	1	−0.6	−0.6		−0.002	−0.002	0.01			0.03
0.64	P_4	14,000		20	20		0.4	0.4		1		
	P_5	2,000							0.03		1	0.08
	P_{10}	900				1						
	$Z_j - C_j$	11,360		14.4	12.8		−0.112	−0.024	−0.32			−0.60*

TABLE 11-15d

							0.40	0.28	0.32	0.72	0.64	0.60
		P_0	P_7	P_8	P_9	P_{10}	P_1	P_2	P_3	P_4	P_5	P_6
0.72	P_7	32.5	1	−0.6	−0.6	$-\frac{3}{8}$	−0.002	−0.002	$-\frac{1}{800}$			
0.64	P_4	14,000		20	20					1		
	P_5	2,000				$12\frac{1}{2}$	0.4	0.4			1	
0.60	P_6	11,250							$\frac{3}{8}$			1
	$Z_j - C_j$	18.110		14.4	12.8	$7\frac{1}{2}$	−0.112*	−0.024	−0.095			

TABLE 11-15e

$C_j \backslash C_i$	Basis	P_0	P_7	P_8	P_9	P_{10}	P_1 (0.40)	P_2 (0.28)	P_3 (0.32)	P_4 (0.72)	P_5 (0.64)	P_6 (0.60)
	P_7	102.5	1	$-\frac{1}{2}$	-0.6	$-\frac{3}{8}$		-0.002	$-\frac{1}{800}$	0.005		
0.40	P_1	35,000		50	20		1	0.4		$\frac{5}{8}$		
0.64	P_5	2,000			20	$\frac{100}{8}$					1	
0.60	P_6	11,250							$\boxed{\frac{3}{8}}$			1
	$Z_j - C_j$	22,030		20	12.8	$7\frac{1}{2}$		-0.024	-0.095^{*}	0.28		

↑　↓

TABLE 11-15f

$C_j \backslash C_i$	Basis	P_0	P_7	P_8	P_9	P_{10}	P_1 (0.40)	P_2 (0.28)	P_3 (0.32)	P_4 (0.72)	P_5 (0.64)	P_6 (0.60)
0.40	P_7	140	1	$-\frac{1}{2}$	-0.6	$-\frac{1}{3}$	1	-0.002		0.005		$\frac{1}{300}$
0.64	P_1	35,000		50	20			$\boxed{0.4}$		$\frac{5}{8}$	1	
0.32	P_5	2,000										
	P_3	30,000				$\frac{100}{3}$			1			$\frac{8}{3}$
	$Z_j - C_j$	24,880		20	12.8	$3\frac{2}{3}$		-0.024^{*}		0.28		$0.25\frac{1}{3}$

↓　↑

TABLE 11-15g. MAXIMUM FEASIBLE SOLUTION

c_i \ c_j							0.40	0.28	0.32	0.72	0.64	0.60
	Basis	P_0	P_7	P_8	P_9	P_{10}	P_1	P_2	P_3	P_4	P_5	P_6
	P_7	150	1	$-\frac{1}{2}$	$-\frac{1}{2}$	$-\frac{1}{3}$				$\frac{1}{200}$	$\frac{1}{200}$	$\frac{1}{300}$
0.40	P_1	35,000		50	50		1			$\frac{5}{2}$		
0.28	P_2	5,000				$\frac{100}{3}$		1			$\frac{5}{2}$	
0.32	P_3	30,000							1			$\frac{8}{3}$
	$Z_j - C_j$	25,000		20	14	$10\frac{2}{3}$				0.28	0.06	$0.25\frac{1}{3}$

the basis vectors are listed.*   Next, a row of C_j's are added, where the C_j's are defined as the coefficients of the corresponding X_j's in the expression for Z given in eq. 1.   Then, a column of C_i's are added, these corresponding to the C_j's, but having the subscript i to denote the row, rather than the subscript j which is used to denote the column. The expression for Z can now be written as

$$Z = \sum_{j=1}^{10} C_j X_j \tag{6}$$

Having entered the equations and the C_j's into the table, we now add a row of numbers labeled Z_j, where j denotes the appropriate column. These Z_j's are determined as follows.   Letting X_{ij} denote the element in the ith row and jth column of the table, then the Z_j's (including Z_0) are defined by

$$Z_j = \sum_i C_i X_{ij} \tag{7}$$

Finally, a row labeled $Z_j - C_j$ is entered into the table and for any column, say j_0, consists of the corresponding C_{j_0} subtracted from the value of Z_{j_0} which was entered in the previous row.

This completes the listing process (Table 11-15a) and constitutes the first full set of calculations.   In the terminology of the earlier discussion, one now has a *feasible* solution to the problem, where this solution is given by the column vector P_0 in terms of the basis vectors P_7, P_8, P_9, P_{10}, namely

$$X_7 = 850; \qquad X_8 = 700; \qquad X_9 = 100; \qquad X_{10} = 900 \tag{8}$$

That is, the initial feasible program consists of "Do not use any of the time available in any of the machine centers; i.e., do nothing," thus resulting in a net profit of $Z = 0$.

Optimum Solution Criteria

Having obtained a feasible program, the question immediately arises as to whether a more profitable program exists.   Accordingly, the following mutually exclusive and collectively exhaustive possibilities must be considered:

M1. Maximum $Z = \infty$ (i.e., maximum Z is infinitely large) and has been obtained by means of the present program.

---

* For this example, the slack vectors form the unit basis.   In some problems for which some of the restrictions are stated either in terms of equalities or in terms of inequalities which impose minimum limits, so-called artificial vectors will have to be introduced in order to form a unit basis (see ref. 4, pp. 15 ff.).   It should be noted also that structural vectors may be such that they may be included in the unit basis.

M2. Maximum Z is finite and has been obtained by means of the present program.

M3. An optimal program has not yet been achieved and a higher value of Z may be possible.

The simplex technique is such that possibilities M1 or M2 *must* be reached in a finite number of steps. Furthermore (remembering that X_{ij} denotes the element in the ith row and jth column of the table), the technique is such that, for a given tableau (i.e., table or matrix):

1. If there exist *any* $Z_j - C_j < 0$, then either M1 or M3 holds.

   a. If all $X_{ij} \leq 0$ in that column (for which $Z_j - C_j < 0$), then M1 is true.
   b. If some $X_{ij} > 0$, further calculations are required, i.e., M3 holds.

2. If *all* $Z_j - C_j \geq 0$, then a maximal Z has been obtained (M2).

Iterative Procedure to an Optimum Solution

In our example (Table 11-15a), $Z_1 - C_1 < 0$ (as are $Z_2 - C_2$ through $Z_6 - C_6$) and, furthermore, some of the coefficients under P_1 are greater than zero. Hence, by condition 1b, further calculations are required (i.e., condition M3 holds).

To discover new solutions, it is possible to proceed in a purely systematic fashion by the simplex technique. Furthermore, any new solution so obtained will never decrease the value of the objective functional (although an increase need not occur).*

The procedure is as follows: Of all the $Z_j - C_j < 0$, choose the most negative of these. (In the particular example, this is $Z_4 - C_4 = -0.72$ and is so indicated by an asterisk in Table 11-15a.) This determines a particular P_j (namely, P_4) which will be introduced into the column labeled "Basis" in Table 11-15b. To determine the vector which this P_j will replace, one first divides each of the positive X_{ij} appearing in the P_j column into the corresponding X_{i0} which appears in the same row under P_0.† The smallest of these ratios then determines the vector to be replaced. That is, in the present example, P_4 is to replace one of the vectors P_7, P_8, P_9, or P_{10}. Under P_4, there are two positive X_{ij}, namely $X_{7,4} = 0.03$ and $X_{8,4} = 0.05$. The division of these X_{ij} into the corresponding X_{i0}'s which appear under P_0 gives a minimum of 14,000 (i.e., 700/0.05). Thus, P_8 is the vector to be replaced by P_4,

---

* As stated earlier, the optimal solution, if one exists, must be reached in a finite number of steps. Hence, the simplex technique is a converging iterative procedure.

† Since the components of P_0 must all be nonnegative, these ratios must, in turn, all be nonnegative.

so that a new basis is formed consisting of the vectors P_7, P_4, P_9, and P_{10}.

If one now lets

Subscript k denote "coming in"

Subscript r denote "going out"

X_{ij}' denote the elements of the new matrix, and

$$\phi = \operatorname*{Min}_{i} \frac{X_{i0}}{X_{ik}}, \qquad X_{ik} > 0 \tag{9}$$

[i.e., ϕ is the minimum of all ratios (X_{i0}/X_{ik}) for $X_{ik} > 0$] then the elements of the new matrix (X_{ij}') are calculated as follows: for the elements of the row corresponding to the vector just entered into the unit basis

$$X_{kj}' = \frac{X_{rj}}{X_{rk}} \tag{10}$$

while the other elements (X_{ij}') of the new matrix are calculated by

$$X_{ij}' = X_{ij} - \left(\frac{X_{rj}}{X_{rk}}\right) X_{ik} \tag{11}$$

where eq. 11 also applies to the X_{i0}'s appearing under P_0 and to the $Z_j - C_j$ in the entire bottom row (but *not* to the Z_j's in the second last row).   Furthermore, the new value of the profit function will be given by *

$$Z_0' = Z_0 - \phi(Z_k - C_k) \tag{12}$$

or, since $C_0 = 0$, the profit function will be given by

$$(Z_0 - C_0)' = (Z_0 - C_0) - \phi(Z_k - C_k) \tag{13}$$

For example, starting with Table 11-15a and proceeding to Table 11-15b, the most negative $Z_j - C_j$ is $Z_4 - C_4 = -0.72$.   Therefore $k = 4$.   Hence, from eq. 9

$$\phi = \operatorname*{Min}_{i} \frac{X_{i0}}{X_{i4}} \quad \text{for all} \quad X_{i4} > 0$$

i.e.

$$\phi = \operatorname{Min} \left(\frac{850}{0.03} = 28,333; \frac{700}{0.05} = 14,000\right) = 14,000$$

Therefore, P_4 will replace P_8; or, in our equations, $k = 4, r = 8$.

---

* In other words, the improvement from one tableau to the next is given by $-\phi(Z_k - C_k)$.   Note the similarity between the improvement here and that obtained in the transportation technique.

The elements in the P_4 row of Table 11-15b are then computed by (see eq. 10)

$$X_{4j}' = \frac{X_{8j}}{X_{84}} = \left(\frac{X_{8j}}{0.05}\right)$$

Therefore

$$X_{40}' = \left(\frac{X_{80}}{0.05}\right) = \left(\frac{700}{0.05}\right) = 14,000$$

$$X_{41}' = \left(\frac{X_{81}}{0.05}\right) = \left(\frac{0.02}{0.05}\right) = 0.4, \text{ etc.}$$

For the elements of the other rows (where $k = 4$, $r = 8$ are substituted into eq. 11)

$$X_{ij}' = X_{ij} - \left(\frac{X_{8j}}{X_{84}}\right) X_{i4} = X_{ij} - \left(\frac{X_{8j}}{0.05}\right) X_{i4}$$

Therefore

$$X_{70}' = X_{70} - \left(\frac{X_{80}}{0.05}\right)(X_{74}) = 850 - \left(\frac{700}{0.05}\right)(0.03)$$

$$= 850 - (14,000)(0.03) = 850 - 420 = 430$$

and

$$(Z_1 - C_1)' = (Z_1 - C_1) - \left(\frac{X_{81}}{X_{84}}\right)(Z_4 - C_4)$$

$$= (-0.40) - \left(\frac{0.02}{0.05}\right)(-0.72)$$

$$= (-0.4) - (0.4)(-0.72) = -0.4 + 0.288 = -0.112$$

etc.

Finally, the new value of the profit functional will be given by

$$(Z_0 - C_0)' = (Z_0 - C_0) - \phi(Z_4 - C_4)$$

$$= 0 - 14,000(-0.72) = +10,080 \quad \checkmark$$

This procedure is carried out in Table 11-15. The process is then repeated until such time as either M1 or M2 holds. For the present example, the solution is obtained after six iterations, i.e., six tableaux or matrices after the first. The final tableau, Table 11-15g, yields the optimal solution.* This optimal solution is also stated, both in terms

---

* If any other optimum solutions existed, they would be indicated by $Z_j - C_j = 0$ for j's other than those appearing in the basis. Here, $Z_j - C_j = 0$ for $j = 1, 2, 3$ and 7 only. Hence no other optimum solutions exist.

of the number of parts and hours required, in Tables 11-16 and 11-17.*

TABLE 11-16. OPTIMUM PROGRAM (NUMBER OF PARTS)

Product R		Product S	
R_1 (Centers I–IIA)	35,000 parts	S_1	0 parts
R_2 (I–IIAA)	5,000 parts	S_2	0 parts
R_3 (I–IIB)	30,000 parts	S_3	0 parts
Total	$R = 70,000$ parts	$S = 0$	
Total profit	$25,000 + 0 = $25,000		

TABLE 11-17. OPTIMUM PROGRAM (HOURS)

Opera-tion	Machine Center	Product R			Product S			Hours Used	Hours Avail.	Sur-plus Hours
		R_1	R_2	R_3	S_1	S_2	S_3			
1	I	350	50	300	0	0	0	700	850	150
2	IIA	700			0			700	700	0
	IIAA		100			0		100	100	0
	IIB			900			0	900	900	0

Thus, one readily sees that the optimal (most profitable) program under the prescribed conditions consists of manufacturing 70,000 units of product R to the complete exclusion of product S. Furthermore, by eq. 1 and also by $(Z_0 - C_0)$ in the optimum tableau, the total profits will be

$$Z = 0.40(35,000) + 0.28(5000) + 0.32(30,000) + 0.72(0)$$

$$+ 0.64(0) + 0.60(0)$$

$$= \$25,000$$

* For a geometric interpretation of the linear programming problem and its solution by the simplex technique, see Appendix 11B. For a short-cut method of solution, see Appendix 11D.

FURTHER RESTRICTIONS IN LINEAR PROGRAMMING PROBLEMS

One might very well raise objections to (or at least raise questions regarding) the preceding linear programming example in that no consideration was given to (1) minimum requirements for product S. (This minimum requirement might arise from contractual needs, expected sales, or from a management policy of producing S as a goodwill or line-completing product.) Furthermore, one might also raise questions regarding the usefulness of the maximum tableau (Table 11-15g), in particular, and the simplex technique, in general, in the event of (2) changes in the amount of time available in any of the machine centers, (3) changes in the price of any of the products and, hence, changes in the profits resulting from the sale of these products, and/or (4) changes in the unit rates brought about by new machines, new dies, new jigs, or improvements in the manufacturing process. Since these are important considerations for any applied problem, let us see how the simplex technique can be employed to take into account these four qualifications or modifications.

The remarkable fact about the simplex technique is that, in general, new optimal programs can be constructed in terms of such *added* restrictions and these essentially new problems do not have to be solved completely from the beginning. This is achieved by means of the $Z_j - C_j$ of the optimal tableau which, in our example, is given in Table 11-15g. The $Z_j - C_j$ represent "opportunity costs." In this particular example, for $j = 1, 2, \cdots, 6$, $Z_j - C_j$ represents the *minimum* cost or loss of profit which can result because of the manufacture of one unit of the product corresponding to X_j. For $j = 7, 8, 9, 10$, $Z_j - C_j$ represents the profit to be gained by making available one additional unit of X_j, namely, one additional unit of time in the corresponding machine center.

With these brief general remarks, let us now consider, in more detail, the four qualifications or modifications of the problem which we have listed.

Minimum Requirement for Product S

Suppose that, for the example just completed, an additional restriction in the form of a minimum requirement of product S had been imposed. This restriction would arise naturally in view of contractual or estimated sales requirements or because of a management policy of having available a certain amount of a given product for, say, goodwill purposes or to complete an existing product line.

The maximum program of Table 11-15g shows that, for the problem as originally stated, no pieces of product S were to be manufactured. Since at least a certain quantity of product S, say S_0, must now be manufactured, one knows that this deviation from the optimal program will result in reduced profits. Furthermore, since the optimum program of Table 11-15g calls for less than S_0 number of units of part S, one obviously should manufacture exactly (and not more than) S_0 units! Consideration of $Z_4 - C_4 = 0.28$, $Z_5 - C_5 = 0.06$ and $Z_6 - C_6 = 0.253$ in Table 11-15g shows that the cheapest method of producing S, i.e., the method which will *reduce* our profits by the least amount, is that represented by P_5, namely using the combination of machine centers I–IIAA. Furthermore, the second cheapest is that represented by P_6 (i.e., I–IIB), and the third cheapest is that represented by P_4 (I–IIA).

Suppose that, in particular, $S_0 = 1000$; in other words, suppose that one *must* manufacture (at least) 1000 units of product S. As just stated, the least reduction in profits which will result from the manufacture of these 1000 units can be obtained by using the combination of machine centers I–IIAA (the process denoted by P_5). The program which achieves this minimum reduction of profit, i.e., the optimal program for the *enlarged* problem, is obtained as shown in Table 11-18.

TABLE 11-18

Optimal Program of Table 11-15g	New Optimal Program for $S_0 = 1000$
$X_7 = \quad\quad 150$	$X_7 = \quad\quad 150 - 1000\ (\frac{1}{200}) = \quad\quad 145$
$X_1 = \quad 35{,}000$	$X_1 = \quad 35{,}000 - 1000\ (0) \quad = \quad 35{,}000$
$X_2 = \quad\quad 5{,}000$	$X_2 = \quad\quad 5{,}000 - 1000\ (\frac{5}{2}) \quad = \quad\quad 2{,}500$
$X_3 = \quad 30{,}000$	$X_3 = \quad 30{,}000 - 1000\ (0) \quad = \quad 30{,}000$
	$X_5 = \quad\quad\quad 0 + 1000 \quad\quad\quad = \quad\quad 1{,}000$
$Z_0 - C_0 = \$25{,}000$	$Z_0 - C_0 = \$25{,}000 - \$1000\ (0.06) = \$24{,}940$

That is, the element in the appropriate column of the optimum tableau (here, the column corresponding to P_5) represents the *optimal changes* to be made in the basis vectors (i.e., vectors which are in the final solution) for each unit of X_j (here, X_5) which is being added as a deviation from the optimum program.

It is important to note that, since the elements X_{i0} of the requirements vector P_0 must be nonnegative (i.e., $X_{i0} \geqq 0$), these optimal changes are permissible only as long as the X_{i0} remain nonnegative. Furthermore, the "opportunity cost," given by $Z_j - C_j$, is valid only as long as the changes produced in the X_{i0}'s do not result in negative values of the X_{i0}.

Thus, to return to the restriction on product S, it can be seen that sequence I–IIAA can be used for at most 2000 units (since $5000 - y(\frac{5}{2})$ $\geqq 0$ implies that $y \leqq 2000$). Suppose, however, that 8000 units of S are required. For $S_0 = 8000$ (actually, for all S_0 such that $2000 < S_0$ $\leqq 13{,}250$), the corresponding optimal program is obtained in two stages, as shown in Table 11-19.

TABLE 11-19

Optimum Program: $S_0 = 8000$

Optimal Program of Table 11-15g	Stage I: P_5	Stage II: P_6
$X_7 = 150$	$X_7 = 150 - 2000\,(\frac{1}{200}) = 140$	$X_7 = 140 - 6000\,(\frac{1}{300}) = 120$
$X_1 = 35{,}000$	$X_1 = 35{,}000 - 2000\,(0) = 35{,}000$	$X_1 = 35{,}000 - 6000\,(0) = 35{,}000$
$X_2 = 5{,}000$	$X_2 = 5{,}000 - 2000\,(\frac{5}{2}) = 0$	$X_2 = 0 - 6000\,(0) = 0$
$X_3 = 30{,}000$	$X_3 = 30{,}000 - 2000\,(0) = 30{,}000$	$X_3 = 30{,}000 - 6000\,(\frac{8}{3}) = 14{,}000$
	$X_5 = 0 + 2000 = 2000$	$X_5 = 2000 - 6000\,(0) = 2000$
		$X_6 = 0 + 6000 = 6000$

$Z_0 - C_0 = \$25{,}000 \quad Z_0 - C_0 = 25{,}000 - 2000\,(0.06) = \$24{,}880 \quad Z_0 - C_0 = 24{,}880 - 6000\,(0.2533) = \$23{,}360$

Similarly, for $13{,}250 < S_0 \leqq 27{,}250$, the corresponding optimal program may be obtained in three stages and is given by eqs. 14

$$X_1 = 35{,}000 - (S_0 - 13{,}250)(\tfrac{5}{2})$$

$$X_4 = S_0 - 13{,}250$$

$$X_5 = 2000$$

$$X_6 = 11{,}250 \tag{14}$$

$$X_7 = 102.5 - (S_0 - 13{,}250)(\tfrac{1}{200})$$

$$Z_0 - C_0 = \$22{,}030.00 - \$(S_0 - 13{,}250)(0.28)$$

Changes in Available Time in Any Machine Center

The values $Z_7 - C_7 = 0$, $Z_8 - C_8 = 20$, $Z_9 - C_9 = 14$, and $Z_{10} - C_{10} = 10\frac{2}{3}$ in Table 11-15g are the benefits to be derived (in terms of *added* profit) by making available one additional unit of time in machine centers I, IIA, IIAA, and IIB respectively. It is interesting to note that it would be more profitable to make available additional (over) time in machine center IIAA than it would be to make available additional hours in machine center IIB. Also, $Z_7 - C_7$ bears out the fact that, since 150 surplus hours are already available in machine center I, there is no value for any additional hours in that center.

Keeping in mind the restriction that $X_{i0} \geq 0$, one can examine the column elements in the same manner as was done in the previous section and see that it would be profitable to make available at most 300, 300, or 450 additional hours in machine centers IIA, IIAA, or IIB, respectively. (These upper limits are based on the premise that the surplus hours in machine center I are to be absorbed, but not exceeded.) Letting H_0 denote the additional hours which may be added, these upper limits are obtained as follows

$$150 + H_0(-\tfrac{1}{2}) \geq 0 \quad \text{implies} \quad H_0 \leq 300$$

and

$$150 + H_0(-\tfrac{1}{3}) \geq 0 \quad \text{implies} \quad H_0 \leq 450$$

Furthermore, for any H_0 within the prescribed limits, the new optimum total profits will be given by

$$(Z_0 - C_0) = 25,000 + H_0 \begin{pmatrix} 20 \\ 14 \\ 10\tfrac{2}{3} \end{pmatrix}$$

More generally, if additional hours are appropriately assigned to machine centers IIA, IIAA, and IIB in the amount H_1, H_2, and H_3, then the total profits will be given by

$$(Z_0 - C_0) = 25,000 + 20H_1 + 14H_2 + 10\tfrac{2}{3}H_3 \tag{15}$$

Changes in Unit Production Rates

Changes in unit production rates may be brought about by the introduction of new dies, special tools, new improvements in the manufacturing process, or even new machines. In the main, such changes will necessitate obtaining a completely new simplex solution. However, in some cases, the former optimal tableaux can still be used. For example, suppose that the time required to produce part R in machine centers IIA and IIAA has been reduced (or is reducible) from 0.02 hour per unit to 0.0175 hour per unit. Since the combination I–IIA is the most profitable for manufacturing part R, all 700 hours available in machine center IIA are first allocated. This requires, in turn, 400 hours in center I. Next, as the second most profitable method,* all 900 hours which are available in center IIB are allocated requiring, in turn, 300 more hours in center I. Finally, the 100 hours available in

---

* One might question selecting sequence I–IIB before sequence I–IIAA even though the unit profits are $0.32 and $0.28 respectively, inasmuch as product R requires 0.03 hour per unit in center IIB as compared with 0.02 hour per unit in center IIAA. However, for the problem as just stated, the critical factor is not the time in centers IIA, IIAA, and IIB, but, rather, the time in center I; hence, the unit profit (or unit profit relative to time in center I) is the governing factor.

center IIAA are allocated, utilizing 57.1 hours in center I. This optimal program is summarized in Table 11-20. (The steps just described hold for all new manufacturing times $t_{IIA,R}$ such that $0.01\frac{3}{11} < t_{IIA,R} < 0.02$.)

TABLE 11-20. $t_{IIA,R} = 0.0175$

Opera-tion	Machine Center	Product R			Product S			Hours Used	Hours Avail.	Sur-plus Hours
		R_1	R_2	R_3	S_1	S_2	S_3			
1	I	400	57.1	300	0	0	0	757.1	850	92.9
2	IIA	700			0			700	700	0
	IIAA		100			0		100	100	0
	IIB			900			0	900	900	0

Profit: $16,000 + 1600 + 9600 = \$27,200$

Optimal programs have also been obtained (in a similar manner) for $t_{IIA,R} = 0.01\frac{3}{11}$ and $t_{IIA,R} = 0.01$ and are given in Tables 11-21 and 11-22 respectively.

TABLE 11-21. $t_{IIA,R} = 0.01\frac{3}{11}$

Opera-tion	Machine Center	Product R			Product S			Hours Used	Hours Avail.	Sur-plus Hours
		R_1	R_2	R_3	S_1	S_2	S_3			
1	I	550	0	300	0	0	0	850	850	0
2	IIA	700			0			700	700	0
	IIAA		0			0		0	100	100
	IIB			900			0	900	900	0

Profit: $22,000 + 0 + 9600 = \$31,600$

TABLE 11-22. $t_{IIA,R} = 0.01$

Opera-tion	Machine Center	Product R			Product S			Hours Used	Hours Avail.	Sur-plus Hours
		R_1	R_2	R_3	S_1	S_2	S_3			
1	I	700	0	150	0	0	0	850	850	0
2	IIA	700			0			700	700	0
	IIAA		0			0		0	100	100
	IIB			450			0	450	900	450

Profit: $28,000 + 0 + 4800 = \$32,800$

Finally, with respect to changes in the unit production rates, it should be pointed out that, should sufficient improvements be effected in the machine centers with respect to product S, new optimum programs can be obtained which will insure the manufacture of some units of product S.

TABLE 11-23a

C_j / C_i	Basis	P_0					0.36	0.24	0.28	0.72	0.64	0.60
			P_7	P_8	P_9	P_{10}	P_1	P_2	P_3	P_4	P_5	P_6
	P_7	150	1	$-\frac12$	$-\frac12$	$-\frac13$				$\frac{1}{200}$	$\frac{1}{200}$	$\frac{1}{300}$
0.36	P_1	35,000		50			1			$\frac52$		
0.24 ↓	P_2	5,000			50			1			$\boxed{\frac52}$	
0.28	P_3	30,000				$\frac{100}{3}$			1			$\frac83$
	Z_j	22,200		18	12	$9\frac13$	0.36	0.24	0.28	0.90	0.60	$0.74\frac23$
	$Z_j - C_j$	22,200		18	12	$9\frac13$				0.18	-0.04^{*}	$0.14\frac23$

TABLE 11-23b

c_i	Basis	P_0	P_7	P_8	P_9	P_{10}	P_1 (0.36)	P_2 (0.24)	P_3 (0.28)	P_4 (0.72)	P_5 (0.64)	P_6 (0.60)
	P_7	140	1	$-\frac{1}{2}$	$-\frac{3}{5}$	$-\frac{1}{3}$		-0.002		$\frac{1}{200}$		$\frac{1}{300}$
0.36	P_1	35,000		50			1			$\frac{5}{2}$		
0.64 ↑	P_5	2,000			20	$\frac{100}{3}$		$\frac{2}{5}$			1	$\frac{8}{3}$
0.28	P_3	30,000							1			
	$Z_j - C_j$	22,280		18	12.8	$9\frac{1}{3}$		0.016		0.18		$0.14\frac{2}{3}$

Changes in Unit Profits

Suppose that, in order to meet competition or for some other reason, the sale price of product R is reduced, say, 4 cents per unit, resulting, in turn, in a reduction of profits of 4 cents per unit. The optimal program for this change in profits can be obtained without having to retrace one's steps completely. For our problem, the procedure may be described as follows:

1. Copy from the optimal tableau, Table 11-15g, the elements which are in the rows of the basis vectors.* (This portion of the table is bounded by a heavy border in Table 11-23a.)

2. Next, insert the new unit profits in the first row and first column (namely: $C_1 = 0.36$, $C_2 = 0.24$, $C_3 = 0.28$, $C_4 = 0.72$, $C_5 = 0.64$, $C_6 = 0.60$, and other $C_j = 0$).

3. Next, calculate

$$Z_j = \sum_{i=1}^{m} C_i X_{ij}, \qquad j = 0, 1, 2, \cdots, n \qquad (7)$$

4. Calculate $(Z_j - C_j)$.

    a. If all $(Z_j - C_j) \geqq 0$, then the old tableau is the optimal tableau relative to the new price structure as well as to the old.

    b. If at least one $(Z_j - C_j) < 0$, then proceed in the usual simplex calculation manner until such time as an optimum program is achieved. This procedure is illustrated in Tables 11-23a and 11-23b.

Thus, the new optimal program (in terms of the given price change) is as given in Table 11-24. That is, with the new pricing policy, pro-

TABLE 11-24

Former Optimum Program		New Optimum Program	
$X_7 =$	150	$X_7 =$	140
$X_1 =$	35,000	$X_1 =$	35,000
$X_2 =$	5,000	$X_5 =$	2,000
$X_3 =$	30,000	$X_3 =$	30,000
$Z_0 - C_0 = \$22,200$ †		$Z_0 - C_0 = \$22,280$	

† This value of $Z_0 - C_0$ reflects the change in price of product R.

fits will be reduced a total of \$2800 if the old optimum program is still used. Furthermore, since the optimum program for the new price

---

* This portion of the matrix is called the *body* and arises from the restrictions. Hence, the body remains unchanged despite the change in unit profits.

will yield a profit of $22,280, the *minimum* reduction in profit will be $2720. This is brought about by substituting 2000 units of product S (I–IIAA) for 5000 parts of product R (I–IIAA).

It should be noted that not only does the simplex technique provide one with a method for studying the effect of changes in the unit costs and rates but it can also be used to determine the effect of *errors* in estimating these production rates and unit costs.

SUMMARY

In summary, then, the transportation technique of solving linear programming problems involves the simplest of arithmetic operations and, consequently, is desirable for use, whenever possible, for large-scale problems. In addition to solving problems such as optimum boxcar distribution and the like, the transportation technique can be used to locate new warehouses and factories, to reduce setup times in the shop, and to allocate products to machines. However, the transportation technique will not handle the general class of linear optimization problems as will the simplex technique.*

On the other hand, not only will the simplex technique † solve the general linear programming problem but, with a minimum of effort, new optimal programs can be determined which take into account added restrictions for the problem or changes in the data for the problem. This is very important in that these "changes" and "restrictions" can be analyzed in advance and thus provide management with a quantitative basis for answering, among others, questions regarding:

1. Addition of extra shifts.
2. Overtime in one center versus straight time in another.
3. Addition of more machines (additional available time in the machine center).
4. Addition of new machines, special tools or improvements (reduction in unit production rates).
5. Changes in prices to meet a competitive market.
6. Cost (i.e., reduction in profits) of good-will items.
7. Direction of sales effort.
8. Optimum product mix.

* The mathematical relationship between the transportation technique and the simplex technique is described in Charnes and Cooper.[3]

† No mention has been made here, as yet, of the relationship between linear programming and the theory of games, the latter to be discussed in Chapter 18. An excellent discussion of this correspondence is given in McKinsey.[33]

Before closing, something should also be stated about nonanalytic techniques. To handle cases where the scope of the problem is such that analytic techniques of solution like the transportation technique and the simplex technique are not practical, nonanalytic techniques of solution have been developed. These are discussed in references 1 and 35, and an example of the use of a nonanalytic procedure is also given in Chapter 13.

Finally, it might be well to restate the general problem of linear programming, namely:

Problem (Statement I). Find the values of X_1, X_2, X_3, $\cdots$, X_n which maximize (minimize)

$$Z = X_1 C_1 + X_2 C_2 + \cdots + X_n C_n$$

subject to the conditions that

$$X_j \geqq 0, \qquad j = 1, 2, \cdots, n$$

and

$$X_1 a_{11} + X_2 a_{12} + \cdots + X_n a_{1n} = b_1$$
$$X_1 a_{21} + X_2 a_{22} + \cdots + X_n a_{2n} = b_2$$

$$\cdot$$
$$\cdot$$
$$\cdot$$

$$X_1 a_{m1} + X_2 a_{m2} + \cdots + X_n a_{mn} = b_m$$

where a_{ij}, b_i, and C_j are given constants $\begin{cases} i = 1, 2, \cdots, m. \\ j = 1, 2, \cdots, n. \end{cases}$

Or, given the column vectors

$$P_j = \begin{bmatrix} a_{1j} \\ a_{2j} \\ \vdots \\ a_{mj} \end{bmatrix}, \qquad j = 1, 2, \cdots, n$$

$$P_0 = \begin{bmatrix} b_1 \\ b_2 \\ \vdots \\ b_m \end{bmatrix}$$

the problem can also be stated as follows:

Problem (Statement II). Determine the values of $X_1, X_2, \cdots, X_n$ which maximize (minimize) the linear functional

$$Z = X_1 C_1 + X_2 C_2 + \cdots + X_n C_n \equiv \sum_{j=1}^{n} X_j C_j$$

subject to the conditions that

$$X_j \geqq 0, \quad j = 1, 2, \cdots, n$$

and

$$X_1 P_1 + X_2 P_2 + \cdots + X_n P_n \equiv \sum_{j=1}^{n} X_j P_j = P_0$$

APPENDIX 11A

Alternate Method of Evaluating Cells in Transportation Technique

In Chapter 11 a method (part of the over-all transportation technique) is presented for "evaluating" those cells in a feasible solution matrix which do not contain circled numbers, i.e., for evaluating "opportunity costs" associated with program possibilities other than the one given in the particular matrix. In this appendix a second technique is presented which not only enables one to make these evaluations in a simple manner but which also yields, as a by-product, additional information regarding the minimum costs of deviating from the given program.*

In order to be able to compare the evaluation technique (or procedure) to be presented here with that presented earlier, let us return to Tables 11-2 and 11-3, namely the cost table and the table listing the first feasible solution of the given transportation problem. The first part of the evaluation procedure is to form a new table (Table 11A-1) corresponding to Table 11-3, but listing the unit costs rather than the amounts to be shipped. These costs are given by the boldface numbers in Table 11A-1.

---

* The evaluation technique presented here is a variation of that originally designed by Dantzig in Chap. XXI of Koopmans [29] and is part of the procedure described in Henderson and Schlaifer.[25] The discussion of determining the costs of deviating from the optimum solution is given in ref. 25.

TABLE 11-2. UNIT SHIPPING COSTS

Destinations / Origins	D_1	D_2	D_3	D_4	D_5
S_1	-10	-20	-5	-9	-10
S_2	-2	-10	-8	-30	-6
S_3	-1	-20	-7	-10	-4

TABLE 11-3. FIRST FEASIBLE SOLUTION

Destinations / Origins	D_1	D_2	D_3	D_4	D_5	Total
S_1	③	⑤	①			9
S_2			③	①		4
S_3				⑤	③	8
Total	3	5	4	6	3	21

Now, add to Table 11A-1 a column labeled "Row Values" and a row labeled "Column Values" and calculate these values as follows:

1. First, assign an arbitrary value to some one row or some one column. For purposes of illustration, let us assign the value 0 (zero) to row S_1.

2. Next, for every cell in row S_1 which contains a circled number representing part of the feasible solution, assign a corresponding column value (which may be positive, negative, or zero) which is such that the sum of the column value and row value is equal to the unit cost rate.

More generally, if r_i is the row value of the ith row, c_j the column value of the jth column, and C_{ij} the unit cost for the cell in the ith

TABLE 11A-1. UNIT COSTS AND FICTITIOUS COSTS CORRESPONDING TO
FIRST FEASIBLE SOLUTION

Origins \ Destinations	D_1	D_2	D_3	D_4	D_5	Row Values
S_1	-10	-20	-5	-27	-21	0
S_2	-13	-23	-8	-30	-24	-3
S_3	7	-3	12	-10	-4	17
Column Values	-10	-20	-5	-27	-21	

row and jth column, then all row and column values are obtained by
the equation

$$r_i + c_j = C_{ij} \tag{A-1}$$

Thus, assuming $r_1 = 0$, we can immediately determine from eq. A-1
that

$$c_1 = -10; \qquad c_2 = -20; \qquad c_3 = -5$$

3. Next, since $c_3 = -5$ and $C_{23} = -8$, we determine that $r_2 = -3$.
4. Since $r_2 = -3$ and $C_{24} = -30$, then $c_4 = -27$.
5. From $c_4 = -27$ and $C_{34} = -10$, one then obtains $r_3 = +17$.
6. Finally, for $r_3 = +17$ and $C_{35} = -4$, one obtains $c_5 = -21$.

It should be noted that this procedure for assigning row and column
values can be used for any solution-matrix which is nondegenerate, i.e.,
given a matrix of m rows and n columns, where the solution consists
of exactly $m + n - 1$ nonzero elements. (Any solution consisting of
less than $m + n - 1$ nonzero elements is said to be degenerate. Simple methods for dealing with degeneracy may be found in Charnes
and Cooper,[3] Henderson and Schlaifer,[25] Dantzig,[10] and others.)

Having computed all row and column values for Table 11A-1, the
table can now be completed by filling in the remaining cells according
to eq. A-1. This results in the lightface figures given in Table 11A-1.

Having completed Table 11A-1, the cell evaluations may now be obtained as follows: Form a new table (Table 11A-2) which consists of

TABLE 11A-2. CELL EVALUATIONS FOR THE FIRST FEASIBLE SOLUTION

Origins \ Destinations	D_1	D_2	D_3	D_4	D_5
S_1	**0**	**0**	**0**	-18	-11
S_2	-11	-13	**0**	**0**	-18
S_3	8	17	19	**0**	**0**

the unit cost rates of Table 11-2 subtracted from the number in the corresponding cell of Table 11A-1. That is, in symbolic notation *

$$\{\text{Table 11A-2}\} = \{\text{Table 11A-1}\} - \{\text{Table 11-2}\}$$

The cells corresponding to movements which are part of the solution will obviously contain zeros. These zeros are given in boldface type in Table 11A-2. The resulting numbers for the remaining cells are given in lightface type and are the cell evaluations to be used in determining a better program or solution. (Comparison with Table 11-4 will show this to be true.)

Having determined these cell evaluations, one then proceeds as previously outlined in the chapter.

APPENDIX 11B

Geometric Interpretation of the Linear Programming Problem

In this appendix a geometric interpretation of the linear programming problem is given. This is done by means of the following specific 2-dimensional example.

---

* One obvious computational short cut is to use one matrix instead of two. For example, the unit costs can be placed in the upper right-hand corner of the cell and the C_{ij} in the upper left-hand corner. The evaluations can then be obtained from just the one table.

Problem: To determine $X, Y \geqq 0$ which maximize $Z = 2X + 5Y$ subject to

$$X \leqq 4$$

$$Y \leqq 3 \qquad \text{(B-1)}$$

$$X + 2Y \leqq 8$$

The system of linear inequalities which constitute the restrictions results in the convex set of points given by polygon $OABCD$ of Fig. 11B-1. That is, any point (X, Y) on or within the polygon satisfies

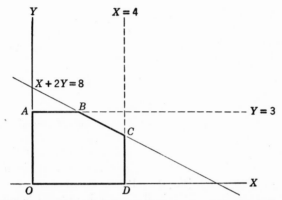

Fig. 11B-1. Region satisfying restrictions stated in Appendix 11B.

the entire system of inequalities B-1. Hence, there exist an infinite number of solutions to system B-1. The linear programming problem, then, is to select, from this infinite number of points, the one or more points which will maximize the function $Z = 2X + 5Y$.

The function $Z = 2X + 5Y$ is a 1-parameter family of straight lines; i.e., the function represents a family of parallel straight lines (of slope $-\frac{2}{5}$) such that Z increases as the line gets farther removed from the origin; see Fig. 11B-2. The problem may then be thought of as one

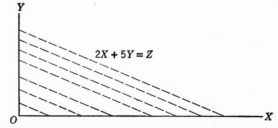

Fig. 11B-2. Family of parallel straight lines, $Z = 2X + 5Y$.

of determining that line of the family, $2X + 5Y = Z$, which is farthest away from the origin but which still contains at least one point of the polygon $OABCD$.

Figure 11B-3 shows how several members of the family $Z = 2X + 5Y$ are related to the polygon $OABCD$ and, in particular, shows that

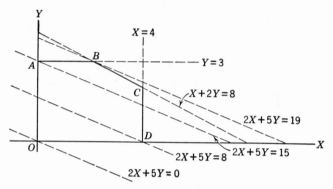

Fig. 11B-3. **Figure for geometric solution of linear programming problem.**

the solution is given by the co-ordinates of point B. Point B is the intersection of $Y = 3$ and $X + 2Y = 8$. Hence, B is given by $(2, 3)$ and, in turn, $Z_{max} = 2(2) + 5(3) = 19$.

In order to exhibit, geometrically, what happens when one solves the problem by means of the simplex technique, the simplex solution of the example of Fig. 11B-3 is given in Tables 11B-1. We see from Tables 11B-1 that the solution progresses from the point $(X \equiv X_1 = 0,$

TABLE 11B-1a

C_i \ C_j		0	0	0	0	2	5
	Basis	P_0	P_3	P_4	P_5	P_1	P_2
0	P_3	4	1	0	0	1	0
0	P_4	3	0	1	0	0	1
0	P_5	8	0	0	1	1	2
	Z_j	0	0	0	0	0	0
	$Z_j - C_j$	0	0	0	0	-2	-5

TABLE 11B-1*b*

C_i \ C_j		0	0	0	0	2	5
	Basis	P_0	P_3	P_4	P_5	P_1	P_2
0	P_3	4	1	0	0	1	0
5	P_2	3	0	1	0	0	1
0	P_5	2	0	-2	1	1	0
	$Z_j - C_j$	15	0	5	0	-2	0

TABLE 11B-1*c*

C_i \ C_j		0	0	0	0	2	5
	Basis	P_0	P_3	P_4	P_5	P_1	P_2
0	P_3	2	1	2	-1	0	0
5	P_2	3	0	1	0	0	1
2	P_1	2	0	-2	1	1	0
	$Z_j - C_j$	19	0	1	2	0	0

$X_3 = 2$

$X_2 = 3$

$X_1 = 2$

$Y \equiv X_2 = 0$) to the point ($X \equiv X_1 = 0$, $Y \equiv X_2 = 3$) to the point ($X \equiv X_1 = 2$, $Y \equiv X_2 = 3$); i.e., referring to Fig. 11B-3, from point O (origin) to point A to point B.

More generally, if we call "corner points" such as O, A, B, C, and D *extreme* points of the polygon $OABCD$, then the optimum solution to the linear programming problem will be at such an extreme point and we reach this optimum (extreme) point by proceeding from one extreme point to another.* The reader will note that, in the example dis-

---

* Mathematically, polygon $OABCD$ constitutes a *convex* set of points; i.e., given any two points in the polygon, then the segment joining them is also in the polygon. An *extreme* point of a convex set is any point in the convex set which does not lie on a segment joining some two other points of the set. Thus, the extreme points of polygon $OABCD$ are points O, A, B, C, and D.

cussed here, the solution proceeded from extreme point O to extreme point A and, finally, to extreme point B.

If one now changes the example slightly to read:

Problem: To determine $X, Y \geq 0$ which maximize $Z = X + 2Y$ subject to the restrictions

$$X \leq 4$$

$$Y \leq 3$$

$$X + 2Y \leq 8$$

then Fig. 11B-4 shows that the solution is given by either extreme point B or extreme point C. This is because $X + 2Y = 8$ is both a

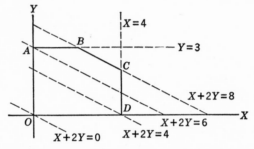

Fig. 11B-4. Geometric solution of linear programming problem with more than one optimum solution.

boundary line of the polygon $OABCD$ and also a member of the family of parallel lines $Z = X + 2Y$. Hence $B = (2, 3)$ and $C = (4, 2)$ both constitute solutions and yield the answer $Z_{\max} = 8$.

Furthermore, any convex linear combination of B and C will also be a solution, namely, the set of all points (X^*, Y^*) given by

$$X^* = a(2) + (1 - a)(4)$$

$$Y^* = a(3) + (1 - a)(2)$$

where $0 \leq a \leq 1$. Geometrically, (X^*, Y^*) is the set of points which make up line segment $\overline{BC}$. The value $a = 0$ corresponds to extreme point C, the value $a = 1$ to extreme point B, and as a is allowed to range from 0 to 1, one is progressing along $\overline{BC}$ from point C to point B.

APPENDIX 11C

The Dual Problem of Linear Programming

In this appendix we consider the dual problem of linear programming and, in particular, exhibit how, given a linear programming problem, its dual problem can be stated. Additionally, we show how the solution of a linear programming problem can be used to determine the solution of its dual problem. We do this by means of the example given in Appendix 11B, namely:

Problem: Determine X, $Y \geqq 0$ which maximize $Z = 2X + 5Y$ subject to

$$X \leqq 4$$

$$Y \leqq 3 \qquad\qquad \text{(C-1)}$$

$$X + 2Y \leqq 8$$

This problem may be displayed in tabular form as is done in Table 11C-1. That is, the restrictions may be "read off" by interpreting a

TABLE 11C-1

$\leqq$

	X	Y	
W₁	1	0	4
W₂	0	1	3
W₃	1	2	8
Max	2	5	

light vertical line as "$+$" and the heavy vertical line as "$\leqq$". Furthermore, the function to be maximized is given by the bottom row, namely $2X + 5Y$. To obtain the dual problem, we extend Table

TABLE 11C-2

	X	Y	Min
W_1	1	0	4
W_2	0	1	3
W_3	1	2	8
Max	2	5	

(with $\leqq$ above the table and $\geqq$ to the left)

11C-1 as is done in Table 11C-2. Then, reading down each column as indicated, we obtain the dual problem, namely:

Dual problem: Minimize $g = 4W_1 + 3W_2 + 8W_3$ subject to *

$$W_1 + W_3 \geqq 2$$
$$W_2 + 2W_3 \geqq 5 \tag{C-2}$$

If we return to the simplex solution of the maximization problem as given in Appendix 11B, we see that the following results are given

$$Z_{\max} = 19$$

and

$$
\begin{aligned}
X_1 &= 2, & Z_1 - C_1 &= 0 \\
X_2 &= 3, & Z_2 - C_2 &= 0 \\
X_3 &= 2, & Z_3 - C_3 &= 0 \\
X_4 &= 0, & Z_4 - C_4 &= 1 \\
X_5 &= 0, & Z_5 - C_5 &= 2
\end{aligned}
\tag{C-3}
$$

Now, X_3, X_4, and X_5 correspond to slack variables. Hence, if we start with the *first* slack variable and renumber the $Z_j - C_j$ in order,

---

* The inequalities, $\geqq$, are converted to equalities by the subtraction of nonnegative slack variables. Then, since -1 cannot be entered into a basis, one may also add *artificial* variables to provide for the basis. Thus, $W_1 + W_3 \geqq 2$ is first converted into $W_1 + W_3 - W_4 = 2$. Then the artificial variable, W_6, may be added to provide $W_1 + W_3 - W_4 + W_6 = 2$. For a detailed discussion, see Charnes, Cooper, and Henderson.[4]

and denote these reordered $Z_j - C_j$ by $Z_j' - C_j'$, we obtain

$$Z_1' - C_1' = 0 \qquad \text{(corresponding to former } Z_3 - C_3)$$

$$Z_2' - C_2' = 1 \qquad \text{(corresponding to former } Z_4 - C_4)$$

$$Z_3' - C_3' = 2 \qquad \text{(corresponding to former } Z_5 - C_5) \qquad \text{(C-4)}$$

$$Z_4' - C_4' = 0 \qquad \text{(corresponding to former } Z_1 - C_1)$$

$$Z_5' - C_5' = 0 \qquad \text{(corresponding to former } Z_2 - C_2)$$

If we then let $W_j = Z_j' - C_j'$, we have the solution to the dual minimization problem. That is, if the minimization problem were to be solved by the simplex technique, the following results would be obtained

$$g_{\min} = 19$$

and

$$W_1 = 0, \qquad -(g_1 - b_1) = 2$$

$$W_2 = 1, \qquad -(g_2 - b_2) = 0$$

$$W_3 = 2, \qquad -(g_3 - b_3) = 0 \qquad \text{(C-5)}$$

$$W_4 = 0, \qquad -(g_4 - b_4) = 2$$

$$W_5 = 0, \qquad -(g_5 - b_5) = 3$$

where b_j are the corresponding coefficients of the W_j in the minimization function.

Conversely, given the solution to the minimization problem (i.e., given eq. C-5), we can determine the solution to the dual maximization problem by starting with the first slack variable W_4, and relabeling the $-(g_j - b_j)$ in order. Hence, solution C-3 would result.

For the dual problems, it can be shown that $Z_{\max} = g_{\min}$; in other words, that the two problems are equivalent.* Hence, in solving a linear programming problem, we are free to work with either the stated problem or its dual. Since, as a rule of thumb, the number of iterations required to solve a linear programming problem is equal to 1 to $1\frac{1}{2}$ times the number of rows (i.e., restrictions), we can, by an appropriate choice, facilitate the computation somewhat, especially in such cases where there exists a sizeable difference in the number of rows for each of the two problems.

* For a proof, see p. 72 of Charnes, Cooper, and Henderson [4] or Chap. XIX of Koopmans.[29]

APPENDIX 11 D

A Short Cut in Solving Linear Programming Problems

One of the many advantages of both the transportation and simplex techniques is that judgment can be used to good advantage in facilitating the computations required in order to arrive at an optimal solution. In the transportation problem involving m rows and n columns, the use of judgment (or a good guess) simply requires designating $m + n - 1$ cells which are expected to correspond to a solution. Having selected these $m + n - 1$ cells, we proceed as in the transportation technique, first filling in these cells with circled numbers and then "evaluating" the remaining cells to determine whether or not we have an optimum solution.

To describe the procedure for utilizing judgment in the simplex technique, it is easiest to proceed by means of an example. In particular, we consider the example of Appendix 11B, and show how, given a "good" guess, we can construct the corresponding simplex matrix and proceed to the optimum solution (if the solution guessed is not already optimum).

Problem: To determine X, $Y \geqq 0$ which maximize $Z = 2X + 5Y$ subject to

$$X \leqq 4$$

$$Y \leqq 3 \tag{D-1}$$

$$X + 2Y \leqq 8$$

Converting this system of inequalities to equalities by means of slack variables S_3, S_4, and S_5 yields

$$X + S_3 = 4$$

$$Y + S_4 = 3 \tag{D-2}$$

$$X + 2Y + S_5 = 8$$

Now, suppose that we "guess" or have reason to believe that the optimum solution is such that it will not involve X; i.e., that the final solution will consist of Y, S_3, and S_5. This means, accordingly, that $X = 0$ and $S_4 = 0$. Hence, to obtain the "solution," i.e., the elements of the basis that would appear in the P_0 column of the simplex tableau,

Linear Programming

339

we need only set $X = 0$ and $S_4 = 0$ in eqs. D-2, yielding

$$S_3 = 4$$

$$Y = 3 \tag{D-3}$$

$$2Y + S_5 = 8$$

so that

$$Y = 3, \quad S_3 = 4, \quad \text{and} \quad S_5 = 2 \tag{D-4}$$

These values are then entered in the simplex tableau (see Table 11D-1) under the column labeled P_0. (Note that P_2 corresponds to Y.)

TABLE 11D-1

C_i \ C_j	Basis	P_0	P_3	P_4	P_5	2 P_1	5 P_2
0	P_3	4	1	0	0	1	0
5	$P_2(Y)$	3	0	1	0	0	1
0	P_5	2	0	-2	1	1	0
	Z_j	15	0	5	0	0	5
	$Z_j - C_j$	15	0	5	0	-2	0

Next, we need to construct the body of the simplex matrix. Since each value of $Z_j - C_j$ corresponds to the *minimum* cost of deviating from the optimum program by one unit of X_j, we can determine, for each j, the corresponding $Z_j - C_j$ and the X_{ij} which appear in that column. For example, consider that we will deviate from the program of $Y = 3$, $S_3 = 4$, and $S_5 = 2$ by insisting that $X = 1$. We then need to determine the *changes* in Y, S_3, and S_5 which result from the unit change in X. Therefore, we need to solve

$$1 + S_3 = 4$$

$$Y = 3 \tag{D-5}$$

$$1 + 2Y + S_5 = 8$$

which result from eqs. D-1 by letting $X = 1$ and $S_4 = 0$.

Solving eqs. D-5 yields

$$X = 1; \qquad Y = 3; \qquad S_3 = 3; \qquad S_5 = 1 \qquad \text{(D-6)}$$

Comparing eqs. D-4 with D-6 then shows that the following changes in Y, S_3, and S_5 occur because of a unit change in X

$$\Delta Y = 0, \qquad \Delta S_3 = 1, \qquad \Delta S_5 = 1 \qquad \text{(D-7)}$$

Therefore, setting up a simplex tableau (see Table 11D-1), we would insert these values under the column labeled P_1 which corresponds to the variable X.

Similarly, for S_4 we need to solve

$$S_3 = 4$$
$$Y + 1 = 3 \qquad \text{(D-8)}$$
$$2Y + S_5 = 8$$

which yields

$$Y = 2, \qquad S_3 = 4, \qquad S_5 = 4 \qquad \text{(D-9)}$$

so that

$$\Delta Y = 1, \qquad \Delta S_3 = 0, \qquad \Delta S_5 = -2 \qquad \text{(D-10)}$$

These values we insert in column P_4 of Table 11D-1.

Next, since P_2, P_3, and P_5 are in the basis, we can complete the corresponding columns (as is done in Table 11D-1) by inserting 0's and 1's in the appropriate places.

Finally, we need only to compute the $Z_j - C_j$'s to determine whether our "solution" is optimal. This is done as at the outset of any simplex solution; i.e., we first compute Z_j by

$$Z_j = \sum_i C_i X_{ij} \qquad \text{(D-11)}$$

and then subtract the corresponding C_j. Since P_2, P_3, and P_5 are in the basis, $Z_2 - C_2$, $Z_3 - C_3$, and $Z_5 - C_5$ are all equal to zero. Additionally, applying eq. D-11, we obtain

$$Z_1 - C_1 = 1(0) + 0(5) + 1(0) - 2 = -2$$
$$Z_4 - C_4 = 0(0) + 1(5) + (-2)(0) - 0 = 5$$

Thus Table 11D-1 is completed and, not having an optimum solution (owing to $Z_1 - C_1$ being negative), we can then proceed to obtain the optimum solution as in Appendix 11B.

The reader should note that Table 11D-1 is identical to Table 11B-1*b* and was generated without a tableau such as is given in Table

11B-1a. The same technique can, of course, also be applied to larger size problems so that, with a good estimate of the variables which will make up the solution, one might be able to eliminate a great amount of computation.

BIBLIOGRAPHY

1. Arnoff, E. Leonard, "An Application of Linear Programming," *Proceedings of the Conference on Operations Research in Production and Inventory Control,* Case Institute of Technology, Cleveland, 1954.
2. Charnes, A., "Optimality and Degeneracy in Linear Programming," *Econometrica, 20,* 160–170 (1952).
3. ———, and Cooper, W. W., "The Stepping Stone Method of Explaining Linear Programming Calculations in Transportation Problems," *Mgmt. Sci., 1,* no. 1, Appendix (Oct. 1954).
4. ———, and Henderson, A., *An Introduction to Linear Programming,* John Wiley & Sons, New York, 1953.
5. Charnes, A., Cooper, W. W., and Mellon, B., "Blending Aviation Gasolines— A Study in Programming Interdependent Activities," in ref. **37**.
6. Charnes, A., and Lemke, C. E., "A Modified Simplex Method for Control of Round-off Error in Linear Programming," Association for Computing Machinery meeting, Pittsburgh, May 2, 1952.
7. ———, "Minimization of Non-Linear Separable Convex Functionals," *Nav. Res. Log. Quart. 1,* 301–312 (1954).
8. Cooper, W. W., and Charnes, A., "Transportation Scheduling by Linear Programming," *Proceedings of the Conference on Operations Research in Marketing,* Case Institute of Technology, Cleveland, 1953.
9. ———, and Farr, D., "Linear Programming Models for Scheduling Manufactured Products," Carnegie Institute of Technology, Pittsburgh, Sept. 1, 1952.
10. Dantzig, G. B., Chaps. I, II, XX, XXI, and XXIII of ref. 29.
11. ———, "Computational Algorithm of the Revised Simplex Method," RAND Memorandum RM-1266, 1953.
12. ———, "Maximization of a Linear Function of Variables Subject to Linear Inequalities," Chap. XXI of ref. 29.
13. ———, "Upper Bounds, Secondary Constraints, and Block Triangularity in Linear Programming," RAND Memorandum 1367, 1954.
14. ———, and Orchard-Hays, W., "Alternate Algorithm for the Revised Simplex Method," RAND Memorandum RM-1268, 1953.
15. ———, and Waters, G., "Product-Form Tableau for Revised Simplex Method," RAND Memorandum RM-1268-A, 1954.
16. Dantzig, G. B., Orden, A., and Wolfe, P., "The Generalized Simplex Method for Minimizing a Linear Form under Linear Inequality Restraints," RAND Memorandum RM-1264, 1954.
17. Dorfman, R., *Application of Linear Programming to the Theory of the Firm,* University of California Press, Berkeley, 1951.
18. Dwyer, Paul S., "The Solution of the Hitchcock Transportation Problem with a Method of Reduced Matrices," University of Michigan, Ann Arbor, Dec. 1955 (hectographed).
19. Flood, M. M., "On the Hitchcock Distribution Problem," *Pac. J. Math., 3,* 369–386 (1953).

20. "The Traveling-Salesman Problem," in J. F. McCloskey and J. M. Coppinger (eds.), *Operations Research for Management II*, The Johns Hopkins Press, Baltimore, 1956.

21. Ford, L. R., and Fulkerson, D. R., "A Simple Algorithm for Finding Maximal Network Flows and an Application to the Hitchcock Problem," RAND Memorandum P-743, 1955.

22. Fulkerson, D. R., and Dantzig, G. B., "Computation of Maximal Flows in Networks," RAND Memorandum RM-1489, 1955.

23. Gale, D., Kuhn, H. W., and Tucker, A. W., "Linear Programming and the Theory of Games," Chap. XIX of ref. 29.

24. Goldstein, Leon, "The Problem of Contract Awards," in ref. 34.

25. Henderson, A., and Schlaifer, R., "Mathematical Programming," *Harv. Busin. Rev.* (May–June 1954).

26. Hildreth, C., and Reiter, S., "On the Choice of a Crop Rotation Plan," Chap. XI of ref. 29.

27. Hitchcock, F. L., "The Distribution of a Product from Several Sources to Numerous Localities," *J. Math. Phys.*, *20*, 224–230 (1941).

28. Hood, W. C., and Koopmans, T. C. (eds.), *Studies in Econometric Method*, Cowles Commission Monograph No. 14, John Wiley & Sons, New York, 1953.

29. Koopmans, T. C. (ed.), *Activity Analysis of Production and Allocation*, Cowles Commission Monograph No. 13, John Wiley & Sons, New York, 1951.

30. ———, "Optimum Utilization of the Transportation System," *Proceedings of the International Statistical Conferences*, Washington, *15* (1947). Cowles Commission Paper, New Series, No. 34.

31. Kuhn, H. W., "The Hungarian Method for the Assignment Problem," *Nav. Res. Log. Quart.*, *2*, 83–98 (1955).

32. ———, and Tucker, A. W., *Contributions to the Theory of Games*, Annals of Mathematics Study No. 24, Princeton University Press, Princeton, 1950.

33. McKinsey, J. C. C., *Introduction to the Theory of Games*, McGraw-Hill Book Co., New York, 1953.

34. Neumann, J. von, and Morgenstern, O., *Theory of Games and Economic Behavior*, Princeton University Press, Princeton, 1947.

35. "New Machine Loading Methods," *Fact. Mgmt.*, *112*, no. 1, 136–137 (Jan. 1954).

36. Orden, A., "Survey of Research on Mathematical Solutions of Programming Problems," *Mgmt. Sci.*, *1*, 170–172 (1955).

37. Project SCOOP, *Symposium of Linear Inequalities and Programming*, Headquarters, U. S. Air Force, Washington, 1952.

38. Symonds, Gifford H., *Linear Programming: The Solution of Refinery Problems*, Esso Standard Oil Co., New York, 1955.

39. Vidale, M. L., "A Graphical Solution of the Transportation Problem," *J. Opns. Res. Soc. Am.*, *4*, no. 2, 193–203 (Apr. 1956).

40. Votaw, D. F., and Orden, A., "The Personnel Assignment Problem," *Symposium on Linear Inequalities and Programming*, Project SCOOP, Headquarters, U.S. Air Force, Washington, 1952.

Chapter 12

The Assignment Problem

INTRODUCTION

In Chapter 11, the solution of linear programming problems by means of the simplex and transportation techniques was discussed. There are, however, some special cases of linear programming problems whose solutions can be obtained by special techniques which greatly reduce the tremendous amount of computation that would otherwise follow from the use of the transportation and simplex techniques. In this chapter, we will consider one such special case—the assignment problem—which has many applications in the areas of allocation and scheduling.

THE ASSIGNMENT PROBLEM

The assignment problem can be stated as follows: Given n facilities and n jobs, and given the effectiveness of each facility for each job (the table which contains the n^2 values of effectiveness is called an $n \times n$, or n^2, matrix), the problem is to assign each facility to one and only one job in such a manner that the given measure of effectiveness is optimized.

The assignment problem presented above can be translated into problems in many management decision fields. As an example, consider the problem which confronts the scheduler of a fleet of tractors and trailers: He has n tractors available at different locations throughout the city and he wants n loaded trailers, lying at the docks of $m \leq n$ shippers, to be picked up and hauled to the freight terminal. His problem is to assign each of the n tractors to corresponding trailers in such a way that a given measure of effectiveness (e.g., the total distance traveled or the total time of travel for tractors) is optimized.

It might be noted that an n^2 matrix has $n!$ possible arrangements for making the assignments. A naïve way of finding an optimal assignment is to enumerate all $n!$ possible arrangements, evaluate their total cost (cost in terms of a given measure of effectiveness), and pick the assignment with the minimum cost. It is easily seen that this method becomes of formidable size for even small or moderate values of n. For example, when $n = 20$, not an uncommon situation, the possible number of arrangements is

$$n! = 20!$$
$$= 2{,}432{,}902{,}008{,}176{,}640{,}000$$

A fast electronic computer programming one arrangement per microsecond and working 8 hours a day, 365 days a year, would take almost a quarter of a million years to find the optimal solution. This example illustrates the need for easy computational techniques for solving the assignment problem.

Mathematical Model

The assignment problem can be stated mathematically as follows:

Given: an n^2 matrix $A_0 = \| a_{ij}^{(0)} \|$ (hereinafter referred to as the *rating matrix*), with $a_{ij}^{(0)} \geq 0$ for $i, j = 1, 2, \cdots, n (n \geq 3)$.

Find: an n^2 matrix $X = \| x_{ij} \|$ (hereinafter referred to as the *assignment* or *permutation matrix*), such that

$$x_{ij} = x_{ij}^2, \, i, j = 1, 2, \cdots, n \, (n \geq 3) \tag{1}$$

$$\sum_{i=1}^{n} x_{ij} = \sum_{j=1}^{n} x_{ij} = 1 \tag{2}$$

$$T = \sum_{i,j} a_{ij}^{(0)} x_{ij} = \text{minimum} * \tag{3}$$

Equations 1 and 2 are conditions which jointly specify that

(a) $x_{ij} = \begin{cases} 1, \text{ if facility } i \text{ is assigned to job } j \\ 0, \text{ otherwise} \end{cases}$

(b) each row and column of matrix X will have one element unity and all other elements zero.

---

* A maximization problem can easily be transformed into a minimization problem as is shown in Example 12-2 in this chapter.

Condition 3, together with eqs. 1 and 2, specify that a set of n elements is to be chosen from matrix A_0, with no two elements in the same row or column, such that the sum of the elements in the set is minimal. When these three conditions are satisfied simultaneously, we obtain the permutation matrix for the optimal solution.

To illustrate these mathematical concepts, we consider the 4×4 (or 4^2) matrix A_0 given in Table 12-1 which shows the cost, $a_{ij}^{(0)}$,

TABLE 12-1. MATRIX A_0. COST MATRIX

Facility \ Job	5	6	7	8
1	1	8	4	1
2	5	7	6	5
3	3	5	4	2
4	3	1	6	3

associated with allocating each of four facilities (numbered 1 through 4) to each of four jobs (numbered 5 through 8). The problem is to assign each facility to a job in such a way that the total cost of the assignment is minimized. (There are $4! = 24$ feasible solutions and therefore 24 possible permutation matrices.)

Table 12-2 shows the permutation matrix X^* for the optimal assignment. The cost associated with this assignment is

$$T^* = a_{15}^{(0)} + a_{27}^{(0)} + a_{38}^{(0)} + a_{46}^{(0)}$$

$$= 1 + 6 + 2 + 1$$

$$= 10 \text{ units}$$

On the other hand, Table 12-3 shows the permutation matrix for the *maximum* cost assignment. The total cost associated with this assignment is

$$T' = a_{16}^{(0)} + a_{28}^{(0)} + a_{35}^{(0)} + a_{47}^{(0)}$$

$$= 8 + 5 + 3 + 6$$

$$= 22 \text{ units}$$

TABLE 12-2.   MATRIX X^*.   OPTIMAL PERMUTATION MATRIX †

Facility \ Job	5	6	7	8	$\sum_j x_{ij}$
1	1				1
2			1		1
3				1	1
4		1			1
$\sum_i x_{ij}$	1	1	1	1	

† As in Chapter 11, zeros are omitted from this and subsequent matrices.

TABLE 12-3.   MATRIX X'.   PERMUTATION MATRIX FOR MAXIMUM
COST ASSIGNMENT

Facility \ Job	5	6	7	8	$\sum_j x_{ij}$
1		1			1
2				1	1
3	1				1
4			1		1
$\sum_i x_{ij}$	1	1	1	1	

Each solution represented in Tables 12-2 and 12-3 satisfies eqs. 1 and 2.

It might be noted parenthetically that there are cases of the assignment problem where eq. 1 can be replaced by the less restrictive condition *

$$x_{ij} \geq 0 \tag{4}$$

However, in this chapter we shall only treat cases for which eq. 1 holds. That is, we shall assume that one facility can be assigned to one job only.

In this form (i.e., with eq. 1) the assignment problem becomes the most degenerate case of the Hitchcock [12] distribution problem (also called the transportation problem) as has been shown by Flood.[5] Several algorithms † for solving the distribution problem exist and this aspect of the problem has been discussed in Chapter 11. It might, however, be pointed out that Flood [5] has extended the graph-theoretic methods employed by Koopmans and Reiter [15] for the nondegenerate case to solve the assignment problem as a special degenerate case of the distribution problem.‡

It is worth noting that the problem as represented by conditions 2, 3, and 4 (i.e., the less restrictive assignment problem obtained by replacing condition 1 by condition 4) can also be solved by using the simplex technique of linear programming. However, for the problem represented by conditions 1, 2, and 3, other techniques of solution offer vastly greater advantages over the simplex technique.

Technique of Solution

Several techniques for solving the assignment problem represented by conditions 1, 2, and 3 have been developed during the past 5 years, and interest in this area seems to be growing. Among the people who have made significant contributions are Dwyer,[3] Flood,[5,7,8] Kuhn,[16] and Votaw and Orden.[18]

Kuhn [16] first developed a computational algorithm for solving the problem based on the following theorem § proved by the Hungarian mathematician König in 1916 and stated by Egerváry: [4]

* See ref. 7, in particular pp. 69–70.
† In particular, see refs. 1, 3, 9, 11, 13, and 15.
‡ For discussion of the mathematical interrelationships between the transportation (distribution) problem and the assignment problem, see ref. 7, in particular pp. 62–63.
§ It appears that the theorem was first proved by Frobenius [2,10] in 1912.

If the elements of a matrix are divided into two classes by a property R, then the minimum number of lines that contain all of the elements with the property R is equal to the maximum number of elements with the property R, with no two on the same line.

In the above theorem, a line means a row or a column of a matrix. This theorem, together with the following important property,[17] is the basis for Kuhn's algorithm for solving the assignment problem:

Given a cost matrix $A = \| a_{ij} \|$, if we form another matrix $B = \| b_{ij} \|$, where

$$b_{ij} = a_{ij} - u_i - v_j \tag{5}$$

and where u_i and v_j are arbitrary constants, the solution of A is identical with that of B.

DUAL OF THE ASSIGNMENT PROBLEM. The dual of the assignment problem * is:

Find a set of constants u_i and v_j such that the following relations hold

$$a_{ij}^{(0)} \geqq u_i + v_j, \quad \text{for} \quad x_{ij} = 0 \tag{6}$$

$$a_{ij}^{(0)} = u_i + v_j, \quad \text{for} \quad x_{ij} > 0 \tag{7}$$

Using relation 6 and making a substitution in eq. 3, we obtain

$$T \geqq \sum_{i,j} (u_i + v_j) x_{ij}$$

$$\geqq \sum_{i,j} u_i x_{ij} + \sum_{i,j} v_j x_{ij}$$

i.e.

$$T \geqq \sum_i \left(u_i \sum_j x_{ij} \right) + \sum_j \left(v_j \sum_i x_{ij} \right)$$

From eq. 2

$$\sum_j x_{ij} = \sum_i x_{ij} = 1$$

Hence

$$T \geqq \sum_i u_i + \sum_j v_j$$

Thus, denoting the right-hand side of this relation by D, the problem associated with minimizing $\sum_{i,j} a_{ij}^{(0)} x_{ij}$ is identical to the following dual problem:

$$\text{Maximize } D = \sum_i u_i + \sum_j v_j \tag{8}$$

subject to $a_{ij}^{(0)} \geqq u_i + v_j$.

In the literature, D is called the *sum of the bounding set.*†

---

* For a discussion of the dual problem of linear programming see Chapter 11, Appendix C.

† For an economic interpretation of u_i and v_j in terms of budgets, see ref. 16, p. 87.

The Assignment Problem

STEPS IN SOLVING ASSIGNMENT PROBLEMS. Dwyer,[3] Flood,[7] and Kuhn [16] have used the dual problem for solving the assignment problem in a particularly effective manner. In this chapter, we will consider Flood's technique for the assignment problem since, for hand computations, it results in a substantial saving in time over the other techniques currently available.

Briefly, Flood's technique involves rapidly reducing the rating matrix A_0, eventually finding a set of n *independent* * zeros one in each row and each column. † This set (not necessarily unique) of n independent zeros gives an optimal solution to the assignment problem.

An outline of the steps involved in this technique is now given:

(a) *Step 1.* Examine the columns of the rating matrix A_0, identifying the smallest element $v_j^{(0)}$ ($= \min_i a_{ij}$) in each column.‡ Form a new matrix A_1 by replacing $a_{ij}^{(0)}$ with $a_{ij}^{(1)} = a_{ij}^{(0)} - u_i^{(0)} - v_j^{(0)}$, for $i, j = 1, \cdots, n$, and where $u_i^{(0)} \equiv 0$.

Notice that here we are reducing matrix A_0 by applying condition 5. Matrix A_1 will have at least one null (i.e., zero) element in each column.

(b) *Step 2.* Find a *minimal* set S_1 of lines, n_1 in number, that includes all null elements of A_1. If $n_1 = n$, there is in A_1 a set of n null elements, no two of which are in the same line, and the elements of A_0 in these n positions constitute the required optimum solution.

Cycle 0

(c) *Step 2'.* If $n_1 < n$, examine the rows of A_1, identifying the smallest element $u_i^{(1)}$ ($= \min_j a_{ij}^{(1)}$) in each row. Form a new matrix A_2 by replacing $a_{ij}^{(1)}$ with $a_{ij}^{(2)} = a_{ij}^{(1)} - u_i^{(1)} - v_j^{(1)}$, for $i, j = 1, \cdots, n$, and where $v_j^{(1)} \equiv 0$.

Matrix A_2 will have at least one null element in each line.

(d) Now follow step 2 as before, denoting the minimal set of lines, n_2 in number, by S_2. If $n_2 = n$, there is in A_2 a set of n null elements, no two of which are in the same line, and the elements of A_2 in these n positions constitute the required optimal solution.

Cycle 1

(e) *Step 3.* If $n_2 < n$, let h_2 denote the smallest element of A_2 not in any line of S_2. Subtract h_2 from all elements of A_2 not in S_2, and add h_2

---

* A set of zeros is said to be *independent* if no two (or more) zeros of this set lie on the same line.

† This is done by applying König's theorem. Hence the name "Hungarian Method" or the "Reduced Matrix Method."

‡ This means that for each column j, we find the smallest element $a_{ij}^{(0)}$ and call it $v_j^{(0)}$.

to all elements which lie at the intersections (if any) of lines of S_2; call the resulting matrix A_3.

(*f*) Check by means of step 2 if $n_3 = n$. If $n_3 = n$, an optimal solution exists as in (*d*) above.

(*g*) If $n_3 < n$, repeat the cycle until at some cycle k, $n_{k+2} = n$. Then an optimal solution exists in matrix A_{k+2} as in (*d*) above.

The flow diagram in Fig. 12-1 indicates the steps and cycles of this technique.

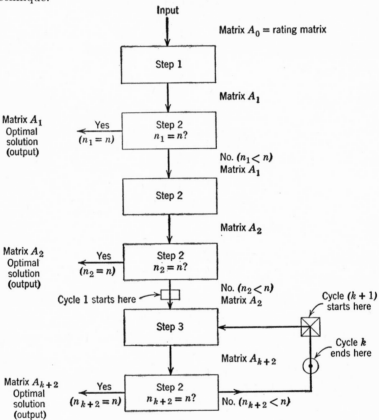

Cycle from step 3 to step 2 until at some cycle k (where k takes on positive integral values), $n_{k+2} = n$. Then matrix A_{k+2} will give the optimal solution(s).

Note: Input to and output from step 3 for the kth cycle are matrices A_{k+1} and A_{k+2} respectively.

Fig. 12-1. Flow diagram for Flood's optimal assignment technique.

Notice that for step 3 of cycle 1, we have matrix A_2 as input and matrix A_3 as output with the characteristics given in columns (1) and (2) of Table 12-4. In general, for the kth cycle ($k = 1, 2, \cdots, K$),

TABLE 12-4

	(1) Input Matrix A_2	(2) Output Matrix A_3	(3) Input Matrix A_{k+1}	(4) Output Matrix A_{k+2}
Element (i,j) of the matrix	$a_{ij}^{(2)}$	$a_{ij}^{(3)}$	$a_{ij}^{(k+1)}$	$a_{ij}^{(k+2)}$
Contribution to the sum of the bounding set D	$\sum_i u_i^{(2)} + \sum_j v_j^{(2)}$	—	$\sum_i u_i^{(k+1)} + \sum_j v_j^{(k+1)}$	—
Minimal set of lines	S_2	S_3	S_{k+1}	S_{k+2}
Number of lines in the minimal set	n_2	n_3	n_{k+1}	n_{k+2}
Minimal element in the matrix that is not in the covering set of lines	h_2	—	h_{k+1}	—

we will have the situation shown in columns (3) and (4) of Table 12-4 in regard to symbols.

It might be noted that step 3 of cycle 1 follows directly from condition 5 and is equivalent to the following two substeps:

(*a*) Replace $a_{ij}^{(2)}$ by $a_{ij}^{(3)\prime}$, where

$$a_{ij}^{(3)\prime} = a_{ij}^{(2)} - u_i^{(2)\prime} - v_j^{(2)\prime} \tag{9}$$

$$u_i^{(2)\prime} = h_2, \, v_j^{(2)\prime} \equiv 0, \, (i, j = 1, 2, \cdots, n) \tag{10}$$

That is, replace $a_{ij}^{(2)}$ by $(a_{ij}^{(2)} - h_2)$, (all i, j).

(*b*) Replace $a_{ij}^{(3)\prime}$ by $a_{ij}^{(3)}$ where

$$a_{ij}^{(3)} = a_{ij}^{(3)\prime} - u_i^{(2)\prime\prime} - v_j^{(2)\prime\prime} \tag{11}$$

Now, set *

$u_i^{(2)\prime\prime} = -h_2$ and $v_j^{(2)\prime\prime} = -h_2$, for elements contained in both lines i and j (written as $i, j, \, \epsilon \, S_2$).

$u_i^{(2)\prime\prime} = -h_2$ and $v_j^{(2)\prime\prime} = 0$, for $i \, \epsilon \, S_2$ but $j \, \notin \, S_2$ (12)

$u_i^{(2)\prime\prime} = 0$ and $v_j^{(2)\prime\prime} = -h_2$, for $j \, \epsilon \, S_2$ but $i \, \notin \, S_2$

$u_i^{(2)\prime\prime} = 0$ and $v_j^{(2)\prime\prime} = 0$, for $i, j \, \notin \, S_2$

Therefore

$$a_{ij}^{(3)} = \begin{cases} a_{ij}^{(3)\prime} + 2h_2, & \text{for both } i, j \, \epsilon \, S_2 \\ a_{ij}^{(3)\prime} + h_2, & \text{for either } i \, \epsilon \, S_2 \text{ } or \text{ } j \, \epsilon \, S_2, \text{ but not both} \\ a_{ij}^{(3)\prime}, & \text{for } i, j \, \notin \, S_2 \end{cases} \tag{13}$$

* The symbol ϵ is used to denote "belongs to," the symbol $\notin$ to denote "does not belong to."

Next, if we replace $a_{ij}^{(3)\prime}$ as given in step (a) above, the net result is

$$a_{ij}^{(3)} = \begin{cases} a_{ij}^{(2)} + h_2, & \text{both } i \in S_2 \text{ and } j \in S_2 \text{ (i.e., for elements at} \\ & \text{the intersections of } i \text{ and } j) \\ a_{ij}^{(2)}, & \text{either } i \in S_2 \text{ or } j \in S_2 \text{ but not both} \\ a_{ij}^{(2)} - h_2, & i, j \notin S_2 \end{cases} \tag{14}$$

Now, since
$$u_i^{(2)} = u_i^{(2)\prime} + u_i^{(2)\prime\prime}$$

$$u_i^{(2)} = \begin{cases} 0, & \text{for } i \in S_2 \text{ (since } h_2 - h_2 \equiv 0) \\ h_2, & \text{for } i \notin S_2 \end{cases} \tag{15}$$

Similarly, since
$$v_j^{(2)} = v_j^{(2)\prime} + v_j^{(2)\prime\prime}$$

$$v_j^{(2)} = \begin{cases} -h_2, & \text{for } j \in S_2 \text{ (since } 0 - h_2 = -h_2) \\ 0, & \text{for } j \notin S_2 \end{cases} \tag{16}$$

Similar remarks apply to step 3 in subsequent cycles.

The values u_i and v_j appearing in conditions 6 and 7 can be computed by applying the following formulas for a problem involving K cycles

$$u_i = u_i^{(0)} + u_i^{(1)} + u_i^{(2)} + \cdots + u_i^{(K+1)}$$

i.e.
$$u_i = u_i^{(0)} + u_i^{(1)} + \sum_{k=1}^{K} u_i^{(k+1)}, \quad i = 1, \cdots, n \tag{17}$$

Similarly
$$v_j = v_j^{(0)} + v_j^{(1)} + v_j^{(2)} + \cdots + v_j^{(K+1)}$$

i.e.
$$v_j = v_j^{(0)} + v_j^{(1)} + \sum_{k=1}^{K} v_j^{(k+1)}, \quad j = 1, 2, \cdots, n \tag{18}$$

From eq. 8 and a theorem relating dual problems, we can then state that the cost of the optimal assignment associated with the minimization problem of condition 3 is exactly the same as that associated with the maximization problem of condition 8, where the u_i and v_j are calculated by use of eqs. 17 and 18.

FURTHER REFINEMENT. The transformation given in step 1 states only one way of starting the solution of the assignment problem. Since our objective is to maximize D, it is desirable that our first transformation should make the *maximum* contribution to the bounding sum $\left(\sum_i u_i + \sum_j v_j \right)$. This is achieved as follows: compare $\sum_i \min_j a_{ij}^{(0)}$ $= \sum_j v_j^{(0)}$ with $\sum_i \min_j a_{ij}^{(0)} = \sum_i u_i^{(0)}$. If $\sum_j v_j^{(0)} \geqq \sum_i u_i^{(0)}$, step 1 and subsequent steps should be carried through as outlined above. However, if $\sum_j v_j^{(0)} < \sum_i u_i^{(0)}$, the $u_i^{(0)}$'s should be subtracted from each element of row i in matrix A_0 in step 1. If this is done, $v_j^{(1)} = \min_i a_{ij}^{(1)}$ will have to be subtracted from each element of matrix A_1 in order to complete step 2'. The remaining steps can then be carried through as previously outlined.

A desirable feature of this technique is that it is self-corrective in the sense that if, in any cycle k, we make an error in selecting the set S_{k+2}' such that $S_{k+2}' > S_{k+2}$, the set that contains the minimal number of lines required to cover all zeros in matrix A_{k+2}, the computations are not thereby invalidated. This type of error will automatically be corrected in subsequent stages.*

EXAMPLE 12-1. To illustrate the application of the assignment technique to a practical problem, consider the following example.

The Hi-Test Gasoline Company is in the business of distributing gasoline from its bulk storage to industrial consumers. For this purpose, it maintains a fleet of motor tractors and tank trailers. Since emptying a tank trailer at the consumer's dock usually takes about 2 hours, the tractor driver spots the loaded trailer at the consumer's dock, picks up an empty trailer from either the same or another consumer, and hauls it back to the bulk storage for refilling.

Let us assume that on a certain morning ten tractors (numbered 1 through 10) have been sent out to deliver ten loaded trailers to consumers located in different parts of the city. After spotting the trailers on consumers' unloading docks, these tractors are required to haul back to the bulk storage ten empty trailers (numbered 11 through 20) from the premises of ten consumers. The problem is to make the assignment of these ten tractors to ten empty trailers (i.e., here $n = 10$) in such a way that the cost of hauling back empty trailers is minimized.

In this problem, the cost (only that part of the cost which varies with the assignment is considered here) of hauling back empty trailers is known to be a function of (1) the distance traveled (the total distance from the point where the tractor drops a loaded trailer to the bulk storage via the point of location of the empty trailer is considered)

* For a technique which gets around the step of drawing of lines, see ref. 3.

TABLE 12-5.　MATRIX A_0.　RATING MATRIX: \$ COST OF TRACTOR-TRAILER ASSIGNMENT

Tractor No. \ Trailer No.	11	12	13	14	15	16	17	18	19	20	$u_i^{(0)} = 0$
1	4.10	4.10	7.90	8.30	2.60	8.70	7.10	9.90	2.20	9.40	0
2	4.60	6.10	4.50	0.90	4.80	6.40	8.80	6.20	0	0.20	0
3	9.70	3.60	5.30	0.90	7.60	2.80	3.50	7.90	4.00	7.00	0
4	2.00	6.50	2.30	5.70	7.40	1.60	2.40	9.70	5.00	1.90	0
5	2.10	1.40	5.00	5.20	1.70	4.70	2.80	6.70	6.30	0.50	0
6	1.70	7.80	3.00	0	1.50	1.00	8.00	6.80	3.00	9.10	0
7	9.10	5.30	0.30	6.40	6.60	3.90	9.80	1.60	2.40	8.10	0
8	4.90	1.70	7.70	5.70	7.90	4.00	9.50	0.80	4.80	2.00	0
9	2.90	8.80	1.80	5.90	6.60	6.20	8.80	0.70	0.30	2.60	0
10	8.40	7.40	0.60	2.60	6.00	7.70	3.70	9.90	0.20	7.90	0
$v_j^{(0)} = \min_i a_{ij}^{(0)}$	1.70	1.40	0.30	0	1.50	1.00	2.40	0.70	0	0.20	

and (2) the speed of travel. Knowing these factors, the rating matrix A_0 (Table 12-5), which gives the cost for each tractor-trailer combination, can be constructed.

The problem is to find the optimal assignment which will reduce the total cost of the assignment. A naïve and exceedingly difficult way of approaching this problem would be to try to determine the cost associated with every feasible assignment and then to pick the assignment with the minimum cost. It should be noted, however, that there are $10! = 3,628,800$ feasible assignments for this problem.

As an alternative, the transportation method of Koopmans and Reiter [15] could be tried. The problem, when solved (by hand) using this method, took 3 hours. The same problem was solved by the author in 20 minutes, using the technique outlined in this chapter.

In order to illustrate the application of the technique presented in this chapter, we proceed as follows:

Step 1. We examine each column of matrix A_0, find the minimum element $v_j^{(0)}$ and write it in the row below matrix A_0. In this example, $\sum_j \min_i a_{ij}^{(0)} = \$9.20$ and $\sum_i \min_j a_{ij}^{(0)} = \$6.80$. Since $\sum_j \min_i a_{ij}^{(0)} > \sum_i \min_j a_{ij}^{(0)}$, the transformation required in step 1 uses $v_j^{(0)}$ values.

Next, we subtract $v_j^{(0)}$ from every element of column j ($j = 11, \cdots, 20$) in matrix A_0 and obtain matrix A_1 (Table 12-6). This matrix has at least one null element in each column.

Step 2. The minimum number of lines which can cover all null elements in matrix A_1 is six. Thus $S_1 = \{$lines 2, 4, 5, 6, 7, 9$\}$ and $n_1 = 6 < n$ ($n = 10$). Hence the optimal solution has not been reached.

Step 2'. Since $n_1 < n$, we start cycle 0 by finding the minimum element $u_i^{(1)}$ in each row of A_1 and writing it on the extreme right side of A_1 in the column labeled $u_i^{(1)}$. We now subtract $u_i^{(1)}$ from every element of row i ($i = 1, \cdots, 10$) and obtain A_2 (Table 12-7). This matrix will have at least one null element in each line.

Step 2. The minimum number of lines which can cover all null elements in matrix A_2 is nine. Hence an optimal solution has not been reached and we proceed to step 3 (cycle 1).

Step 3. We find h_2, the smallest element of A_2, ignoring all elements covered by lines of S_2. In our example, referring to Table 12-7, we see that $h_2 = a_{4,11}^{(2)} = 0.30$. We add 0.30 to every element at the intersection of lines of S_2, and subtract 0.30 from every element of A_2 not in S_2 to obtain matrix A_3 (Table 12-8).

TABLE 12-6. MATRIX A_1. REDUCED MATRIX

Trac-tor No. \ Trailer No.	11	12	13	14	15	16	17	18	19	20	$u_i^{(1)} = \min_j a_{ij}$
1	2.40	2.70	7.60	8.30	1.10	7.70	4.70	9.20	2.20	9.20	1.10
2 ***	2.90	4.70	4.20	0.90	3.30	5.40	6.40	5.50	0	0	0
3	8.00	2.20	5.00	0.90	6.10	1.80	1.10	7.20	4.00	6.80	0.90
4 ***	0.30	5.10	2.00	5.70	5.90	0.60	0	9.00	5.00	1.70	0
5 ***	0.40	0	4.70	5.20	0.20	3.70	0.40	6.00	6.30	0.30	0
6 ***	0	6.40	2.70	0	0	0	5.60	6.10	3.00	8.90	0
7 ***	7.40	3.90	0	6.40	5.10	2.90	7.40	0.90	2.40	7.90	0
8	3.20	0.30	7.40	5.70	6.40	3.00	7.10	0.10	4.80	1.80	0.10
9 ***	1.20	7.40	1.50	5.90	5.10	5.20	6.40	0	0.30	2.40	0
10	6.70	6.00	0.30	2.60	4.50	6.70	1.30	9.20	0.20	7.70	0.20
$v_j^{(1)} \equiv 0$	0	0	0	0	0	0	0	0	0	0	

* * * indicates lines of S_1.

$S_1 = \{2, 4, 5, 6, 7, 9\}$; $n_1 = 6 < n$.

Next Step: Cycle 0:

Subtract $u_i^{(1)}$ from every element of row i ($i = 1, \cdots, 10$) to obtain matrix A_2.

TABLE 12-7. MATRIX A_2. REDUCED MATRIX

Trailer No. / Tractor No.	11	12	13	14	15	16	17	18	19	20	$u_i^{(2)}$
1	1.30	1.60	6.50	7.20	0	6.60	3.60	8.10	1.10	8.10	0.30
2	2.90	4.70	4.20	0.90	3.30	5.40	6.40	5.50	0	0	0.30
3	7.10	1.30	4.10	0	5.20	0.90	0.20	6.30	3.10	5.90	0.30
4	0.30	5.10	2.00	5.70	5.90	0.60	0	9.00	5.00	1.70	0.30
5	0.40	0	4.70	5.20	0.20	3.70	0.40	6.00	6.30	0.30	0.30
6	0	6.40	2.70	0	0	0	5.60	6.10	3.00	8.90	0
7	7.40	3.90	0	6.40	5.10	2.90	7.40	0.90	2.40	7.90	0.30
8	3.10	0.20	7.30	5.60	6.30	2.90	7.00	0	4.70	1.70	0.30
9	1.20	7.40	1.50	5.90	5.10	5.20	6.40	0	0.30	2.40	0.30
10	6.50	5.80	0.10	2.40	4.30	6.50	1.10	9.00	0	7.50	0.30
$v_j^{(2)}$	0	-0.30	-0.30	-0.30	-0.30	0	-0.30	-0.30	-0.30	-0.30	

*** indicates lines of S_2.

$S_2 = \{6, 12, 13, 14, 15, 17, 18, 19, 20\}$; $n_2 = 9 < n$.

Next Step: Cycle 1:

Since $h_2 = 0.30$, add 0.30 to every element at the intersections of lines of S_2 (elements $a_{6,12}^{(2)}$, $a_{6,13}^{(2)}$, $\cdots$, $a_{6,20}^{(2)}$) and subtract 0.30 from every element of A_2 not in S_2, resulting in matrix A_3.

TABLE 12-8. MATRIX A_3. REDUCED MATRIX

Trailer No. / Tractor No.	11	12	13	14	15	16	17	18	19	20	$u_i^{(3)}$
1	1.00	1.60	6.50	7.20	0	6.30	3.60	8.10	1.10	8.10	0
2	2.60	4.70	4.20	0.90	3.30	5.10	6.40	5.50	0	0	0.10
3	6.80	1.30	4.10	0	5.20	0.60	0.20	6.30	3.10	5.90	0.10
4	0	5.10	2.00	5.70	5.90	0.30	0	9.00	5.00	1.70	0
5	0.10	0	4.70	5.20	0.20	3.40	0.40	6.00	6.30	0.30	0.10
6	0	6.70	3.00	0.30	0.30	0	5.90	6.40	3.30	9.20	0
7	7.10	3.90	0	6.40	5.10	2.60	7.40	0.90	2.40	7.90	0
8	2.80	0.20	7.30	5.60	6.30	2.60	7.00	0	4.70	1.70	0.10
9	0.90	7.40	1.50	5.90	5.10	4.90	6.40	0	0.30	2.40	0.10
10	6.20	5.80	0.10	2.40	4.30	6.20	1.10	9.00	0	7.50	0.10
$v_j^{(3)}$	0	-0.10	0	-0.10	0	0	0	-0.10	-0.10	-0.10	

*** indicates lines of S_3.

$S_3 = \{1, 4, 6, 7, 12, 14, 18, 19, 20\}$; $n_2 = 9 < n$.

Next Step: Cycle 2:

Since $h_3 = 0.10$, add 0.10 to every element at the intersections of lines of S_3 ($a_{1,12}^{(3)}$, $a_{1,14}^{(3)}$, $\cdots$, $a_{7,20}^{(3)}$) and subtract 0.10 from every element of A_2 not in S_3 to obtain A_4.

TABLE 12-9. MATRIX A_4. REDUCED MATRIX

Trailer No. / Tractor No.	11	12	13	14	15	16	17	18	19	20	$u_i^{(4)}$
1	1.00	1.70	6.50	7.30	0	6.30	3.60	8.20	1.20	8.20	0
2	2.50	4.70	4.10	0.90	3.20	5.00	6.30	5.50	0	0	0
3	6.70	1.30	4.00	0	5.10	0.50	0.10	6.30	3.10	5.90	0
4	0	5.20	2.00	5.80	5.90	0.30	0	9.10	5.10	1.80	0
5	0	0	4.60	5.20	0.10	3.30	0.30	6.00	6.30	0.30	0
6	0	6.80	3.00	0.40	0.30	0	5.90	6.50	3.40	9.30	0
7	7.10	4.00	0	6.50	5.10	2.60	7.40	1.00	2.50	8.00	0
8	2.70	0.20	7.20	5.60	6.20	2.50	6.90	0	4.70	1.70	0.20
9	0.80	7.40	1.40	5.90	5.00	4.80	6.30	0	0.30	2.40	0.20
10	6.10	5.80	0	2.40	4.20	6.10	1.00	9.00	0	7.50	0
$v_j^{(4)}$	0	0	0	0	0	0	0	-0.20	0	0	

*** indicates lines of S_4.
$S_4 = \{1, 2, 3, 4, 5, 6, 7, 10, 18\}$; $n_4 = 9 < n$.
Next Step: Cycle 8:
Since $h_4 = 0.20$, add 0.20 to every element at the intersections of lines S_4 and subtract 0.20 from every element of A_4 not in S_4 to obtain A_5.

We repeat steps 2 and 3, starting with A_3, until in cycle 3 we reach A_5 (Table 12-10), wherein $n_5 = 10 = n$. The optimal solution can therefore be found from matrix A_5. This optimal assignment is indicated by [0]'s (to be read as independent zeros) in A_5. This assignment is: 1–15, 2–20, 3–14, 4–17, 5–11, 6–16, 7–13, 8–12, 9–18, and 10–19. This is to be interpreted as follows: Tractor no. 1 should be assigned to haul trailer no. 15, etc.

Using eq. 3, we can compute the total cost associated with the optimal assignment. This cost is (by reference to rating matrix A_0, Table 12-5):

$$T^* = 2.60 + 0.20 + 0.90 + 2.40 + 2.10$$

$$+ 1.00 + 0.30 + 1.70 + 0.70 + 0.20$$

i.e.

$$T^* = \$12.10$$

Although it is not necessary to compute the u_i's and v_j's for the purpose of obtaining the optimal assignment, we can verify the cost of our optimal assignment by using eqs. 15 through 18 and picking up the components of u_i's and v_j's from Tables 12-5 through 12-10 as follows:

$$u_1 = u_1{}^{(0)} + u_1{}^{(1)} + u_1{}^{(2)} + u_1{}^{(3)} + u_1{}^{(4)}$$

$$= 0 + 1.10 + 0.30 + 0 + 0$$

$$= 1.40$$

$$u_2 = u_2{}^{(0)} + u_2{}^{(1)} + u_2{}^{(2)} + u_2{}^{(3)} + u_2{}^{(4)}$$

$$= 0 + 0 + 0.30 + 0.10 + 0$$

$$= 0.40$$

Similarly we can compute $u_3, \cdots, u_{10}$ and $v_1, \cdots, v_{10}$. These values, together with the $a_{ij}{}^{(0)}$'s, are shown in Table 12-11. It is seen that

$$D^* = \sum_i u_i + \sum_j v_j = \$12.10$$

which checks with the value of T^* already obtained.

Table 12-11 also shows that wherever $x_{ij} = 1$ (a_{ij}'s corresponding to these values have been shown bracketed in the table), $a_{ij} = u_i + v_j$. Everywhere else, $a_{ij} > u_i + v_j$. Hence conditions 6 and 7 are also satisfied.

COMMENTS ON EXAMPLE 12-1. It might be noted that for the purpose of optimal assignment, matrices A_0 through A_5 represent the same problem. However, reduced matrices A_2 through A_5 are not

TABLE 12-10. MATRIX A_5. FINAL MATRIX

Trailer No. / Tractor No.	11	12	13	14	15	16	17	18	19	20
1	1.00	1.70	6.50	7.30	[0]	6.30	3.60	8.40	1.20	8.20
2	2.50	4.70	4.10	0.90	3.20	5.00	6.30	5.70	0	[0]
3	6.70	1.30	4.00	[0]	5.10	0.50	0.10	6.50	3.10	5.90
4	0	5.20	2.00	5.80	5.90	0.30	[0]	9.30	5.10	1.80
5	[0]	0	4.60	5.20	0.10	3.30	0.30	6.20	6.30	0.30
6	0	6.80	3.00	0.40	0.30	[0]	5.90	6.70	3.40	9.30
7	7.10	4.00	[0]	6.50	5.10	2.60	7.40	1.20	2.50	8.00
8	2.50	[0]	7.00	5.40	6.00	2.30	6.70	0	4.50	1.50
9	0.60	7.20	1.20	5.70	4.80	4.60	6.10	[0]	0.10	2.20
10	6.10	5.80	0	2.40	4.20	6.10	1.00	9.20	[0]	7.50

*** indicates lines of S_5.

$S_5 = \{1, 2, 3, 4, 5, 6, 7, 8, 9, 10\}$; $n_5 = 10 = n$; hence the optimal solution may be obtained from the set of null elements in A_5. The optimal assignment, which is unique in this example, is indicated by the symbol [0].

TABLE 12-11. MATRIX A_0. DEMONSTRATION OF DUALITY

Trailer No. / Tractor No.	11	12	13	14	15	16	17	18	19	20	u_i
1	4.10	4.10	7.90	8.30	[2.60]	8.70	7.10	9.90	2.20	9.40	1.40
2	4.60	6.10	4.50	0.90	4.80	6.40	8.80	6.20	0	[0.20]	0.40
3	9.70	3.60	5.30	[0.90]	7.60	2.80	3.50	7.90	4.00	7.00	1.30
4	2.00	6.50	2.30	5.70	7.40	1.60	[2.40]	9.70	5.00	1.90	0.30
5	[2.10]	1.40	5.00	5.20	1.70	4.70	2.80	6.70	6.30	0.50	0.40
6	1.70	7.80	3.00	0	1.50	[1.00]	8.00	6.80	3.00	9.10	0
7	9.10	5.30	[0.30]	6.40	6.60	3.90	9.80	1.60	2.40	8.10	0.30
8	4.90	[1.70]	7.70	5.70	7.90	4.00	9.50	0.80	4.80	2.00	0.70
9	2.90	8.80	1.80	5.90	6.60	6.20	8.80	[0.70]	0.30	2.60	0.60
10	8.40	7.40	0.60	2.60	6.00	7.70	3.70	9.90	[0.20]	7.90	0.60
v_j	1.70	1.00	0	-0.40	1.20	1.00	2.10	0.10	-0.40	-0.20	

Note: "[ ]" in i, j cell denotes $x_{ij} = 1$. All other $x_{ij} = 0$.

necessarily unique since usually many alternative choices for selecting the set of lines for covering all null elements exist and the matrix resulting from each transformation will depend upon which set of covering lines is selected.

VARIATIONS OF THE ASSIGNMENT PROBLEM

We shall now consider three variations of the optimization problem.

$n \times m$ $(m < n)$ Matrix

Sometimes the optimal assignment problem is presented in a form in which the matrix is not square. It is easy to convert such a matrix into a square matrix as is shown in the following example.

EXAMPLE 12-2. A trucking company engaged in the business of handling less-than-truck loads (LTL) maintains separate fleets of intracity and intercity trucks. Local pickups are made by intracity trucks and brought to the city freight terminal where the loads are sorted and transferred to appropriate intercity trucks.

The freight terminal can accommodate six intracity trucks simultaneously. There is a cost (of sorting and transferring of loads) associated with the spotting of each truck on each one of the six spots.

On a certain day, four intracity trucks (numbered 1 through 4) are to be simultaneously spotted at the terminal. Table 12-12 shows the cost matrix A. This matrix can be converted into a square matrix A_0

TABLE 12-12. MATRIX A. RATING MATRIX: $ COST OF TRUCK-TO-SPOT ASSIGNMENT

Spot \ Truck	1	2	3	4
7	3	6	2	6
8	7	1	4	4
9	3	8	5	8
10	6	4	3	7
11	5	2	4	3
12	5	7	6	2

by introducing two dummy trucks 5 and 6 as is shown in Table 12-13. Since there is no cost associated with spotting these dummy trucks on any one of the spots, the corresponding $a_{ij}^{(0)}$'s are all zero.

TABLE 12-13.   MATRIX A_0

Spot \ Truck	1	2	3	4	5	6
7	3	6	2	6	0	0
8	7	1	4	4	0	0
9	3	8	5	8	0	0
10	6	4	3	7	0	0
11	5	2	4	3	0	0
12	5	7	6	2	0	0
$v_j^{(0)} = \min_i a_{ij}^{(0)}$	3	1	2	2	0	0

We can now proceed to solve the matrix according to the method already outlined.   The optimal assignment is indicated by [0]'s in Table 12-14.   The solution is to be interpreted as follows:

Assign truck 1 to spot 9
Assign truck 2 to spot 8
Assign truck 3 to spot 7
Assign truck 4 to spot 12
Leave spots 10 and 11 vacant

The cost associated with this assignment is

$$\$(3 + 1 + 2 + 2) = \$8.00$$

It is also seen that for this example

$$v_j = v_j^{(0)}, \text{ for } j = 1, \cdots, 4$$

and $u_i = 0, \text{ for } i = 7, \cdots, 12$

It is easily seen from Table 12-13 that duality conditions 6 and 7 are also satisfied.

TABLE 12-14. MATRIX A_1. OPTIMAL ASSIGNMENT SHOWN BY [0]

Truck / Spot	1	2	3	4	5	6
7	0	5	[0]	4	0	0
8	4	[0]	2	2	0	0
9	[0]	7	3	6	0	0
10	3	3	1	5	0	[0]
11	2	1	2	1	[0]	0
12	2	6	4	[0]	0	0

Maximization Problem

Examples considered so far are essentially problems of minimization. However, it is easily seen that the same technique could be used to tackle problems of maximization.

One such problem is to assign persons to jobs in such a way that the expected profit is maximized. The technique for solving this type of problem will be illustrated by means of an example which, although fictitious, has all the flavor of a real problem.

EXAMPLE 12-3. Let us suppose that Womanpower, Inc., is in the business of supplying female help in a small commercial town. It maintains a salaried staff of four women (numbered 1 through 4) who beside being versatile in many common types of jobs are also experts in their own individual fields. The company maintains a roster of housewives trained in various jobs and who are willing to work on a temporary basis on days when more than four jobs have to be done. Clients are usually charged for services according to the productivity of girls assigned (e.g., number of letters typed, number of invoices prepared, number of orders packed, etc.)

On a certain day, the company has orders from clients for four jobs (numbered 5 through 8) for each of which the expected productivity of each salaried girl is known from past experience. A profit matrix C showing the day's expected profit in assigning girl i ($i = 1, \cdots, 4$) to job j ($j = 5, \cdots, 8$) can now be constructed (Table 12-15). The objective is to assign the four girls to the four jobs so as to maximize the day's expected profit.

TABLE 12-15. Matrix C. Profit Matrix: Day's Expected Profit
(in Dollars)

Girl \ Job	5	6	7	8
1	1	8	4	1
2	5	7	6	5
3	3	5	4	2
4	3	1	6	3

In order to solve this problem by Flood's technique, all we have to do is to convert matrix C into matrix A_0 by means of the following step $1'$:

Step 1'. We find max c_{ij} in matrix C. Then we construct matrix A_0 by making the following transformation

$$a_{ij}^{(0)} = (\max_{i,j} c_{ij}) - c_{ij} \qquad (19)$$

Matrix A_0 will have at least one null element.

We now follow the same procedure as that for minimization problems and pick out four independent zeros. The reader can easily verify that the optimal assignment is 1–6, 2–8, 3–5, and 4–7, and the day's expected profit for this assignment is $\$(8 + 5 + 3 + 6) = \$22.00$.

Further Restrictions

For illustration purposes, in the above examples we have considered cases where all $a_{ij}^{(0)}$'s were finite elements, but this need not be the case. For instance, if legal or other restrictions prohibit the assignment of any particular facility to any particular job, the matter can very easily be taken care of by associating an arbitrarily high (infinite) cost with the corresponding $a_{ij}^{(0)}$, i.e.

$$a_{ij}^{(0)} = \infty \qquad (20)$$

The activity will automatically be excluded from the optimal solution.

Use is made of this device in the traveling-salesman problem which is described in Chapter 16.

SUMMARY

In this chapter, a special type of linear programming problem—the assignment problem—has been discussed. The assignment problem is a mathematical "twin" of the distribution (the so-called transportation) problem for which many solution algorithms exist. For hand computations, the use of the Hungarian method for solving the assignment problem as developed by Flood is particularly effective.

BIBLIOGRAPHY

1. Charnes, A., and Cooper, W. W., "The Stepping Stone Method of Explaining Linear Programming," *Mgmt. Sci.*, *1*, no. 1, 49–69 (Oct. 1955).
2. Dulmage, L., and Halperin, I., "On a Theorem of Frobenius-König and J. von Neumann's Game of Hide and Seek," *Trans. roy. Soc. Can.*, Third Series, Sec. III, *49*, 23–29 (June 1955).
3. Dwyer, P. S., "The Solution of the Hitchcock Transportation Problem with a Method of Reduced Matrices," Statistical Laboratory, University of Michigan, Dec. 1955 (privately circulated).
4. Egerváry, J., "Matrixok Kombinatorius Tulajdonságairól," *Matematikai és Fizikai Lapok*, *38*, 16–28 (1931). Translated by H. W. Kuhn as "Combinatorial Properties of Matrices," *ONR Logistics Project*, Princeton University, Princeton, 1953 (mimeographed).
5. Flood, M. M., "On the Hitchcock Distribution Problem," *Pac. J. Math.*, *3*, no. 2, 369–386 (June 1953).
6. ———, "Operations Research and Logistics," *Proceedings of First Ordnance Conference on Operations Research*, Report No. 55-1, Office of Ordnance Research, Durham, pp. 3–25, Jan. 1955.
7. ———, "The Traveling-Salesman Problem," *J. Opns. Res. Soc. Am.*, *4*, no. 1, 61–75 (Feb. 1956).
8. ———, "The Traveling-Salesman Problem," in F. C. McCloskey and J. M. Coppinger (eds.), *Operations Research for Management*, The Johns Hopkins Press, Baltimore, 1956.
9. Ford, L. R., Jr., and Fulkerson, D. R., "A Simplex Algorithm for Finding Maximal Network Flows and an Application to the Hitchcock Problem," RAND Report RM-1604, RAND Corporation, Santa Monica, Dec. 20, 1955.
10. Frobenius, G., "Ueber Matrizen Mit Nicht Negativen Elementen," *Sitzungsberichte der Berliner Akad.*, *23*, 456–477 (1912).
11. Gleyzal, A., "An Algorithm for Solving the Transportation Problem," *J. Res. Nat. Bur. Stand.*, *54*, no. 4, 213–216 (Apr. 1955).
12. Hitchcock, F. L., "The Distribution of a Product from Several Sources to Numerous Localities," *J. Math. Phys.*, *20*, 224–250 (1941).
13. Houthakker, H. S., "On the Numerical Solution of the Transportation Problem," *J. Opns. Res. Soc. Am.*, *3*, no. 2, 210–214 (May 1955).

368 **Introduction to Operations Research**

14. König, D., *Theorie der Endlichen und Unendlichen Graphen*, Chelsea Publishing Co., New York, 1950.
15. Koopmans, T. C., and Reiter, S., "A Model of Transportation," in T. C. Koopmans (ed.), *Activity Analysis of Production and Allocation*, Cowles Commission Monograph No. 13, John Wiley & Sons, New York, 1951.
16. Kuhn, H. W., "The Hungarian Method for the Assignment Problem," *Nav. Res. Log. Quart.*, *2*, nos. 1 and 2, 83–98 (Mar.–June 1955).
17. Neumann, J. von, "A Certain Zero-Sum Two-Person Game Equivalent to the Optimal Assignment Problem," in H. W. Kuhn and A. W. Tucker (eds.), *Contributions to the Theory of Games II*, Annals of Mathematics Study No. 28, Princeton University Press, Princeton, pp. 5–12, 1953.
18. Votaw, D. F., and Orden, A., "The Personnel Assignment Problem," in A. Orden and L. Goldstein (eds.), *Symposium on Linear Inequalities and Programming*, Project SCOOP, Headquarters, U.S. Air Force, Washington, pp. 155–163, 1952.

Chapter 13

Some Illustrations
of Allocation
Problems

In Chapter 11 two analytic techniques for solving linear programming problems were presented, namely the transportation and simplex techniques. The transportation technique can be used with a great deal of ease (by clerical help, for example) but as explained in Chapter 11 is applicable only to a restricted group or class of linear programming problems. On the other hand, the simplex technique is applicable to the general linear programming problem but, even though the mathematics involved in the technique are only at the level of grade-school arithmetic, such an enormous bulk of arithmetic is usually encountered that one must either resort to high-speed electronic computers or introduce simplifications in order to reduce the scope and size of the problem.

In many industrial situations, especially where direct access to electronic computers is not available, the use of high-speed electronic computers is not practical even though machine time can be rented from a service bureau. In many cases, decisions must be made so soon after the receipt of the essential data that sufficient time does not exist for the use of such computer services. This might occur in day-to-day machine loading problems and other problems being handled on a continuing basis.

To offer some means of solving such linear programming problems on at least a near-optimal basis, a nonanalytic (so-called quick and dirty) technique is discussed in this chapter by means of an actual industrial problem and a hypothetical example. Then, lest one think that all linear programming problems must be solved by nonanalytic procedures, highlights of several case studies in which analytic techniques were used are also discussed.

NONANALYTIC SOLUTION OF
AN ALLOCATION PROBLEM

The problem concerns a producer of antibiotics and may be described as follows: The production of antibiotics involves many steps culminating in a semiautomatic filling operation during which small vials are filled and then capped after a short trip along conveyor belts from the sterile filling area to the capping machine center. The filling machines used are specialized pieces of equipment that may be either purchased or rented; they have different capacities, different filling rates, and different costs of operation. The production scheduler for the filling operation receives, in advance, a statement of the monthly production requirements. The scheduler must then draw up a production schedule that states not only *how much* of each product is to be filled by *which* machine but also *when* these products are to be filled. In other words, the production scheduler must give answers to the following questions:

1. How much? (lot size, etc.)
2. Where? (allocation)
3. When? (scheduling)

The first question, "how much?", involves such things as determination of economic lot sizes. The second, or "where?", refers to allocating the products to the filling machines, and the "when?" is concerned with the scheduling, or the actual timing of the various steps and materials in the filling operation. Now, the process is such that, once the filling schedule is completed, the scheduler can then work backwards to schedule the entire production of antibiotics for all of the steps required. In this case, there is no problem in scheduling forward to the capping machines inasmuch as the caps are identical for all vials, and since all capping machines are of the same make and model and have plenty of unused capacity.

Where does linear programming fit into this picture? Once the quantities to be produced are determined, linear programming can then be used to answer question 2; i.e., it can provide the scheduler with a tool for *allocating* the products to the various filling machines. Notice particularly that linear programming *allocates;* it does not answer question 3, i.e., it does not *schedule.* In other words, after an optimum allocation has been determined, there still remains the task of scheduling.

Now, our particular company produces 12 different basic antibiotics which appear either in powder form or in oil or aqueous suspensions.

If we count as separate products those antibiotics which appear in more than one form, we then get a total of 16 products. Furthermore, any given product may appear in as many as six different vial sizes, so that, all told, there are produced 53 different combinations.

In the filling department, there are nine filling machines. Of these, three are so-called wet-fill machines, i.e., they fill those products which appear in aqueous or oil suspension, and the other six are dry-fill machines. The products they fill are mutually exclusive and collectively exhaustive; in other words, none of the 16 products referred to can be filled on both sets of machines. Thus, two smaller problems replace the first over-all one.

The problem to be discussed here is that of allocating the dry-fill products so as to minimize the total cost of the filling operation. These dry-fill products, incidentally, constitute 10 of the 16 products and 31 of the original 53 combinations.

Mathematical Statement of Problem

For this problem, we adopt the following notation:

x_{ij} = amount of the jth product to be filled on the ith machine

c_{ij} = cost of filling the jth product on the ith machine

t_{ij} = time required to fill one vial of the jth product on the ith machine

p_j = amount needed of the jth product for this scheduling period

b_i = rated capacity limit of the ith machine

m = the number of dry-filling machines, namely six

n = the number of different products * to be filled in any scheduling period, $n \leq 31$

Source of the Given Constants

Costs. Production costs are standard costs designed to include setup, internal maintenance, external maintenance, cleanup, adjustments in run, operating labor, operating supplies, and scrap and waste. Using this notation, the total cost C of filling the products will be given by

$$C = \sum_{i=1}^{m} \sum_{j=1}^{n} x_{ij}c_{ij} = \sum_{i,j} x_{ij}c_{ij}$$

* In the discussion which follows, different vial sizes of the same antibiotic are treated as separate products. The determination of the filling sequence is a separate (scheduling) problem *not* answered by linear programming (allocation) techniques.

while other pertinent items such as time consumed and quantities produced are given by the following expressions:

1. Total time used on the ith machine by all products:

$$\sum_{j=1}^{n} t_{ij} x_{ij}$$

2. Total amount of the jth product which is filled on all machines:

$$\sum_{i=1}^{m} x_{ij}.$$

Thus, our linear programming problem can be stated as follows: * Given c_{ij}, t_{ij}, p_j, b_i ($i = 1, 2, \cdots, m$; $j = 1, 2, \cdots, n$), determine the $x_{ij} \geq 0$ which minimize

$$C = \sum_{i,j} c_{ij} x_{ij}$$

subject to the restrictions

$$\sum_{j=1}^{n} t_{ij} x_{ij} \leq b_i, \qquad i = 1, 2, \cdots, m$$

$$\sum_{i=1}^{m} x_{ij} \geq p_j, \qquad j = 1, 2, \cdots, n$$

Notice that all costs and times are assumed to be *linear;* i.e., it is assumed that it costs ten times as much to fill ten vials as it does to fill one vial and, furthermore, that it takes ten times as long to do so. The linearity assumption is, ordinarily, necessary for a problem of this type if one is to be able to apply the techniques referred to in the foregoing—hence, the name *linear* programming.†

Where the costs listed were independent of the machine, they were omitted from the study since they would not affect the total cost under any change in allocation. Furthermore, for this problem, the variations in setup cost from machine to machine for any given product were so small that setup costs could also be neglected. (This assumption, incidentally, eliminates a nonlinear cost factor; however, in this problem, an appreciable setup cost would not have presented too great a problem inasmuch as the products are normally run in specified lot

---

* The problem could also have been stated in terms of maximum profits, optimum inventory levels, and the like. It should be emphasized, however, that, unlike the situation discussed here, minimum costs do not necessarily imply maximum profits.

† These methods may also be applied to certain special nonlinear optimization problems. See, e.g., Lemke and Charnes.[2]

sizes so that a setup cost per vial per machine could have been realistically assigned.) Combining the remaining costs yields a matrix of incremental production costs per 1000 vials as shown in Table 13-1.*

TABLE 13-1. Production Costs per 1000 Vials

Machine Product	1	2	3	4	5	6
1	1.417	2.747	2.373	1.564	3.252	2.060
2	1.425	2.450	2.236	1.509	3.084	2.141
3	1.368	2.402	2.188	1.452	2.994	2.061
4	1.368	2.900	2.686	1.452	2.994	2.061
5	1.355	2.470	2.201	1.460	2.978	2.048
6	2.703			2.806	3.138	2.192
7					6.118	4.227
8					10.040	
9	1.365	2.400	2.185	1.448	2.990	2.056
10					6.109	4.216
11	2.612			2.693	2.990	2.056
12					6.109	4.216
13	1.425	2.450	2.236	1.509	3.085	2.141
14	1.425	2.450	2.236	1.509	3.085	2.141
15					3.355	2.384

RATES. Rates were obtained by direct observation and from standard rates based on time studies and are given in Table 13-2.*

MACHINE CAPACITIES. The total ideal available time must be adjusted to allow for rest periods, setup time, breakdowns, queuing disturbances, etc. This results in a rated available capacity. For the

* Blanks in the table mean that the product could not be filled on the corresponding machine.

TABLE 13-2. Pharmaceutical Filling Rates (Minutes per Vial), Parts Requirements, and Rated Available Times

Machine Product	1	2	3	4	5	6	Requirements
1	0.0125	0.0200	0.0200	0.0125	0.0625	0.0417	55,500
2	.0125	.0200	.0200	.0125	.0625	.0417	22,799
3	.0125	.0200	.0200	.0125	.0625	.0417	35,933
4	.0125	.0250	.0250	.0125	.0625	.0417	53,097
5	.0125	.0200	.0200	.0125	.0625	.0417	514,793
6	.0250			.0250	.0625	.0417	43,987
7					.1250	.0833	77,697
8					.2000		4,363
9	.0125	.0200	.0200	.0125	.0625	.0417	447,060
10					.1250	.0833	11,494
11	.0250			.0250	.0250	.0417	215,646
12					.1250	.0833	12,023
13	.0125	.0200	.0200	.0125	.0625	.0417	25,154
14	.0125	.0200	.0200	.0125	.0625	.0417	44,963
15					.0625	.0417	4,046
Time available	7920	7920	7920	7920	7920	7920	

Some Illustrations of Allocation Problems

initial study, the rated available time was taken to be equal for machines, namely 7920 minutes per month.

TOTAL AMOUNTS TO BE PRODUCED OF EACH PRODUCT. The production requirements are obtained by the production scheduling department from the sales department and are based on sales forecasts and contracts. This set of data is easy for the production planning department to obtain and, for a specific month, might appear as in the right-hand column of Table 13-2.

For the month's production as given in Table 13-2, the linear programming problem can now be stated as follows: Given c_{ij}, t_{ij}, p_j, b_i ($i = 1, 2, \cdots, 6; j = 1, 2, \cdots, 15$), determine $x_{ij} \geq 0$ which minimize

$$C = \sum_{i=1}^{6} \sum_{j=1}^{15} c_{ij} x_{ij}$$

subject to the restrictions

$$\sum_{i=1}^{6} x_{ij} \geq p_j, \qquad j = 1, 2, \cdots, 15$$

$$\sum_{j=1}^{15} t_{ij} x_{ij} \leq b_i, \qquad i = 1, 2, \cdots, 6$$

That is, we must determine the values of the 90 variables x_{ij} so as to minimize the 90-term cost equation and, at the same time, satisfy the 21 restrictive inequations just given.

This problem, and others that appear in this and similar forms, can be solved by the second of the two techniques of linear programming to which reference has been made, namely the simplex technique. However, no attempt will be made to use this technique to carry out the solution here, for if one were to exhibit just the first step, or tableau, in the calculational procedure one would have a matrix (or chart) consisting of 127 columns and 23 rows.* Furthermore, using a rule of thumb that applies to simplex calculations, final answers would be obtained only after 22 to 34 more such tableaux or matrices.

Computation Procedures

Realizing the large number of calculations needed, one might then naturally raise the question, "How is the solution to this problem to be obtained in practice?" That is, what can be said, in general, about obtaining solutions to problems of similar magnitude?

---

* Actually, some of the 127 columns are not required since the corresponding x_{ij} are obviously equal to zero (e.g., x_{71}, x_{81}, x_{86}, etc.).

First of all, how about manual or desk calculator computation? To solve the problem described here would take one person approximately 15 to 22 days—one working month—and would undoubtedly involve computational errors. If we neglected the probability of error, this method of procedure would obviously still be of doubtful value except for problems involving rather long-range planning, i.e., where a month's time is of relative unimportance.

How about automatic computing equipment? As shown in Chapter 11, the simplex technique necessitates selecting the most negative number from a given set of numbers and then choosing the smallest positive number in a corresponding set of ratios. Accordingly, the smaller automatic computers [and this would include machines up to the size and capacity of the IBM CPC (Card-Programmed Electronic Calculator)] would require many manual operations which would greatly extend the total elapsed time of solution and, hence, might be impractical even though faster than hand computation. The answer, in so far as automatic computing equipment is concerned, seems to lie in machines such as the IBM 701 or IBM 704 or the Remington-Rand UNIVAC. Instead of requiring 15 to 22 days on a desk calculator, these latter machines can present the solution in less than 1 hour's time. Added to this, of course, must be the time required to prepare the data for input, interpret the results, etc.; but, in total, there would be a substantial saving of time compared with the original 15 to 22 days.

What can be accomplished, however, if access to automatic computers is not readily available or if their use is deemed impractical for some reason? The answer, here, seems to lie in nonanalytic or, if you wish, trial-and-error techniques which may yield quite satisfactory results that are often very close to the optimal solution. In fact, in the problem stated here, it was decided to follow this course of action and excellent results were obtained.

Just what is this nonanalytic or trial-and-error technique? For purposes of illustration, and to avoid involvement in a mass of numbers, let us consider an example that was cited in an article written by M. G. Melden.[3] This example concerns the minimization of machine time in the production of six parts in a 3-machine center. The basic data are given in Table 13-3 and include number of parts required, the rated available capacity of each machine, and the production hours required per unit per machine. The technique may be described as a common-sense technique and goes something like this:

STEP 1. For each part to be manufactured, select that machine which will produce the part in the best fashion (i.e., with least cost, least running time or maximum profit, depending on what the objective may be). This yields an "ideal" schedule,* namely one which does not take into account capacity limitations on the equipment.†

TABLE 13-3. PARTS AND TIME REQUIREMENTS (HOURS PER UNIT)

Machine \ Part	1	2	3	4	5	6	Available Machine Hours
1	3	3	2	5	2	1	80
2	4	1	1	2	2	1	30
3	2	2	5	1	1	2	160
Parts Required	10	40	60	20	20	30	270

STEP 2. Adjust this schedule, by trial and error, accepting next best choices until the given capacity limitations are satisfied or until the desired objective is satisfactorily achieved.‡

With the example of six parts and three machines as stated in Table 13-3, this technique would first yield the ideal program given in Table 13-4. In this ideal program, machine 2 is overloaded, since 100 hours have been allocated and only 30 hours are available. On the other hand, machines 1 and 3 still have 50 and 100 hours available respectively. Therefore, the planner needs to reduce or eliminate the overload on machine 2 by essentially shifting some of its loadings to machines 1 and 3 according to next best choices.

The obvious changes in loadings would be, in this case, those that increase the time by only 1 hour per unit. Thus, part 2 could be reallocated from machine 2 to machine 3 and part 3 could be reallocated to machine 1. This might suggest an allocation such as is given in

* It should be emphasized that, in reality, one has thus far obtained only an "ideal allocation." The schedule, as such, still remains to be completed.

† It may well be the case that the capacity limitations cannot be satisfied without resorting to extra shifts or overtime. In that instance, the desired objective might be to minimize the total overtime or to spread the overtime evenly over certain machines.

‡ If all of the capacity limitations are satisfied with this ideal program, then there is obviously no problem here.

TABLE 13-4. "Ideal Schedule"

Machine \ Part	1	2	3	4	5	6	Machine Hours Available	Machine Hours Scheduled
1						30	80	30
2		40	60				30	100
3	10			20	20		160	60
Parts required	10	40	60	20	20	30	270	190

Table 13-5, wherein 25 units of part 3 are now to be made on machine 1 and all 40 units of part 2 are to be made on machine 3. Note that machine 1 is now fully loaded, machine 2 is now overloaded by 5 hours, while machine 3 still has 20 hours of unused capacity. A little reflection then suggests the final set of shifts as indicated in Table 13-6,

TABLE 13-5. Adjusted Interim Schedule

Machine \ Part	1	2	3	4	5	6	Machine Hours Available	Machine Hours Scheduled
1			25			30	80	80
2			35				30	35
3	10	40		20	20		160	140
Parts required	10	40	60	20	20	30	270	255

where, for this example, all three machines are now fully loaded and no overtime is needed. It should be pointed out that the solution as given in Table 13-6 is actually the optimum solution, as can be verified by use of the simplex technique.

TABLE 13-6. OPTIMUM SCHEDULE

Machine \ Part	1	2	3	4	5	6	Machine Hours Available	Machine Hours Scheduled
1			30			20	80	80
2			30				30	30
3	10	40		20	20	10	160	160
Parts required	10	40	60	20	20	30	270	270

Although a time comparison is probably not fair with such a small-scale example, it might, nevertheless, be pointed out that the corresponding solution by the simplex technique involves an 11 by 34 matrix and requires 11 steps or iterations (i.e., there will be 11 such matrices) and would require approximately 4 hours of computation by an experienced person. This may be compared with the few minutes required for the nonanalytic (trial-and-error) procedure just described.

To return to the general antibiotic problem, excellent results can be obtained by the nonanalytic technique in at most a few hours and while, in general, this technique does not yield the optimal solution, it does nevertheless yield a distinct improvement over the techniques of allocation that were practiced by this particular company. In other words, while the technique may not be the ultimate allocation procedure—this might well require the use of electronic computers—it does represent a definite step in the right direction and paves the way for further improvements.*

OPTIMUM UTILIZATION OF STEEL-PROCESSING FACILITIES

Another illustration of an allocation problem arises in the study of the optimum utilization of steel-processing facilities. Although the

* For a refinement of the operational use of the technique described herein, see ref. 4.

In this particular problem, the cost of obtaining the "optimum" solution would exceed the added profits to be gained; hence, the "quick-and-dirty" solution is, in a sense, itself optimum.

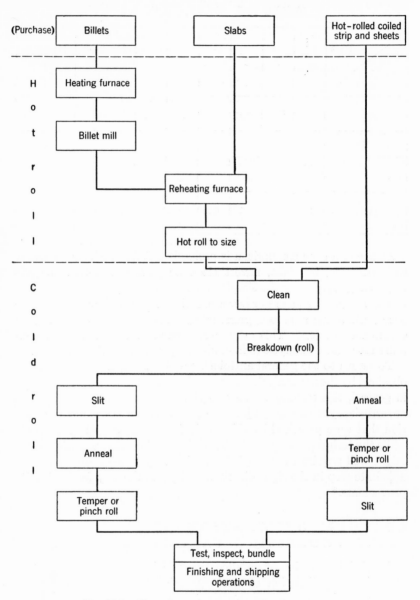

Fig. 13-1. Flow chart: hot- and cold-roll operations.

solution to this problem also involved nonanalytic procedures, the purpose of the discussion here is not to illustrate another application of nonanalytic procedures but, rather, to show the special devices which were necessary in order to make the problem amenable to solution.

The operations and facilities under study were those associated with the production of cold-rolled steel products. These products can be obtained either by starting with semiprocessed materials called *slabs* or *billets* and processing them through hot- and cold-roll operations or by processing purchased hot-rolled strip and sheets in the cold-roll mill. The production sequence is shown in highly simplified form in Fig. 13-1 and is seen to include heating, rolling, slitting, and annealing operations. As Fig. 13-1 shows, one may vary, or permute, the sequence of operations. Additionally, many products may require several passes through some of the operations (e.g., the anneal and roll sequence is usually repeated for narrow-gauge products, since they cannot be reduced to the desired size in one pass without having the metal lose some of the required characteristics). Finally, within each operation center, there is a choice as to the equipment to be used to perform that operation.

Accordingly, in order to determine the optimum utilization of the steel-making facilities, one needs to determine the types and sizes of semiprocessed materials (such as slabs, billets, sheets, or strip) and the practices (i.e., sequence of operations and specific machine assignments) to be used in the fulfillment of customer orders.

Data Required for Solution of Problem

It is readily apparent that this is an allocation problem and one to which the techniques of linear programming might be applicable. However, before being able to apply linear programming techniques, it was necessary to procure data such as 1. standard product costs, 2. setup times, 3. production rates, 4. machine capacities, and 5. amount required of each product. Additionally, *it was necessary to render these data available in a readily usable form.*

The need to make the required data available in a readily usable form was emphasized when considering the standard product costs. These costs were available only on a large collection of individual cards for each operation in a manufacturing sequence and, as such, were not in a form directly of use for the study.* This is evidenced by the fact that, under the existing procedure, it took approximately 60 to 75

---

* It should be pointed out that the cost computations for each operation include determining scrap losses, overhead costs, and the like.

minutes to obtain the standard product cost for each product, given the sequence of operations and the essential characteristics (such as temper, finish, edge, gauge, width, and quantity) of the product. Thus, if one were to consider only 100 orders per week and an average of four alternate practices * for each order, approximately 400 to 500 man-hours would have been required each week under the existing procedure in order to derive just the standard production costs. It was obvious that this time and manpower requirement was prohibitive if linear programming techniques were to be of any practical use in solving the weekly allocation problem.

To resolve the difficulty, it was necessary to develop a means of presenting accurate cost data in a convenient and readily accessible form. This was finally accomplished by means of graphs, which gave the standard product cost (for width, gauge, and size of order) for the entire manufacturing sequence, and, additionally, showed the relative costs of alternative manufacturing practices (with respect to basic materials, sequence of operations, and choice of machines). The development of these costing graphs is discussed in the next section.

DEVELOPMENT OF COST GRAPHS. To illustrate the development of the cost graphs, consider, for the moment, just one of the machine centers, namely that of the breakdown (rolling) equipment or train sets. A product of a given finished width may be obtained by first rolling some multiple of that width and later slitting to size. Since the train sets have varying capacities with respect to width, one's choice of the number of multiples may then determine the corresponding train set to be used. Further complications arise due to the fact that there is usually a choice of facility for each width (because of overlapping in capabilities of train sets). Thus, for a given finished width of product, one has to determine the type and width of starting materials, the sequence of operations, and the choice of equipment. Fortunately, however, although an exceedingly large number of combinations exist in theory, only a few (approximately two to eight) choices exist in practice.

For train sets, it can be shown that, for a specific gauge, the unit cost of production (exclusive of setup costs) varies inversely with the width. Thus, if one considers, for example, a train set on which one can roll products 4 inches to 24 inches wide (i.e., in-process width), the lowest unit cost (i.e., cost per pound) will be achieved at the widest width, here 24 inches. Then, as the finished width decreases from 24

* Although there may be a high number of possible alternate practices, the number of possibilities that need be considered realistically varies from two to eight, depending upon the product.

inches, the unit cost will increase according to the law of proportionality

$$\text{Cost} = k/(\text{finished width})$$

until the finished width reaches 12 inches. On a machine capable of rolling 24-inch-wide material, it is not economical to roll a single 12-inch width. Rather, one would roll 24-inch material (i.e., two multiples) and later slit the material in two.* Thus, except for the added cost of slitting, one can roll 12-inch material at the same unit cost as 24-inch material. Similar discussion applies to 8 inches, 6 inches, etc., namely for 3, 4, $\cdots$ multiples. Figure 13-2 represents the typical

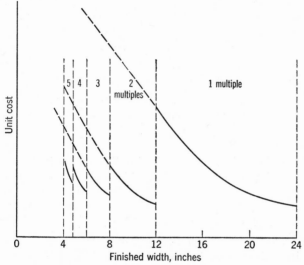

Fig. 13-2. Unit cost as a function of finished width.

total unit cost curve (including setup costs) which results when one considers the possibility of rolling in multiples. In Fig. 13-2 the unit cost is plotted against the finished width.†

Cost curves such as shown in Fig. 13-2 were established for a "standard" product ‡ for all pertinent equipment in the various operations

* For purposes of this discussion, scrap allowances necessary for slitting, edging, etc., are assumed to be zero.

† The reader should note in Fig. 13-2 that for a finished width, say, 7 inches, one has, in theory, three choices for the one train set, namely to roll at 7, 14, or 21 inches and slit subsequently, if needed. The solid curve in Fig. 13-2 represents the cheapest, i.e., rolling at 21 inches, while the dashed curves represent the more costly choices and are obtained by extending the cost curves which exist for the greater widths.

‡ The "standard" product was one consisting of a certain temper, finish, edge, and gauge. In addition, a "standard" size of order was also assumed.

centers. Parallel curves were developed for varying gauges and, additionally, an auxiliary table of factors was calculated in order to be able to take into account variations in the size of the order. Then these cost curves were superimposed for each operation, thereby yielding a visual comparison of unit costs in any operations center.

Total cost curves were also derived for the more common sequences of operations; i.e., total cost curves were obtained for an entire practice. These cost curves were also arranged so as to provide a visual comparison of total unit costs for the various choices of practices which could be used to produce a product of the desired finished width.

These cost curves were developed only after continued cross-checking with existing standard product costs. After being developed, they were checked for a wide range of items, and the costs obtained by using the curves differed from the accepted standard product costs by negligible amounts. Additionally, instead of the 60 to 75 minutes per cost as previously required, standard product costs could very easily be obtained in less than 5 minutes.

Observations

Once having developed a means of rapidly obtaining accurate cost data, the solution of the allocation problem followed quickly by use of specially devised nonanalytic procedures.

In summary, two important observations should be made. First, as originally posed, the problem was to determine the optimum utilization of only the company's hot-rolling mill. However, analysis of the organization quickly revealed that this question could not be answered without studying the cold-rolling mill as well. Consideration of just the hot-roll facilities would not have led to an optimum solution. Second, the major difficulty was not in the solution of a unit cost matrix but, rather, in the determination of the cost matrix itself. Once a practical means of producing unit costs had been devised, the allocation problem could be quickly solved.

OPTIMUM COAL-PURCHASING PROGRAM

In this section another allocation problem is discussed, namely that dealing with the purchase of coal from mines for delivery to power plants of an electric utility company. This problem was readily solved by the simplex technique, but only after the introduction of a special device which will now be discussed.

For the electric utility company studied, a certain level of energy output is required.* This energy is generated at several company plants using fuel purchased from a variety of bituminous coal fields. The available coals have a range of characteristics and costs. The significant characteristic which enables one to differentiate between one coal source and another is the Btu content per pound, inasmuch as this then determines the number of tons of a particular coal which must be purchased for, shipped to, and handled at any plant.

Costs per ton delivered at each plant were easily determined. These costs included the cost of coal at the source, transportation costs, and handling costs at the destination.

Although it was easy to determine the total energy requirements (in kilowatt-hours) for each plant, one could not readily translate these requirements into tons of coal because of variations in the Btu content of the various grades of coal. The simple, but essential, device employed here consisted of 1. converting the energy requirements for each plant from kilowatt-hours to Btu's, and 2. expressing the cost of coal as a function of its Btu content rather than on a tonnage basis.†

Once this transformation was made, the optimum coal-purchasing program was easily determined by the simplex technique.‡ The optimum tableau resulting from the simplex technique was also analyzed to consider the effect of variations in the given restrictions, thereby helping to evaluate existing purchasing policies.

DETERMINATION OF THE OPTIMUM BURDEN FOR A BLAST FURNACE

A very fruitful application of linear programming techniques was made in a study (completed in 1954) dealing with the determination of the best (optimum) burdens for the blast furnace production of pig iron. This is essentially a "diet mix" problem in which one seeks to produce an end product (i.e., pig iron) of certain predetermined metallurgical specifications (with respect to manganese, sulphur, phosphorus, etc.) by an appropriate mixture of the various iron-bearing input materials.

In the usual "diet mix" problem, one seeks simply to *blend* various

---

* The required level is determined by forecasts and current weather conditions. Protection against errors in forecasts is provided by means of 1. "spinning spare," i.e., machines which are immediately able to take up any slack, and 2. interconnections with neighboring utilities.

† That is, the Btu was used as the common unit in order to be able to treat both tonnages and kilowatt-hours.

‡ Restrictions on the solution included energy requirements at each plant and maximal and minimal purchasing requirements at each coal mine.

input materials so as to produce an output product of certain specifications. This is true in mixing cattle feed, in blending ores for product sales, etc. However, in the blast furnace problem described here, one additional feature is present which requires resolution—that associated with the *conversion* (rather than blending) of the iron-bearing input materials into pig iron and slag. As in the coal-purchasing problem just described, the available ores each have different characteristics. Additionally, for each ore there is a corresponding requirement of coke and limestone which varies with the type and grade of ore. Therefore, one seeks a common unit for all materials which, in this problem, is taken to be the "ore required per ton of hot metal."

To determine the "ore required per ton of hot metal," one needs to know the amount of iron and manganese natural in the ore. If, for example, one determines that the iron plus manganese in the hot metal will be 95% of its weight or 1900 pounds per net ton and, further, that only 75% of the manganese will be reduced into the hot metal, one determines the *theoretical* ore required to produce a net ton of hot metal. For example, given an ore with iron content of 49.78% and manganese content of 0.77%, the theoretical ore required per ton of hot metal equals

$$\frac{1900}{0.4978 + (0.75)(0.0077)} = 3773 \text{ pounds}$$

To this theoretical ore must be added the estimated flue dust loss which, if assumed to be 25% of the −20 mesh material in the theoretical ore, yields a total of theoretical ore plus flue dust of *

$$\frac{3773}{1.00 - (0.25)(0.25)} = 4025 \text{ pounds}$$

Next, an additional 2% is added to represent the efficiency loss. This yields (4025 + 80) or 4105 pounds of ore required to produce one net ton of hot metal.

For every ore, one must also determine the corresponding amount of coke and limestone required in the blast furnace. The amount of required coke (i.e., the coke rate) is determined by calculations based largely upon formulas developed by Flint.[1] This involves the determination of the effective carbon in the coke as a function of the carbon, ash and sulphur in the coke, the moisture in the blast, etc.

For the illustrative ore cited above, the base coke rate is 1740 pounds per ton of hot metal for a given furnace operation. This coke rate is

---

* For our example, the theoretical ore contains 25% of −20 mesh ore.

then adjusted for 1. the change of slag volume from the ore, and 2. ore fines (i.e., materials of less than -20 mesh). These adjustments are also made on the basis of formulas developed by Flint. Finally, other corrections to the coke rate are made for special materials.

The amount of limestone (flux) required is determined by a straight-forward metallurgical calculation.

The cost of producing one net ton of hot metal is then determined by adding the costs of the theoretical ore, the coke rate, and the limestone. For example, the ore cited above costs $11.93 per gross ton of ore or $21.86 for the total ore (i.e., 4105 pounds or 1.8326 gross tons) required to produce one net ton of hot metal. When one adds the cost of coke and limestone, the total cost of producing one net ton of hot metal becomes $36.65. Similarly, costs are then determined for the other available ores.

Having determined these costs and having previously determined the metallurgical properties and availabilities (i.e., contractual limitations) of each of the ores, one can then readily obtain the optimum loading (i.e., mix of ores) of the blast furnace so as to produce pig iron of specific characteristics at the lowest cost.

The problem described here was solved by means of the simplex technique and using an IBM 701 electronic computer. In addition, related problems were solved wherein one considered the effect of variations in 1. the metallurgical requirements for the pig iron, and 2. the availability of certain ores. The former helped to evaluate the importance of the restrictions (e.g., is one required to make "too good" a grade of pig iron?), while the latter served to evaluate the pricing structures of the various competing ore suppliers.

In this example, too, one again encounters the type of situation which occurs so frequently in linear programming problems, namely, that the formulation of the problem and the rendering and determination of the basic data constitute the major portion of the task and that, once this is done, the formal solution is easy to obtain.

BIBLIOGRAPHY

1. Flint, R. V., "Multiple Correlation of Blast Furnace Variables," *Blast Furnace, Coke Oven and Raw Materials, Proceedings of American Institute of Mining and Metallurgical Engineers Conference*, Pittsburgh, Mar. 31–Apr. 2, 1952, pp. 49–73.
2. Lemke, C. E., and Charnes, A., "Extremal Problems in Linear Inequalities," Technical Report No. 36, Carnegie Institute of Technology, Pittsburgh, 1953.
3. Melden, Morley G., "Operations Research," *Fact. Mgmt.*, *111*, no. 10, 113–120 (Oct. 1953).
4. "New Machine Loading Methods," *Fact. Mgmt. 112*, no. 1, 136–137 (Jan. 1954).

PART
VI

WAITING-TIME

MODELS

A waiting-time problem arises when either units requiring service or the facilities which are available for providing service stand idle, i.e., wait. Problems involving waiting time fall into two different types depending on their structure.

The first type of problem involves arrivals which are randomly spaced and/or service time of random duration. This class of problems includes situations requiring either determination of the optimal number of service facilities or the optimal arrival rate (or times of arrival), or both. The class of models applicable to the solution of these facility and scheduling problems is called *waiting-line* theory or (by the British) *queuing* theory.

Waiting-line theory dates back to the work of Erlang in 1908. In Erlang's and subsequent work up to approximately 1945, applications were restricted in the main to operation of telephone systems. Since then the theory has been extended and applied to a wide variety of phenomena.

The construction of models of waiting-line processes usually involves relatively complex mathematics. Even an introduction to the subject must be fairly complex. However, many waiting-line problems can be solved more simply by use of Monte Carlo procedures. An introduction to the theory of waiting lines and a simplified illustration of the use of

Monte Carlo procedures for solving a waiting-line problem are given in Chapter 14.

Chapter 15 consists of a "classic" study involving waiting-line theory. This case, which originally appeared in the *Journal of The Operations Research Society of America*, was awarded the Lanchester Prize by The Johns Hopkins University and the Society as the best article published in the field of Operations Research in 1954.

The second type of waiting-time problem is not concerned with either controlling the times of arrivals or the number of facilities, but rather is concerned with the order or sequence in which service is provided to available units by a series of service points. This is called the *sequencing* problem. Such problems involve combinatorial analysis for their solution. Models and solutions for some simple sequencing problems are discussed in Chapter 16. Some related problems are also considered.

Chapter 14

Queuing Models

INTRODUCTION

The length of a waiting line depends primarily on time; i.e., under fixed conditions of customer arrivals and service facilities, queue length is a function of time. Hence the process of waiting-line formation is sometimes referred to as a "stochastic process." A process is stochastic if it includes random variables whose values depend on a parameter such as "time."

In developing a model for the probability distribution of queue length, certain assumptions must be made about features pertinent to the formation of the queue:

1. The manner in which units (customers at a counter, trucks at a loading dock, raw material at a machine center, etc.) arrive and become part of the waiting line. This is the system's *input*.

2. The number of service units (called *stations*) operating on the units requiring service and the *service policy;* e.g., limitations on the amount of service that can be rendered or is allowed.

3. The order in which units are served: the *queue discipline*.

4. The service provided and its duration: the system's *output;* e.g., customers waited on, packages wrapped, trucks loaded, etc.

In waiting-line situations, problems arise because of either: 1. too much demand on the facilities, in which case we may say either that there is an excess of waiting time or that there are not enough service facilities; or 2. too little demand, in which case there is either too much idle facility time or too many facilities. One would like to obtain an optimum balance between the costs associated with waiting time and idle time. But what does such balance mean?

Let us assume the following situation for the arrival of units and the servicing of these units at a single counter:

Arrivals

1. An average of six per hour, or one every 10 minutes.
2. Within each 10-minute interval the time of arrival of the one unit is "random."
3. Each unit takes its place in line in order of appearance and takes its place at the counter for service the moment the counter is free.

Servicing

1. An average of ten per hour, or one every 6 minutes.
2. Each unit served is given *exactly* 6 minutes of service, and the units are taken in order of arrival.

Suppose the arrivals for a certain period of time are: 8:07, 8:14, 8:25, 8:39, 8:43, and 8:56. Then the schedule showing the times at which service begins and ends, the amounts of idle time for the counter, the amounts of waiting for the arrival units, and the maximum queue length during each of the 10-minute intervals for the hour, are as shown in Table 14-1. From Table 14-1 we observe that only once dur-

TABLE 14-1

Time of Arrival	Time Service Begins	Time Service Ends	Idle Time	Waiting Time	Queue Length
8:07	8:07	8:13	0	0	0
8:14	8:14	8:20	1	0	0
8:25	8:25	8:31	5	0	0
8:39	8:39	8:45	8	0	0
8:43	8:45	8:51	0	2	1
8:56	8:56	....	5	0	0

ing the hour does a queue begin to form, namely at 8:43 when the arrival unit is required to wait for 2 minutes. The total waiting time is 2 minutes, and the total idle time is 19 minutes.

When the service time is increased one expects the queue length and the waiting time to increase. The data for the same set of arrivals when the service time is one every 9 minutes are given in Table 14-2.

TABLE 14-2

Time of Arrival	Time Service Begins	Time Service Ends	Idle Time	Waiting Time	Queue Length
8:07	8:07	8:16	0	0	0
8:14	8:16	8:25	0	2	1
8:25	8:25	8:34	0	0	0
8:39	8:39	8:48	5	0	0
8:43	8:48	8:57	0	5	1
8:56	8:57	....	0	1	1

We observe from Table 14-2 that the total idle time has decreased from 19 minutes to 5 minutes, while the total waiting time has increased from 2 minutes to 8 minutes.

Although in this simple illustration the time period is too short to permit a queue of great length, it is possible to recognize some of the features of queuing that create problems of considerable magnitude. One can see, for example, the necessity of manipulating the service facility so that an optimum balance may be achieved between the cost of idle time and the cost of waiting time.

By increasing one's investment in labor and equipment, one can decrease waiting time and losses in business which result from waiting lines. It is desirable, then, to obtain a minimum sum of these two costs: costs of investment and operation and costs due to waiting. This optimum balance of costs can be obtained by *scheduling* the flow of units requiring service and/or employing the proper amount of facilities. That is, if facilities are fixed, one may be able to schedule the flow of the input so as to minimize the sum of waiting time and idle time costs. If the flow is not subject to control, then one can install that amount of equipment and/or employ that number of personnel which minimizes the over-all costs of operation. If both the arrival time and the facilities can be controlled, one seeks both to schedule the input and to provide facilities which minimize the over-all cost.

A SINGLE-STATION QUEUING PROBLEM

Consider the problem of determining the probability of a given queue length and the expected queue length for the case of a single station for which both input and output are assumed to be random. In this case it is further assumed that the servicing rate is independent of the number of units in line, and that the units that make up the line are serviced in order of appearance in the line.

The following notation will be used:

n = number of units in the waiting line at time t

$P_n(t)$ = probability of n units in the queue at time t

$\lambda \Delta t$ = probability of a new unit entering the line in the time interval t to $t + \Delta t$, which implies that λ = mean arrival rate

$\mu \Delta t$ = probability that a unit being serviced is completed in the time interval t to $t + \Delta t$, which implies that μ = mean service rate

$\bar{n}$ = mean length of (i.e., number of units in) the waiting line

A set of differential equations from which $P_n(t)$ (and subsequently $\bar{n}$) may be obtained can be formulated by using the fundamental properties of probability in the following manner:

The probability that there will be n units (when $n > 0$) in the line at time $(t + \Delta t)$ may be expressed as the sum of four independent compound probabilities:

1. The product of the probabilities that

a. There are n units in line at time t $[P_n(t)]$
b. There are no arrivals during the Δt interval $[1 - \lambda(\Delta t)]$
c. There are no units serviced during the Δt interval $[1 - \mu(\Delta t)]$

2. The product of the probabilities that

a. There are $(n + 1)$ units in line at time t $[P_{n+1}(t)]$
b. There is one unit serviced during the Δt interval $[\mu(\Delta t)]$
c. There are no arrivals during the Δt interval $[1 - \lambda(\Delta t)]$

3. The product of the probabilities that

a. There are $(n - 1)$ units in line at time t $[P_{n-1}(t)]$
b. There is one arrival during the Δt interval $[\lambda(\Delta t)]$
c. There are no units serviced during the Δt interval $[1 - \mu(\Delta t)]$

4. The product of the probabilities that

a. There are n units in line at time t $[P_n(t)]$
b. There is one arrival during the Δt interval $[\lambda(\Delta t)]$
c. There is one unit serviced during the Δt interval $[\mu(\Delta t)]$

The probabilities of more than one unit arriving or being serviced during the Δt interval are assumed to be negligible.

These four probabilities may be transformed as follows:

1. $P_n(t)(1 - \lambda \Delta t)(1 - \mu \Delta t) = P_n(t)[1 - \lambda \Delta t - \mu \Delta t] + o_1(\Delta t).$*
2. $P_{n+1}(t)(\mu \Delta t)(1 - \lambda \Delta t) = P_{n+1}(t)\mu \Delta t + o_2(\Delta t).$
3. $P_{n-1}(t)(\lambda \Delta t)(1 - \mu \Delta t) = P_{n-1}(t)\lambda \Delta t + o_3(\Delta t).$
4. $P_n(t)(\lambda \Delta t)(\mu \Delta t) = o_4(\Delta t).$

* The $o_i(\Delta t)$ are higher order terms in Δt that are assumed to be negligible compared to those in Δt.

$(1 - \partial)(1 - \rho) = 1 - \partial - \rho$

By adding these probabilities, we obtain for the probability of n units in line at time $(t + \Delta t)$

$$P_n(t + \Delta t) = P_n(t)[1 - \lambda \Delta t - \mu \Delta t] + P_{n+1}(t)\mu \Delta t + P_{n-1}(t)\lambda \Delta t$$
$$+ o_1(\Delta t) + o_2(\Delta t) + o_3(\Delta t) + o_4(\Delta t) \quad (1)$$

This equation may be rewritten as follows

$$\frac{P_n(t + \Delta t) - P_n(t)}{\Delta t} = \lambda P_{n-1}(t) + \mu P_{n+1}(t) - (\lambda + \mu)P_n(t)$$
$$+ o_1(\Delta t) + o_2(\Delta t) + o_3(\Delta t) + o_4(\Delta t)$$

Upon letting Δt approach zero, we then obtain the differential equation

$$\frac{dP_n(t)}{dt} = \lambda P_{n-1}(t) + \mu P_{n+1}(t) - (\lambda + \mu)P_n(t), \quad (n > 0) \quad (2)$$

When the length of the waiting line at time t is considered to include the unit being serviced (if there is one at the time), and when it is recognized that $n \geq 0$ in every situation, it follows that the four probabilities listed in the foregoing must be modified for the case $n = 0$. In this situation, the probability that there will be 0 units in the line at time $t + \Delta t$ is the sum of the two independent probabilities:

1. $P_0(t)(1 - \lambda \Delta t)$: Probability of 0 units in the line at time t, and 0 arrivals in Δt.

2. $P_1(t)(\mu \Delta t)(1 - \lambda \Delta t)$: Probability of 1 unit in the line at time t, 1 unit serviced in Δt and 0 arrivals in Δt.

Upon adding these two independent probabilities we obtain for the probability of a queue of length 0 at time $t + \Delta t$

$$P_0(t + \Delta t) = P_0(t)(1 - \lambda \Delta t) + P_1(t)\mu \Delta t - \lambda \mu P_1(t)(\Delta t)^2 \quad (3)$$

from which it follows that

$$\frac{P_0(t + \Delta t) - P_0(t)}{\Delta t} = -\lambda P_0(t) + \mu P_1(t) - \lambda \mu P_1(t)(\Delta t)$$

and

$$\frac{dP_0(t)}{dt} = -\lambda P_0(t) + \mu P_1(t), \quad (n = 0) \quad (4)$$

The differential equations 2 and 4 express implicitly the relationship between waiting time and servicing time and thus furnish the basis for solutions to many waiting-line problems. Solutions are usually difficult to obtain, depending upon the complexity of $P_n(t)$. However, one may readily obtain a solution in the case in which it is assumed that $P_n(t)$ is independent of t and equals P_n. Then, since this probability does not change with time, its rate of change is equal to zero

$$\frac{dP_n}{dt} = 0, \qquad n = 0, 1, 2, \cdots$$

Equations 2 and 4 in this situation become

$$0 = \lambda P_{n-1} + \mu P_{n+1} - (\lambda + \mu)P_n \qquad (n > 0) \qquad (2a)$$

$$0 = -\lambda P_0 + \mu P_1 \qquad\qquad\qquad (n = 0) \qquad (4a)$$

Equations $2a$ and $4a$ are difference rather than differential equations and may be solved for P_0, P_1, $\cdots$, P_n, $\cdots$ by successive substitution and utilization of the fact that $\sum_0^\infty P_i = 1$. This technique is as follows: we may write

$$P_0 = P_0$$

$$P_1 = \left(\frac{\lambda}{\mu}\right) P_0 \qquad \text{(From eq. } 4a\text{)}$$

$$P_2 = \left(\frac{\lambda}{\mu}\right)^2 P_0 \qquad \text{(From letting } n = 1 \text{ in eq. } 2a$$
$$\qquad\qquad\qquad\qquad \text{and substituting for } P_1\text{)}$$

$$P_3 = \left(\frac{\lambda}{\mu}\right)^3 P_0 \qquad \text{(From letting } n = 2 \text{ in eq. } 2a$$
$$\qquad\qquad\qquad\qquad \text{and substituting for } P_2\text{)}$$

$$\vdots$$

$$P_n = \left(\frac{\lambda}{\mu}\right)^n P_0$$

Summing corresponding members of these equations, we obtain

$$\sum_0^\infty P_i = P_0 \sum_0^\infty \left(\frac{\lambda}{\mu}\right)^n \qquad (5)$$

Now let us assume that $\lambda/\mu < 1$ (i.e., the mean arrival rate is less than the mean service rate, a condition that must hold to prevent queue growth beyond bound). Since

$$\sum_0^\infty P_i = 1 \qquad \text{and} \qquad \sum_0^\infty (\lambda/\mu)^n = 1/[1 - (\lambda/\mu)]$$

by the equation for the sum of an infinite geometric series, we have

$$\frac{1}{1 - \lambda/\mu} P_0 = 1$$

Hence

$$P_0 = 1 - (\lambda/\mu) \qquad (6)$$

By substituting this value of P_0 in the foregoing expression for P_n, it follows that *the probability of a waiting line of length n* is given by

$$P_n = \left(\frac{\lambda}{\mu}\right)^n \left(1 - \frac{\lambda}{\mu}\right) \qquad \text{if } \frac{\lambda}{\mu} < 1 \qquad (7)$$

The ratio λ/μ is sometimes called "traffic intensity." It is the expected service per unit of time, measured in what Kendall calls "erlangs" in honor of A. K. Erlang who contributed greatly to the theory of queues.

We may find $\bar{n}$, the mean length of the waiting line, as follows: By definition, since $\Sigma P_n = 1$

$$\bar{n} = \sum_0^\infty n P_n \qquad (8)$$

Substituting in eq. 8 the value of P_n given in eq. 7, eq. 8 becomes

$$\bar{n} = \sum_0^\infty n \left(\frac{\lambda}{\mu}\right)^n \left(1 - \frac{\lambda}{\mu}\right)$$

$$= \left(1 - \frac{\lambda}{\mu}\right) \sum_0^\infty n \left(\frac{\lambda}{\mu}\right)^n$$

$$= \left(1 - \frac{\lambda}{\mu}\right) \left[\frac{\lambda}{\mu} + 2\left(\frac{\lambda}{\mu}\right)^2 + 3\left(\frac{\lambda}{\mu}\right)^3 + \cdots\right]$$

$$= \left(\frac{\lambda}{\mu}\right) \left(1 - \frac{\lambda}{\mu}\right) \left[1 + 2\left(\frac{\lambda}{\mu}\right) + 3\left(\frac{\lambda}{\mu}\right)^2 + \cdots\right] \qquad (9)$$

To evaluate this expression we may first obtain the sum of the series within brackets by the use of integration and differentiation. Let us call the series $S(\lambda/\mu)$ and proceed as follows:

Integrate $S(\lambda/\mu)$ term by term and obtain

$$\int_0^{\lambda/\mu} S\left(\frac{\lambda}{\mu}\right) d\left(\frac{\lambda}{\mu}\right) = \frac{\lambda}{\mu} + \left(\frac{\lambda}{\mu}\right)^2 + \left(\frac{\lambda}{\mu}\right)^3 + \cdots$$

which is a geometric series having the sum $(\lambda/\mu)/[1 - (\lambda/\mu)]$. Now differentiate this sum with respect to λ/μ and obtain $1/[1 - (\lambda/\mu)]^2$.

This means that

$$S\left(\frac{\lambda}{\mu}\right) = \frac{1}{[1 - (\lambda/\mu)]^2} \tag{10}$$

Hence, substituting this value in eq. 9 we obtain

$$\bar{n} = \left(\frac{\lambda}{\mu}\right)\left(1 - \frac{\lambda}{\mu}\right)\frac{1}{[1 - (\lambda/\mu)]^2} \tag{11}$$

so that, for the given conditions, the mean length of a waiting line is given by

$$\bar{n} = \frac{\lambda/\mu}{1 - (\lambda/\mu)}, \quad \frac{\lambda}{\mu} < 1 \tag{12}$$

Example of a Single-Station Model

For a single station at which the mean arrival rate λ is known to be 10 units per day and the mean service rate μ is 20 units per day, we would have $\lambda/\mu = \frac{10}{20} = \frac{1}{2}$. Then by substituting this value in eqs. 7 and 12, we obtain

$$P_n = (\tfrac{1}{2})^n(1 - \tfrac{1}{2})$$

and

$$\bar{n} = \frac{\frac{1}{2}}{1 - \frac{1}{2}} = 1$$

The probabilities of $0, 1, 2, \cdots, n$ units in the waiting line at any time are:

n	0	1	2	3	4	$\cdots$
P_n	$\frac{1}{2}$	$\frac{1}{4}$	$\frac{1}{8}$	$\frac{1}{16}$	$\frac{1}{32}$	$\cdots$

It is interesting to note (see eq. 12) that, for increasing values of the traffic intensity ratio λ/μ, the expected length of the queue increases rapidly, and as λ/μ approaches unity, $\bar{n}$ becomes infinitely large. (Strictly speaking, of course, the equation for $\bar{n}$ ceases to hold when λ/μ equals 1.) By substituting several values of λ/μ in eq. 12, the behavior of the average queue length can be illustrated as follows:

Traffic intensity λ/μ	$\frac{1}{2}$	$\frac{3}{4}$	$\frac{7}{8}$	$\frac{15}{16}$	$\frac{31}{32}$	$\cdots$
Expected queue length $\bar{n}$	1	3	7	15	31	$\cdots$

Time Between Arrivals

Consider a unit service time T. Suppose the number of arrivals in this period has a Poisson distribution.* Then, if a is the mean length

* That is, if λ is the expected number of arrivals in the period, then the probability $f(n)$ of exactly n arrivals in the period is

$$f(n) = \lambda^n e^{-\lambda}/n!$$

of the intervals between arrivals in the period, it follows that λ, the mean number of arrivals for the period, is given by

$$\lambda = T/a$$

For example, suppose $T = 1$ hour and $\lambda = 6$ arrivals per hour. Then a, the mean interval between arrivals, is 10 minutes ($\frac{1}{6}$ hour); i.e.,

$$a = T/\lambda = \tfrac{1}{6}$$

The probability density function for the time t_a between two successive arrivals may be obtained as follows: Let $p(t_a)$ be the probability of no arrivals in the period t_a following an arrival. Then, since $\lambda \Delta t_a$, i.e., $(T/a)\Delta t_a$, is the probability of one arrival during the interval $(t_a, t_a + \Delta t_a)$, we have for the probability of no arrivals $[p(t_a)]$ followed by one arrival $[(T/a)\Delta t_a]$ during this latter interval the product $p(t_a)[(T/a)\Delta t_a]$. Without loss of generality, we may take $T = 1$ and write this probability as $p(t_a)(\Delta t_a)/a$. That is to say

$$p(t_a) - p(t_a + \Delta t_a) = p(t_a)(\Delta t_a)/a$$

or, since $p(t_a) - p(t_a + \Delta t_a) = -\Delta p(t_a)$, we may write

$$-\Delta p(t_a) = p(t_a)(\Delta t_a)/a \tag{13}$$

the probability of exactly 1 arrival in the interval Δt_a. This means that $p(t_a)/a$ is the probability density function for the time between arrivals.

To illustrate the foregoing incremental relationship (eq. 13), consider the following interval which has been subdivided into four equal

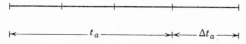

Fig. 14-1.   Time scale.

subintervals in any one of which there can be either 0 or 1 arrival. Let there be a probability of $\frac{1}{3}$ of there being 0 arrivals in any one of the four subintervals; see Fig. 14-1. In this situation, we then have

$$p(t_a) = (\tfrac{1}{3})^3 = \tfrac{1}{27} = \text{probability of no arrivals during the first three subintervals}$$

$$(\Delta t_a)/a = 1 - \tfrac{1}{3} = \tfrac{2}{3} = \text{probability of one arrival during the fourth (or any one) subinterval}$$

Therefore, the probability of no arrivals in the first three subintervals followed by one arrival during the fourth subinterval is given by

$$p(t_a)(\Delta t_a)/a = (\tfrac{1}{27})(\tfrac{2}{3}) = \tfrac{2}{81}$$

Alternatively, this result may be obtained as follows

$$p(t_a + \Delta t_a) = (\tfrac{1}{3})^4 = \tfrac{1}{81}$$

$$p(t_a) = (\tfrac{1}{3})^3 = \tfrac{1}{27}$$

so that

$$-\Delta p(t_a) = p(t_a) - p(t_a + \Delta t_a) = \tfrac{1}{27} - \tfrac{1}{81} = \tfrac{2}{81}$$

and one can see that eq. 13 holds.

If now we divide both sides of eq. 13 by $-\Delta t_a$, we may write

$$\frac{\Delta p(t_a)}{\Delta t_a} = \frac{-p(t_a)}{a}$$

Upon letting Δt_a approach zero, we obtain

$$\frac{dp(t_a)}{dt_a} = \frac{-p(t_a)}{a} \tag{14}$$

But since $1/a = \lambda$, we may write

$$\frac{dp(t_a)}{dt_a} = -\lambda p(t_a) \tag{15}$$

The solution of this differential equation yields

$$p(t_a) = Ke^{-\lambda t_a} \tag{16}$$

The constant K is determined to be equal to 1 from the condition

$$p(0) = 1$$

Hence

$$p(t_a) = e^{-\lambda t_a} \tag{18}$$

Therefore, the probability density function for the time between arrivals * is $\lambda e^{-\lambda t_a}$.

* The details in arriving at eq. 18 are as follows: We have

$$\frac{dp(t_a)}{dt_a} = -\lambda p(t_a) \qquad \text{or} \qquad \frac{dp(t_a)}{p(t_a)} = -\lambda \, dt_a$$

Integrating, we obtain

$$\log_e p(t_a) = -\lambda t_a + C \qquad \text{or} \qquad p(t_a) = e^{-\lambda t_a + C}$$

which may be written

$$p(t_a) = Ke^{-\lambda t_a}, \qquad \text{where } K = e^C$$

Since

$$p(0) = 1$$

it follows that $K = 1$.

Hence $p(t_a) = e^{-\lambda t_a}$.

Service Time

We have already examined the problem of expected queue length when both input and output are assumed to be random. It has been shown by Kendall [20] that when the input at a single station obeys the negative exponential distribution obtained in the previous section, the expected queue length $\bar{n}$ can be expressed in terms of the mean arrival rate, the mean service rate, and the variance of the service time. In the symbolism used in this chapter, this equation can be expressed as

$$\bar{n} = \frac{\lambda}{\mu} + \frac{\lambda^2(\sigma_{ts}^2) + (\lambda/\mu)^2}{2[1 - (\lambda/\mu)]} \qquad (19)$$

in which

$$\sigma_{ts}^2 = \text{variance of the service time } t_s$$

Equation 19 for $\bar{n}$ indicates that the expected queue length increases with variance of service for fixed values of λ and μ. For constant λ and μ the minimum expected queue length results when $\sigma_{ts}^2 = 0$, i.e., when the service time is constant. That is to say, *for given mean arrival rate λ and constant service time μ*

$$\bar{n} = \frac{\lambda}{\mu} + \frac{(\lambda/\mu)^2}{2[1 - (\lambda/\mu)]} \qquad (20)$$

If, as was the case earlier in this chapter, the distribution of service time is assumed to be negative exponential with mean μ, then it can be shown that $\sigma_{ts}^2 = 1/\mu^2$ and eq. 19 reduces algebraically to

$$\bar{n} = \frac{\lambda/\mu}{1 - \lambda/\mu} \quad \checkmark$$

which agrees with eq. 12.

Again we observe in eq. 19 that, when the mean arrival rate approaches the mean service rate (i.e., $\lambda \rightarrow \mu$), the expected queue length increases beyond bound. Also we see that for a given service time distribution, the expected queue length can only be reduced by a reduction in the ratio λ/μ. We can, therefore, restate the essence of the queuing problem in terms of this ratio λ/μ. When λ/μ is reduced, the value of $1 - (\lambda/\mu)$ is increased, and the queue length decreases. This means that the solution to a queuing problem requires a balancing of the costs of reduction of queue length against the costs associated with station facilities not being used.

Waiting Time

The expected waiting time of arrivals at a single station with random input can be formulated as follows:

Let $\quad\quad \bar{t}_w =$ expected waiting time

and $\quad\quad \bar{t}_s =$ expected time spent in service

Then

$\bar{t}_w + \bar{t}_s =$ total expected time consumed in both waiting and service

When the mean arrival rate is λ, then

$$\bar{n} = \lambda(\bar{t}_w + \bar{t}_s)$$

from which

$$\bar{t}_w = \frac{\bar{n}}{\lambda} - \bar{t}_s \qquad (21)$$

For the case of *random input and random output*

$$\bar{n} = \frac{\lambda/\mu}{1 - \lambda/\mu}$$

and it can be shown that

$$\bar{t}_s = \frac{1}{\mu}$$

By substitution in the expression for $\bar{t}_w$, we obtain

$$\bar{t}_w = \frac{1}{\mu - \lambda} - \frac{1}{\mu} \qquad (22)$$

as an equation for expected waiting time at a single station.

For *random input and a given distribution of service time with variance* σ_{ts}^2 *and mean* $\bar{t}_s$, the equation for expected waiting time at a single station becomes *

$$\bar{t}_w = \frac{1}{\lambda}\left[\frac{\lambda}{\mu} + \frac{\lambda^2(\sigma_{ts}^2) + (\lambda/\mu)^2}{2[1 - (\lambda/\mu)]}\right] - \bar{t}_s \qquad (23)$$

* When

$$\sigma_{ts}^2 = \frac{1}{\mu^2} \quad \text{and} \quad \bar{t}_s = \frac{1}{\mu}$$

as in the case for a negative exponential time distribution of mean μ, eq. 23 becomes

$$\bar{t}_w = \frac{1}{\lambda}\left[\frac{\lambda}{\mu} + \frac{(\lambda/\mu)^2}{1 - (\lambda/\mu)}\right] - \frac{1}{\mu} = \frac{1}{\mu - \lambda} - \frac{1}{\mu}$$

which is eq. 22.

GENERAL SINGLE-STATION QUEUING PROBLEM

In the general queuing problem in which the rates of arrival and service are dependent on the length of the line, the fundamental equations are

$$\frac{dP_n(t)}{dt} = -(\lambda_n + \mu_n)P_n(t) + \lambda_{n-1}P_{n-1}(t) + \mu_{n+1}P_{n+1}(t) \quad (24)$$

$$\frac{dP_0(t)}{dt} = -\lambda_0 P_0(t) + \mu_1 P_1(t) \quad (25)$$

The process giving rise to these equations is usually known as the "birth and death" process. To illustrate this process, let us consider the following example.

A certain restaurant serves meals from 5 p.m. to 9 p.m. We shall assume, for the moment, that there is no restriction on the number of persons that can be served. We shall further assume that customers arrive at random and hence, in our notation, that the probability of a customer's arriving during $(t, t + \Delta t)$ is $\lambda \Delta t$. Also, the probability of a customer's leaving during $(t, t + \Delta t)$ is assumed to be $n\mu\Delta t$. That is, the service rate increases as the restaurant fills up. Thus we have for the arrival and service rates in eqs. 24 and 25

$$\lambda_n = \lambda, \qquad \mu_n = n\mu$$

The appropriate differential equations for determining $P_n(t)$, the probability of n customers in the restaurant at time t, are

$$\frac{dP_n(t)}{dt} = -(\lambda + n\mu)P_n(t) + \lambda P_{n-1}(t)$$
$$+ (n + 1)\mu P_{n+1}(t), \qquad (n > 0) \quad (26)$$

$$\frac{dP_0(t)}{dt} = -\lambda P_0(t) + \mu P_1(t) \quad (27)$$

An explicit solution for $P_n(t)$ takes the form

$$P_n(t) = \frac{e^{-\lambda/\mu(1 - e^{-\mu t})}[(\lambda/\mu)(1 - e^{-\mu t})]^n}{n!} \quad (28)$$

when the initial conditions are $P_0(0) = 1$, $P_i(0) = 0 (i \geq 1)$. We note that in the limit as $t \to \infty$

$$\lim_{t \to \infty} P_n(t) = P_n = \frac{e^{-(\lambda/\mu)}(\lambda/\mu)^n}{n!} \quad (29)$$

Thus, for a sufficiently long period, we find that the probability of exactly n customers is given by a Poisson distribution, with mean λ/μ. For example, in the early evening we might find that $\lambda/\mu = 9$. In this case $e^{-(\lambda/\mu)}$ is about 0.0001 so that the probability of zero customers being served is $P_0 = 0.0001$. At a later time, λ/μ might be 0.1, and $P_0 = e^{-(\lambda/\mu)} = 0.9048$.

Let $\bar{n}(t)$ represent the mean or expected number of customers being served at any time t. The value of $\bar{n}$ can be determined without the use of the explicit solution as follows: We have

$$\bar{n}(t) = \Sigma n P_n(t) \tag{30}$$

$$\frac{d\bar{n}(t)}{dt} = \Sigma n d P_n(t)/dt$$

$$= \lambda - \mu\bar{n}(t) \tag{31}$$

The solution for the expected value of $\bar{n}$ when the initial number of people in line is 0 is

$$\bar{n}(t) = \frac{\lambda}{\mu}(1 - e^{-\mu t}) \tag{32}$$

A MULTISTATION (OR MULTICHANNEL) QUEUING PROBLEM

The example just discussed would be more realistic if there were an assumption about the limit on the number of customers that can be served. Let us interpret this restriction in the discussion of another example. The orders coming into a shipping department are assumed, just as for the restaurant customers in the previous problem, to be random and the probability of an order arriving during $(t, t + \Delta t)$ to be $\lambda \Delta t$. We shall assume further that a definite number S of employees in the office handle the orders. Then when all S are working, suppose new orders coming in cannot be handled immediately and must be put into a _waiting line_. If the amount of time spent in processing an order produces a situation similar to the occupation of restaurant tables, we say that there is an _exponential holding time_ or service time. We now define the system to be in state E_n if n is the total number of orders being processed or in the waiting line. A waiting line exists only when the system is in a state E_n with $n > S$ and there are $n - S$ orders in the waiting line.

As long as at least one employee is not busy, we have the same situation as in the previous example. However, if the system is in state

Queuing Models

E_n with $n > S$, then there are only S orders being serviced and hence $\mu_n = S\mu$ for $n \geq S$.

The following system of differential equations is appropriate for this example

$$\frac{dP_0(t)}{dt} = -\lambda P_0(t) + \mu P_1(t) \qquad\qquad (n = 0) \quad (33)$$

$$\frac{dP_n(t)}{dt} = -(\lambda + n\mu)P_n(t) + \lambda P_{n-1}(t) + (n + 1)\mu P_{n+1}(t) \qquad (34)$$

$$(0 < n < S)$$

$$\frac{dP_n(t)}{dt} = -(\lambda + S\mu)P_n(t) + \lambda P_{n-1}(t) + S\mu P_{n+1}(t) \qquad (n \geq S) \quad (35)$$

The solution of these equations is a very complicated expression. We shall determine the limiting probabilities as $t \to \infty$. It can be shown that a unique limit

$$\lim_{t \to \infty} P_n(t) = P_n$$

exists for all n. Hence the differential equations for the limiting probabilities become

$$\lambda P_0 = \mu P_1 \qquad\qquad (n = 0) \quad (36)$$

$$(\lambda + n\mu)P_n = \lambda P_{n-1} + (n + 1)\mu P_{n+1} \qquad (1 \leq n < S) \quad (37)$$

$$(\lambda + S\mu)P_n = \lambda P_{n-1} + S\mu P_{n+1} \qquad (n \geq S) \quad (38)$$

$$P_n = P_0 \frac{(\lambda/\mu)^n}{n!} \qquad\qquad (n \leq S) \quad (39)$$

$$P_n = P_0 \frac{(\lambda/\mu)^n}{S!\, S^{n-S}} \qquad\qquad (n \geq S) \quad (40)$$

The condition

$$\lambda/\mu < S$$

is needed if the P_n (for all n) are to form a unique probability distribution. If this condition does not hold, it is implied that the waiting line gradually grows beyond bound.

The probability of having to wait in line is the sum of all probabilities that all service facilities are being used or that S or more customers are in line. Let this probability be W. Then

$$W = \sum_{n=S}^{\infty} P_n$$

$$= \frac{P_0}{S!} \left(\frac{\lambda}{\mu}\right)^S \sum_{n=0}^{\infty} \left(\frac{\lambda}{\mu S}\right)^n$$

$$W = \left(\frac{\lambda}{\mu}\right)^S \frac{P_0}{S!\left(1 - \frac{\lambda}{\mu S}\right)} \tag{41}$$

Also of interest is the probability that the time of waiting in line plus the time of service is larger than a given time t. We denote this probability by $P(>t)$. The derivation is rather lengthy and will not be given here; but the result is

$$P(>t) = e^{-\mu t}\left\{1 + \frac{W}{S}\left[\frac{1 - e^{-\mu S t[1-(\lambda/\mu S)-(1/S)]}}{1 - (\lambda/\mu S) - (1/S)}\right]\right\} \tag{42}$$

The probability of spending a time between t and $t + \Delta t$ waiting in line and being serviced is

$$\frac{d[P(>t)]}{dt} \Delta t$$

The average time in the system becomes

$$\int_0^{\infty} t\frac{d[P(>t)]}{dt}\, dt = \bar{t}_w + \frac{1}{\mu} \tag{43}$$

where $\bar{t}_w$ is the average time spent waiting in line and $1/\mu$ equals the average servicing time.

Solving this equation for $\bar{t}_w$ we find the average waiting time for the case of multichannel servicing facilities to be

$$\bar{t}_w = \frac{P_0}{\mu S(S!)[1 - (\lambda/\mu S)]^2}\left(\frac{\lambda}{\mu}\right)^S \tag{44}$$

in which P_0 may be determined from the condition $\sum_{n=0}^{\infty} P_n = 1$. It turns out that

$$P_0 = \frac{1}{\sum_{n=0}^{S-1} (\lambda/\mu)^n/n! + \{(\lambda/\mu)^S/[S!(1 - \lambda/\mu S)]\}} \tag{45}$$

The analytical approach to queuing problems has been used in a variety of situations. Among these have been the multichannel cases in which the servicing consists of separate phases [26] and the mathematical description of the growth of populations of organisms.[20]   Kendall [20] lists several of the various types of problems that have been attacked on the basis of assumptions made concerning input (regular, random, or "erlang"), service time distributions, and number of servers, and tells where accounts of the various types of waiting-line systems are to be found in the literature.

Cobham [10] has developed a model for priority service systems for: *a.* single channels, arbitrary service time, and random arrivals; and *b.* multiple channels, exponential service time, and random arrivals. Solution of this model involves an infinite iterative procedure.   Holley [18] suggests an alternative procedure which avoids the infinite iteration.   Gaver [17] has investigated the influence of servicing time on waiting time of units requiring service.   Barrer [3] has studied the problem involving fixed time of availability of units requiring service (impatient customers) and random selection of units for service (indifferent clerks).

MONTE CARLO TECHNIQUE APPLIED TO QUEUING PROBLEMS

The theory of queuing provides techniques for determining such things as the average queue length and average waiting time when the arrival and service rates are known.   If costs can be assigned to waiting time and service, the problem of establishing a proper balance between these costs can be determined.   In situations where input parameters cannot be controlled, manipulation of output facilities can be made "on paper" to give estimates of expected results.   For example, by substituting various values for the service rate (μ and σ_{ts}^2) the effect upon average waiting time ($\bar{t}_w$), and associated costs, can be examined. Analysis of this type, however, need not be made by means of the formal approach already described, but may be made by the use of Monte Carlo techniques.

Let us consider a specific case—that of home delivery of packages of goods purchased at a department store.   If we try to build up a large enough truck fleet and obtain sufficient personnel for assuring 1-day delivery to every customer, a very large capital investment may be required and a good deal of idle time of men and equipment may result.   If a very small truck fleet is maintained, we shall either lose customers because of slow delivery time or sometimes have to use overtime or rented facilities to make the deliveries.   How then can we decide what size fleet to use and how much overtime or rental of facilities to authorize?

One possible but not very practical approach to this problem would be to try out in actual operations each of several alternative policies for a while and see what happens. Obviously, it would be very expensive to disrupt normal operations to this extent. Furthermore, it would be very difficult to try out each alternative under the same conditions. Herein lie the great advantages of the Monte Carlo technique; it requires no disruption of operations, and yet makes possible the evaluation (under given conditions) of as many alternative solutions to a waiting-line problem as may be desired. How would such a solution be obtained for the problem of determining the optimum size of a truck fleet?

The first thing to study is the average rate at which packages arrive at the loading point for delivery (*mean arrival rate*). This average may not be a constant quantity but may vary considerably. What, then, is the nature of this variation? By analysis of records of past requirements, we can determine how the number of packages requiring delivery per day has varied over, say, the last year, and express this variation in terms of the estimated standard deviation of the distribution of arrival times.

The distribution of the number of packages arriving for delivery may take on any one of a variety of forms. Let us assume, however, that the distribution is normal with a mean of 1000 packages per day and a standard deviation of 100 packages. That is, the mean arrival rate is $\lambda = 1000$ per day.

The next thing to be determined is the average number of packages that can be delivered by a truck in a day (*mean service rate*). The service rate is not constant but is subject to variation. We shall suppose that analysis also indicates this distribution to be normal with an average of 100 and a standard deviation of 10. That is, the mean service rate is $\mu = 100$ per day.

To determine how many trucks we ought to have, two more pieces of information are needed. The first is the cost per day of operating a delivery truck. This involves the fixed as well as the variable costs. We shall assume this cost to be $25.00 per day.

In addition, we need to know the costs per day of delivery delay. In many cases, it is very difficult to estimate this cost. Despite difficulties, however, this cost can frequently be determined satisfactorily from available records of sales and deliveries. Essentially, what is involved in such a determination is a statistical study of the difference in business obtained from customers who have always received delivery within 1 day and those who have had to wait for varying lengths of time on varying numbers of occasions. For illustrative purposes, let us side-step the complication of considering this delay cost by posing the problem relative to a policy which requires that all packages be delivered on the day they are available for delivery. To fulfill this requirement overtime may be required. Overtime will be assumed to cost \$8.00 per hour, and the required hours of overtime will be based on the delivery rate for that day.

We begin by preparing a table such as is shown in Table 14-3. Then, in effect, we shall run the delivery system "on paper" with each of

TABLE 14-3

		No. of Packages to Be Delivered			No. of Packages Capable of Being Delivered			Cost of Overtime	
(1)	(2)	(3)	(4)	(5)	(6)	(7)	(8)	(9)	(10)
No. of Trucks in Fleet	Day	Table Value	Converted Value: $1000 + 100$ (3) * = No. of Pkgs. Arr.	Total Requirement: (4) + Previous (8)	Table Value: Av. No. of Deliveries per Truck	Converted Value: (1) $[100 + 10$ (6)] Total No. of Deliveries	No. Left Over if No Overtime (5) − (7)	No. to Be Delivered at Overtime Rate (4) − (7)	$\left[\dfrac{(9) \div (7)}{(1)\,8}\right] \times (\$8.00)$
	1	2.455	1246	1246	−0.323	968	278	278	\$184
	2	−0.531	947	1225	−1.940	806	419	141	112
10	3	−0.634	937	1356	0.697	1070	286	0	
	4	1.279	1128	1414	3.521	1352	62	0	
	5	0.046	1005	1067	0.321	1032	35	0	
Total									\$296
	1	2.455	1246	1246	−0.323	1161	85	85	\$56
	2	−0.531	947	1032	−1.940	967	65	0	
12	3	−0.634	937	1002	0.697	1284			
	4	1.279	1128	1128	3.521	1623			
	5	0.046	1005	1005	0.321	1239			
Total									\$56
	1	2.455	1246	1246	−0.323	1452			
	2	−0.531	947	947	−1.940	1209			
15	3	−0.634	937	937	0.697	1605			
	4	1.279	1128	1128	3.521	2028			
	5	0.046	1005	1005	0.321	1548			
Total									\$0

* Numbers in parentheses refer to entry on same line in column headed by that number.

three fleets. We can run the system for any length of time we care to and for as many fleet sizes as desired. But since our purpose is illustration, one sample period of 5 consecutive days will be considered.

Columns (1) and (2) in Table 14-3 are self-explanatory. Column (3) requires some explanation. It will be recalled that a distribution of the number of packages for delivery is required, and that in our case

the distribution is assumed to be normal. Now we wish to draw a
certain kind of sample from this distribution. Since about 1000 delivery requirements occur most frequently, we want the chance of
drawing values close to 1000 to reflect this fact. That is, we want the
probability of drawing a certain number of deliveries for the sample to be equal to the probability that such a number will actually
occur in practice. We start at the top of column (3) in Table 7-5, a
table of random normal numbers, and transcribe five successive numbers into column (3) of Table 14-3.* Negative numbers indicate values less than the average, and positive numbers indicate values more
than the average. To convert standard units to number of deliveries
required we must multiply the number of standard units by 100 to
get the deviation from the average and add this quantity to the average, 1000. The resulting values are shown in column (4) of Table 14-3.
The number of deliveries is similarly determined in columns (6) and
(7) except that in this case we multiply the number of standard units
by 10. Then in column (9) we can show the number of undelivered
packages which, it is assumed, are delivered on overtime. Assuming
the same rate of service the cost of the overtime deliveries is computed
in column (10).

The total cost per week for each fleet can now be computed. Since
a truck costs \$25.00 per day, it costs \$125.00 per 5-day week. Multiplying by the number of trucks and adding overtime costs we obtain
the following results:

(a)　10 trucks: (10 × \$125) + \$296 = \$1546
(b)　12 trucks: (12 × \$125) +　\$56 = \$1556
(c)　15 trucks: (15 × \$125)　　　　= \$1875

In this case, the 10-truck fleet is the most economical.

In practice, the sample of weeks would be much larger and other sizes
of truck fleets would also be tried. By statistical procedures to be
discussed in Chapter 20, we can test the significance of the difference
between the resulting costs. If the differences obtained are not found
to be significant, a larger sample is required.

With relatively little additional computation we can determine the
effect on costs of changing the delivery policy. For example, we can
evaluate a policy of delivering all packages within 2, 3, or any specified
number of days. Or we can consider renting trucks on overloaded
days. By computing the costs associated with such alternative policies
management would be in a position to evaluate the alternatives.

* Of course, we may start anywhere in the table of random numbers.

In some cases the analysis of past data on arrival and service rates may not yield a distribution (such as Poisson or normal) which can be expressed mathematically. Then the data themselves may be used in the following way:

Separate lists of past arrival and service rates are prepared and each entry is numbered consecutively. Then by use of a table of random numbers a sample of arrival and service rates can be drawn and used in the same way as was done in the foregoing. Such a procedure assumes independence of these two rates. In many cases such an assumption may not be justified since, for example, the men may work faster as their load increases. In such a case, paired data (arrival and service rate) should be sampled, rather than independent samples of each.

It is important to remember that the illustration given here was deliberately oversimplified. In practice we might want to take into account such things as seasonal variations in delivery requirements, or even variations in arrival or delivery rates by days of the week. We might want to consider truck breakdowns, bad weather, absenteeism, or variations in delivery rate of drivers as a function of their load. All of these things can be done by use of the Monte Carlo technique once the data describing each of these conditions have been collected.

AN APPLICATION OF QUEUING
THEORY IN THE AIRCRAFT INDUSTRY

At Boeing Aircraft the problem arose as to the optimum number of clerks that should be placed in the company's factory tool cribs. The cribs, 60 in number and scattered throughout the factory, store tools for use by the mechanics. They are kept by clerks who hand out the tools from behind a counter as the mechanics arrive and request them, and take them back when the tools are returned. The problem was recognized as a queuing problem and was studied by the Analysis Section of the Mathematical Services Group in the Physical Research Unit of the company.[7]

The serving times of the mechanics by the clerks were obtained by sampling. An observer simply watched the mechanics arriving at the counter, and with a stop watch measured the length of time it took to serve a man. In this way a satisfactory distribution of serving time was obtained.

To obtain the distribution of arrivals, *all* arrivals were measured. To facilitate this data-taking, the following system was used. A box-mounted panel was made on which were installed two small hand-operated switches and two signal lights. Inside was a 6-volt battery.

Whenever one of the switches was depressed, a signal was fed to a 2-channel Brush recorder, one switch controlling one channel. The recording pen of the recorder deflected and made a mark on the recording paper, and the corresponding signal light went on. The observer then simply depressed the switch briefly each time a man arrived at the counter and thus recorded the number of arrivals.

The electric device was also used to record serving or transaction times. In this case, the switch was kept depressed as long as the transaction was being carried on, and was released when the transaction ended, thus making a continuous trace on the recording paper. The data obtained on the paper tapes were finally transformed to units of time, and service and arrival distributions were made up.

If each mechanic arrived at a counter at the very moment when service of the previous mechanic was completed, there would be no waiting line and hence no time lost either by the mechanics or by the serving clerks. But serving times vary and arrivals occur at random. Hence, a queue of mechanics would form at certain times, while at others some or all of the clerks would be idle. The problem was to minimize the total cost of waiting (idle) time of both mechanics and clerks. Since control can be exercised over the number of clerks at a counter, the problem became one of determining that number of clerks which would result in the minimum total cost of idle time.

For one particular tool crib, the average time between arrivals of mechanics was found to be 35 seconds. Also, for this same crib the average serving time for the individual mechanics was found to be 50 seconds. We have used λ to stand for the average arrival rate and μ to stand for the average service rate over a fixed length of time. If we select the average serving time as this fixed unit, it follows that

$$\lambda = \frac{\frac{1}{35}}{\frac{1}{50}} = \frac{\text{mechanics arriving per second}}{\text{average serving time per second}}$$

$$= 1.43 \text{ mechanics arriving per average serving time}$$

i.e., for this crib, the average number of arrivals per average serving time (i.e., per 50-second interval) is 1.43 mechanics. The average service rate for the 50-second time interval is, of course

$$\mu = 1$$

To find the average waiting time T_w (in average serving time units of 50 seconds), we must use eq. 44 for the case of multichannel servicing facilities in which s refers to the number of clerks at the counter.

That is

$$T_w = \frac{P_0}{s\mu(s!)[1 - (\lambda/\mu s)]^2} \left(\frac{\lambda}{\mu}\right)^s$$

To find P_0 we use eq. 45. Then upon substituting for P_0, s, μ, and λ, we may calculate the average waiting time (in units of average servicing time) of the mechanics for this tool crib.

Table 14-4 illustrates the calculations made for two, three, and four

TABLE 14-4

				T_w	
				Av. Serving	
λ	μ	s	P_0	Time Units	Seconds
1.43	1	2	0.166	1.040	52.0
1.43	1	3	0.228	0.135	6.8
1.43	1	4	0.237	0.025	1.3

clerks. The entry $P_0 = 0.166$ in Table 14-4 was obtained as follows. Using the values $\lambda = 1.43$, $\mu = 1$, and $s = 2$ in eq. 45, we find

$$P_0 = \frac{1}{\sum_{n=0}^{1} (1.43)^n/n! + (1.43)^2/\{2![1 - (1.43/2)]\}}$$

$$= \frac{1}{(1 + 1.43) + 3.58} = \frac{1}{6.01} = 0.166$$

The calculation for the corresponding entry for T_w for two clerks is as follows

$$T_w = \frac{0.166}{2(1)(2!)[1 - (1.43/2)]^2} (1.43)^2$$

$$= \frac{0.166}{(4)(0.285)^2} (1.43)^2 = 1.04$$

the number of 50-second average serving time units. The average waiting time in seconds is, therefore, 1.04×50 seconds, or 52 seconds. The other entries in the table are calculated in a similar manner.

Since on the average one caller arrives every 35 seconds, in a working day of 7.5 hours the expected number of arrivals is

$$\frac{(7.5)(3600)}{35} = 770$$

For this number of arrivals there would be required at the rate of 50 seconds' service for each a total of

$$\frac{770(50)}{3600} = 10.7 \text{ hours}$$

of service on the part of the clerks in 1 working day. Since one clerk alone would furnish only $7\frac{1}{2}$ hours of service, he could not handle the tool crib without there developing a longer and longer waiting line throughout the day. If there were two clerks furnishing 15 hours of service, there would be $15 - 10.7$ or 4.3 hours of idle time on the part of these clerks. But for two clerks we have seen that the expected waiting time for each mechanic is 52 seconds. Hence for an expected number of 770 arrivals per day the expected waiting time would be 770×52 seconds, or approximately 11.1 hours.

If we let \$2 per hour represent the labor cost of clerks and \$5 per hour the cost of a mechanic, we see that the idle time for the two clerks represents $4.3 \times \$2$ or \$8.60 as contrasted with $11.1 \times \$5$ or \$55.50 cost due to mechanics' waiting time. The total cost of waiting on the part of the two clerks and the mechanics is \$64.10.

For three clerks the cost can be similarly computed. It turns out to be \$31. However, for four clerks the total cost rises to \$40, and the cost continues to rise for additional clerks. Hence, under the assumptions stated, the optimum number of clerks is three.

For facility of operation the computations of cost were made for various input rates, for various numbers of clerks, and for various ratios of cost of mechanics' idle time to that of clerks' idle time. These results were then plotted as a family of curves which could be referred to so that a decision as to the optimum number of clerks to be used at any tool crib could readily be made by reference to a chart.

CONCLUSION

Monte Carlo techniques can be used to solve any queuing problem for which the required data can be collected. In some cases, the use of mathematical theory can cut down on the work required to obtain a solution.* In still more cases, by combining the theory and Monte Carlo techniques a solution can be found without much difficulty. At

---

* Camp [9] has developed analytic techniques which can guide the use of Monte Carlo techniques in such a way as to reduce the amount of computation required. This he does by the application of (a) servomechanism theory to establish upper and lower boundaries on expected values, and (b) the technique based on state probabilities.

Massachusetts Institute of Technology work is already under way which is directed toward producing tables which will further facilitate solutions to queuing problems. Computers and analogue devices have been used successfully to simulate waiting-line processes and to provide estimates of the characteristics of the processes.

Much of the applied work done to date in this area indicates that intuition is a poor guide to solving queuing problems. Analyses using the tools described in this chapter have almost always yielded significant improvements in operations.

BIBLIOGRAPHY

1. Adler, R. B., and Fricker, S. J., "The Flow of Scheduled Air Traffic—I and II," M.I.T. RLE Technical Report No. 198, May 2, 1951, and No. 199, Aug. 13, 1951.
2. Bailey, N. T. J., "On Queuing Processes with Bulk Service," *J. R. statist. Soc.*, *16*, no. 2, 80–87 (1954).
3. Barrer, D. Y., "A Waiting Line Problem Characterized by Impatient Customers and Indifferent Clerks," Third Annual Meeting, Operations Research Society of America, New York, June 4, 1955.
4. Bell, G. E., "Operational Research into Air Traffic Control," *J. R. aero. Soc.*, *53*, 965–976 (Oct. 1949).
5. Benson, F., and Cox, D. R., "The Productivity of Machines Requiring Attention at Random Intervals," *J. R. statist. Soc.*, *13*, 65–82 (1951).
6. Berkeley, G. S., "Traffic and Trunking Principles in Automatic Telephony," Ernest Benn, Ltd., London, 1949.
7. Brigham, Georges, "On a Congestion Problem in an Aircraft Factory," *J. Opns. Res. Soc. Am.*, *3*, no. 4, 412–428 (Nov. 1955).
8. Brisby, M. D. J., and Eddison, R. T., "Train Arrivals: Handling Costs, and the Holding and Storage of Raw Materials," *J. Iron Steel Inst.*, *172*, pt. 2, 171–183 (Oct. 1952).
9. Camp, G. D., "Bounding the Solutions of Practical Queuing Problems by Analytic Methods," in J. F. McCloskey and J. M. Coppinger (eds.), *Operations Research for Management II*, The Johns Hopkins Press, Baltimore, 1956.
10. Cobham, Alan, "Priority Assignment in Waiting Line Problems," *J. Opns. Res. Soc. Am.*, *2*, no. 1, 70–76 (Feb. 1954).
11. Crommelin, C. D., "Delay Probability Formulae When the Holding Times Are Constant," *P. O. Elect. Engrs' J.*, *25*, pt. 1, 41–50 (Apr. 1932).
12. Eddison, R. T., and Owen, D. G., "Discharging Iron Ore," *Operat. Res. Quart.*, *4*, no. 3, 39–50 (Sept. 1953).
13. Edie, L. C., "Traffic Delays at Toll Booths," *J. Opns. Res. Soc. Am.*, *2*, no. 2, 107–138 (May 1954).
14. Everett, J. L., "State Probabilities in Congestion Problems Characterized by Constant Holding Times," *J. Opns. Res. Soc. Am.*, *1*, no. 5, 279–285 (Nov. 1953).
15. Feller, W., *An Introduction to Probability Theory and Its Applications*, John Wiley & Sons, New York, 1950.

16. Fry, T. C., *Probability and Its Engineering Uses*, D. Van Nostrand Co., New York, 1928.
17. Gaver, D. P., "The Influence of Servicing Times in Queuing Processes," *J. Opns. Res. Soc. Am.*, *2*, no. 2, 139–149 (May 1954).
18. Holley, J. L., "Waiting Lines Subject to Priorities," *J. Opns. Res. Soc. Am.*, *2*, no. 3, 341–343 (Aug. 1954).
19. Jackson, R. R. P., "Queuing Systems with Phase Type Service," *Operat. Res. Quart.*, *5*, no. 4, 109–120 (Dec. 1954).
20. Kendall, D. G., "On the Role of Variable Generation Time in the Development of a Stochastic Birth Process," *Biometrika*, *35*, 316 (Dec. 1948).
21. ———, "Some Problems in the Theory of Queues," *J. R. statist. Soc.*, (B), *13*, no. 2, 151–173 (1951).
22. ———, "Stochastic Processes Occurring in the Theory of Queues and Their Analysis by the Method of the Imbedded Markov Chain," *Ann. math. Statist.*, *24*, no. 3, 338–354 (Sept. 1953).
23. Lindley, D. V., "The Theory of Queues With a Single Server," *Proc. Cambr. phil. Soc.*, *48*, pt. 2, 277–289 (Apr. 1952).
24. Marshall, B. D., Jr., "Queuing Theory" in J. F. McCloskey and F. N. Trefethen (eds.), *Operations Research for Management*, The Johns Hopkins University Press, Baltimore, 1954.
25. "Marshalling and Queuing," *Operat. Res. Quart.*, *3*, no. 1, 1–15 (Mar. 1952).
26. M.I.T. Interim Report No. 2, "Fundamental Investigations in Methods of Operations Research," Apr. 1, 1954–Nov. 30, 1954.
27. *M.I.T. Summer Short Course in Operations Research*, Technology Press, Massachusetts Institute of Technology, Cambridge, 1953.
28. Molina, E. C., "Applications of the Theory of Probabilities to Telephone Trunking Problems," *Bell Syst. Tech. J.*, *6*, 461 (1927).
29. Morse, P. M., "Stochastic Properties of Waiting Lines," *J. Opns. Res. Soc. Am.*, *3*, no. 3, 255–261 (Aug. 1955).
30. ———, Garber, H. N., and Ernst, M. L., "A Family of Queuing Problems," *J. Opns. Res. Soc. Am.*, *2*, no. 4, 444–445 (Nov. 1954).
31. Pollaczek, F., "Sur l'application de la théorie des fonctions au calcul de certaines probabilités continués utilisées dans la théorie des réseaux téléphoniques," *Ann. Inst. Poincaré*, *10*, no. 1, 1 (1946).
32. ———, "Über eine Aufgabe der Wahrscheinlichkeitstheorie," *Math. Z.*, *32*, 64–100 and 729–750 (1930).

Chapter 15

Traffic Delays
at Toll Booths*

The business of the Port of New York Authority is public service, which it renders by the construction and operation of various facilities and the promotion and protection of commerce in the Port district. Its operations involve such items as ramp co-ordination, fire fighting and other emergency work, baggage handling, and parking-lot operations at airports; dock-space allocation, warehousing, and materials handling at seaports; truck loading, bus loading and dispatching, and rail and truck freight distribution at land terminals; and vehicular-traffic control, accident prevention, and the collection of vehicular tolls—with which this chapter deals—at tunnels and bridges. Although the list is incomplete, it is sufficient to indicate a fertile area for Operations Research.

O.R. methods are being applied to this public service by the Operations Standards Division of the Operations Department, a staff department filling the role of consultant on operating problems encountered by four line departments, each of which is responsible for the physical and financial results of one of the four groups of facilities previously mentioned. O.R. methods are now being extended to the Comptroller's Department, where sample auditing of various accounts is being investigated. The division's introduction to O.R. came about during a comprehensive study of the Port Authority police force—a group of 1000 men comprising the largest single class of employees in the Port Authority.

* By *Leslie C. Edie.* Reprinted from *Journal of the Operations Research Society of America*, 2, no. 2, 107–138 (May 1954).

The purpose of the police study was to determine whether the police staffing of the various facilities was sound and economical. Achieving this purpose necessitated careful analysis of the numerous operations conducted by the police and the establishment of standards for these operations. Good standards are sometimes rather difficult to establish, and the complete police study, which was originally scheduled to take 6 months, actually required 14. The additional time was largely consumed in operational analyses, such as the one covered in this chapter, which were not foreseen in the beginning, but which proved to be well worth while. The annual operating savings effected soon after completion of the study amounted to more than ten times the cost of the study itself with potential future savings of more than 20 times the study cost. These are annual savings, repeated each year. In addition, capital savings were achieved of nearly ten times the study cost. O.R. can be credited with important portions of these financial results, and for such other results as better service to the public and benefits to police personnel.

TOLL COLLECTION

The collection of vehicular tolls is a major part of the Port Authority police operations: more than one-fourth of the police personnel are utilized in this function. In the preliminary stages of our analysis, it was observed that the results obtained from toll operations were not altogether satisfactory. The quality of the service varied appreciably from time to time, being considerably better than necessary in some instances, thus involving idle toll collectors, and being unsatisfactory in others, resulting in patron complaints. The average delay, for instance, was observed to vary from 2 to 50 seconds.

Prior to our operational analysis, toll booths were manned almost entirely on the basis of opinion and judgment and the manpower supplied was first determined by budget procedures. A facility included in its budget the number of toll collectors it believed was required in the forthcoming year. These requirements were then reviewed by management in the light of the expected annual traffic, past experience, and a rule of thumb about how much traffic could be handled by a toll collector. The manpower authorized and provided by this budget procedure was then allocated by the facility to various days of the week and tours, and was based on the composite judgment of the toll sergeants, who supervised the toll operations, and their superiors. This is a typical management process.

On a given tour the actual number of toll booths manned at any particular time was left to the discretion of the toll sergeant on duty, who made the best use he could of the manpower at his disposal. Toll sergeants are rotated around the three tours and alternated between tolls and traffic duty, making it difficult for a sergeant to become thoroughly familiar with traffic on any tour. The principal operation required of the toll sergeant is compromising the frequently conflicting requirements of traffic on the one hand with personal and meal reliefs for the toll collectors on the other. Since the toll sergeants have varying experience and different ideas about how to operate, the results were not consistent. Some exercised good judgment, and some did not; interviews with toll collectors indicated that their relief requirements were in too many cases being unsatisfactorily met. Precedence was generally given to the patron at the expense of the toll collector when conflicts arose, but, since toll collecting is a rather nerve-wracking job, extended working periods without a relief are very undesirable.

From the foregoing discussion, the general objectives of the study can be seen to be: 1. to evaluate the grade of service given to patrons and determine how it varies with the volume of traffic handled by toll lanes; 2. to establish the optimum standards of service; and 3. to develop a more precise method of controlling expenses and service while at the same time providing for well-spaced reliefs to the toll collector.

OBSERVATIONS

The first type of data recorded was traffic arrivals at the toll plaza. One observer counted the number of vehicles arriving in 30-second intervals and recorded the count along with the time, as shown in the first two columns of Table 15-1. Intervals of 30 seconds were found to be about the shortest that could be used to permit the observer to make recordings without losing the count.

The second type of data recorded was the extent of the backup in each open toll lane. These data, recorded by a second observer, were also taken at 30-second intervals and in synchronism with the traffic arrival recordings.

The third type of data was the toll transaction count. These data were recorded at half-hour intervals and whenever there was a change in the number or type of toll lanes. In some cases the number and type of lanes opened were left to the toll sergeant, but in other cases the number and type were regulated by the survey group in order to obtain information on specific arrangements and to create moderate amounts of congestion. These data provide a check on the arrival count, with which they should agree when adjusted for the change in accumulation at the beginning and end of an observation period. More important, they also permit computations to be made for each lane individually, as well as for all lanes collectively.

TABLE 15-1. SAMPLE OF RECORDED DATA

Time, P.M.	Traffic Arrivals	Vehicles in			Total	Lanes Occupied
		Lane A	Lane 6	Lane 10		
8:58	10	2	2	1	5	3
8:59	6	0	1	0	1	1
	1	0	1	0	1	1
9:00	3	1	0	0	1	1
	4	0	1	1	2	2
9:01	5	1	1	0	2	2
9:15 *	6	0	1	0	1	1
	5	1	2	0	3	2
9:16	6	5	0	1	6	2
	4	2	1	0	3	2
9:17	4	1	0	1	2	2
	2	0	0	0	0	0
9:18	7	1	1	3	5	3
Totals *	205	41	55	38	134	76

	Transactions †			
9:18	2102	79,785	97,466	
8:58	2034	79,698	97,416	
Totals	68	87	50	205

* Fourteen minutes omitted.
† Similar to cash-register tally number.

Table 15-1 shows a sample of all three types of data, taken at the Lincoln Tunnel when three left-hand toll booths were open in one direction and were handling traffic at the rate of 615 vehicles per hour. It also shows the preliminary steps taken in analyzing the data, these being the totals of each column, the total backup for the three lanes at each observation, and the number of lanes occupied at each observation.

COMPUTATIONS

One of the principal factors of interest is average delay. It is first desirable, however, to calculate the over-all time taken per vehicle to clear the toll lanes; this includes both the delay, or waiting time, and the booth-holding or servicing time. The over-all time used by all vehicles to get through the toll lanes, based on the sample observations, is 4020 seconds, and the average is 19.6 seconds.

The total booth time used in handling vehicles during the observation period of Table 15-1 is the total number of occupancies observed—given by the total of the last column—multiplied by the observation interval, or 2280 seconds. The average booth-holding time is 11.1 seconds. The average delay per vehicle is the over-all time per vehicle less the booth-holding time, or 8.5 seconds.

Another item of interest is the average delay expressed as a multiple of holding time, here called "delay ratio." This item is of particular interest because of its use in delay theories, and also because it provides a measurement of delay that is independent of fluctuations in holding time. The delay ratio is average delay per vehicle divided by average booth-holding time, or 0.77.

The percentage of vehicles delayed might well be used as a measurement of the grade of toll-booth service. This can be obtained by counting the number of instances in which two or more vehicles were observed at a single booth and dividing this count by the total number of booth occupancies observed. Another factor is average delay of delayed vehicles. This is the average delay to all vehicles divided by the percentage delayed.

The maximum delay can be estimated from the maximum backup and the average booth-holding time. In the example, the maximum backup observed was six vehicles. This is found by inspection of the data. The sixth vehicle waited for the five preceding ones, each assumed to have taken the average booth-holding time. Thus, the maximum delay is 55.5 seconds.

The availability of an empty toll lane is still another factor that could be used to measure the grade of toll-booth service. At first thought one might state that this is complementary to the percentage of vehicles delayed, since any vehicle may go either into an occupied lane and be delayed or an empty lane and not be delayed, and if drivers always picked an unoccupied lane when available this would be the case. Unfortunately, however, drivers often pick an occupied lane instead of an empty one even though an empty lane is always available, and in so doing can delay all vehicles. The number of instances when there were one or more lanes empty in the example was 31 out of 40, thus giving a percentage availability of 77.5. The complement to the percentage delayed is 55.

In addition to the previously mentioned items, any one of which could be used to specify the grade of toll-booth service being given, there is interest in the percentage occupancy of the toll booths, which is given by the number of occupancies observed, divided by the total number of observations. In the example, this is 63.3.

These calculations have been made for the three toll lanes as a group. By using the transaction counts shown at the bottom of Table 15-1, all the items can be calculated for each lane individually.

Having shown how a number of tentative service criteria can be determined from the data, we shall, in the balance of the chapter, concern ourselves with only those that were actually used to arrive at service standards. Before going into an analysis of these, let us consider the analysis of traffic arrivals.

TRAFFIC-ARRIVAL ANALYSIS

The traffic-arrival patterns were analyzed by forming frequency distributions of the number of vehicles arriving in 30-second intervals at various volumes. Observations were formed into 200 vehicles-per-hour groups, and in each group the number of occurrences of arrivals of 0, 1, 2, 3, etc., vehicles was counted and organized into a table. The empirical frequency of occurrences of each arrival class was computed as a percentage of the total number of intervals observed. These percentages were then plotted against the arrival classes, as shown in Fig. 15-1, and frequency polygons were drawn. These frequency distributions have rather good resemblances to the distributions one would expect with pure-chance traffic. One feature to be noted, however, is the tendency for the right-hand tails of the distributions at the higher volumes to be somewhat prolonged. The extension of the distribution for the highest volume shown out to 28 along the abscissa should be noted in particular.

Comparison for the same volumes of traffic can be made with the theoretical distributions which are shown in Fig. 15-2. The similarity to the actual distributions is quite evident; however, it will be noted that the right-hand tails are not as prolonged. These theoretical distributions are Poisson at the lower volumes and normal at the higher volumes.

A more easily observed comparison between the actual and the two theoretical distributions is shown in Fig. 15-3, where they are plotted together. These distributions pertain to a volume of 655 vehicles per hour at the Lincoln Tunnel. The mean arrival rate is 5.46 vehicles per 30-second interval, and the standard deviation is 2.73 vehicles per 30-second interval. In computing the Poisson and normal values the sample mean was used, but in the case of the normal distribution the standard deviation used was the theoretical one for a pure-chance dis-

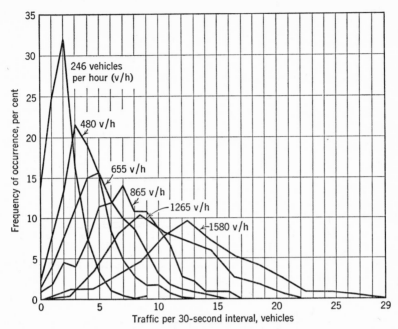

Fig. 15-1. Frequency distribution of traffic arrivals.

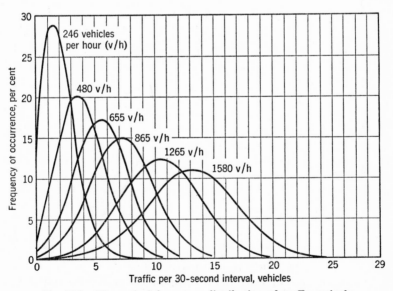

Fig. 15-2. Theoretical frequency distribution of traffic arrivals.

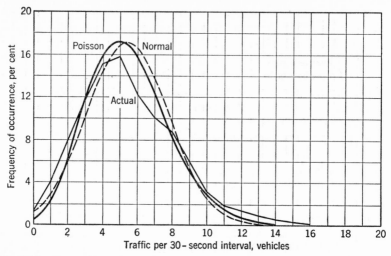

Fig. 15-3. Comparison of actual and theoretical traffic arrivals for 655 vehicles per hour at Lincoln Tunnel.

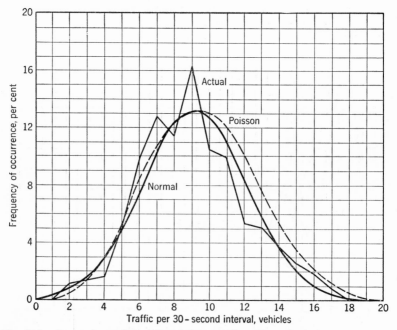

Fig. 15-4. Comparison of actual and theoretical traffic arrivals for 1100 vehicles per hour at George Washington Bridge.

tribution. In this example the Poisson, shown as a solid curve, appears to give a better fit to the actual than the normal.

The arrival distributions at the George Washington Bridge, as well as at the Lincoln Tunnel, were analyzed in the same manner with similar results, as shown in Fig. 15-4. This figure applies to a volume of 1100 vehicles per hour, with a mean of 9.17 and a standard deviation of 3.00. Here the normal curve, shown as a solid curve, appears to fit slightly better than the Poisson.*

Table 15-2 shows the goodness of fit for a number of traffic volumes investigated. There is a very evident tendency for the fit of both distributions to deteriorate at the higher traffic volumes, although both continue to show a satisfactory fit better than 0.05. This deterioration, however, is of some interest since it corresponds with the extended right-hand tails of the actual distributions that were previously noted. Both the extended tails and the poorer fit at higher volumes can be explained by the development of congestion, which causes the operation of one vehicle to interfere with the operation of another. At

---

* The Poisson distribution is given by the expression $P(x) = e^{-m}m^x/x!$, where $P(x)$ in this case is the probability of x vehicles arriving in any interval when the average arrival rate is m. It will be noted that the Poisson distribution is fully specified by a single parameter, the mean.

The normal distribution is given by the expression

$$F(x) = \exp\left[-(x - m)^2/2s^2\right]/s\sqrt{2\pi}$$

where $F(x)$ is the probability of x vehicles arriving in any interval when the average arrival rate is m and the standard deviation is s. For pure-chance traffic, where p is the probability of any random vehicle arriving in a particular interval, q the probability of it not arriving, and n the total number of vehicles in the hour, the standard deviation is $s = \sqrt{npq}$.

Both of these distributions are close approximations of the binomial distribution given by the expression $P(x) = C_x^n p^x q^{n-x}$, when n, the number of vehicles, is large and p is small. In the distribution of hourly vehicular traffic arrivals in 30-second intervals, small p is $1/120$, q is $119/120$, and n is the total traffic volume. However our interest is more in the Poisson and normal distributions than the binomial, since they are easier to deal with.

To learn which of these two theoretical distributions gives the better fit, the chi-square test of fitness can be used. The chi-square value is given by the expression

$$\chi^2 = \sum_{x=0}^{n} (f_o - f_t)^2/f_t$$

where f_o is the observed frequency and f_t the theoretical. When these values have been computed, they may be looked up in a table of chi-square values to obtain the probability level of fit. A perfect fit would show a probability level of 1.00, but a fit showing a probability level better than 0.05 is generally taken as satisfactory.

426 Introduction to Operations Research

still higher volumes it is apparent that the fit would break down, and under bumper-to-bumper congestion the distribution would tend to become constant. The volume at which the fit becomes unsatisfactory depends, of course, on the number of lanes in the roadway. The column indicating the theoretical better fit is based on the theory that the Poisson expresses the better approximation to the binomial below a mean value of 5 and the normal the better approximation above this

TABLE 15-2. TRAFFIC-ARRIVAL GOODNESS OF FIT

Traffic Volume	Poisson	Normal	Theoretical Best Fit
246	0.754	0.235	Poisson
480	0.966	0.743	Poisson
655	0.738 *	0.459	normal
865	0.842	0.882	normal
1100	0.718	0.812	normal
1265	0.359 *	0.295	normal
1580	0.191	0.575	normal

value. This mean corresponds with a traffic volume of 120×5 equals 600 vehicles per hour. Two exceptions to this theory, noted by asterisks in the table, are not considered significant. The results support the belief that the true distribution, before congestions enter as a factor, is binomial, and consequently is a pure-chance distribution.

OCCUPANCY VERSUS DELAY RATIO

Having established the randomness of traffic we thought that we would be able to draw curves of traffic volumes versus each of the various service criteria, and then find a delay theory that would agree closely enough with the empirical curves for at least some of these criteria to be predictable from theory. Unfortunately, such was not the case; for some delay factors satisfactory empirical curves could not be drawn because of the wide dispersion of points. To determine accurately the correlation curves for some of the service criteria directly from computed points would have required a very large amount of data.

The most obvious relation to seek to establish—that between traffic volumes and average delay in seconds—fell into this category. One reason for this is that average delay measured in seconds is a function not only of traffic volume but also of booth-holding time. Because of differences in traffic composition, holding times are different at different facilities, and the data taken at one facility are not usable for an-

other. Another factor is that holding time is partly under the control
of the toll collectors, who in some cases knew they were being observed
and were naturally influenced to keep holding times lower than usual.
These factors made the direct plotting of average delay for each facility unsatisfactory.

To get around the difficulty our attention was directed to curves of
occupancy versus delay ratio. This relation is independent of holding
time, permitting data from different facilities to be combined. The
scattering of the points was appreciably reduced and, with the greater
number of observations available from combining all facilities, satisfactory empirical curves could be drawn. A further consideration is
that delay theory is developed on the basis of holding-time units, and
it was desired to compare the empirical results with the theories of
Erlang,[2] Molina,[1] and the joint theory of Pollaczek and Crommelin.[3]

Erlang's theory is given by the equation

$$d = \frac{(y^x/x!)[x/(x-y)^2]}{\left(\begin{array}{c}\{1 + y + (y^2/2!) + (y^3/3!) + \cdots \\ + [y^{x-1}/(x-1)!] + (y^x/x!)[x/(x-y)]\}\end{array}\right)}$$

where d is average delay in units of holding time, x is the number of
traffic channels, and y is the traffic intensity in erlangs.[2] An erlang is
defined as the average occupancy during a time T, divided by T. It
is a dimensionless unit, being similar in this respect to the decibel used
to express values of attenuation. For example, if three channels are
each occupied one-half the time of a period T, the total occupancy is
$1.5T$ and the traffic intensity is 1.5 erlangs. The number of erlangs
also expresses the average number of traffic elements handled simultaneously. Erlang's delay equation is based on an assumption of exponentially distributed holding times, where $P(t) = e^{-t/h}$ gives the
probability of an element of traffic selected at random having a holding time of at least t, when the average holding time is h.

Molina's equation constitutes a correction factor applied to Erlang's
equation to alter it for constant holding-time distribution.[1] The correction factor is given by the expression

$$[x/(x+1)][1 - (y/x)^{x+1}]/[1 - (y/x)^x]$$

The Pollaczek-Crommelin equation, based on an assumption of constant holding-time distribution,[3] is given by the expression

$$d = \sum_{w=1}^{\infty} e^{-wy} \left(\sum_{u=wx}^{\infty} \frac{(wy)^u}{u!} - \frac{x}{y} \sum_{u=wx+1}^{\infty} \frac{(wy)^u}{u!} \right)$$

Figure 15-5 shows a comparison between values predicted by these equations and the empirical results for a single toll booth. The empirical values are shown as plotted points. It can be seen that, as expected, the Pollaczek-Crommelin equation shows a good fit, whereas

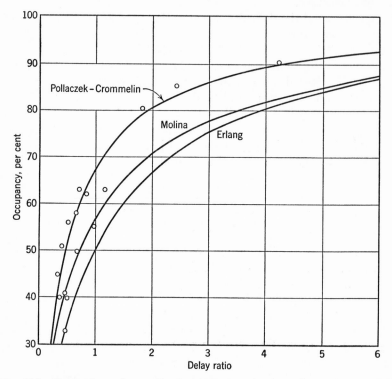

Fig. 15-5. Comparison of actual points and theoretical occupancy delay curves for one toll booth.

both Molina's and Erlang's equations give delays considerably greater than the empirical results. This indicates that booth-holding times are essentially constant in distribution, and that the Pollaczek-Crommelin equation more accurately portrays average delay at the higher occupancies than does Molina's, although there is not much choice between them at lower occupancies. A sampling of holding times by means of stop-watch timing also indicated booth-holding times were more nearly constant than exponential in distribution.

In the case of four toll booths, shown in Fig. 15-6, the empirical results show greater delays than any of the theories, and Erlang's equation for exponentially distributed holding times is closer to the empirical results than the constant holding-time equations. The reason for this is that previously mentioned: traffic lines up at one booth while another toll lane is empty. Because the traffic was found to be random, and because of the fit of the Pollaczek-Crommelin equation to one toll booth, this poor traffic distribution is virtually the sole cause of the much greater delays found than that given by the constant

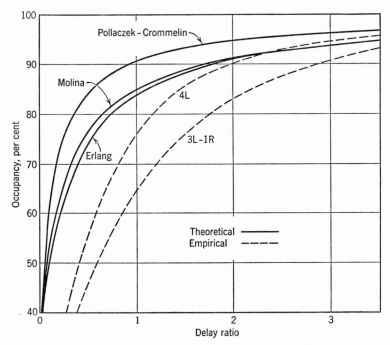

Fig. 15-6. Comparison of actual and theoretical occupancy delay curves for four toll booths.

holding-time equation. Our efforts to adjust the equation for this factor were not successful, so it was necessary to proceed with empirical values.

It will be noted that two empirical curves are shown for the case of four toll booths, one curve applying to four left-hand toll booths and the other to three lefts and one right. Left-hand toll booths are those on the driver's side of a vehicle passing through the lane, and right-hand toll booths are the opposite. Both curves have been shown to illustrate the inferiority of the right-hand booths.

This is illustrated even more clearly in Table 15-3, which shows the percentage increase in delay ratio for equal occupancies and the reduction in occupancy for equal delays when a right-hand booth is substituted for a left. In the first comparison it will be noted that this results in an increase in delay of approximately 50%. The increased delay is suffered by all traffic in the aggregate, not just by the traffic handled at the right-hand booth.

TABLE 15-3. Comparison of Four Left-Hand with Three Left-, One Right-Hand Booths

Percentage of Equal Occupancy for 4 Left-Hand Booths	Corresponding Percentage for 3L-1R	Delay Ratio for 4L	Corresponding Delay Ratio for 3L-1R	Increase in Delay for 3L-1R, %	Value of RH Versus LH, %
50	40	0.40	0.60	50	20
60	50	0.60	0.85	41	33
70	60	0.85	1.25	47	43
80	70	1.25	1.80	44	50
90	83	2.00	3.00	50	69

In the second comparison it will be noted that at moderate delay levels a right-hand toll booth has less than one-half the value of a left-hand toll booth. The value of a right-hand booth increases as congestion at the toll plaza increases, thus indicating the overflow character of the right-hand booths. As a consequence of these findings the Port Authority is reconstructing all major toll plazas to provide only left-hand toll booths.

TRAFFIC VERSUS HOLDING TIME

To convert the dimensionless ratios of occupancy and delay into the practical units of vehicles per hour and seconds of delay requires a determination of holding-time values. In some delay problems, holding time is unaffected by the traffic congestion and by the number of channels employed. This is the case, for instance, when dealing with telephone traffic. But in the case of toll operations, as shown in Fig. 15-7, for the George Washington Bridge, holding time was found to be a function of traffic volume and the number of toll booths employed. It can be seen that holding time is appreciably longer at low volumes of traffic per lane than it is at high volumes. As traffic per lane approaches zero, the holding time approaches a maximum value of approximately 13 seconds, and as traffic volume rises to the maximum that can be handled per lane, the holding time approaches a minimum value of $8\frac{1}{2}$ seconds. It will also be noted from the figure that the greater the number of toll lanes used, the sooner the holding time begins to drop. However, once it begins to drop, it does so in the same manner for all groups of booths, i.e., in proportion to increases in traffic per lane, the slope being approximately 1 second to 50 vehicles per lane per hour.

The explanations for this phenomenon seem apparent. In the first place, holding time decreases as traffic per lane increases because both toll collectors and patrons tend to expedite the operation under the pressure of backed-up traffic. This seems to be a fairly common phenomenon in waiting problems involving people who are aware of the

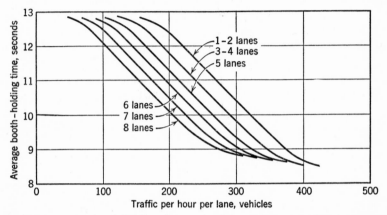

Fig. 15-7. Average booth-holding time per vehicle at George Washington Bridge.

amount of congestion. In our field observations it was noticed that when traffic was light there was considerably more conversation between collector and patron than when traffic was heavy. Another factor is that, when there is a waiting line at a toll booth, patrons have an opportunity, while waiting, to get their tolls ready; whereas with an empty lane the patron might drive right up to the booth before reaching for his toll—and then have to search to find it.

The explanation for the quicker drop in holding time for larger groups of lanes appears to lie in the nonuniform distribution of traffic between the open lanes. Certain lanes, particularly those having left-hand booths, and those located near the center of the plaza, are considerably favored by patrons over the others. The greater pressure of traffic in these favored lanes brings about a reduction in holding time, even though the average traffic per lane over all lanes may still be low. Since the favored lanes handle the most traffic, they have a proportionately greater effect on the average over-all lanes than do the less favored lanes.

When the curves of traffic per lane versus holding time were plotted, it was found that there were few values at the high traffic volumes to define clearly the location of the curves at these levels of traffic. The reason for this is that, to obtain points at heavy loadings per lane, the creation of heavy congestion would be required. This would result in complaints that might be embarrassing to answer. Therefore we sought other methods of finding where the curves leveled off.

The principal method used consisted of stop-watch measurements of toll transaction times and the calculation of vehicle times for various types of transactions. Booth-holding time is made up of two parts: One is the time taken by the toll collector to receive the toll from the patron and, if necessary, to give change or a receipt. The other is the time taken by the vehicle to move into toll-paying position. The collection, or transaction, time is taken as the interval between the time the wheels of a vehicle stop rolling when it moves into a lane and the time they again start rolling when the vehicle moves out of the lane. The vehicle time is taken as the interval between the time one vehicle starts to leave and the following vehicle comes to a stop in toll-paying position.

Using this breakdown of the holding time, it was relatively easy to make stop-watch measurements of minimum transaction times, just by watching the wheels of the vehicles as they came to a stop and started up again in lanes having long lines. It would also have been easy to measure the vehicle time in a similar fashion, but this was not considered necessary since information is readily available on the acceleration and deceleration of automotive vehicles, and these times could be determined from available curves.

The observations on transaction times, which were made on several hundred vehicles, and the determination of vehicle times from acceleration-deceleration curves resulted in a breakdown of minimum booth-holding times by types of vehicles and types of toll booths. This is shown in Table 15-4. With this information it is possible to calculate

TABLE 15-4. BREAKDOWN OF AVERAGE MINIMUM HOLDING TIMES FOR
DIFFERENT VEHICLES

Vehicle	Vehicle Time, Seconds	Toll Time, Seconds		Holding Time, Seconds	
		LH	RH	LH	RH
Passenger car	5.0	3	4	8	9
Bus	6.5	3	4	9.5	10.5
Truck	6.0	5	6.5	11.0	12.5
Tractor-trailer	7.5	6.5	8.0	14.0	15.5

minimum holding times for traffic composed of various percentages of passenger cars, buses, trucks, and tractor-trailer units. For example, traffic at the Lincoln Tunnel is, at peak periods, composed of about 64% passenger vehicles, 15% buses, 14% trucks, and 7% tractor-trailer units. The minimum holding times for left-hand and right-hand toll booths can be computed as follows:

Left-Hand Booths

$$\text{H.T.} = 0.64 \times 8 + 0.15 \times 9.5 + 0.14 \times 11 + 0.07 \times 14$$

$$= 5.1 + 1.4 + 1.5 + 1.0 = 9.0 \text{ seconds}$$

Maximum booth capacity = 3600/9 = 400 vehicles per hour.

Right-Hand Booths

$$\text{H.T.} = 0.64 \times 9 + 0.15 \times 10.5 + 0.14 \times 12.5 + 0.07 \times 15.5$$

$$= 5.8 + 1.6 + 1.8 + 1.1 = 10.3 \text{ seconds}$$

Maximum booth capacity = 3600/10.3 = 350 vehicles per hour.

As a check against this method, another method was utilized. At the George Washington Bridge during 18 peak periods in which there was heavy congestion due solely to overloaded toll booths, the average traffic per lane was 403 vehicles. Assuming a 95% occupancy at these times, a minimum holding time of $0.95 \times (3600/403) = 8.5$ was indicated. This compares exactly with the results of the toll-time and vehicle-time analysis with equal numbers of left- and right-hand booths handling a composition of traffic consisting entirely of passenger cars, which was virtually the composition at the George Washington Bridge on the occasions mentioned. This method is applicable only at a bridge, because at a tunnel entrance the congestion caused by the tunnel itself during peak traffic periods prevents traffic from moving out of toll booths when the transaction is over, thus artificially lengthening the holding time, and at a tunnel exit the tunnel holds back traffic, thus preventing saturation of the toll booths.

DEVELOPMENT OF AVERAGE DELAY CURVES

Having established the relation of traffic per lane versus holding time, in addition to the relation of percentage of occupancy versus delay ratio, it is now practical to develop the relation of traffic versus average delay in seconds that was originally sought. Table 15-5 shows sample computations of points for a curve for four left-hand toll booths using values taken from the previous two types of curve. Table 15-5 applies to the George Washington Bridge only, since the holding-time values given in the third column apply only to this facility. These points were computed by first assuming a traffic volume per lane, and working from there. Take the point given by 300 vehicles per lane per hour. The next column shows the total traffic volume of 1200 for the four lanes. The third column gives the booth-holding time, 9.8 seconds, which was read from the holding-time curves. The booth-holding time multiplied by the vehicles per lane gives 2940 booth-seconds of traffic

TABLE 15-5. TRAFFIC VERSUS DELAY POINTS FOR FOUR LEFT-HAND BOOTHS

Vehicles per Lane per Hour	Total Vehicles	Holding Time, Seconds	Booth-Seconds	Occu-pancy, %	Delay Ratio	Delay, Seconds
100	400	12.9	1290	36.0	0.20	2.6
150	600	12.7	1910	53.0	0.45	5.7
200	800	11.8	2360	65.5	0.73	8.6
250	1000	10.8	2700	75.0	1.02	11.0
300	1200	9.8	2940	81.6	1.31	12.8
350	1400	8.9	3120	86.7	1.66	14.8
375	1500	8.7	3260	90.6	2.00	17.4
385	1540	8.6	3310	91.9	2.36	20.3
400	1600	8.5	3400	94.4	3.40	28.9

per lane shown in the fourth column. Dividing the latter value by the 3600 booth-seconds available in 1 hour gives the 81.6% occupancy shown in the next column. Entering the occupancy-delay-ratio curve for four left-hand toll booths at this occupancy gives a delay ratio of 1.31, and multiplying the delay ratio by the holding time of 9.8 seconds yields an average delay value of 12.8 seconds.

When points had been computed and plotted for all the various booth combinations generally used at the George Washington Bridge, the result was a family of curves, as shown in Fig. 15-8. From these curves, it is apparent that the traffic-carrying capacity of different toll booths for a given delay is not constant but instead varies appreciably between different combinations of booths for a given amount of delay. Before this analysis was made, it was generally assumed by the management in scheduling manpower that one toll booth was just about like another in all circumstances. Again the overflow nature of the right-hand toll booths shows up here. The curves for combinations of four lefts with one to four rights all merge into the curve for four left-hand booths alone at a volume of about 400 vehicles per hour. Below this volume the right-hand booths carry virtually no traffic.

One solution to the delay problem has now been achieved, but, before it is used, some indication of its accuracy would be desirable. To see whether the curves actually portrayed what was given by the original observations, values read from the curves were compared with the direct computations of average delays from the data. In so doing it was found that for observation periods of approximately 20 minutes

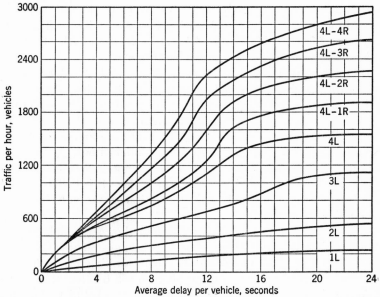

Fig. 15-8. **Average delay for various volumes of traffic at George Washington Bridge.**

the average error was 2.64 seconds. Considering that the values computed from the data represent the mean of a sample of the population, it can be estimated that for a sample of three times this size the probable error would be less by a factor of one to the square root of 3, making it 1.53 seconds. The average delay of all observations was 11 seconds, thus indicating that for hourly periods the curves would predict average delay with a probable error of about 15%. This, fortunately, was close enough for our purposes. If it had not been, we would have had to turn to some other criteria that could be predicted for purposes of setting service standards and determining how many toll booths were required for various volumes of traffic.

ANALYSIS OF TRAFFIC BACKUP

Very often in waiting problems, knowledge of the average delay involved is insufficient. An analyst is interested in this, but he is also interested in the boundary conditions of what the worst delays may be under given circumstances. If, on the occasion of an important appointment, a motorist is delayed several minutes waiting in a line of many vehicles to get through the toll booths, he would likely find little consolation in being told that by using Port Authority facilities regularly he could expect his average delay to be very nominal. This realization leads to an analysis of traffic-backup behavior.

One way of analyzing backup behavior is simply to plot values of the greatest backups observed against the traffic volume handled for each combination of toll lanes. When this is done, the problem of wide scattering again arises. For this particular relation the scattering is worse than for any other investigated. From the limited amount of data taken, only the roughest idea can be obtained of what maximum backup to expect and how often to expect it for a given combination of toll booths handling a given volume of traffic. It is therefore necessary to employ the methods of mathematical statistics to determine the relation.

In organizing and summarizing the data shown in Table 15-1 for purposes of statistical analysis of backup behavior, it was decided to consider the number of vehicles in the longest waiting line, rather than the total amount of backup behind all open toll booths. The reason, of course, is that we are concerned with the one motorist who incurs the worst delay, and total backup is not a measure of this because of the nonuniform distribution of backup between the open lanes.

The first steps in the analysis of backup are similar to those taken in the analysis of traffic arrivals. One difference, however, is the use of much smaller samples. In the traffic-arrival analysis, the data were grouped into 200-vehicle volumes. By so grouping, samples consisting of a few hundred intervals could be obtained, and the frequency polygons resulting from the samples were fairly smooth. In studying traffic arrivals, consideration did not have to be given to the number and types of toll booths employed, but, for the backup analysis, observations have to be so segregated. The toll-booth arrangements are, in practice, changed two or more times an hour because of changing traffic volume and because the reliefs given to toll collectors sometimes result in a booth of one type being substituted for one of the other type. It is therefore expedient in analyzing backup behavior, as was also the case in the average delay analysis, to use periods of about

20 minutes. This provides samples of only about 40 intervals—two a minute for 20 minutes. To smooth out the irregularities in the frequency distribution resulting from the small samples, a 3-point weighted moving average can be employed.

Figure 15-9 shows the results obtained in plotting frequency distributions of the backup in the longest line for a combination of three left-hand toll booths, after the observed distributions had been smoothed

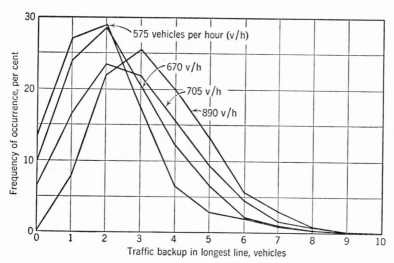

Fig. 15-9. Actual frequency distribution of traffic backup for three left lanes.

by averaging and had been converted to a base of 100 to give frequency as a percentage of total occurrences. These curves include cases from both the Lincoln Tunnel and the George Washington Bridge. The first two curves, for volumes of 575 and 670 vehicles per hour, are from the tunnel, and the other two, for volumes of 705 and 890 vehicles per hour, are from the bridge. It will be noted that the distributions resemble the traffic-arrival distributions, as one might expect, since holding times are essentially constant in distribution and therefore the cause of variations in backup is largely the variation in traffic arrivals.

Figure 15-10 shows Poisson distributions corresponding to the actual distributions shown in Fig. 15-9. Except for the irregularities of the actual distributions, they resemble the Poisson distributions. In computing values for the Poisson distributions, the same mean value of backup found in the actual distributions was employed. This feature is different from the traffic-arrival analysis since in the latter it was unnecessary to determine the mean value empirically; it is given directly from the traffic volume and observation interval. There is no doubt a definable relation between traffic volume and the mean value of backup for a given booth combination, but we could develop no formula, either theoretical or empirical, that would predict the mean value of backup for a given volume of traffic.

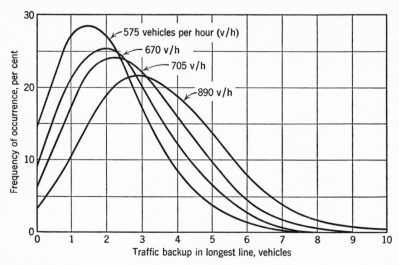

Fig. 15-10. Theoretical frequency distribution of traffic backup for three left lanes.

How closely the Poisson distribution fits the actual distribution of backup is illustrated more clearly in Fig. 15-11, which shows both distributions plotted together. This case covers a condition of three left-hand toll booths handling traffic at the rate of 615 vehicles per hour at the Lincoln Tunnel. This, incidentally, portrays the values given in the sample data presented in Table 15-1. For this case, the mean value of backup is 2.16 vehicles, and the standard deviation is 1.52 vehicles. The standard deviation of the mean, which will be used later, is 0.15. The chi-square probability level for the Poisson is 0.64. For a normal distribution the chi-square probability is only 0.01.

The results at the George Washington Bridge are comparable to those at the Lincoln Tunnel, as shown in Fig. 15-12. This is at a slightly higher volume of 705 vehicles per hour, and the mean backup value is 2.79 vehicles, the standard deviation is 1.67, and the standard deviation of the mean is 0.31. The chi-square probability level (used here as a rough indicator of goodness of fit) for the Poisson is 0.55, and, for a normal distribution, less than 0.01.

In the same way that the traffic-arrival patterns at the tunnel and the bridge are nearly identical, the backup behavior is also nearly identical. The identity is so close that we were quite unable to differentiate between the two facilities. This was rather surprising since

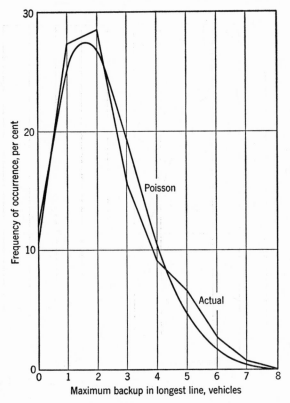

Fig. 15-11. Actual and theoretical backup for 615 vehicles per hour in three left lanes at Lincoln Tunnel.

there were quite discernible differences in average delay values between facilities because of differences in traffic composition and holding time. We spent a considerable amount of effort trying to find differences in backup values, but without success. It was decided that, except for conditions approaching saturation, the greater amount of backup caused by a longer holding time for a given traffic volume is reflected more in time units than in vehicle units. As a specific illustration, the mean value of backup for 615 vehicles per hour and three left-hand toll booths was found to be 2.16 vehicles, and the booth holding time was

11.1 seconds. This represents a backup in time units of 2.16 × 11.1 = 24.0 seconds. If the holding time increased, say, 20% to 13.3 seconds and the time backup also increased 20% to 28.8 seconds, the vehicle backup would remain the same at 2.16. Something close to this seems to happen for small differences in holding time.

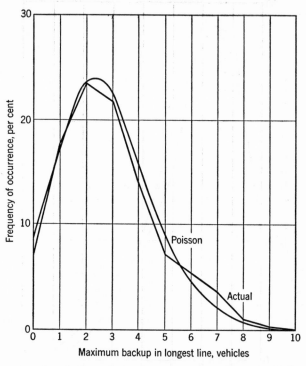

Fig. 15-12. Actual and theoretical maximum backup for 705 vehicles per hour in three left lanes at George Washington Bridge.

In all cases of backup distribution, the normal showed a poorer fit than the Poisson so that the latter can be considered the true nature of the backup distribution—up to a point. Table 15-6 indicates that the Poisson distribution does not hold indefinitely as traffic volumes are increased. Starting with a rather remarkable fit of 0.93, at a volume of 575 vehicles per hour, the goodness of fit drops off gradually, reaching an unsatisfactory value at a traffic volume of about 800 vehicles per hour. This particular volume applies only to three left-hand toll booths, but the same deterioration of fit was observed at other volumes for all toll-booth combinations as the traffic volumes approached values of approximately 60 to 75% of saturation. The reason for this deterioration appears to be the increasing carry-over of vehicles from one interval to the next as saturation is approached. The traffic volume at which the Poisson distribution broke down was termed the "Poisson point."

TABLE 15-6. RELATION OF GOODNESS OF FIT OF BACKUP TO POISSON DISTRIBUTION FOR THREE LEFT-HAND TOLL BOOTHS

Traffic Volume	Goodness of Fit
575	0.93
615	0.64
625	0.55
670	0.85
705	0.55
750	0.05
867	0.01
890	0.32

TRAFFIC VOLUME VERSUS MEAN VALUE OF BACKUP

Having established the range of usefulness of the Poisson distribution, the next step is that of establishing the relation between traffic volumes and the mean value of backup, the mean value being the sole parameter necessary to specify the entire distribution. The only satisfactory method found to determine mean values was to draw an empirical curve, as shown in Fig. 15-13. To assist in locating the curve, the points were plotted to show plus and minus one standard deviation of the mean. In many cases, as in this one, most of the points were more or less clustered within the range of traffic volumes customarily handled by the booth combination concerned. To obtain empirical values at higher traffic volumes would have required the deliberate creation of excessive congestion, which would make some patrons very unhappy. Fortunately, this was unnecessary because it is obvious that the curves approach the full occupancy capacity of the booth combination asymptotically. Full occupancy capacity is known to be approximately 400 vehicles per hour for left-hand booths at the Lincoln Tunnel and 450 at the George Washington Bridge. To be on the safe side, the lower value was used, and the curve for three left-hand booths was drawn to approach a volume of 1200 vehicles per hour.

Combining similar curves for various toll-booth combinations results in the family of curves shown in Fig. 15-14. When the Poisson points were plotted on this chart they were found to be very nearly in the straight line shown dotted and labeled the "Poisson line."

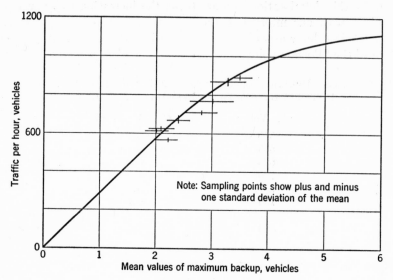

Fig. 15-13.   Mean values of maximum backup.

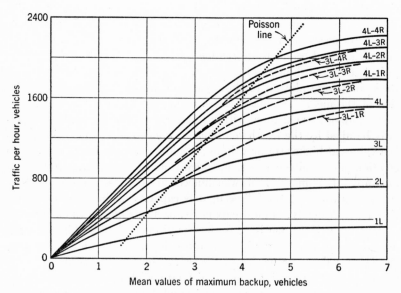

Fig. 15-14.   Mean values of maximum backup.

PROBABLE MAXIMUM BACKUP

Knowledge of the mean values of backup in the longest line, plus knowledge that the distribution of this variable is Poisson, permit us to investigate the boundary values, which can be determined by Poisson summations. The question is: What boundary values are we interested in? Or in telephone terminology: What loss probability should be used? The answer to this question depends somewhat on judgment.

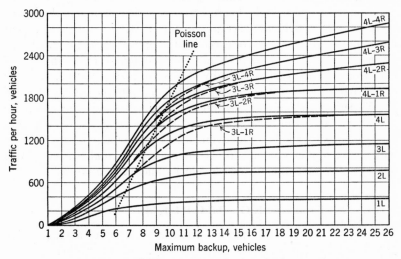

Fig. 15-15. Probable maximum backup in longest line.

If the loss probability is made too large, say 0.1, the boundary value will be exceeded so frequently that it will be a poor measure of the maximum delay that a patron incurs. On the other hand, if the loss probability is made too small, say 0.001, the boundary condition will occur so infrequently as to be misleading in the other direction. Looking at this question in a slightly different way, if we consider the period of interest to be 1 hour composed of 120 30-second intervals, and the boundary value of backup is taken as that having a probability of 0.1 of being equaled or exceeded, the expected number of intervals of occurrence will be $0.1 \times 120 = 12$. If the loss probability is taken as 0.001, then the expected number of intervals that will occur in 1 hour will be 0.12, and the maximum will be expected to occur only once in over 8 hours. It therefore appears logical to choose a loss probability of 0.01 to define what is called the "probable maximum backup," since this maximum can be expected to occur or be exceeded for about one 30-second interval out of an hour. The family of curves shown in Fig. 15-15 gives backup values at that probability level. These curves have again been extrapolated considerably beyond the data, and the extrapolation has been made by approaching asymptotically traffic volumes of 400 times the number of toll booths.

As in the case of the average delay curves, it was considered advisable to establish the reliability of the probable maximum backup curves by a comparison with observed values. For some 53 periods of observation at the Lincoln Tunnel and the George Washington Bridge covering from one to eight booths, over a period of about 20 hours, there were 26 individual observations out of 2379 in which the actual maximum backup equaled or exceeded the probable maximum backup given by Fig. 15-15. The probability of equaling or exceeding values read from the curves indicated by this is $26/2379 = 0.0109$, an error of 9% from the objective of establishing the $p(0.01)$ values. Out of the 53 periods, which averaged about 20 minutes each, there were 10 periods in which the backup exceeded the prediction for one or more intervals of 30 seconds. The average excess amounted to 1.4 vehicles and the maximum was 4. For 41 intervals the actual maximum was less by an average amount of 1.5 vehicles and a maximum of 4.

THE OPTIMIZING PROBLEM

Having solved the waiting-line problem in terms of average delay per vehicle and probable maximum backup, the next problem is that of establishing an optimum level of service, i.e., of setting service standards. One way is to select an upper limit of average delay, such as 20 seconds, and to open another toll booth when this limit is reached. Such an arbitrary decision is difficult to support, and is hardly to be recommended in Operations Research. Furthermore, the objective is not so much to place an upper limit on delay as it is to control delay more closely than had been done in the past. The principal dissatisfaction with former methods of manning toll booths was that they varied so widely—from less than 2 to nearly 50 seconds under substantially normal off-peak conditions.

In order to reduce the extreme swings of average delay and at the same time to optimize the service, it is suggested that the standard be a middle value rather than a maximum. As traffic increases, the average delay should swing above the standard by an amount equal to the drop below the standard when an additional booth is manned. The question is how to select this middle value of delay in a logical manner with a minimum of arbitrariness.

One way would be to assign relative values to traffic volumes handled and serviced; for example, let 10 vehicles per booth-hour be considered equivalent in value to an increase in delay of 1 second. This method of equating would be hard to support logically. A better one along the same line would be to consider patron time and toll-collector time of equal value. Thus, another booth would be opened when the traffic volume times the reduction in delay to be achieved by another booth would equal 3600 seconds. Although this principle makes a certain amount of sense, it was not used.

Another way is to consider the point of diminishing returns. This method has the advantage of being less controversial and comprises a concept widely accepted and understood by management people. In this case the cost is characterized by the delay and the return by the traffic volume. The point where return starts diminishing in relation to the cost is that of minimum curvature of the curves. Above this point the increases in traffic volume attained for each increment of increase of delay become smaller and smaller, approaching zero as the delay approaches infinity.

The points of diminishing return defined in this way can be determined by inspection. For the George Washington Bridge they vary from $10\frac{1}{2}$ to 16 seconds with a weighted average of about 12 seconds. For the Lincoln and Holland tunnels, they average about 10 and 11 seconds respectively. Since it was desired to provide uniform service at the three crossings, the middle value of 11 seconds was adopted as the standard for all three.

Now, capacity standards can be established for the various groups of toll booths by equalizing the swing on each side of the standard delay as additional booths are provided. Doing so at the George Washington Bridge resulted in Table 15-7. It will be noted that the backup

TABLE 15-7. George Washington Bridge Toll-Booth Capacity

Booths		Capacity, Vehicles per Hour	Delay, Seconds	Backup, Number of Cars
Left-Hand	Right-Hand			
1		225	0–16.9	6
2		450	5.1–15.5	7
3		750	6.5–14.0	8
4		1050	8.0–11.5	8
4	1	1250	10.5–12.0	9
4	2	1525	10.0–11.8	10
4	3	1850	10.2–11.5	11
4	4	2150	10.5–11.5	12

values at the booth capacities for the standard average delay increase as the number of booths is increased, ranging from 6 with one booth to 12 with eight booths. Fortunately, this is a desirable result since experience has shown that patrons are more willing to accept longer lines as traffic volumes increase. Apparently they intuitively feel that a backup of 12 cars when eight toll booths are open is qualitatively different from a backup of 12 cars with only one toll booth open.

HOURLY TRAFFIC PATTERN

At this point, two service criteria—average delay and maximum backup—can be satisfactorily predicted when the traffic volume is

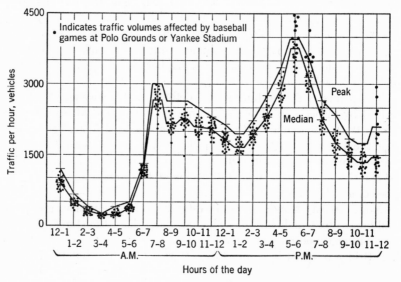

Fig. 15-16. Hourly volume of westbound traffic on George Washington Bridge.

known, and a standard for one has been established. The question that next arises is how well traffic volumes can be predicted. This question requires a study of the hourly pattern of traffic throughout the day and the dispersion from day to day. This analysis was made by plotting hourly volumes on charts having time of day as abscissas and traffic volumes as ordinates. In making this analysis it was found that the days in the middle of the week had almost identical patterns and could be combined. Figure 15-16 shows a pattern found for Tuesdays, Wednesdays, and Thursdays combined at the George Washington Bridge for the summer of 1952. On the other days of the week each day was so different that it required separate treatment.

As can be seen in Fig. 15-16, two curves were drawn through certain of the plotted points. One curve was drawn through median points, which was the simplest way of obtaining an estimate of expected values of traffic without many computations. Another curve was drawn through the peak values as the simplest means of estimating the highest values of traffic to be expected.

Inspection of the curves indicates a spread between median and peak figures of from 10 to 60% at the George Washington Bridge. At the tunnels the spread was less, ranging from 10 to 30%. These variations limit how closely toll booths can be scheduled in advance to provide optimum service, which brings us to the last part of the problem, the scheduling of toll booths and collectors.

THE SCHEDULING PROBLEM

In the scheduling of toll booths throughout a day, the number of booths required was first determined from the capacities of various booth combinations derived on the basis of optimum average delay for the median traffic volumes. Because of the rapid rise and fall of traffic at daily peaks, it was necessary to do this by half-hours. When done, the peak values of traffic for each half-hour period were studied for the maximum backup that might occur. Concern was then given to those cases where maximum backups several vehicles above the Poisson points were indicated. Our ability to predict backups satisfactorily no doubt fell off rather rapidly in this region. Since saturation of booth capacity was being approached, traffic volumes slightly higher could cause a significant jump in backups. Judgment was used here to determine how much of a gamble to take. Although more precise methods could be used, they were unnecessary. Judgment suggested a gamble on backups up to three vehicles above the Poisson points. Therefore, when the spread between median and peak traffic was great enough to result in backups exceeding this standard, an additional booth was provided.

This process resulted in a schedule of booths throughout the day, from which could be determined the total number of booth-hours required for the day. One more step remained in the problem, that of determining how many toll collectors were required to keep the scheduled number of booths open, and still permit toll collectors' personal and meal reliefs to be given within certain restrictions. These restrictions were: 1. working periods of not less than 1 nor more than 3 hours between reliefs or ends of the collector's tour, 2. meal reliefs in the middle 4 hours of an individual's tour; and 3. starting times not earlier than 6 A.M. and quitting times not later than 12:30 A.M.

The scheduling of manpower in such a manner requires the preparation of a Gantt-type chart for each day, showing the working and idle periods for every toll collector. Toll-collector starting times and relief periods must be juggled in an effort to provide exactly the number of collectors needed to give the optimum service each half-hour of the day. This is largely a trial-and-error problem, and preparation of such schedules may be very time-consuming when the objective is to make the schedule as efficient as possible.

The efficiency of such a schedule is given by the ratio of the number of collectors required by the booth-hours to the number supplied by the schedule. As an example, the midweek days at the George Washington Bridge during the summer of 1953 required 344 booth-hours per day. The net working time per toll collector per day is $6\frac{1}{4}$ hours; thus the minimum number of collectors that would meet booth-hour requirements is $344/6.25 = 55.04$. If a schedule uses 57 men, its efficiency is $55.04/57 = 97\%$. The first schedules made were not very efficient, and there was always a question whether a given schedule was the most efficient that could be made as long as the number of collectors used exceeded the first integral number above requirements. A great deal of time can be wasted in trying to reduce the number of collectors employed, when it actually is not possible to do so within the restrictions imposed.

Analysis and experience show, however, that the efficiency of such a schedule depends largely on the magnitude and duration of peak periods. By considering the relief requirements during the morning and evening peaks, and the period just after midnight, an estimate can be made of the number of collectors required on each tour. This analysis is made by totaling the number of booth-hours required for the peak $3\frac{1}{2}$ hours and dividing by 3. Doing so allows a $\frac{1}{2}$-hour relief period for each toll collector. Continuing with the example of the George Washington Bridge midweek days, there are 70 booth-hours in the morning peak, requiring $70/3 = 23.3$, or 24, men; 71.5 booth-hours in the evening peak, requiring $71.5/3 = 23.8$, or 24, men; and 21 booth-hours after midnight, requiring $21/3 = 7$ men. The total for the three tours comes out to 55 men, thus indicating that a schedule close to actual requirements is possible. The actual schedule used 56 men for a scheduling efficiency of $55.04/56 = 98.3\%$. In most cases traffic patterns enable scheduling efficiencies of 95% or better.

RESULTS

With the development of an efficient method of scheduling, the last problem of the study was solved. A big question, however, remained before the results could be recommended to management. This question was: Would a method of manning toll booths based on these techniques really work any better than the former method of just giving a toll sergeant approximately the right number of collectors and letting him use his own judgment about how many booths should be kept open as traffic varied and when collectors should be given reliefs. The only way to find out was to try it. If it worked continuously for a week, it should be able to work indefinitely.

A trial was conducted at the Lincoln Tunnel. The numbers of toll booths required every half-hour for the entire week were predicted in both directions of traffic. This entailed 512 predictions of booth requirements. Each toll collector was given a slip showing his booth assignments and relief periods and was instructed to follow the schedule strictly. During the entire week, the prearranged schedules were followed without a hitch. At no time did excessive backups occur, and at no time did reliefs have to be deferred. The movement of collectors and the opening and closing of booths took place without the attention of the toll sergeant. At times the number of booths was slightly excessive, but not to the extent previously occurring under the former method. Needless to say, there is a good deal of satisfaction in seeing the validity of so much work actually established.

BIBLIOGRAPHY

1. Berkeley, G. S., *Traffic and Trunking Principles in Automatic Telephony*, Ernest Benn, Ltd., London, 1949.
2. Brockmeyer, E., Holstrom, H. L., and Jensen, Arne, *The Life and Work of A. K. Erlang*, Copenhagen Telephone Co., Copenhagen, 1948.
3. Crommelin, C. D., *P.O. Elect. Engrs' J.*, *26*, pt. 4 (Jan. 1934).
4. Greenshields, B. D., Shapiro, D., and Erickson, E. L., "Traffic Performance at Urban Street Intersections," Yale University, New Haven, 1947.

Chapter 16

Sequencing Models

INTRODUCTION

The class of waiting-line problems considered in Chapter 14 involved determining the amount of facilities which would minimize the sum of the costs associated with both "customer" and facility waiting time. In this chapter we turn to the converse problem, one in which the facilities are fixed and arrivals and/or the sequence of servicing the waiting customers are subject to control. The problem is to *schedule* arrivals or *sequence* the jobs to be done so that the sum of the pertinent costs is minimized.

"Scheduling" is used here to refer to the *timing* of arrivals (and/or departures) of units requiring service. For example, a train or bus schedule indicates the planned time of arrivals and departures. "Sequencing" is used here to refer to the *order* in which units requiring service are serviced. For instance, production lots waiting at the "entrance" to a machine center can be put into a sequence in which they are to be worked. The terms scheduling and sequencing are often used interchangeably. This usage tends to obscure a fundamental difference in the underlying structure of the two types of problems. The scheduling problem is solvable by Queuing Theory for it has the same structure as the type of facility problem discussed in Chapter 14. The scheduling problem differs from the type of problem discussed in Chapter 14 only in the nature of the control variable: number of service points or time (or rate) of arrivals. Since the models and techniques discussed in Chapter 14 are applicable to scheduling, this type of problem is not discussed further here. In this chapter we are primarily concerned with the sequencing problem.

Mathematical analysis of the sequencing problem has just begun. Relatively little progress has been made to date. The formulation of the problem itself is still incomplete because it is concerned only with minimizing some function of time. The characteristic of O.R. problems which involves balancing conflicting objectives has not yet been brought into the formulation of the sequencing problem. Yet these conflicts exist in real situations. For example, in sequencing production lots over a series of machines, we are not only concerned with minimizing total elapsed time (in order to reduce the cost of in-process inventory and to increase output for a fixed investment) but usually are also concerned with providing equal incentive opportunities to the operators of the different machines. These and other considerations such as shipping priorities (and the associated costs of delay) are generally in conflict with the objective of minimizing some function of processing time.

There is little doubt that these complexities will eventually be formulated into the sequencing problem. In fact, there have already been moves in this direction. For example, Rowe and Jackson [17] have formulated and made progress on solving sequencing problems involving priorities.

These remarks are not intended to minimize the importance of the work that has been done and which is discussed in this chapter. They are intended to put the reader on guard against uncritical application of the techniques to be discussed.

Sequencing problems have most frequently been encountered in the context of a production department. Little wonder; the more effective use of available facilities—greater output—is a constant objective of production organizations. Management has been willing to support many types of investigation into the possibility of improving utilization of available facilities by bettering decision rules concerning the scheduling or sequencing of work over those facilities.

Many production control departments attempt to achieve effective utilization of facilities by means of such visual aids as the Gantt chart, Produc-trol boards, and Sched-U-Graphs. (See Chap. 10 in Moore.[15]) Useful as such devices are, they nevertheless often fail to yield optimum sequences or even to indicate how far from an optimum is a sequence which they do yield.

In order to appreciate the complexity of sequencing, consider the case in which four jobs must be done, each requiring time on each of five machines. There can be $(4!)^5$, or 7,962,624 different sequences, some of which, however, may not be feasible due to the fact that the required operations must be performed in a specified order. Obviously, any technique which will direct us to an optimal or approximately optimal sequence without trying all or most of the possibilities has considerable value.

As indicated, acceptable sequences of jobs are frequently restricted by "precedence requirements" which arise from the technology of the manufacturing process. For example, a part must be degreased before it is painted, and a hole must be drilled before it is threaded. In all such cases, it is necessary that a work element which must follow another be assigned to the same work station where the preceding element is to be performed or to a work station which follows later in the sequence.

TWO STATIONS AND n JOBS—NO PASSING

Consider the very simple case of n jobs to be processed on two machines, A and B, each job requiring the same sequence of operations and no passing allowed. Whichever job is processed first on machine A must also be processed first on machine B and whichever job is processed second on machine A must also be processed second on machine B, etc. This condition exists, for example, in many chemical processes where the material flows from work station to work station on conveyors or through pipes. It is assumed, however, that the material can be held between work stations; e.g., the work to be done can be temporarily stored on the conveyor belt or in the pipes or storage tanks until the next station is ready for it. In the meantime the preceding work station is left clear to start work on another job. Without loss of generality, it can also be assumed that all jobs must first go to machine A and then machine B. Let

A_i = time required by job i on machine A
B_i = time required by job i on machine B
T = total elapsed time for jobs $1, \cdots, n$
X_i = idle time on machine B from end of job $i-1$ to start of job i

The problem is to determine a sequence $(i_1, \cdots, i_n)$, where $(i_1, \cdots, i_n)$ is a permutation of integers 1 through n, which will minimize T. There are $n!$ possible sequences. A possible sequence, say for $n = 5$, can be represented on a Gantt chart * such as is done in Fig. 16-1.

Figure 16-1 represents the sequence (1, 2, 3, 4, 5). Job 1 occupies machine A for A_1 hours, while machine B is idle. As soon as job 1 comes off machine A, job 2 goes on it, and job 1 goes to machine B, etc.

* For details on the use of a Gantt chart see Moore,[15] pp. 228–235.

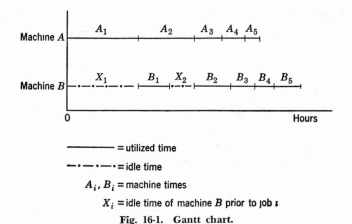

Fig. 16-1. Gantt chart.

The total elapsed time T is determined by the point of time at which job 1 goes on machine A and the point of time at which job 5 comes off machine B. At any instant of time machine B is either working or idle. The total time machine B has to work is $\sum_{i=1}^{5} B_i$; this is determined by the technology of the process, not by the sequence. Now

$$T = \sum_{i=1}^{5} B_i + \sum_{i=1}^{5} X_i \qquad (1)$$

The problem is to minimize T, but since $\sum_{i=1}^{5} B_i$ is fixed, the problem becomes that of minimizing $\sum_{i=1}^{5} X_i$.

It is obvious from Fig. 16.1 that

$X_1 = A_1$
$X_2 = A_1 + A_2 - B_1 - X_1$, if $A_1 + A_2 \geq X_1 + B_1$
$\quad = 0$, if $A_1 + A_2 < X_1 + B_1$

The expression for X_2 can be rewritten as follows

$$X_2 = \max (A_1 + A_2 - B_1 - X_1, 0)$$

$$= \max \left(\sum_{i=1}^{2} A_i - \sum_{i=1}^{1} B_i - \sum_{i=1}^{1} X_i, 0 \right)$$

Using the same type of notation

$$X_1 + X_2 = \max (A_1 + A_2 - B_1, X_1)$$

$$= \max \left(\sum_{i=1}^{2} A_i - \sum_{i=1}^{1} B_i, A_1 \right)$$

Similarly

$$X_3 = \max \left(\sum_{i=1}^{3} A_i - \sum_{i=1}^{2} B_i - \sum_{i=1}^{2} X_i, 0 \right)$$

$$\sum_{i=1}^{3} X_i = \max \left(\sum_{i=1}^{3} A_i - \sum_{i=1}^{2} B_i, \sum_{i=1}^{2} X_i \right)$$

$$= \max \left(\sum_{i=1}^{3} A_i - \sum_{i=1}^{2} B_i, \sum_{i=1}^{2} A_i - B_1, A_1 \right)$$

Let

$$D_n(S) = \sum_{i=1}^{n} X_i$$

where $D_n(S)$ is a function of the sequence S. Then, in general

$$D_n(S) = \sum_{i=1}^{n} X_i = \max \left(\sum_{i=1}^{n} A_i - \sum_{i=1}^{n-1} B_i, \sum_{i=1}^{n-1} A_i - \sum_{i=1}^{n-2} B_i, \cdots, A_1 \right)$$

$$= \max_{1 \leq u \leq n} \left(\sum_{i=1}^{u} A_i - \sum_{i=1}^{u-1} B_i \right) \qquad (2)$$

This means that the expression within the parenthesis is evaluated separately for each positive value of u (1 through n) and the maximum of all these values is $D_n(S)$.

The problem can now be stated as follows: to put the jobs in a sequence which minimizes $D_n(S)$. Johnson [13] and Bellman [3] have analytically determined the decision rule for the optimal sequence. Johnson's derivation is given in Note 1 at the end of this chapter. The decision rule can be transformed into the following procedure which is illustrated by considering the situation represented in Table 16-1.

TABLE 16-1. MACHINE TIMES (IN HOURS) FOR FIVE JOBS AND TWO MACHINES

i	A_i	B_i
1	3	6
2	7	2
3	4	7
4	5	3
5	7	4

Procedure for Finding the Optimal Sequence [13]

1. Examine the A_i's and B_i's and find the smallest value [min (A_i, B_i)]. In this illustrative case, this value is $B_2 = 2$.

2. If the value determined falls in the A_i column, schedule this job first on machine A. If the value falls in the B_i column (as it does in this case), schedule the job last on machine A. Hence, job 2 goes last on machine A.

3. Cross off the job just assigned and continue by repeating the procedure given in steps 1 and 2. In case of a tie, choose any job among those tied. In this illustrative case, once job 2 is assigned, the minimum value which remains is 3, and it occurs in A_1 and B_4. We have a choice, so let us arbitrarily select A_1. Then job 1 goes on machine A first. Now B_4 is the minimum remaining value. Hence, job 4 goes on machine A next to last. The minimum remaining value is 4, and it occurs in A_3 and B_5. Then we can put job 3 on machine A second and job 5 on third. The resulting sequence is optimal and is 1, 3, 5, 4, 2.

This sequence and the total elapsed time can be shown on a Gantt chart as is done in Fig. 16-2. From Fig. 16-2 it can be seen that the

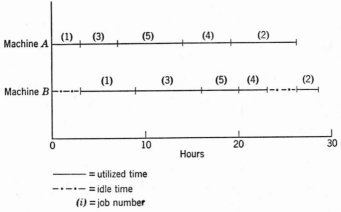

Fig. 16-2. Gantt chart for optimal sequence involving five jobs and two machines.

total elapsed time is 28 hours and that the idle time on machine B is 6 hours.

Several properties of this problem should be noted. First, it is assumed that the order of completion of jobs has no significance; i.e., no product is needed more quickly than another. The introduction of completion priorities complicates the problem. This complication will be referred to later in the chapter. Second, it is assumed that in-process storage space is available and that the cost of in-process inventory is the same for each job or is too small to be taken into account. For processes which are short in duration this is usually the case. But for extended processes the situation may require consideration of this inventory cost.

THREE STATIONS AND n JOBS—NO PASSING

Here we consider a case similar to the preceding one except that three stations are involved. Each job requires the same sequence of operations and no passing is allowed. Expanding the notation used in the preceding discussion, we let

Y_i = the idle time of the third machine before it starts work on the ith job

C_i = working time of the third machine on the ith job

The total elapsed time is now expressed as

$$T = \sum_{i=1}^{n} C_i + \sum_{i=1}^{n} Y_i \qquad (3)$$

Hence, the problem of minimizing T is the same as that of minimizing $\sum_{i=1}^{n} Y_i$, since $\sum_{i=1}^{n} C_i$ is fixed. Johnson [13] has found an optimum solution * to this problem for the special case where either

1. Min $A_i \geq$ max B_i (the least time required on machine A for any job is equal to or greater than the greatest time required on machine B for any job),
or
2. Min $C_i \geq$ max B_i.

The first of these conditions is satisfied by means of an exact equality in the illustrative data given in Table 16-2.

---

* Johnson showed that for the general case of three stations and n jobs

$$\sum_{i=1}^{n} Y_i = \max_{1 \leq u \leq v \leq n} (H_v + K_u)$$

where

$$H_v = \sum_{i=1}^{v} B_i - \sum_{i=1}^{v-1} C_i, \, v = 1, 2, \cdots, n$$

$$K_u = \sum_{i=1}^{u} A_i - \sum_{i=1}^{u-1} B_i, \, u = 1, 2, \cdots, n$$

TABLE 16-2. MACHINE TIMES (IN HOURS) FOR FIVE JOBS AND THREE
MACHINES

i	A_i	B_i	C_i
1	8	5	4
2	10	6	9
3	6	2	8
4	7	3	6
5	11	4	5

To obtain an optimal sequence a new table, such as that shown in
Table 16-3, is formed. The procedure (described in the preceding) for

TABLE 16-3. SUMS OF MACHINE TIMES (IN HOURS) FOR FIVE JOBS FOR
FIRST AND INTERMEDIATE MACHINES AND INTERMEDIATE AND LAST
MACHINES

i	$A_i + B_i$	$B_i + C_i$
1	13	9
2	16	15
3	8	10
4	10	9
5	15	9

obtaining an optimal sequence for two stations can be applied to Table
16-3. In this case, the following would be optimal sequences:

$$3, 2, 1, 4, 5$$
$$3, 2, 4, 5, 1$$
$$3, 2, 4, 1, 5$$
$$\cdots$$

In situations where the conditions $\min A_i \geq \max B_i$ or $\min C_i \geq$
$\max B_i$ do not hold, no general procedure is available as yet for obtaining an optimal sequence. It follows, of course, that no general
solution is yet available for the more general problem of n jobs and m
machines, each job following an identical route with no passing allowed.
However, the following statement holds: For optimal sequences (the
criterion being the total elapsed time), the total idle time of the last
machine must be minimized.

Identical Routing, Passing Permitted

Although each of n jobs may have to pass through each of m stations according to a specific route, the process characteristics do not
always require that the order in which n jobs pass through each of the

stations be identical; i.e., passing is permitted. Bellman [3] and Johnson [13] have shown, however, that for two or three station processes, the optimal sequence always involves the same ordering of jobs over each station. This result, however, does not necessarily hold where more than three stations are involved.

DIFFERENT ROUTING

In many production operations, particularly in job shops, the various jobs which must be done require different routing through the work stations or centers.

Two Jobs and m Stations

Let us consider the case in which two jobs have to be processed on m machines using two different routes. No alternative routing is permissible for either job and each machine can work on only one job at a time. Storage space for in-process inventory is assumed to be available. The problem considered here is to find a sequence which will minimize the total elapsed time.

There are 2^m possible sequences, not all of which are technologically feasible. In this situation there might be many more unfeasible sequences than feasible ones. Hence, it would be very desirable to be able to eliminate the unfeasible sequences. Furthermore, among the remaining feasible solutions there are some which could not possibly be optimum and it would be very desirable to be able to identify these also. Akers and Friedman [1] have developed a technique for accomplishing such elimination, a technique which employs symbolic logic (specifically, Boolean algebra). This technique yields a subset of sequences, one or more of which is optimal.

To describe and illustrate the technique, consider the case * of two parts (jobs), and four machines, a, b, c, and d. Suppose the required sequences of stations for each job are as follows:

Job 1: a, b, c, d

Job 2: d, b, a, c

Let A stand for the instruction: on machine a, process job 1 before job 2. Let $\bar{A}$ stand for the instruction: on machine a, process job 2 before job 1. Similarly, B, $\bar{B}$, C, $\bar{C}$, D, and $\bar{D}$ represent corresponding instructions for machines b, c, and d. For example, in this notation,

* This illustration is taken from Akers and Friedman.[1]

$A\bar{D}$ stands for the instruction: on machine a process job 1 before job 2 *and* on machine d process job 2 before job 1. The 16 possible sequences (called "programs") of jobs over machines can be represented in this notation, as is done in Table 16-4.

TABLE 16-4. ALL PROGRAMS FOR TWO JOBS ON FOUR MACHINES

Program No.	1	2	3	4	5	6	7	8	9	10	11	12	13	14	15	16
	$\bar{A}$	A	$\bar{A}$	A	$\bar{A}$	A	$\bar{A}$	A	$\bar{A}$	A	$\bar{A}$	A	$\bar{A}$	A	$\bar{A}$	A
	$\bar{B}$	$\bar{B}$	B	B	$\bar{B}$	$\bar{B}$	B	B	$\bar{B}$	$\bar{B}$	B	B	$\bar{B}$	$\bar{B}$	B	B
	$\bar{C}$	$\bar{C}$	$\bar{C}$	$\bar{C}$	C	C	C	C	$\bar{C}$	$\bar{C}$	$\bar{C}$	$\bar{C}$	C	C	C	C
	$\bar{D}$	$\bar{D}$	$\bar{D}$	$\bar{D}$	$\bar{D}$	$\bar{D}$	$\bar{D}$	$\bar{D}$	D	D	D	D	D	D	D	D

Table 16-4 can be transformed into "binary" language by letting "1" represent an instruction that holds, and "0" represent an instruction that does not hold. We place the four instructions A, B, C, and D in the left-hand column and for each sequence indicate whether or not each of the instructions holds by referring back to Table 16-4. The results are shown in Table 16-5. Wherever an A appears in Table 16-4, 1 appears in Table 16-5; and wherever an $\bar{A}$ appears in Table 16-4, 0 appears in Table 16-5, etc.

TABLE 16-5. BINARY TABLE FOR PROGRAMS FOR TWO JOBS AND FOUR MACHINES

Instruction \ Program No.	1	2	3	4	5	6	7	8	9	10	11	12	13	14	15	16
A	0	1	0	1	0	1	0	1	0	1	0	1	0	1	0	1
B	0	0	1	1	0	0	1	1	0	0	1	1	0	0	1	1
C	0	0	0	0	1	1	1	1	0	0	0	0	1	1	1	1
D	0	0	0	0	0	0	0	0	1	1	1	1	1	1	1	1

The next step is to determine which sequences are not technologically feasible. To do this we refer to the prescribed routings for each job:

$$\text{Job 1:} \quad a, b, c, d$$

$$\text{Job 2:} \quad d, b, a, c$$

It is obvious that before job 1 can go on machine d it must go on machine a. Also, before job 2 can go on machine a it must go on machine d. Hence, any sequence which includes $\bar{A}D$ is technologically unfeasible. The unfeasibility can be demonstrated as follows:

1. $\bar{A}$ asserts that job 2 must precede job 1 on machine a.

2. But job 2 cannot go onto machine a until it has gone on machine d and

3. Since statement D is asserted to be true, it specifies that job 2 cannot go onto machine d until after job 1 has. However, job 1 cannot go onto machine d until it has gone on machine a.

4. Therefore, this sequence could never get started.

The principle just demonstrated has been generalized by Akers and Friedman in their Theorem I as follows:

A necessary and sufficient condition that a 2-job program be technologically feasible is that for each pair of machines, x and y, where x precedes y for job 1 and x follows y for job 2, the term $\bar{X}Y$ not appear in the program.

On the basis of this theorem, we can, in the illustration, eliminate all programs that include $\bar{A}D$, $\bar{A}B$, $\bar{B}D$, and $\bar{C}D$. Those programs involving $\bar{A}C$, for example, cannot be eliminated on these grounds since both jobs 1 and 2 go onto machine a before machine c.

Now we want to separate and retain for consideration those programs for which statements $\bar{A}D$, $\bar{A}B$, $\bar{B}D$, and $\bar{C}D$ are not true. This is done as follows. Each column in Table 16-5 is examined and marked 1 if "not $(\bar{A}D)$" is true, and 0 if it is false. For example; each program for which $\bar{A}D$ is true will have 0 in the first row and 1 in the fourth row. That is, a 0 in the first row of Table 16-5 is equivalent to $\bar{A}$ and a 1 in the fourth row is equivalent to D. Similarly, in Table 16-5

$$\bar{A}B = 0 \text{ in the first row, 1 in second}$$

$$\bar{B}D = 0 \text{ in second row, 1 in fourth}$$

$$\bar{C}D = 0 \text{ in third row, 1 in fourth}$$

The result of following this procedure is shown in Table 16-6.

TABLE 16-6. Binary Number for Technologically Feasible Programs

Program No. / Instruction	1	2	3	4	5	6	7	8	9	10	11	12	13	14	15	16
Not ($\bar{A}D$)	1	1	1	1	1	1	1	1	0	1	0	1	0	1	0	1
Not ($\bar{A}B$)	1	1	0	1	1	1	0	1	1	1	0	1	1	1	0	1
Not ($\bar{B}D$)	1	1	1	1	1	1	1	1	0	0	1	1	0	0	1	1
Not ($\bar{C}D$)	1	1	1	1	1	1	1	1	0	0	0	0	1	1	1	1
Logical Product	1	1	0	1	1	1	0	1	0	0	0	0	0	0	0	1

The feasible programs are those which satisfy all four conditions and hence have a 1 in each row. We reject every column which has one or more 0's in it. This operation is equivalent to forming the *logical product* of rows and entering 1 under a column if it has all 1's and 0 otherwise. Nine out of the 16 possible programs have been eliminated; 7 remain.

Akers and Friedman have shown that the number of feasible programs N is given by

$$N = 1 + m + \sum_{k=2}^{m} i_k \qquad (4)$$

where i_k is the number of times that k specific machines ($k = 2, 3, \cdots, m$) appear in the same order (regardless of intervening machines) in both job routings.

In the example under consideration

$$m = 4$$
$$k = 2, 3, 4$$
$$i_2 = 2[(a, c) \text{ and } (b, c)]$$
$$i_3 = 0$$
$$i_4 = 0$$

Hence

$$N = 1 + 4 + 2 + 0 + 0 = 7$$

These feasible programs are shown in Table 16-7. The feasible programs are now examined to determine whether or not they are optimal relative to a specified measure of effectiveness.

TABLE 16-7. TECHNOLOGICALLY FEASIBLE PROGRAMS

Instruction / Program No.	1	2	4	5	6	8	16
A or $\bar{A}$	$\bar{A}$	A	A	$\bar{A}$	A	A	A
B or $\bar{B}$	$\bar{B}$	$\bar{B}$	B	$\bar{B}$	$\bar{B}$	B	B
C or $\bar{C}$	$\bar{C}$	$\bar{C}$	$\bar{C}$	C	C	C	C
D or $\bar{D}$	$\bar{D}$	$\bar{D}$	$\bar{D}$	$\bar{D}$	$\bar{D}$	$\bar{D}$	D

Examination of program 16 (A, B, C, D) reveals this could not be optimal because it requires job 2 to wait until job 1 is completed. It will be recalled that job 2 starts on machine d. Thus the two jobs are processed separately and only one machine is used at a time. It is obvious, then, that any program which contains D cannot be optimal. Our purpose is to eliminate all such programs.

The characteristic of program 16 which we have just considered can be stated as follows: There exists in it a machine x on which the two jobs are processed consecutively in time and while this machine operates all other machines are idle. Such a machine is called a *free machine* for the given program. Akers and Friedman generalize this characteristic as follows:

> A necessary and sufficient condition that a feasible 2-job program belong to the set of optimal programs is that it contain no free machines.*

Elimination of programs that contain free machines is carried out by means of the following principle:

> A necessary and sufficient condition that a feasible program contain no free machines is that, for each machine y,
>
> (1) When there exist machines x and z located as shown below
>
> Job 1: $\cdots xy \cdots z \cdots$
> Job 2: $\cdots x \ \cdots yz \cdots$
>
> then the term $X\bar{Y}Z$ must not appear in the program (in the special case

---

* The sections in reduced type are virtually direct quotes from Akers and Friedman.[1] They have been modified slightly so that the terminology can be kept consistent with that of the preceding portion of this chapter.

where y is the first machine for job 1, X is omitted; and when y is the last machine for job 2, Z is omitted), and

(2) When there exist machines u and v located as shown below

$$\text{Job 1:} \quad \cdots u \ \cdots yv \cdots$$
$$\text{Job 2:} \quad \cdots uy \cdots \ v \cdots$$

then the term $\overline{U}Y\overline{V}$ must not appear in the program (in the special case when y is the first machine for job 2, $\overline{U}$ is omitted, and when y is the last machine for job 1, $\overline{V}$ is omitted).

Applying (1) and letting y stand for machine a and z for machine c, we get the special situation

$$\text{Job 1:} \quad y \cdots z \cdots$$
$$\text{Job 2:} \quad \cdots yz$$

Hence, programs containing $\overline{Y}Z$ (i.e., $\overline{A}C$) must be eliminated.

Applying (1) again, this time letting x stand for machine b and y for machine c, we get the special situation

$$\text{Job 1:} \quad \cdots xy \cdots$$
$$\text{Job 2:} \quad \cdots x \cdots y$$

Hence programs containing $X\overline{Y}$ (i.e., $B\overline{C}$) must be eliminated.

Now we return to Table 16-7 and determine which feasible programs also satisfy the three conditions for optimality: not (D), not $(\overline{A}C)$, and not $(B\overline{C})$. The results are shown in Table 16-8.

TABLE 16-8. FEASIBLE PROGRAMS WHICH SATISFY NECESSARY
CONDITIONS OF OPTIMALITY

Program No. / Instruction	1	2	4	5	6	8	16
Not (D)	1	1	1	1	1	1	0
Not $(\overline{A}C)$	1	1	1	0	1	1	1
Not $(B\overline{C})$	1	1	0	1	1	1	1
Logical Product	1	1	0	0	1	1	0

There are four programs, then, which satisfy the necessary (but not necessarily the sufficient) conditions for both technological feasibility and optimality: 1, 2, 6, and 8. All that remains now is to put in machine time values for each operation and evaluate each of these four programs by means of a device like the Gantt chart. Thus, in the previous example, let us suppose that machine times for the different operations are as given in Table 16-9.

TABLE 16-9. MACHINE TIMES IN HOURS

Machine Job	a	b	c	d
1	2	4	5	1
2	2	5	3	6

The Gantt charts for the four programs, then, are given in Fig. 16-3.

Program 8 has the minimum elapsed time and is therefore optimal for this example.

n Jobs and m Stations

The Akers-Friedman technique for "reducing" the sequencing problem of two jobs over m stations or machines can be extended to apply to the case of n jobs and m machines. In such a case there are $(n!)^m$ different programs to be considered. Feasibility Theorem I must be replaced by Theorem II (developed by Akers and Friedman) which states:

A necessary and sufficient condition that an n-job program be technologically feasible is that corresponding to every "loop" existing between α operating sequences, $(2 \leq \alpha \leq n)$, i.e.

$$\text{Job 1:} \quad \cdots a_1 \cdots z_1 \cdots$$
$$\text{Job 2:} \quad \cdots b_2 \cdots a_2 \cdots$$
$$\text{Job 3:} \quad \cdots c_3 \cdots b_3 \cdots$$
$$\text{Job } \alpha - 1: \quad \cdots y_{\alpha-1} \cdots x_{\alpha-1}$$
$$\text{Job } \alpha: \quad \cdots z_\alpha \cdots y_\alpha \cdots,$$

the complete term

$$A_{(2<1)}B_{(3<2)}C_{(4<3)} \cdots Y_{(\alpha<\alpha-1)}Z_{(1<\alpha)}$$

must not appear in the program. Here $K_{(i<j)}$ means that on machine k job i is done before job j.

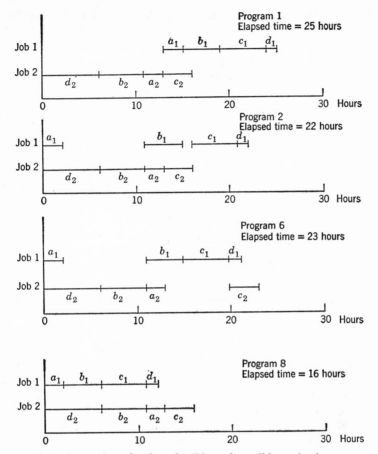

Fig. 16-3. Gantt chart for four feasible and possibly optimal programs.

As has been demonstrated in this section, small problems can be
solved by hand using the nonnumerical technique developed by Akers
and Friedman. An advantage of the technique is that it can also be
programmed on an electronic computer and this is a great help for
problems of moderate or large size.

It is to be noted that data on machine times are not required until
all nonfeasible programs and those that cannot possibly be optimal
are eliminated. Hence a great merit of the technique arises in situations where the routes for jobs are fixed but the machine times are
subject to fluctuations because of design changes or changes in materials (e.g., different grades of castings require heat treatment for different time intervals). In such situations, a subset of feasible and pos-

sibly optimal programs can be kept in readiness and tested for optimality every time the machine times change.

APPROACHES TO MORE COMPLEX
SEQUENCING PROBLEMS

In this chapter we have considered only relatively simple problems. Models and analytic solutions do not exist for more complex problems in which alternative routes are permissible, where more than one machine of a given type exists, where the machine times and/or costs are of a probabilistic nature, or where machines are subject to breakdowns and operators may be absent from or injured at work. At present each of these more complex cases has to be treated individually and a tailor-made solution found.

There are at least two fruitful approaches to these more complex problems. One approach is to break the problem into subproblems which can then be handled by means of separate techniques, each of which is valid in its own domain. Such a procedure has all the dangers inherent in treating a system in parts; i.e., of suboptimization. The effectiveness of the over-all operation might be decreased by such a procedure. To the extent that supoptimization increases the over-all effectiveness of the system the O.R. work is judged "good." Therefore, even when suboptimization is necessary because of the inadequacy of available techniques, the operations researcher must keep his eye on the total system.*

The second approach to sequencing problems consists of the use of Monte Carlo procedures. Such an approach makes use of the probability distributions of such characteristics of the system as the processing time on each machine and the availability of the machine. In addition, we can introduce the effects of probabilities of alternative routings for jobs, availability of more than one similar machine, fluctuations in the working pace of operators during different shifts, and seasonal variations in any of these variables. In effect, the system can be simulated by an analogue which includes as many of the system's complexities as we desire and have capacity to handle. Once such an analogue is constructed we can compare either alternative sequencing policies or specific sequences. For example, we might compare the following two policies with regard to a specified measure of the system's effectiveness:

1. For any machine consider the jobs allotted to it and assign to it first the job that has the least number of days left before its due date.

* For further information on this point, see Hitch.[12]

As an illustration, consider the case of a single machine which, on March 1, has five jobs assigned to it under the conditions shown in columns (2), (3), and (4) in Table 16-10.

TABLE 16-10. ILLUSTRATIVE MACHINE SCHEDULE

(1)	(2)	(3)	(4)	(5)	(6)	(7)
	Expected Operating Time on		Days Until		Days Until Due Date Minus	
Job No.	Machine in Days	Due Date	Due Date	Se- quence I	Operating Time	Sec- quence II
593	3	3/20	20	4	17	4
465	10	3/22	22	3	12	2
607	1	3/20	20	1	19	5
305	2	3/12	12	2	10	1
336	7	3/23	23	5	16	3

Columns (1), (2), (3), and (4) of Table 16-10 are filled in from data that are known. The sequence shown in column (5) follows from a policy of working on jobs in the same order as column (4). By simulation of the system (and this can take account of the known probability distributions of jobs taking longer or shorter times than their expected operating times) the average effectiveness of this policy can be estimated. Such a procedure is sometimes referred to as operational gaming or operational experimentation.*

2. A second possible sequencing policy is illustrated in columns (6) and (7) of Table 16-10. It is carried out as follows: For any machine, consider the jobs assigned to it and assign to it first the job which has the least number of days left before its due date, excluding the operating time for the operation under consideration.

If we repeat simulated runs on a probabilistic basis a large number of times,† we can compare the results of these two and other sequencing policies and determine which has the highest average effectiveness.

The use of high-speed electronic computers facilitates simulation, particularly where complex situations are involved. De Carlo [8] discusses this use of computers in some detail. Preliminary experiments along these lines have been carried out by Rowe and Jackson.[17] Rothman [16] has handled a large job shop system using a large electronic computer.

* For details on this approach see Cushen [6] and Thornthwaite.[19]
† For techniques useful for reducing the number of Monte Carlo runs see Kahn and Marshall.[14]

The analogue used by Rothman * allowed for variations in arrival and service time, for breakdown of equipment, for absenteeism, material shortage, etc. It included a rule for changing sequences in successive runs on the computer. An empirical determination was made of the number of alternatives required to reach a point at which further significant improvements were not likely to be made. Each alternative sequence was evaluated by obtaining an average running cost extracted from eight runs per sequence. The sequence with the lowest estimated expected cost was then selected.

The solution of large-scale sequencing problems by use of simulation has only begun to be explored. Further development can be expected in the near future.

RELATED PROBLEMS

There are two types of problems which are related to the sequencing problem and which have been receiving increased attention. The first, the (*assembly*) *line-balancing problem*, also involves minimization of total elapsed time in a sequence of operations. The second, the *traveling-salesman problem*, involves routing a salesman through a sequence of locations so as to minimize either the distance traveled or the time or cost of travel. More generally, it involves sequencing each of a set of jobs (e.g., visiting a location) for a facility (e.g., a salesman) so as to minimize some characteristic of movement from one job to the next. Although the available solutions or approximations to solutions of the line-balancing and traveling-salesman problems are not presented here, they are discussed so as to acquaint the reader with their nature and to indicate where further information can be found.

The (Assembly) Line-Balancing Problem

An assembly line is made up of a sequence of work stations (service points) which must be passed through in a pre-established order. Consider an assembly line which is used to turn out only one type of product. There is a problem in designing the assembly line so as to minimize the processing time. The assembly operation can be broken down into a set of work elements. The assembly-line-balancing problem consists of combining work elements into subtasks, i.e., groupings of work elements to be carried out at one location called the work station. Ideally, all work stations on an assembly line should have equal work content (measured in terms of time) assigned to them. If this were

* Presented in a talk by H. R. J. Grosch at the Short Course in Operations Research at Case Institute of Technology (1954). See also ref. 16.

possible there would be no idle time at any work station and the assembly line would be perfectly balanced. If, however, the work contents of stations on the assembly line differ from each other, the work station with the largest work content becomes the bottleneck and the speed of the assembly line has to be adjusted to this station. As a result of this there is wasted or idle time at some work stations and the assembly process is slowed up. This is called line imbalance.

In designing an assembly line, therefore, it is desirable to minimize the total idle time for work stations by suitable grouping of work elements. Such minimization is very difficult to obtain in real situations which are complicated by the fact that the times required to perform each work element and subtask vary for the same worker or machine and for different workers. Also, the personnel that man an assembly line frequently change. The problem can be simplified by assuming constant time-requirements for each work element and subtask. This simplification has made it possible to make an initial attack on the problem.

Assuming constant time-requirements for work elements, the problem has been formulated as one of finding the optimal combination of work elements which can be grouped into work stations so that the total delay is eliminated or minimized. The total delay is the sum of delays per cycle at every work station, where delay is defined as the idle nonproductive time which is lost at each work station due to line imbalance.

The problem involves restrictions (called precedence requirements) which arise from the technology of the assembly process. For instance, all work inside an electric appliance must be completed before the outside cover is bolted down. In all such cases it is necessary that a work element which must follow another be assigned either to the same work station at which the preceding element is to be performed or to a work station which follows later in the sequence.

Two approaches to the problem have been taken. The first, by Bryton,[5] takes the number of work stations as fixed and seeks to minimize the total delay time by minimizing the cycle time (i.e., the time allowed at a station per unit of product) at the station with the largest work content. Bryton has developed a way of finding a local minimum but, as yet, no systematic way of finding the absolute minimum.

The second formulation, made by Salveson,[18] assumes fixed cycle time and involves finding the optimal number of work stations. Salveson has developed a computational technique which yields an optimal solution in most cases. Both Salveson's and Bryton's techniques can be programmed for electronic computers.

The assembly-line-balancing problem has many applications outside of production context. For example, a railroad in the piggy-back business may have a fixed time (analogous to the assembly-line cycle time) before the departure of the freight train within which it has to pick up a given number of loaded trailers from shippers' docks located in different parts of the city. Assuming that all tractors required for making the pickups are located at the freight terminal and the time required for hauling each trailer is known (analogous to the work element time), if we set the objective as one which involves the use of minimum number of tractors (analogous to finding the minimum number of work stations) the problem corresponds to that of assembly-line-balancing; i.e., using the minimum number of tractors so that the sum of idle times for all tractors that are employed is minimized. This problem can have precedence requirements in the sense that some trailers have to be picked up before others.

The Traveling-Salesman (or Routing) Problem

The traveling-salesman problem is a "classical" mathematical problem which involves finding an optimal route between a series of locations under the condition that each location is visited once and only once and a return is made to the point of origin. An optimal route is defined as one for which the sum of the distances (or travel cost or time) is minimum. This routing problem, then, involves sequencing locations so as to minimize some function of a characteristic of the travel between them.

This problem also appears in another apparently disconnected context. Consider a production or assembly line on which a number of different but related products are manufactured. These products may have common parts; e.g., in a line of metal kitchen cabinets some have common doors, tops, sides, etc. Then the cost of setting up the line for a specific item depends on which item precedes it. If the two items have many common parts the setup cost is relatively low, otherwise it is relatively high. The problem then is to get a sequence of items for production such that the sum of the setup costs is minimized.

This problem appears to be conceptually related to the sequencing problem discussed in this chapter but actually it is more similar in structure to the assignment problem considered in Chapter 12. Like the assignment problem it can be put into matrix form but, because loops are not permitted, the requirements for a solution are not exactly the same. It is sometimes possible, however, to solve this problem in an optimal way by treating it as an assignment problem [10] and then checking to see if the solution contains any loops. If it does not have loops, then the solution is optimum. If the loops are present, then the assignment problem approach serves as an initial preparation for subsequent computations of the traveling-salesman problem.

Suppose, for example, that we have five products to be produced, A, B, C, D, and E. Then we can set up a matrix such as is shown in Table 16-11. Since we never want an item to follow itself an infinite

TABLE 16-11. Cost Matrix for Routing Problem

To From	A	B	C	D	E
A	∞	$K_{AB}{}^*$	K_{AC}	K_{AD}	K_{AE}
B	K_{BA}	∞	$K_{BC}{}^*$	K_{BD}	K_{BE}
C	K_{CA}	K_{CB}	∞	$K_{CD}{}^*$	K_{CE}
D	K_{DA}	K_{DB}	K_{DC}	∞	$K_{DE}{}^*$
E	$K_{EA}{}^*$	K_{EB}	K_{EC}	K_{ED}	∞

cost is assigned to each cell on the diagonal.† In each of the other cells the cost of setting up the item designated by the column after the item designated by the row is entered. For example, K_{BA} is the cost of setting up A after B has been run. Now the assignment technique is applied. It will designate one cell in each row and column such that the sum of the costs in these cells is minimum. The solution thus obtained may, however, not be feasible. For example, it may designate cells ED and DE, which requires D to follow E and E to follow D. Suppose, however, that E is the last item run in the preceding period and that the minimum cost solution is defined by the cells with asterisks in them. Then the optimum sequence for this period would be A, B, C, D, E. This is called the slant ‡ solution. More generally, the following statement could be made: [10] If the slant of the cost matrix represents the optimal solution of the assignment problem, then the slant also represents the optimal solution of the traveling-salesman or routing problem.

† Notice that we are in effect making use of condition 20 of the assignment problem discussed in Chap. 12.

‡ The *slant* of a $n \times n$ matrix is defined as the set of n elements consisting of all elements immediately above the main diagonal together with the element in the last row of the first column.

Although no general analytic solution to this type of problem is available, a solution can always be obtained by trying all the possibilities. This may require more time than is available.* Some progress toward analytic solutions has been made. Dantzig, Fulkerson, and Johnson [7] have suggested four devices which are sometimes useful in solving "symmetric" versions of the problem. This is a version in which the distance (cost or time) between two points is the same regardless of the direction. Flood [9,10] has suggested a technique of solving symmetric cases and has developed a technique for testing trial solutions for optimality in nonsymmetric cases.

It should be noted that in some cases considerable improvement over current procedures can be obtained with rather rough approximations to a solution of this type of problem. Such a case has been discussed by Hare and Hugli.[11]

SUMMARY

The sequencing problem is one of the most challenging problems which has been posed in O.R. So far, general decision rules have been found for only the simpler cases.

Johnson's procedure [13] for determining an optimal sequence which will minimize the total elapsed time for processing n jobs, each following an identical route over two work stations, is extremely simple and can be easily applied by shop personnel. A similar procedure is also available for a special case of n jobs, each following an identical route over three work stations.

The case of n jobs each requiring time (and following a different route) on each of m work stations necessitates an examination of $(n!)^m$ programs. Many of these turn out to be technologically infeasible and can therefore be eliminated from consideration. Of those that remain, some could not possibly be optimal and should also be eliminated. This elimination can be carried out by the nonnumerical technique of Akers and Friedman.[1]

The assembly-line-balancing problem usually arises in repetitive processes and involves allocating work elements to work stations in such a way that, for a given cycle time, the total idle time for the whole assembly line is minimized. Precedence requirements among

* Consider, for instance, a problem involving the sequencing of 20 jobs on one facility. There can be $20! = 2,432,902,008,176,640,000$ different sequences. A fast electronic computer programming one sequence per microsecond and working 8 hours a day, 365 days a year, would take almost a quarter of a million years to find the solution—an impossible situation for all practical purposes.

the work elements make the problem complex. The application of Salveson's technique [18] will usually lead to an optimal solution.

The traveling-salesman or routing problem involves sequencing items so as to minimize the sum of the costs, times, distances, or some other measure of effectiveness associated with going from one to the other, where each item must occur once and only once in the sequence. This problem does not as yet have a general analytical solution. In some cases it can be solved by treating it as an assignment problem.[10] In other cases the techniques developed by Dantzig, Fulkerson, and Johnson [7] and Flood [9, 10] may be helpful.

At the present time the most fruitful approach to the complex sequencing problems which occur in reality seems to be that of operational experimentation and gaming which may involve use of Monte Carlo procedures. The fruitfulness of this approach is enhanced by the availability of high-speed electronic computers.

Note 1. Proof of Optimal Sequencing Decision Rule for n Jobs on Two Machines

The sequencing problem involved here is characterized by n jobs on two machines, A and B, each requiring the same sequence of operations, and no passing allowed. The pertinent symbolism used in the chapter is

A_i = time required by job i on machine A

B_i = time required by job i on machine B

X_i = idle time on machine B from end of job i-1 to start of job i

$$D_n(S) = \sum_{i=1}^{n} X_i = \text{total idle time on machine } B \text{ for sequence } S$$

The problem is one of finding a sequence S^* of jobs $(1, \cdots, n)$ such that $D_n(S^*) \leq D_n(S_0)$ for any S_0.

Johnson [13] and Bellman [3] have shown that an optimal sequence is yielded by the following rule: Job j precedes job $j + 1$ if

$$\text{Min } (A_j, B_{j+1}) < \min (A_{j+1}, B_j) \tag{5}$$

and job j is indifferent to job $j + 1$ (i.e., either precedes the other) if

$$\text{Min } (A_j, B_{j+1}) = \min (A_{j+1}, B_j) \tag{6}$$

Johnson's [13] proof for this rule proceeds as follows:

We start with a sequence S' and from it obtain another sequence S'' by interchanging the jth and the $(j + 1)$st jobs. The two sequences are

$$S' = 1, 2, 3, \cdots, j - 1, j \quad , j + 1, j + 2, \cdots, n$$

$$S'' = 1, 2, 3, \cdots, j - 1, j + 1, j \quad , j + 2, \cdots, n$$

Let

$$K_u = \sum_{i=1}^{u} A_i - \sum_{i=1}^{u-1} B_i$$

and K_u' represent the K_u value for S' and K_u'' represent the K_u value for S''. From eq. 2

$$D_n(S) = \max_{1 \leq u \leq n} \left(\sum_{i=1}^{u} A_i - \sum_{i=1}^{u-1} B_i \right)$$

we get

$$D_n(S) = \max_{1 \leq u \leq n} K_u$$

Then $K_u' = K_u''$ for $u = 1, 2, \cdots, j - 1, j + 2, \cdots, n$; but K_j' and K_{j+1}' need not be equal to K_j'' and K_{j+1}'' respectively. This might make $D_n(S')$ different from $D_n(S'')$.

Two statements can now be made:

a. If $\max (K_j', K_{j+1}') = \max (K_j'', K_{j+1}'')$, then $D_n(S') = D_n(S'')$

and, relative to the criterion of minimizing total elapsed time, it makes no difference which sequence is used.

b. If, however, $\max (K_j', K_{j+1}') < \max (K_j'', K_{j+1}'')$, then S' is preferable to S'', i.e., job j should precede job $j + 1$. The relation involved in this statement can be rewritten by first expanding the K_j's; i.e.

$$K_j' = \sum_{i=1}^{j} A_i - \sum_{i=1}^{j-1} B_i$$

$$K_{j+1}' = \sum_{i=1}^{j+1} A_i - \sum_{i=1}^{j} B_i$$

Therefore

$$\text{Max } (K_j', K_{j+1}') = \max \left(\sum_{i=1}^{j} A_i - \sum_{i=1}^{j-1} B_i, \sum_{i=1}^{j+1} A_i - \sum_{i=1}^{j} B_i \right) \quad (7)$$

Similarly

$$K_j'' = \sum_{i=1}^{j-1} A_i + A_{j+1} - \sum_{i=1}^{j-1} B_i$$

$$K_{j+1}'' = \sum_{i=1}^{j+1} A_i - \sum_{i=1}^{j-1} B_i - B_{j+1}$$

and therefore

$$\text{Max } (K_j{}'', K_{j+1}{}'')$$

$$= \max \left(\sum_{i=1}^{j-1} A_i + A_{j+1} - \sum_{i=1}^{j-1} B_i, \sum_{i=1}^{j+1} A_i - \sum_{i=1}^{j-1} B_i - B_{j+1} \right) \quad (8)$$

Subtracting $\sum_{i=1}^{j+1} A_i - \sum_{i=1}^{j-1} B_i$ from the right-hand terms of eqs. 7 and 8 we can then get the following result: if

$$\text{Max } (-A_{j+1}, -B_j) < \max (-A_j, -B_{j+1}) \quad (9)$$

then

$$\text{Max } (K_j{}', K_{j+1}{}') < \max (K_j{}'', K_{j+1}{}'') \quad (10)$$

Multiplying eq. 9 by -1 (which involves changing the inequality sign), we get

$$\text{Min } (A_{j+1}, B_j) > \min (A_j, B_{j+1})$$

This is the same as

$$\text{Min } (A_j, B_{j+1}) < \min (A_{j+1}, B_j)$$

Then statement b can be rewritten as the following rule: Job j precedes job $j + 1$ when

$$\text{Min } (A_j, B_{j+1}) < \min (A_{j+1}, B_j)$$

Johnson has shown that this result is transitive and its importance lies in the fact that it indicates that starting with any sequence S_0, the optimal sequence S^* can be obtained by the successive interchange of consecutive jobs applying the above rule. Each such interchange will give a value of $D_n(S)$ smaller than or the same as before the interchange.

BIBLIOGRAPHY

1. Akers, S. B., Jr., and Friedman, J., "A Non-Numerical Approach to Production Scheduling Problems," *J. Opns. Res. Soc. Am., 3*, no. 4, 429–442 (Nov. 1955).
2. Barankin, E. W., "The Scheduling Problem as an Algebraic Generalization of Ordinary Linear Programming," Discussion Paper No. 9, Logistic Research Project, University of California, Los Angeles, Aug. 28, 1952.
3. Bellman, R., "Mathematical Aspects of Scheduling Theory," RAND Report P-651, RAND Corporation, Santa Monica, Apr. 11, 1955.
4. ———, and Gross, O., "Some Combinatorial Problems Arising in the Theory of Multi-stage Processes," *J. Soc. Indust. Appl. Math., 2*, no. 3, 175–183 (Sept. 1954).
5. Bryton, B., *Balancing of a Continuous Production Line*, M.S. Thesis, Northwestern University, Evanston, June 1954.

6. Cushen, W. E., "Operational Gaming in Industry," in J. F. McCloskey and J. M. Coppinger (eds.), *Operations Research for Management II*, The Johns Hopkins Press, Baltimore, 1956.

7. Dantzig, G., Fulkerson, R., and Johnson, S., "Solution of a Large-Scale Traveling-Salesman Problem," *J. Opns. Res. Soc. Am.*, *2*, 393–410 (1954).

8. De Carlo, C. R., "The Use of Automatic and Semi-Automatic Processing Equipment in Production and Inventory Control," *Proceedings of the Conference on Operations Research in Production and Inventory Control*, Case Institute of Technology, Cleveland, 1954.

9. Flood, M. M., "Operations Research and Logistics," *Proceedings: First Ordnance Conference on OR*, Office of Ordnance Research, Durham, pp. 3–25, Jan. 1955.

10. ————, "The Traveling-Salesman Problem," *J. Opns. Res. Soc. Am.*, *4*, no. 1, 61–75 (Feb. 1956).

11. Hare, V. C., and Hugli, W. C., "Applications of Operations Research to Production Scheduling and Inventory Control, II," *Proceedings of the Conference on "What Is Operations Research Accomplishing in Industry?"*, Case Institute of Technology, Cleveland, 1955.

12. Hitch, C., "Sub-Optimization in Operations Problems," *J. Opns. Res. Soc. Am.*, *1*, no. 3, 87–99 (May 1953).

13. Johnson, S. M., "Optimal Two- and Three-Stage Production Schedules with Setup Times Included," *Nav. Res. Log. Quart.*, *1*, no. 1, 61–68 (Mar. 1954).

14. Kahn, H., and Marshall, A. W., "Methods of Reducing Sample Size in Monte Carlo Computations," *J. Opns. Res. Soc. Am.*, *1*, no. 5, 263–278 (Nov. 1953).

15. Moore, F. G., *Production Control*, McGraw-Hill Book Co., New York, 1951.

16. Rothman, S., "A Problem in Production Scheduling," General Electric Co., Evendale, Ohio, 1953 (privately circulated).

17. Rowe, A. J., and Jackson, J. R., "Research Problems in Production Routing and Scheduling," Research Report No. 46, Management Sciences Research Project, University of California, Los Angeles, Oct. 26, 1955.

18. Salveson, M. E., "The Assembly Line Balancing Problem," *J. Indust. Eng.*, *6*, no. 3, 18–25 (May–June 1955).

19. Thornthwaite, C. W., "Operations Research in Agriculture," *J. Opns. Res. Soc. Am.*, *1*, no. 2, 33–38 (Feb. 1953).

PART REPLACEMENT
VII MODELS

This part consists of only one chapter (Chapter 17) which deals with some theory and applications of replacement or renewal models. The work presented here is part of the results obtained through a basic research program sponsored by and conducted at Case Institute.

Most of the studies of replacement processes have been done outside of O.R.* O.R. has extended application of the theory to phenomena not previously treated, and is beginning to extend the theory itself.

Replacement processes fall into two classes depending on the life pattern of the equipment involved; i.e., whether the equipment deteriorates or becomes obsolete (i.e., becomes less efficient) because of the use or introduction of new developments (e.g., machine tools), or does not deteriorate but is subject to failure or "death" (e.g., light bulbs).

For deteriorating items, the problem consists of balancing the cost of new equipment against the cost of maintaining efficiency on the old and/or that due to the loss of efficiency. Although no general solution to this problem has been ob-

* Two organizations should be cited for their major contribution to the development of this area: the Machinery and Allied Products Institute (MAPI) and the National Center for Education and Research in Dynamic Equipment Policy.

tained, models have been developed and solutions have been found for various sets of assumptions about the conditions of the problem.

Grant [20] has solved the replacement problem for the situation in which a. there will be no new more efficient equipment made available before replacement, b. the value of money remains constant over the useful life of the equipment, and c. annual operating costs do not decrease. Terborgh's [41] model assumes a constant rate of technological improvement. He computes the past rate of obsolescence and projects it into the future. He also uses a predicted price of new equipment in the future but does not take into account possible errors in the predictions.

Dean [11,12] has criticized the use of a fixed discount rate (as employed by Grant) to compute the cost of investment. He employs a method which involves a comparison of alternative investments. Consequently, in his model investment costs change with business conditions and opportunities.

The underlying mathematics of replacement processes has a relatively long history. The problem has attracted the attention of many prominent mathematicians, statisticians, economists, and actuaries. Among them are Blackwell,[4] Brown,[6] Chung and Pollard,[8] Chung and Wolfowitz,[9] Doob,[14] Feller,[18] Karlin,[24] and Preinreich.[37]

Following the work of Alchian [1] at RAND, Bellman [2] has applied the functional equation technique of the theory of dynamic programming to the replacement problem. For a given output of equipment and its cost of upkeep as a function of time, and under the assumptions that replacement is possible only at specified times and that delivery of equipment is immediate, Bellman has found the policy which maximizes the over-all discounted return.

In the case of replacement of items that fail, the problem is one of determining which items to replace (e.g., all but those installed in the last week) and how frequently to replace them so as to minimize the sum of the following costs:

1. the cost of the equipment involved (e.g., purchasing or production cost),
2. the cost of replacing the unit, and
3. the cost associated with failure of the unit (e.g., loss in earnings or profit due to unusable equipment).

At one extreme a policy might be to replace items only when they fail. Such a policy minimizes equipment cost (since it maximizes usage), but the costs of individual replacement and failure may be high. At the other extreme all units might be replaced when (or before) the first one fails. This leads to a high equipment cost but a low failure cost. It may reduce replacement cost because of the economy of mass replacement. The optimum policy usually falls between these extremes.

Life spans of items that fail are usually probabilistic. A good deal of work has been done in the area of life testing to determine the distribution of probabilities of failure as a function of time. The literature on this subject is extensive.

Goodman [19] has developed a method for measuring and comparing lives of alternative pieces of equipment without keeping track of individual items. Epstein and Sobel [15, 16] have done considerable work on the statistics of life-testing items for which conditional probability of failure is constant. Davis [10] and others have found that vacuum tubes have this failure characteristic. The significance of this characteristic has been explored by Boodman [5] in an O.R. study entitled "The Reliability of Airborne Radar Equipment." Shellard [40] has carried this work further by developing methods for computing the probability of failure of equipment (which consists of many components the failure of any of which results in failure of the equipment itself) as a function of time. Shellard has also investigated the possible improvement in the reliability of such equipment by replacement of components at a specified age.

Once a distribution of life spans has been obtained, it is usually necessary to generate an expression for the expected number of failures as a function of time. In most operating situations, failures are replaced as they occur, i.e., between group replacements. Because of this condition, an expression for the expected number of failures is difficult to evaluate analytically. Several procedures for approximating the values of the expected number of failures have been developed. One involving normally distributed life patterns has been developed at M.I.T.[39] In Chapter 17, discrete approximations to the continuous distribution of life spans are employed. In addition, Monte Carlo techniques have been used with increasing frequency for generating values of these expectations.

A decision rule for replacing light bulbs was developed at the General Electric Company's Lamp Division. This rule assumes a maximum of one failure per location between group replacements. In Chapter 17, this replacement problem is solved without use of the restrictive assumption of one possible failure.

A useful review of equipment replacement rules from an industrial point of view has been published by the American Management Association.[42]

Replacement Models

INTRODUCTION

The theory of replacement is concerned with the prediction of replacement costs and the determination of the most economical replacement policy. Prediction of costs for a group of items with a probabilistic life span (e.g., light bulbs, radio tubes) involves estimation of the probability distribution of life spans and calculation from these of predicted number of failures as a function of the age of the group of items. A rather large literature on this subject contains several schemes for approximating the number of failures.[6, 7, 17, 18, 30, 37]

In the case of items whose efficiency declines over their life spans (e.g., machine tools, vehicles), prediction of costs involves determining those factors which contribute to increased operating cost, forced idle time, increased scrap, increased repair, etc.

The alternative to the increased cost of operating aging equipment is the cost of replacing old equipment with new. There is some age at which replacement of old equipment is more economical than continuation at the increased operating cost. At that age, the saving from use of new equipment more than compensates for its initial cost.

This chapter is concerned with methods for comparing alternative replacement policies. This involves identifying certain cost relationships pertinent to the minimization of costs, and developing some methods for predicting costs based on probability distributions of life spans.

REPLACEMENT OF ITEMS
THAT DETERIORATE

The measure of efficiency used here for comparisons of alternative replacement policies is the *discounted value of all future costs* associated with each policy. Discounted cost is the amount required at the time of the policy decision to build up a fund at compound interest large enough to pay the pertinent cost when due.

Relevant Costs in Replacement Theory Considerations

In general, the costs to be included in considering replacement decisions are *all* costs that depend upon the choice or age of the machine. While only cash costs rather than accrued costs are appropriate, it is necessary occasionally to consider the accrued costs when they affect the cash flow. The most prominent example of this relation is the effect of depreciation allowances on income tax payments.

In special problems, certain costs need not be included in the calculations. For example, in considering the optimum time of replacement for a particular machine, costs that *do not* change with the *age* of the machine need not be considered. Such costs might be the direct operating cost of labor, power, and the like.

In the problem of choosing between two machines, those costs that are constant over time for each machine will still have to be included if they differ between machines. Only costs that are the same for the two machines can be excluded in the comparison.

Maintenance costs are an especially troublesome factor. However, we can assume that there is a maintenance policy that has been found to be optimal and use the costs associated with that policy. Determination of optimal maintenance policy is another problem.

Since costs are incurred over a period of time, and since money has a value over time, the use of neither the minimum of a sum of undiscounted costs nor the minimum of average discounted costs over the period between replacements is satisfactory. Tables 17-1 and 17-2 illustrate these points.

Consider the two cost patterns shown in Table 17-1 for machines 1 and 2 over a period of 3 years. For each machine, the total outlay for three years is $2200. However, machine 2 requires a higher initial outlay, and, in fact, is actually more costly than machine 1 when the value of money is taken into account. While the extra initial outlay of $500 in year 1 in the case of machine 2 results in a saving of $500 in year 2, it would require only $455 invested at 10% in year 1 to produce the extra $500 required in year 2 by machine 1. Thus, although the total outlay is the same for the three years for either machine, the cost pattern for machine 1 is actually $45.46 less costly than that for machine 2, when the cost of money is taken into account.

TABLE 17-1. Two Cost Patterns

Cost at Beginning of Year, Dollars			Discounted Cost (10% Rate),* Dollars	
Year	Machine 1	Machine 2	Machine 1	Machine 2
1	900	1400	900.00	1400.00
2	600	100	545.45	90.91
3	700	700	578.52	578.52
Total	2200	2200	2023.97	2069.43
Difference		0		45.46

* The discounted cost is the present value of the cost, and is obtained by the expression $C_n/(1 + r)^{n-1}$, in which C_n is the cost at the beginning of the nth year, r is the annual discount rate (worth of money), and n is the number of years.

Again let the value of money be assumed to be 10% per year; but suppose machine 1 is to be replaced every 3 years and machine 2 is to be replaced every 6 years with yearly outlays as indicated in Table 17-2.

TABLE 17-2. Yearly Outlays for Replacing Machines

Year	Machine 1, Dollars	Machine 2, Dollars
1	1000	1700
2	200	100
3	400	200
4		300
5		400
6		500

The total discounted cost of machine 1 for *3* years is

$$\$1000 + \frac{\$200}{1.10} + \frac{\$400}{1.10^2} = \$1512$$

or $504 per year.

For machine 2, the discounted cost for *6* years is

$$\$1700 + \frac{\$100}{1.10} + \frac{\$200}{1.10^2} + \frac{\$300}{1.10^3} + \frac{\$400}{1.10^4} + \frac{\$500}{1.10^5} = \$2765$$

or $461 per year.

The apparent advantage is with machine 2. However, the comparison is unfair since the periods are different, 3 years in one case and 6 years in the other. The total discounted cost of adopting machine 1 for *6* years is

$$\frac{\$1000}{1} + \frac{\$200}{1.10} + \frac{\$400}{1.10^2} + \frac{\$1000}{1.10^3} + \frac{\$200}{1.10^4} + \frac{\$400}{1.10^5} = \$2647$$

or $118 less than that for machine 2 for the same period.

The two machines may be compared for equal periods simply by considering two life cycles of machine 1. Ordinarily the comparison can only be made by considering periods of infinite length. The method for so doing is discussed in the next section.

Cost Equation

Consider a series of time periods 1, 2, 3, 4, $\cdots$, of equal length, and let the costs incurred in these periods be $C_1, C_2, C_3, C_4, \cdots$, respectively. *It is assumed throughout the discussion of the replacement of items that deteriorate that these costs are monotonically increasing.* Assume that each cost is paid at the beginning of the period in which it is incurred, that the initial cost of new equipment is A, and that the cost of money is $100r\%$ per period. Then the discounted value K_n of *all* future costs associated with a policy of replacing equipment after each n periods is given by

$$K_n = \left(A + C_1 + \frac{C_2}{1+r} + \frac{C_3}{(1+r)^2} + \cdots + \frac{C_n}{(1+r)^{n-1}} \right)$$
$$+ \left(\frac{A+C_1}{(1+r)^n} + \frac{C_2}{(1+r)^{n+1}} + \cdots + \frac{C_n}{(1+r)^{2n-1}} \right) + \cdots \quad (1)$$

which may also be written

$$K_n = \left(A + \sum_{i=1}^{n} \frac{C_i}{(1+r)^{i-1}} \right) + \frac{1}{(1+r)^n} \left(A + \sum_{i=1}^{n} \frac{C_i}{(1+r)^{i-1}} \right)$$
$$+ \frac{1}{(1+r)^{2n}} \left(A + \sum_{i=1}^{n} \frac{C_i}{(1+r)^{i-1}} \right) + \cdots \quad (2)$$

The right-hand side of eq. 2 may be written as the product of the common factor within the large parentheses and a convergent geometric series. Hence, K_n may be expressed in the following form

$$K_n = \frac{A + \sum_{i=1}^{n} [C_i/(1 + r)^{i-1}]}{1 - [1/(1 + r)]^n} \tag{3}$$

K_n is the amount of money required *now* to pay all future costs of acquiring and operating the equipment when it is renewed each n years. It is not suggested that any company would actually set up a fund of this size. However, if K_n is less than K_{n+1}, then replacing the equipment each n years is preferable to replacing each $n + 1$ years. Furthermore, if the best policy is replacement every n years, then the two inequalities

$$K_{n+1} - K_n > 0 \quad \text{and} \quad K_{n-1} - K_n > 0$$

must hold.

Now, it can be shown * that $K_{n-1} - K_n > 0$ is equivalent to

$$\frac{C_n}{1 - [1/(1 + r)]} < K_{n-1} \tag{4}$$

and that $K_{n+1} - K_n > 0$ is equivalent to

$$\frac{C_{n+1}}{1 - [1/(1 + r)]} > K_n \tag{5}$$

These two inequalities, 4 and 5, must hold for K_n to be a minimum,† i.e., for replacement after n periods to be the best policy, and can be interpreted in a very meaningful way.

Consider, first, inequality 4

$$\frac{C_n}{1 - X} < K_{n-1} \tag{4a}$$

where we have let $X = 1/(1 + r)$. It follows that $C_n < (1 - X)K_{n-1}$, so that, substituting the expression for K_{n-1} obtained by substituting $n - 1$ for n in eq. 3, one obtains

$$C_n < (1 - X)\frac{(A + C_1 + C_2X + \cdots C_{n-1}X^{n-2})}{1 - X^{n-1}} \tag{4b}$$

or

$$C_n < \frac{(A + C_1) + C_2X + \cdots + C_{n-1}X^{n-2}}{1 + X + X^2 + \cdots + X^{n-2}} \tag{4c}$$

* See Note 1 at the end of this chapter.

† While inequalities 4 and 5 are certainly necessary conditions, it can be shown that they are also sufficient conditions for the case where the C_n are monotonic increasing, i.e., when $C_n < C_{n+1}$ for all n.

The expression on the right-hand side of inequality 4c is the *weighted average* of all costs up to and including period $n - 1$. The weights 1, X, X^2, $\cdots$, X^{n-2} are the *discount factors* applied to the costs in each period.

The other inequality may be put in a similar form

$$C_{n+1} > K_n(1 - X) \tag{5a}$$

$$C_{n+1} > \frac{1 - X}{1 - X^n}(A + C_1 + C_2X + \cdots + C_nX^{n-1}) \tag{5b}$$

or

$$C_{n+1} > \frac{(A + C_1) + C_2X + \cdots + C_nX^{n-1}}{1 + X + X^2 + \cdots + X^{n-1}} \tag{5c}$$

As a result of these two inequalities, rules for minimizing costs may be stated as follows:

1. *Do not replace* if the next period's cost is *less* than the *weighted average* of previous costs.

2. *Replace* if the next period's cost is *greater* than the *weighted average* of previous costs.

A geometrical interpretation of these rules is presented in Fig. 17-1. The sum of the discounted costs is plotted on the vertical axis and the sum of the weights is plotted on the horizontal axis. Then the slope of the line from the origin to the plotted point is the weighted average cost. Now consider two successive points on the chart, P_n and P_{n+1}. The difference in vertical height between the points is $C_{n+1}X^n$ and the horizontal distance is X^n. Hence the slope of the line between P_n and P_{n+1} is $(C_{n+1}X^n)/X^n = C_{n+1}$. If C_{n+1} is less than the slope to P_n, then the slope to P_{n+1} will be less than the slope to P_n. (For example, in Fig. 17-1, this is true for $n = 1$.) Therefore, do not replace. If C_{n+1} is greater than the slope from the origin to P_n, then the slope from the origin to P_{n+1} will be greater than the slope to P_n. (For example, in Fig. 17-1, this is true for, say, $n = 6$.) Therefore, replace. The figures used in Fig. 17-1 are derived from the costs given in Table 17-3.

In this table the minimum value of column (7) occurs after three periods. This minimum is predicted by comparing the cost in the fourth period [30, as shown in column (2)], with the weighted average after three periods, 27.16 [column (7)].

In Fig. 17-1, it is seen that the minimum slope of any line from the origin to any point P_1, P_2, $\cdots$, P_8 occurs at P_3. It is also seen that the slope declines from P_1 to P_2 because the slope between P_1 and P_2 is less than the slope from the origin to P_1.

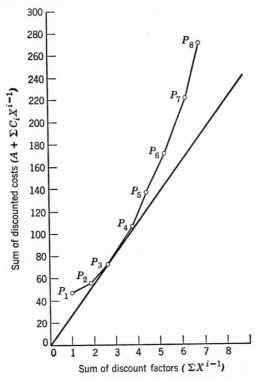

Fig. 17-1. Relation of sum of discounted costs to sum of discount factors. (Data from Table 17-3.)

More generally, the slope of the line from the origin to any point P_d equals

$$\frac{A + \sum_{i=1}^{d} C_i X^{i-1}}{1 + X + X^2 + \cdots + X^{d-1}}$$

$$= \frac{(1 - X)\left(A + \sum_{i=1}^{d} C_i X^{i-1}\right)}{(1 - X)(1 + X + X^2 + \cdots + X^{d-1})} = (1 - X)K_d \quad (6)$$

Therefore, since $1 - X$ is a positive constant for a given value of r, the *minimum* slope will also reveal the minimum K_d and, hence, that policy which minimizes cost.

TABLE 17-3. REPLACEMENT COSTS ($A = 50$, $r = 0.05$)

(1)	(2)	(3)	(4)	(5)	(6)	(7)
Period (i)	Cost (C_i)	$X^{i-1} \equiv \left(\dfrac{1}{1+r}\right)^{i-1}$	$C_i X^{i-1}$	$A + \Sigma C_i X^{i-1}$	ΣX^{i-1}	$\dfrac{A + \Sigma C_i X^{i-1}}{\Sigma X^{i-1}} = (1-X)K_n$
1	0*	1.0000	0.00	50.00	1.0000	50.00
2	10	0.9524	9.52	59.52	1.9524	30.49
3	20	0.9070	18.14	77.66	2.8594	27.16 Replace
4	30	0.8638	25.92	103.58	3.7232	27.82
5	40	0.8227	32.91	136.49	4.5459	30.02
6	50	0.7835	39.18	175.67	5.3294	32.96
7	60	0.7462	44.77	220.44	6.0756	36.28
8	70	0.7107	49.75	270.19	6.7863	39.81
9	80	0.6768	54.14	324.33	7.4631	43.46
10	90	0.6446	58.01	382.34	8.1077	47.16

Column (1): Number of elapsed periods.
Column (2): Cost incurred in each period.
Column (3): Discount factor applicable in the respective period.
Column (4): Cost in each period, discounted to the beginning of period 1 [column (2) × column (3)].
Column (5): Accumulation of column (4).
Column (6): Accumulation of column (3).
Column (7): Ratio of column (5) to column (6).

* $A + C_1 = 50$, where $A = 50$, $C_1 = 0$.

Use of the Cost Equation

In the previous section, it was shown how the cost equation, eq. 3, was derived, how certain inequalities were derived from it to provide the optimum time of replacement for a given piece of equipment, and how these relations might be expressed graphically. For equipment already owned, the historical record of costs may be used to signal replacement, either by use of the chart or by use of the equation. The actual minimum K_n need not be calculated. It has been established that selecting n by the foregoing method yields the minimum costs. This is somewhat similar to the calculus procedure of finding the value of the independent variable for which a function may have a minimum by setting the derivative equal to zero and solving for the appropriate value of the variable. It is not necessary to find the actual minimum value of the function.

In considering new or alternate pieces of equipment other than those currently in use, however, it is necessary to compare the actual minimum values of K_n for each piece of equipment. While the cost figures are readily derived from historical data for existing equipment, some method for "predicting" the cost record for new equipment is required. The MAPI formula is a short cut to such a determination, based on some rather strict assumptions.[41] First, it is assumed that costs increase linearly from the time a machine is new until it is scrapped. Second, the rate of increase is not measured directly but is deduced from an arbitrary assignment of a "service life" based on shop experience.

No such simplifying assumptions are made here. Rather, it is left to the user of the method to decide upon a method of predicting costs that is particularly appropriate to the immediate problem at hand. In some cases, sufficient information of an engineering nature may be available to the user that will permit relatively accurate appraisals of future costs. On the other hand, paucity of information may require the extreme simplifying assumptions of the type used in the MAPI formulation.

Once cost estimates are obtained, however, the method described in this chapter can be used to determine the "best" policy, and, hence, estimate the minimum (expected) cost associated with the new equipment. Then a comparison with costs for existing equipment is simple and direct.

Suppose that this comparison indicates the new equipment is more economical with respect to discounted cost. This does not necessarily indicate immediate replacement. The present equipment may be quite new and still be operating efficiently. It can be shown that the proposed replacement should not be installed until the operating cost per period of the old equipment reaches the weighted average cost of using the new equipment.

Let

K_n' = minimum discounted value of all future costs of new equipment

$D_1, D_2, D_3, \cdots, D_m$ = costs in each *future* period incurred with present equipment

$X = 1/(1 + r)$, the discount factor where r is the interest rate

Π_m = discounted value of all future costs if present equipment is discarded after m periods

Then, proceeding as before, we find

$$\Pi_m = D_1 + D_2 X + D_3 X^2 + \cdots + D_m X^{m-1} + K_n' X^m$$

$$\Pi_{m+1} = D_1 + D_2 X + D_3 X^2 + \cdots + D_m X^{m-1}$$
$$\quad\quad + D_{m+1} X^m + K_n' X^{m+1} \tag{7}$$

$$\Pi_{m-1} = D_1 + D_2 X + D_3 X^2 + \cdots + D_{m-1} X^{m-2} + K_n' X^{m-1}$$

Subtracting, we obtain

$$\Pi_{m+1} - \Pi_m = D_{m+1} X^m + K_n'(X^{m+1} - X^m) \tag{8}$$

$$\Pi_m - \Pi_{m-1} = D_m X^{m-1} + K_n'(X^m - X^{m-1}) \tag{9}$$

From eq. 8, it follows that $\Pi_{m+1} > \Pi_m$ is equivalent to

$$[D_{m+1} X^m + K_n'(X^{m+1} - X^m)] > 0$$

i.e.,

$$[D_{m+1} + K_n'(X - 1)] > 0$$

or, equivalently

$$D_{m+1} > (1 - X)K_n' \tag{10}$$

Similarly, from eq. 9, it follows that $\Pi_m < \Pi_{m-1}$ is equivalent to

$$D_m < (1 - X)K_n' \tag{11}$$

These inequalities involving D_{m+1} and D_m show that minimum cost is achieved by continuing the use of the old equipment until the cost for the next period is greater than $(1 - X)K_n'$. We may recall (see eq. 4b) that $(1 - X)K_n'$ is the weighted average of the costs of using the equipment for n periods between replacements.

In some cases, the expectation of improved processes or equipment induces a delay in replacement of current equipment with similar or even with improved alternative equipment. The analysis used in this chapter can evaluate the wisdom of such a policy in specific cases where the cost characteristics and the time of availability of the new process are known.

REPLACEMENT OF ITEMS THAT FAIL

A second major class of replacement problems is concerned with items that do not deteriorate markedly with service but which ultimately fail after a period of use. The period between installation and failure is not constant for any particular type of equipment but will follow some frequency distribution. We shall assume that we have the probability distribution of item lives. From this we may derive the conditional probability of failure in some small interval of time, say time t to $t + \Delta t$. This conditional probability may either decrease with t, stay constant, or increase with t. The notion of decreasing conditional probabilities is most familiar in the case of "infant mortality." In such a case, the ability of a unit to survive the initial period of life increases its expected life. Industrial equipment with this type of distribution of life spans is exemplified by aircraft engines. As a result, artificial (in the sense of no useful output) aging of engines is carried on as part of the production process to produce engines with longer expected lives and lower initial probability of failure. After the initial period, of course, the probability of failure increases with age.

Constant probability of failure is associated with items that fail from random causes, such as physical shocks, not related to age. In such a case, virtually all items fail before aging has any effect. For example, vacuum tubes in air-borne equipment have been shown to fail at a rate independent of the age of the tube.[5, 10]

In this section, we shall be concerned primarily with items that fail with increasing probability as they age. This type of item provides the more interesting problems in replacement policy. Replacement of failed items is a trivial problem in most cases. It is usually a problem of capital investment or comparison of the productivity of the item with its cost. If the item is vital to the operation of a complex system of which it is a part, the productivity of the entire system depends upon the replacement. For example, a pump failure in a refinery may close down the entire system. Replacement of the pump is a trivial cost compared to the value of continuing operations. *We shall assume for the rest of this chapter that all failures will be replaced.*

The problem here is to plan replacement of items that have *not* failed. So far we have discussed items that were replaced when they deteriorated in performance. In this part of the chapter, however, deterioration is not a factor. Replacing a used but still functioning item with a new item is justified only if the cost of replacement is higher after failure than before, and if the new item reduces the probability of failure. Clearly, the latter condition does not hold when probability of failure decreases or stays constant with age.

The foregoing considerations indicate that replacement policy depends upon the probability of failures. It is therefore of considerable importance to estimate the probability distribution of failures. Statistical techniques used in such "life testing" are being developed rapidly and a growing literature on the subject is becoming available.[15, 16, 19]

Although knowledge of the probability distribution of failures is of great importance, it is extremely useful to supplement this knowledge with a method for detecting imminent failures. That is, it is useful to know that four of ten items are expected to fail in the next week, but it is even better to know which four items will fail.

It may be economical to replace all ten items if four are expected to fail. However, if the four potential failures are identifiable, only those four need be replaced and the other six may be kept for at least an additional week. Obviously, fewer replacements are needed to keep failures down to a given level if the imminent failures can be identified. This saving in replacements and failures is the payoff associated with inspection procedures. Such payoff increases as better discrimination between imminent failures and usable items is achieved and the gains may more than offset the inspection costs. Actually, the results of inspection will yield a probability of failure rather than a certain prediction of failure or survival in the following period. It remains yet to determine the maximum probability of failure for which an item will still be retained.

In the following section, we shall explicitly introduce the cost of the alternatives of replacement or retention and develop a policy that minimizes expected costs as a function of cost of replacement, cost of failure, and probability of failure.

The problem of replacement of existing "live" units will be illustrated by reference to the problem of group relamping or replacement of all light bulbs in an installation at specified intervals. For some intervals, the combined cost of group relamping and of replacing individual bulbs which fail between group relampings is minimized. Determination of the optimum interval is our problem. We shall consider the probability of failure, the costs of failure and of replacement, the total cost equation, and the solution for the optimum group replacement interval.

Mortality Curves

The initial information on the life characteristics of a light bulb may be shown in the form of a mortality curve. A group of N light bulbs is installed, and at the end of t equal time intervals the number of bulbs surviving equals some function of t, say $S(t)$. The proportion of the initial bulbs remaining is, then, $s(t) = [S(t)]/N$. A typical mortality table is shown in Table 17-4 giving the number of survivors out

TABLE 17-4. LIFE CHARACTERISTICS OF A LIGHT BULB: ORIGINAL
POPULATION OF 100,000 UNITS

(1) Time Units Elapsed t	(2) Survivors $S(t)$	(3) Reduction in Survivors $S(t-1) - S(t)$	(4) Probability of Failure $p(t)$	(5) Conditional Probability of Failure $v_{t,0}$
0	100,000			
1	100,000	0	0	**0**
2	99,000	1,000	0.01	0.0100
3	98,000	1,000	.01	.0101
4	97,000	1,000	.01	.0102
5	96,000	1,000	.01	.0103
6	93,000	3,000	.03	.0312
7	87,000	6,000	.06	.0645
8	77,000	10,000	.10	.1149
9	63,000	14,000	.14	.1818
10	48,000	15,000	.15	.2381
11	32,000	16,000	.16	.3333
12	18,000	14,000	.14	.4375
13	10,000	8,000	.08	.4444
14	6,000	4,000	.04	.4000
15	3,000	3,000	.03	.5000
16	2,000	1,000	.01	.3333
17	1,000	1,000	.01	.5000
18	0	1,000	.01	1.0000

Column (1): Number of elapsed periods.
Column (2): Survivors at end of period, based on figures supplied by a major light bulb manufacturer.
Column (3): Rate of change of column (2).
Column (4): Column (3) divided by 100,000.
Column (5): Column (3) divided by value in column (2) for previous period.

of an original group of 100,000 bulbs at regular intervals of time. In Fig. 17-2, the number surviving is plotted against elapsed time units. The resulting curve, $S(t)$, is the mortality curve. Without reference to the statistical problems involved, we shall regard the proportion of survivals at time t as the probability of survival till time t for a single new bulb which is chosen at random.

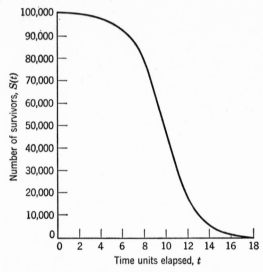

Fig. 17-2. **Number of survivors after t periods of time. (Data from Table 17-4.)**

Life Spans

Perhaps a more familiar presentation of the life characteristics of a group of bulbs is in the form of a probability distribution of life spans. Such a probability distribution may be derived from the mortality table by taking $[S(t-1) - S(t)]/N = p(t)$, the proportion of units failing in time period t. These calculations are made easily by taking the first differences or reduction in survivors from period to period as shown in column (3) of Table 17-4, and then dividing by 100,000 to get column (4), hereafter taken as the probability of failure. This probability is plotted against t in Fig. 17-3.

Conditional Probability of Failure

Another descriptive notion of life characteristics is the conditional probability of failure, or its complement—the probability that an item at time t will survive to time $t + 1$. Again, this may be derived from the mortality table by considering the frequency of failure in a period relative to the number of survivors at the beginning of the period, namely

$$v_{t,0} = \frac{S(t-1) - S(t)}{S(t-1)} = 1 - \frac{S(t)}{S(t-1)}$$

The conditional probabilities are plotted in Fig. 17-4.

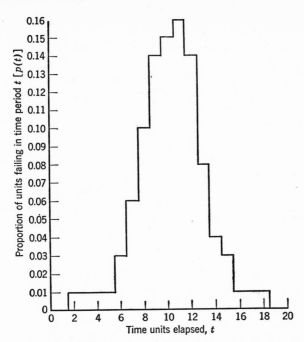

Fig. 17-3. Probability of failure in *t*th period of bulb installed at beginning of first period. (Data from Table 17-4.)

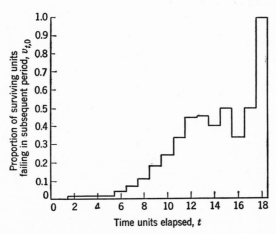

Fig. 17-4. Conditional probability of failure in *t*th period. (Data from Table 17-4.)

Replacement Process

We assume throughout the rest of this chapter that failures occur only at the end of a period. Consequently, replacements of failures which occur at the end of, say, the third period will be of age zero at the *beginning* of the fourth period. This assumption saves us the difficulty of considering fractional periods or continuous variations in time at this stage. During the first t time intervals, all failures are replaced as indicated in the foregoing. At the end of the tth time interval, *all* units are replaced regardless of their ages. The problem is to find that value of t which will minimize total cost.

RATE OF REPLACEMENT: METHOD I. As the replacement process is carried on, the failures to be replaced are, at first, the original installations and, later, some of the replacements and, eventually, when all of the original units are gone, the replacements themselves that have failed during the process.

The general expression for the number of units failing in time interval t is

$$f(t) = N \left\{ p(t) + \sum_{x=1}^{t-1} p(x)p(t - x) \right.$$
$$\left. + \sum_{b=2}^{t-1} \left[\sum_{x=1}^{b-1} p(x)p(b - x) \right] p(t - b) + \cdots \right\} \quad (12)$$

where

N = total units in the installation

$p(x)$ = probability of failure at age x

The expression within the braces of eq. 12 contains terms for the probability of a first failure, the probability of a second failure, a third failure, etc., in that order, for any one of the units in time interval t. Clearly, $p(t)$ is the probability of a first failure, derived earlier from the mortality data. The second term in the right-hand member of the expression, namely $\sum_{x=1}^{t-1} p(x)p(t - x)$, is the probability of a failure of an earlier replacement occurring in time interval t. This is the compound probability of two independent events: failure at age x, and failure of the replacement at age $t - x$.

Expansion of the sum just given may indicate this more clearly. For example, let $t = 6$, i.e., the sixth time interval. We then have

$$\sum_{x=1}^{5} p(x)p(6 - x)$$
$$= p(1)p(5) + p(2)p(4) + p(3)p(3) + p(4)p(2) + p(5)p(1)$$

Each of the terms represents the probability of an event such that a second failure occurs in the sixth period.

The probability of a third failure in the tth period is the probability of a second failure in the $(t - b)$th period times the probability of a failure in the bth period, summed for all values of b less than t, and is given by the third term within the braces in eq. 12. This argument is developed in the same way as for second failures and can be extended to fourth, fifth, and nth failures as well. As a result, we can derive a complicated expression for $f(t)$. It will be well to examine a numerical example of the calculation at this point, using the values of $p(t)$ given in Table 17-4.

Starting with 100,000 units at time 0, we find from the probability distribution of life spans [column (4), Table 17-4] that there are no failures in the first period. In the second, 1% or 1000 units fail. In

TABLE 17-5.* TOTAL FAILURES (REPLACEMENTS) IN EACH PERIOD t

(1)	(2)	(3)	(1)	(2)	(3)
		Replacements			Replacements
Period	Current [$f(t)$]	Cumulative [$\Sigma f(t)$]	Period	Current [$f(t)$]	Cumulative [$\Sigma f(t)$]
1	0	0	21	12,047	162,167
2	1,000	1,000	22	11,706	173,873
3	1,000	2,000	23	10,820	184,693
4	1,010	3,010	24	9,697	194,390
5	1,020	4,030	25	8,700	203,090
6	3,030	7,060	26	8,288	211,378
7	6,040	13,100	27	8,413	219,791
8	10,090	23,190	28	8,862	228,653
9	14,201	37,391	29	9,523	238,176
10	15,392	52,783	30	10,100	248,276
11	16,665	69,448	31	10,413	258,689
12	15,000	84,448	32	10,507	269,196
13	9,480	93,928	33	10,348	279,544
14	6,175	100,103	34	9,999	289,543
15	6,160	106,263	35	9,636	299,179
16	5,521	111,784	36	9,079	308,258
17	7,309	119,093	37	9,220	317,478
18	9,317	128,410	38	9,271	326,749
19	10,181	138,591	39	9,447	336,196
20	11,529	150,120	40	9,669	345,865

Column (1): Periods since original installation.
Column (2): Calculated as described in text.
Column (3): Cumulative sum of values in column (2).

* Data based on Table 17-4.

the third period, 1% of the original units fail. However, this is still
the first period for the 1000 replacements, and hence none of those fail.
In the fourth period, 1% of the original units fail and 1% of the first
1000 replacements fail. Hence, 1010 replacements are needed altogether. Thus the units installed in any period will be replaced in each
of the 18 periods following installation and will contribute to the total
rate of failure in each of those intervals.

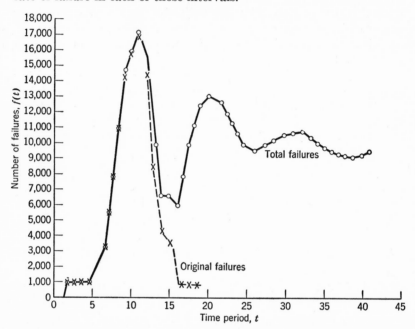

Fig. 17-5. Failures in each period t of 100,000 original light bulbs and total
failures in each period t. (Data from Tables 17-4 and 17-5.)

In the case at hand, the rate of failure is shown period by period in
Table 17-5. For example, the number of failures in period 20 is found
by summing 1% of the failures in period 18, 1% of period 17, 1% of 16,
1% of 15, 3% of 14, 6% of 13, etc., using the probability of failure
appropriate to the elapsed time between installation and period 20.

In Fig. 17-5, the number of failures in each period is plotted against
time. Superimposed on the same chart is the number of failures from
the original installation by periods. It is noteworthy that the two
curves are very close for the first few periods and then diverge widely
as second and later replacements become increasingly important.

The up-and-down movement of the rate-of-failure curve (Fig. 17-5)
and its gradual convergence to a fixed value is of interest as well. It

has been proved (p. 276 [17]) that the limiting rate of failure is the number of units in the installation times the inverse of the mean life span. In this case, it can be shown that the average life span is 10.3 time units; hence the limiting rate of replacement is 100,000/10.3, or 9709 failures per time period. This rate is used later in determining the cost conditions under which group replacement is never warranted.

The procedure used for computing the number of failures in Table 17-5 assumes that a failure in the ith period is not replaced until the

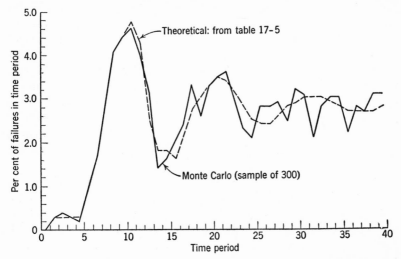

Fig. 17-6. Comparison of distributions of failures computed theoretically and by Monte Carlo technique.

beginning of the $(i + 1)$st period. But even where the periods are of considerable duration, this assumption leads to very little bias in estimating the cumulative number of failures. To obtain more accurate estimates by use of the Monte Carlo technique, an extremely large sample would be required and would not be practical unless electronic computers were available. A comparison between the distribution of failures given in column (3) of Table 17-5 and plotted in Fig. 17-5 (expressed as a per cent of the number originally installed) and one computed from a sample of 300 using the Monte Carlo technique is shown in Fig. 17-6.

RATE OF REPLACEMENT: METHOD II. It is worth considering the problem of determining the rate of replacement from a slightly different point of view. Recall that we computed the conditional probability of failure at given ages. Suppose we know the age distribution of the 100,000 units at a given time. Then we can compute the expected number of failures in the next period by multiplying the number in each age group by the probability of failure for that age group, and then summing over all age groups. For computational purposes, this approach is tedious and uneconomical since it involves determining the age distribution at the end of each period of time. The method discussed in the previous section involved determining only the failures in each period. However, the method described in this section clarifies certain fundamental notions touched on earlier.

Consider a row vector A_i which consists of 18 elements, each element giving the number of units of each age 0, 1, 2, $\cdots$, 17, respectively, at the beginning of the ith period. We can construct a matrix which transforms the age vector at the beginning of any period into the age vector at the end of that period. Call this matrix $V = \{v_{ij}\}$ where v_{ij} is the probability that a unit of age i will be transformed into a unit of age j in the next period and i and j each run from 0 to 17. Clearly, an item either fails or becomes one period older. A failed item is replaced by a new item and hence is, in a sense, transformed into an item of age 0. Thus, if $j \neq 0$ *and* $j \neq i + 1$, then $v_{ij} \equiv 0$ for every i. On the other hand, if $j = 0$ *or* $j = i + 1$, then $v_{ij} \geq 0$.

Also $v_{i,0} + v_{i,i+1} = 1$, since the events of failing or surviving the ith period are mutually exclusive and collectively exhaustive. $v_{i,0}$ is the probability of failure of an item of age i, during the ith period and hence is the conditional probability shown in Table 17-4. Using Table 17-4, we may now write the transformation matrix for our example as follows

$$
V = \begin{bmatrix}
0 & 1 & 0 & 0 & 0 & 0 & 0 & 0 & 0 & \cdots \\
0.0100 & 0 & 0.9900 & 0 & 0 & 0 & 0 & 0 & 0 & \cdots \\
0.0101 & 0 & 0 & 0.9899 & 0 & 0 & 0 & 0 & 0 & \cdots \\
0.0102 & 0 & 0 & 0 & 0.9898 & 0 & 0 & 0 & 0 & \cdots \\
0.0103 & 0 & 0 & 0 & 0 & 0.9897 & 0 & 0 & 0 & \cdots \\
0.0312 & 0 & 0 & 0 & 0 & 0 & 0.9688 & 0 & 0 & \cdots \\
0.0645 & 0 & 0 & 0 & 0 & 0 & 0 & 0.9355 & 0 & \cdots \\
0.1149 & 0 & 0 & 0 & 0 & 0 & 0 & 0 & 0.8851 & \cdots \\
\vdots & & & & & & & &
\end{bmatrix}
$$

If A_1 is the row vector which gives the age distribution of the units at the beginning of time period 1, then

$$A_2 = A_1 V$$

is the age distribution at time period 2,

$$A_3 = A_2 V = (A_1 V)V = A_1 V^2$$

is the age distribution at time period 3, etc. In general, the age distribution for time period n is given by

$$\mathbf{A}_n = \mathbf{A}_1 V^{n-1} \tag{13}$$

For example, starting with 100,000 new units, $\mathbf{A}_1$ is given by

$$\mathbf{A}_1 = (100{,}000; 0; 0; 0; \cdots; 0)$$

i.e., we have 100,000 units of age *zero* at the beginning of time period 1. Then, applying the rules for matrix multiplication

$$\mathbf{A}_2 = \mathbf{A}_1 V = (0; 100{,}000; 0; 0; \cdots; 0)$$

i.e., at the beginning of time period 2, all 100,000 units are of age *one*, no units having failed.

Proceeding further

$$\mathbf{A}_3 = \mathbf{A}_2 V = (1000; 0; 99{,}000; 0; 0; \cdots; 0)$$

or, 99,000 units are now of age 2 at the beginning of time period 3 while 1000 other units have failed and have been replaced by units which are now of age *zero*.

$\mathbf{A}_4$ is given by

$$\mathbf{A}_4 = \mathbf{A}_3 V = (1010; 1000; 0; 97{,}990; 0; 0; \cdots; 0)$$

etc.

Since V is a square matrix with nonnegative elements and all row sums equal 1, (since $v_{i,0} + v_{i,i+1} = 1$), the higher powers of V converge to a matrix V^*.[21] Hence, for n sufficiently large, we may write

$$\mathbf{A}_n = \mathbf{A}_1 V^* \qquad \text{and} \qquad \mathbf{A}_{n+1} = \mathbf{A}_1 V^*$$

so that

$$\mathbf{A}_n = \mathbf{A}_{n+1} \qquad \text{(for } n \text{ sufficiently large)} \tag{14}$$

This result indicates that eventually a stable age distribution is attained. Included in the stable age distribution is a stable number of zero age units which is equivalent to a stable rate of failure.

Another interesting relationship may be observed between the stable age distribution and the mortality curve. As just shown, $\mathbf{A}_n = \mathbf{A}_{n+1}$, for sufficiently large n. However, by definition

$$\mathbf{A}_{n+1} = \mathbf{A}_n V$$

Hence, for n sufficiently large

$$\mathbf{A}_n = \mathbf{A}_n V$$

so that

$$\mathbf{A}_n[I - V] = 0$$

where I is the identity matrix which consists of unit elements on the diagonal and zero nondiagonal elements and which has the property

$$IV = VI = V$$

The matrix V has elements in the first column $v_{i,0}$, namely the conditional probability of failure in the ith period. The only other nonzero element in each row is $v_{i,i+1}$, the conditional probability of survival in the ith period. Clearly

$$v_{i,i+1} + v_{i,0} = 1 \tag{15}$$

or

$$v_{i,i+1} = 1 - v_{i,0}$$

Hence the matrix $I - V$ is written

$$I - V = \begin{bmatrix} 1 - v_{10} & -(1 - v_{10}) & 0 & 0 & 0 \\ -v_{20} & 1 & -(1 - v_{20}) & 0 & 0 \\ -v_{30} & 0 & 1 & -(1 - v_{30}) & 0 \\ -v_{40} & 0 & 0 & 1 & -(1 - v_{40}) & \cdots \\ \vdots & \vdots & \vdots & \vdots & \vdots \end{bmatrix} \tag{16}$$

Expanding the matrix equation $\mathbf{A}_n(I - V) = 0$, we obtain the set of equations

$$a_0(1 - v_{10}) - a_1 v_{20} - a_2 v_{30} - \cdots - a_i v_{i+1,0} - \cdots = 0$$

$$-a_0(1 - v_{10}) + a_1 \qquad\qquad\qquad\qquad\qquad = 0$$

$$-a_1(1 - v_{20}) + a_2 \qquad\qquad\qquad\qquad\qquad = 0$$

$$\vdots \tag{17}$$

$$-a_{i-1}(1 - v_{i,0}) + a_i \qquad\qquad\qquad\qquad = 0$$

$$\vdots$$

where a_i are elements of the vector $\mathbf{A}_n$.

Rewriting the first equation of this set, we have

$$a_0 = a_0 v_{10} + a_1 v_{20} + \cdots + a_i v_{i+1,0} + \cdots \tag{18}$$

This equation indicates again that the replacements in a period may be found by summing over all ages the number of units of that age times the conditional probability of failure in the next period.

The other equations of the set may be rewritten

$$a_1/a_0 = 1 - v_{10}$$

$$a_2/a_1 = 1 - v_{20}$$

$$\cdot$$
$$\cdot$$
$$\cdot$$

$$\frac{a_i}{a_{i-1}} = 1 - v_{i,0}$$

$$\cdot$$
$$\cdot$$
$$\cdot$$

(19)

The conditional probability $v_{i,0}$ was found earlier by dividing the failures in the ith period of life by the number of units of age $i - 1$ at the beginning of the period. This may be written

$$v_{i,0} = \frac{S(i - 1) - S(i)}{S(i - 1)}$$

(20)

Hence

$$1 - v_{i,0} = 1 - \frac{S(i - 1) - S(i)}{S(i - 1)} = \frac{S(i)}{S(i - 1)}$$

(21)

But we see above that

$$1 - v_{i,0} = \frac{a_i}{a_{i-1}}$$

hence

$$\frac{a_i}{a_{i-1}} = \frac{S(i)}{S(i - 1)}$$

(22)

This relationship shows that the limiting relative age distribution for a group of units which are replaced only as they fail may be predicted from the mortality table. In the case of light bulbs, the age distribution is needed to determine the light level produced by a group of bulbs of mixed ages, since light output per bulb declines with age. The relationship between the limiting age distribution and the mortality table thus permits an estimation of the light level that will be produced if group replacement is not undertaken.

Cost of Replacement

A second fundamental requirement of a useful replacement policy is that the cost of replacement after failure be greater than the cost of replacement before failure. This difference in cost is the source of savings required to compensate for the expense of reducing probability of a failure by replacing surviving units. Corresponding to various specific industrial situations, there are a number of reasons why replacing failures may be more costly than replacing live items. For example, the cost of replacing a failure involves cost of the unit itself, cost of labor, cost of lost production because of delay, and cost of damage to material and equipment because of fire, wrecks, or other hazards. Furthermore, the sum of these costs may not be constant for each failure but may depend on the number of failures in each period as, for example, delays in servicing failures when there are a relatively large number of them per period of time. However, for our example of group replacement of light bulbs, we shall assume that the cost of replacing failures is constant.

Group replacing can cost less than replacement of failures by virtue of labor savings, volume discounts on materials, or for other reasons. It is sufficient to specify that replacement costs per unit for group replacement be constant and be less than costs per unit for replacement of failures.

Cost Equations

Let us construct an equation for the cost of maintaining a system as a function of the control variable t, the number of periods between group replacements.

Let $K(t)$ = total cost from time of group installation until the end of t periods. If the entire group is replaced at intervals of length t periods, then

$$\frac{K(t)}{t} = \text{average cost per period of time}$$

Furthermore, let

C_1 = unit cost of replacement in a group
C_2 = unit cost of individual replacement after failure
$f(X)$ = number of failures in the Xth period
N = number of units in the group

Then, the total cost $K(t)$ will be given by

$$K(t) = NC_1 + C_2 \sum_{X=1}^{t-1} f(X)$$

in which NC_1 is the cost of replacing the bulbs as a group, and C_2

$\sum_{X=1}^{t-1} f(X)$ is the cost of replacing the individual failures at the end of each of $t-1$ periods before the group is again replaced. Therefore, the cost *per period* is given by

$$\frac{K(t)}{t} = \frac{NC_1}{t} + \frac{C_2}{t}\sum_{X=1}^{t-1} f(X) \qquad (23)$$

In this development, we are using the cost per period, rather than the discounted sum of all future costs as was done in the early part of this chapter. There is no necessity to do so, but it is assumed that the length of time involved here is relatively short and the effect of discounting correspondingly minor. In problems involving equipment with longer lives, the equation should properly include discount factors.

Minimization of Costs

Costs are minimized for a policy of group replacing after $\hat{t}$ periods if *

$$\left. \begin{array}{l} \dfrac{K(\hat{t})}{\hat{t}} < \dfrac{K(\hat{t}+1)}{\hat{t}+1} \quad \text{or, equivalently,} \quad \dfrac{K(\hat{t}+1)}{\hat{t}+1} - \dfrac{K(\hat{t})}{\hat{t}} > 0 \\[2ex] \text{and if} \\[2ex] \dfrac{K(\hat{t})}{\hat{t}} < \dfrac{K(\hat{t}-1)}{\hat{t}-1} \quad \text{or, equivalently,} \quad \dfrac{K(\hat{t}-1)}{\hat{t}-1} - \dfrac{K(\hat{t})}{\hat{t}} > 0 \end{array} \right\} \qquad (24)$$

Let us rewrite cost equation 23 as follows

$$\frac{K(\hat{t}+1)}{\hat{t}+1} = \frac{NC_1}{\hat{t}+1} + \frac{C_2}{\hat{t}+1}\sum_{X=1}^{\hat{t}} f(X) \qquad (25a)$$

where we have let $t = \hat{t} + 1$; and, for $t = \hat{t}$

$$\frac{K(\hat{t})}{\hat{t}} = \frac{NC_1}{\hat{t}} + \frac{C_2}{\hat{t}}\sum_{X=1}^{\hat{t}-1} f(X) \qquad (25b)$$

---

* These conditions are necessary but *not* sufficient. For example, consider the function $F(t) = t \sin t$, $0 \le t \le 4\pi$, which satisfies these conditions for, not one, but two values of t, although the function has but one *true* (as opposed to *relative*) minimum point.

Subtracting, we obtain

$$\frac{K(\hat{t}+1)}{\hat{t}+1} - \frac{K(\hat{t})}{\hat{t}} = NC_1\left(\frac{1}{\hat{t}+1} - \frac{1}{\hat{t}}\right) + C_2\sum_{X=1}^{\hat{t}-1}f(X)\left(\frac{1}{\hat{t}+1} - \frac{1}{\hat{t}}\right)$$

$$+ \frac{C_2}{\hat{t}+1}f(\hat{t})$$

$$= \frac{-NC_1 - C_2\sum_{X=1}^{\hat{t}-1}f(X) + C_2\hat{t}f(\hat{t})}{(\hat{t}+1)\hat{t}} \qquad (26)$$

For the expression on the left of eq. 26 to be positive, it is then necessary that

$$C_2\hat{t}f(\hat{t}) > NC_1 + C_2\sum_{X=1}^{\hat{t}-1}f(X)$$

or

$$C_2 f(\hat{t}) > \frac{NC_1 + C_2\sum_{X=1}^{\hat{t}-1}f(X)}{\hat{t}} \qquad (27)$$

By a similar construction, we can find that

$$\frac{K(\hat{t}-1)}{\hat{t}-1} > \frac{K(\hat{t})}{\hat{t}}$$

implies that

$$C_2 f(\hat{t}-1) < \frac{NC_1 + C_2\sum_{X=1}^{\hat{t}-2}f(X)}{\hat{t}-1} \qquad (28)$$

Inequations 27 and 28 describe necessary conditions for optimum group replacement and may be interpreted as follows:

$[NC_1 + C_2\sum_{X=1}^{\hat{t}-1}f(X)]/\hat{t}$ is the average cost per period if all bulbs are replaced at the end of t periods.

$C_2 f(\hat{t})$ is the cost for the $\hat{t}$th period if group replacement is not made at the end of the $\hat{t}$th period. That is, the $f(\hat{t})$ individual failures are replaced at a cost of C_2 each, if and only if the group is not replaced at that time.

Thus, inequation 27 shows that *one should group-replace at the end of the tth period if the cost of individual replacements for the tth period is greater than the average cost per period through the end of t periods.*

Similarly, inequation 28 shows that *one should not group-replace at the end of the tth period if the cost of individual replacements at the end of the tth period is less than average cost per period through the end of t periods.*

We shall now show how we may determine the optimal t, i.e., $\hat{t}$, for group replacement under the assumption that the ratio $C_1/C_2 = 0.25$. The numerical values of the individual costs are irrelevant as may be shown by dividing the appropriate inequalities by C_2, so that inequations 27 and 28 become

$$f(\hat{t}) > \frac{N(C_1/C_2) + \sum_{X=1}^{\hat{t}-1} f(X)}{\hat{t}} \tag{29}$$

and

$$f(\hat{t} - 1) < \frac{N(C_1/C_2) + \sum_{X=1}^{\hat{t}-2} f(X)}{\hat{t} - 1} \tag{30}$$

In this case, $N(C_1/C_2) = 25,000$. Hence, we wish to find t, such that

$$\hat{t}f(\hat{t}) - \sum_{X=1}^{\hat{t}-1} f(X) > 25,000$$

$$\tag{31}$$

$$(\hat{t} - 1)f(\hat{t} - 1) - \sum_{X=1}^{\hat{t}-2} f(X) < 25,000$$

In Table 17-6, we show the values of the left-hand terms of the two inequalities 31 for each of several values of t. In addition, the costs are shown in terms of C_2, using the cost function $K(t)$ shown earlier and with $C_1 = 0.25C_2$. It is indicated that the average cost by group replacement is a minimum ($4580C_2$) at the end of seven periods, and that the two inequalities 31 are actually satisfied only for that value of t; i.e., for $\hat{t} = 7$.

In Fig. 17-7, total costs are charted against t, the number of periods between group replacements. Average cost equals total cost divided by t, which ratio is the slope of a line from the origin to each point on the curve. The cost minimizing replacement policy can be determined visually from the figure. This chart is identical to Fig. 17-1 except that discounting of future costs is not taken into account here.

The solution just given holds for cases where $C_1/C_2 = 0.25$. It is useful to provide a solution for any value of C_1/C_2. Notice that columns (4) and (5) of Table 17-6 must bracket $N(C_1/C_2)$ for the optimum value of t. By dividing these columns by N (= 100,000), we ob-

TABLE 17-6. AVERAGE COSTS FOR ALTERNATIVE GROUP REPLACEMENT POLICIES: $C_1/C_2 = 0.25$

(Data: From Table 17-5)

(1) t	(2) $f(t)$ (Current)	(3) $\sum_{x=1}^{t} f(X)$ (Cumulative)	(4) $(t-1)f(t-1) - \sum_{1}^{t-2} f(X)$	(5) $tf(t) - \sum_{1}^{t-1} f(X)$	(6) Total Cost $K(t) = NC_1 + C_2 \sum_{1}^{t-1} f(X)$	(7) Average Cost per Period $[K(t)/t]$
1	0	0	0	0	$25,000C_2$	$25,000C_2$
2	1,000	1,000	0	2,000	$25,000C_2$	$12,500C_2$
3	1,000	2,000	2,000	2,000	$26,000C_2$	$8,667C_2$
4	1,010	3,010	2,000	2,040	$27,000C_2$	$6,750C_2$
5	1,020	4,030	2,040	2,090	$28,010C_2$	$5,602C_2$
6	3,030	7,060	2,090	14,150	$29,030C_2$	$4,838C_2$
7	6,040	13,100	14,150	35,220	$32,060C_2$	$4,580C_2$ *
8	10,090	23,190	35,220	67,620	$38,100C_2$	$4,762C_2$
9	14,201	37,391	67,620	104,619	$48,190C_2$	$5,354C_2$
10	15,392	52,783	104,619	116,529	$62,391C_2$	$6,239C_2$

Column (1): Number of periods between group replacements.
Column (2): Number of replacements from Table 17-5.
Columns (3), (4), (5): Calculated as indicated in column headings.
Column (6): Calculated as indicated with $C_1 = 0.25C_2$.
Column (7): Column (6) divided by column (1).

* Therefore $\hat{t} = 7$.

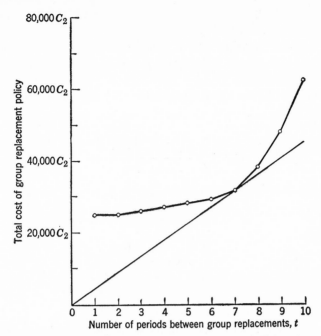

Fig. 17-7. Total costs for alternative group replacement policies plotted against periods between replacements: $C_1/C_2 = 0.25$. (Data from Table 17-6.)

tain values which must bracket C_1/C_2 in order that t be optimum. These values are given in Table 17-7.

TABLE 17-7. Optimizing Value of t for Cost Ratios C_1/C_2

Cost Ratio Range	$\hat{t}$ *
0	1
0 through 0.02	2
0.02	3
0.02 through 0.0204	4
0.0204 through 0.0209	5
0.0209 through 0.1415	6
0.1415 through 0.3522	7
0.3522 through 0.6762	8
0.6762 through 1.0462	9
1.0462 through 1.1653	10

* $\hat{t}$ is that value of t which yields the minimum cost.

The foregoing has shown how to locate the optimum number of periods between group replacements. However, it has not considered the alternative policy of only replacing individual failures, i.e., of never group-replacing.

Now suppose that the rate of failures per period $f(t)$ converges to $\bar{f}(t)$. Then, if no group replacement is ever made, the cost per period will converge to $C_2\bar{f}(t)$.

It has already been noted (inequation 27) that, if $\hat{t}$ is the optimum value of t

$$C_2f(\hat{t}) > \frac{NC_1 + C_2\sum_{X=1}^{\hat{t}-1}f(X)}{\hat{t}}$$

Now, if $\bar{f}(t) > f(\hat{t})$, then, obviously

$$C_2\bar{f}(t) > C_2f(\hat{t})$$

Therefore

$$C_2\bar{f}(t) > \frac{NC_1 + C_2\sum_{X=1}^{\hat{t}-1}f(X)}{\hat{t}}$$

and group replacement is economical.

To exhibit a necessary condition for which group replacement is not economical, we note from inequation 28 that *

$$C_2f(\hat{t}-1) < \frac{NC_1 + C_2\sum_{X=1}^{\hat{t}-1}f(X)}{\hat{t}}$$

Then, if $\bar{f}(t) < f(\hat{t}-1)$

$$C_2\bar{f}(t) < C_2f(\hat{t}-1) < \frac{NC_1 + C_2\sum_{X=1}^{\hat{t}-1}f(X)}{\hat{t}}$$

and group replacement is not economical. That is, the loss that would be incurred in the discard of surviving items is never compensated by the reduced number of failures.

Finally, if $\bar{f}(t) < f(\hat{t})$ and $f(\hat{t}-1) < \bar{f}(t)$, then the comparison is less obvious and the economy of group replacement must be more closely examined. Specifically, t is determined by the survival curve and by the costs C_1 and C_2. Hence $f(\hat{t})$ may be less than $\bar{f}(t)$ for some values of C_1 and C_2 and greater than $\bar{f}(t)$ for others. However, we

* This follows from the algebra of inequalities; i.e., given $a/b < r/s$, then $a/b < (r+a)/(s+b)$.

can find the largest value of the ratio C_1/C_2 for which group replacement is economical. This is done as follows:

Let the optimum group replacement cost and the cost of individual replacement be equal to each other. This gives

$$\frac{NC_1 + C_2 \sum_1^{\hat{t}-1} f(X)}{\hat{t}} = C_2 \bar{f}(t)$$

Then

$$NC_1 + C_2 \sum_1^{\hat{t}-1} f(X) = \hat{t} C_2 \bar{f}(t)$$

$$NC_1 = \hat{t} C_2 \bar{f}(t) - C_2 \sum_1^{\hat{t}-1} f(X)$$

$$\frac{C_1}{C_2} = \frac{\hat{t} \bar{f}(t) - \sum_1^{\hat{t}-1} f(X)}{N} \tag{32}$$

Since $\bar{f}(t)$ is 9709 in the numerical example, it follows that the conditions

$$f(\hat{t} - 1) < \bar{f}(t) \qquad \text{and} \qquad \bar{f}(t) < f(\hat{t})$$

both occur for $\hat{t} = 8$. That is, referring to Table 17-5, we see that

$$6040 < 9709 \qquad \text{and} \qquad 9709 < 10{,}090$$

Thus, substituting numerical values into eq. 32, we have

$$\frac{C_1}{C_2} = \frac{(8)(9709) - 13{,}100}{100{,}000} = 0.64572 \text{ or } 0.65$$

Hence, for $C_1/C_2 > 0.65$, group replacement is never economical.

In Fig. 17-8, values of $\hat{t}$ may be read for corresponding values of C_1/C_2. The chart depends only on the knowledge of $s(t)$, the mortality curve, and, in the case of light bulbs, can easily be supplied by the lamp manufacturer. Each user can isolate the cost C_1 and C_2 and then determine the optimum policy by reference to Fig. 17-8.

We may verify the utility of Fig. 17-8 for determining the optimum value of t by the following example. Let $C_1/C_2 = 0.10$. Then, by using the equation for average cost, eq. 23

$$\frac{K(t)}{t} = \frac{NC_1 + C_2 \sum_{X=1}^{t-1} f(X)}{t} = \frac{100{,}000(0.10C_2) + C_2 \sum_{X=1}^{t-1} f(X)}{t}$$

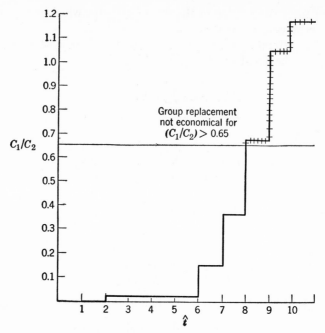

Fig. 17-8. Optimum replacement policy for any value of C_1/C_2. (Data from Table 17-7.)

we can compute directly the cost of each policy and select the best. These costs are given in Table 17-8. Thus, by direct computation, it

TABLE 17-8. Costs for t, $K(t)$, and $K(t)/t$

t	$K(t)$	$K(t)/t$
1	$10,000C_2$	$10,000C_2$
2	$10,000C_2 + \quad\;\; 0C_2$	$5,000C_2$
3	$10,000C_2 + \quad 1,000C_2$	$3,667C_2$
4	$10,000C_2 + \quad 2,000C_2$	$3,000C_2$
5	$10,000C_2 + \quad 3,010C_2$	$2,602C_2$
6	$10,000C_2 + \quad 4,030C_2$	$2,338C_2$
7	$10,000C_2 + \quad 7,060C_2$	$2,437C_2$
8	$10,000C_2 + 13,100C_2$	$2,887C_2$
9	$10,000C_2 + 23,190C_2$	$3,688C_2$

is seen that, for $C_1/C_2 = 0.10$, $\hat{t} = 6$. This can be verified either from Table 17-7 or from Fig. 17-8, both of which show that, for $C_1/C_2 = 0.10$, $\hat{t} = 6$ is the optimum number of periods between group replacements.

Other Models

Although the solutions presented apply only to the particular model described earlier, models of other characteristics may be approached in the same way. For example, a model could be concerned with group replacement in which new bulbs are used for group replacement only, and used bulbs replace failures in between group replacements. A different model is needed when surviving bulbs are replaced at a fixed age, rather than at fixed intervals of time. The considerations of this chapter have been limited to demonstrating an approach to two basic replacement problems, one involving deterioration, and the other involving probabilistic life spans of equipment.

Note 1

This note will derive expressions 4 and 5.
Let $X = 1/(1 + r)$ so that K_n will be given by

$$K_n = \frac{A + \sum_{i=1}^{n} C_i X^{i-1}}{1 - X^n}$$

Then, by substituting $n + 1$ for n

$$K_{n+1} = \frac{A + \sum_{i=1}^{n+1} C_i X^{i-1}}{1 - X^{n+1}} = \frac{A + \sum_{i=1}^{n} C_i X^{i-1} + C_{n+1} X^n}{1 - X^{n+1}}$$

$$= \frac{(1 - X^n) K_n + C_{n+1} X^n}{1 - X^{n+1}}$$

$$= \frac{1 - X^n}{1 - X^{n+1}} K_n + \frac{C_{n+1} X^n}{1 - X^{n+1}}$$

Hence

$$K_{n+1} - K_n = K_n \left(\frac{1 - X^n}{1 - X^{n+1}} - 1 \right) + \frac{C_{n+1} X^n}{1 - X^{n+1}}$$

$$= \frac{K_n (X^{n+1} - X^n) + C_{n+1} X^n}{1 - X^{n+1}}$$

Now, if $K_{n+1} - K_n > 0$, then

$$[K_n(X^{n+1} - X^n) + C_{n+1}X^n] > 0$$

since $X < 1$ or, equivalently

$$(1 - X^{n+1}) > 0$$

Upon dividing by X^n, we obtain

$$K_n(X - 1) + C_{n+1} > 0$$

Hence

$$C_{n+1} > (1 - X)K_n$$

i.e.,

$$\frac{C_{n+1}}{1 - X} > K_n$$

or, equivalently,

$$\frac{C_{n+1}}{1 - 1/(1 + r)} > K_n \qquad \text{Q.E.D.}$$

To prove the other inequality, we note from the foregoing that

$$K_n - K_{n+1} = \frac{K_n(X^n - X^{n+1}) - C_{n+1}X^n}{1 - X^{n+1}}$$

so that, by replacing n by $n - 1$, we obtain

$$K_{n-1} - K_n = \frac{K_{n-1}(X^{n-1} - X^n) - C_n X^{n-1}}{1 - X^n}$$

Then, if $K_{n-1} - K_n > 0$

$$K_{n-1}(X^{n-1} - X^n) - C_n X^{n-1} > 0$$

since $X < 1$.

Therefore, dividing by X^{n-1},

$$(1 - X)K_{n-1} - C_n > 0$$

Hence

$$\frac{C_n}{1 - X} < K_{n-1}$$

or, equivalently, since $X = 1/(1 + r)$,

$$\frac{C_n}{1 - 1/(1 + r)} < K_{n-1} \qquad \text{Q.E.D.}$$

BIBLIOGRAPHY

1. Alchian, A., "Economic Replacement Policy," RAND Report No. R-224, Apr. 1952.
2. Bellman, R., "Notes in the Theory of Dynamic Programming—III: Equipment Replacement Policy," RAND Report No. P-632, Jan. 1955.
3. Benson, C. B., and Kimball, B. F., "Mortality Characteristics of Physical Property Based Upon Location Life Table and Re-Use Ratios," *Econometrica*, *13*, 214 (1945).
4. Blackwell, D., "Extension of a Renewal Theorem," *Pac. J. Math.*, *3*, 315–332 (1953).
5. Boodman, D. M., "The Reliability of Airborne Radar Equipment," *J. Opns. Res. Soc. Am.*, *1*, 39–45 (Feb. 1953).
6. Brown, A. W., "A Note on the Use of a Pearson Type III Function in Renewal Theory," *Ann. math. Statist.*, *11*, 448–453 (1940).
7. Campbell, N. R., "The Replacement of Perishable Members of an Operating System," *J. R. statist. Soc.*, *VII*, Sec. B, 110–130 (1941).
8. Chung, K. L., and Pollard, H., "An Extension of Renewal Theory," *Proc. Amer. math. Soc.*, *3*, 303–309 (1952).
9. Chung, K. L., and Wolfowitz, J., "On a Limit Theorem in Renewal Theory," *Ann. Math.*, 55–56, 1–6 (1952).
10. Davis, D. S., "An Analysis of Some Failure Data," *J. Amer. statist. Ass.*, *47*, 113–150 (June 1952).
11. Dean, Joel, *Capital Budgeting*, Columbia University Press, New York, 1951.
12. ———, *Capital Expenditures, Management and the Replacement of Milk Trucks*, Joel Dean Associates, New York (pamphlet).
13. ———, "Replacement Investments," Chap. VI in *Capital Budgeting*, Columbia University Press, New York, 1951.
14. Doob, J. L., "Renewal Theory from the Point of View of Probability," *Trans. Amer. math. Soc.*, *63*, 422–438 (1948).
15. Epstein, B., and Sobel, M., "Life Testing—I," *J. Amer. statist. Ass.*, *48*, 486–502 (1953).
16. ———, "Some Theorems Relevant to Life Testing from an Exponential Distribution," *Ann. math. Statist.*, *25*, 373–381 (June 1954).
17. Feller, W., *An Introduction to Probability Theory and Its Applications*, Vol. I, John Wiley & Sons, New York, 1950.
18. ———, "On the Integral Equation of Renewal Theory," *Ann. math. Statist.*, *13*, 243–267 (Sept. 1941).
19. Goodman, L., "Methods of Measuring Useful Life of Equipment under Operational Conditions," *J. Amer. statist. Ass.*, *48*, 503–530 (Sept. 1953).
20. Grant, E., *Principles of Engineering Economy*, 3rd ed., Ronald Press Company, New York, 1950.
21. Herstein, I., and Debrew, G., "Non-Negative Square Matrices," *Econometrica*, *21*, 597–607 (Oct. 1953).
22. Jeming, Joseph, "Estimates of Average Service Life and Life Expectancies and the Standard Deviation of Such Estimates," *Econometrica*, *11*, 141–150 (1943).
23. Kai Lai Chung, "On the Renewal Theorem in Higher Dimensions," Parts 1 and 2, *Skand. Aktuar Tidskr.* (1952).
24. Karlin, S., "On the Renewal Equation," *Pac. J. Math.*, *5*, 229–257 (1955).

25. Kendall, D. G., "Random Fluctuations in the Age-Distribution of a Population Whose Development Is Controlled by the Simple Birth and Death Process," *J. R. statist. Soc.*, *12*, Sec. B, 278 (1950).
26. ———, "Stochastic Processes and Population Growth," *J. R. statist. Soc.*, *11*, Sec. B, 230 (1949).
27. Kimball, Bradford F., "A System of Life Tables for Physical Property Based on the Truncated Normal Distribution," *Econometrica*, *15*, 342 (1947).
28. Kurtz, E. B., *Life Expectancy of Physical Property*, Ronald Press Co., New York, 1930.
29. Leslie, P. H., "On the Use of Matrices in Certain Population Problems," *Biometrika*, *33*, 183–212 (1945).
30. Lotka, A. J., "A Contribution to the Theory of Self-Renewing Aggregates, with Special Reference to Industrial Replacement," *Ann. math. Statist.*, *10*, 1–25 (1939).
31. ———, "Industrial Replacement," *Skand. Aktuar Tidskr.*, 51 (1933).
32. ———, "On an Integral Equation in Population Analysis," *Ann. math. Statist.*, *10*, 144–161 (1939).
33. ———, "Population Analysis: A Theorem Regarding the Stable Age Distribution," *J. Wash. Acad. Sci.*, *27*, 299 (1937).
34. ———, "The Stability of the Normal Age Distribution," *Proc. nat. Acad. Sci.*, *8*, 339 (1922).
35. ———, "The Theory of Industrial Replacement," *Skand. Aktuar Tidskr.*, 1–14 (1940).
36. Preinreich, G. A. D., "The Economic Life of Industrial Equipment," *Econometrica*, *8*, 12 (1940).
37. ———, *The Present Status of Renewal Theory*, Waverly Press, Baltimore, 1940.
38. ———, "The Theory of Industrial Replacement," *Skand. Aktuar Tidskr.*, 1–19 (1939).
39. *Problems for Short Course in Operations Research, Summer, 1953*, Massachusetts Institute of Technology, Cambridge (hectographed).
40. Shellard, G. G., "Failure of Complex Equipment," *J. Opns. Res. Soc. Am.*, *1*, 130–136 (1953).
41. Terborgh, B., *Dynamic Equipment Policy*, McGraw-Hill Book Co., New York, 1949.
42. *Tested Approaches to Capital Equipment Replacement*, Special Report No. 1, American Management Association, New York, 1954.
43. Winfrey, R., and Kurtz, E. B., "Life Characteristics of Physical Property," Bulletin 103, Iowa State College, Ames, *30*, no. 3 (1931).

PART VIII

COMPETITIVE MODELS

All the models which have been discussed up to this point have dealt with conflicts of interest internal to the organization, such as a conflict between interests in minimizing manufacturing costs and in minimizing capital invested in inventory. The models discussed in this part of the book take into account conflict external to the organization, or at least that form of external conflict called "competition." Competition manifests itself in the problems to be considered because the effectiveness of decisions by one party is dependent on decisions by another party. Competitive problems of two types are considered: games and bidding.

Chapter 18 is an introduction to the theory of games. This theory has received a good deal of attention in the recent literature but as yet it has found relatively few practical applications. That is, the mathematical phases of the theory have not found much direct application in O.R. but, nevertheless, the underlying logic and conceptualization have significance in O.R.

Everyone is interested in games and in learning how to win "without actually cheating." For this reason the theory has received considerable popular attention. However, the intent of game theory is very serious and its development is directed toward yielding a better understanding of competitive economic behavior. As yet only relatively simple gaming situations have been mathematized, but the mathematics of even the simple games is extremely complex. As indicated, the theory has a value which is independent of the mathematics. It has brought to consciousness the possibility of rational choice of policy in noncompetitive as well as competitive situations.

Chapter 19 considers several models of competitive bidding situations. This work is very recent and represents only a beginning in an important area of competitive behavior. It has already been successfully applied to an industrial problem. Unfortunately, this application cannot be presented for reasons of industrial security. A paraphrased version of the application, however, is presented.

Chapter 18

The Theory of Games

INTRODUCTION

Analysis of the mathematical form and underlying principles of games was made by von Neumann [17] as early as 1928. In this early work von Neumann was not so much interested in executive-type problems as he was in the logical foundations of quantum mechanics. It was not until 1944, when von Neumann and Morgenstern published their now well known *Theory of Games and Economic Behavior*,[18] that the mathematical treatment of games "took fire." It had a major impact on the development of linear programming and Wald's statistical decision theory.* It also started a new way of thinking about competitive decisions.

THE NATURE OF GAMES

Every game has a goal or end-state for which the players strive by selecting courses of action permissible under the rules. In some cases the object of the game is to reach the goal as efficiently as possible. Here efficiency is measured by a score as in golf or baseball. In golf, for example, the goal is to complete 18 (or some other specified number of) holes with as low a score as possible. In some cases efficiency is measured by time or number of choices, and the objective is to get there first.

In other games, the goal is such that only one person or team can

---

* See references in Chapters 20 and 21.

attain it, and the objective is to attain it. Checkmate in chess, for example, is such a goal.

The game may have alternative goals as in playing dice: to throw a 7 or 11 on the first throw and not to throw a 2, 3, or 12; or if a 4, 5, 6, 8, 9, or 10 is obtained on the first throw, the objective is to get the same number again before a 7 is thrown.

A one-person game such as solitaire or golf (under some circumstances) is not competitive. The person is playing for score or to reach a goal. This is very similar to the type of decision situation discussed in Chapter 5 where the objective is to reach one or more goals with maximum effectiveness. The approach (decision strategy) outlined there is applicable to such one-person games. Our concern here will be with games which involve competition, actions, and counteractions. Consequently, the term *game* will be used to refer only to competitive games.

A game is competitive if there is an end-state (winning) such that each player desires it, but not all can obtain it. Hence the players are in conflict relative to this goal. But this conflict is made to serve a common objective by virtue of the rules of the game. Each player has a set of possible *choices*. To select one is to *move*. A *play* is a sequence or set of choices which brings the game to an end-state.

In many games, the attainment of the goal is accompanied by a payment of some kind, usually money. These payments and receipts (negative payments) are, in a sense, a way of scoring the game, i.e., compensating for effectiveness. We shall assume that "winning" a game can always be translated into monetary terms since our interest is in economic games, in other words, business competition.

A *zero-sum* game is one in which the payments, upon completion of the game, are equal to zero. Thus, if A pays B \$1.00, then B pays A $-\$1.00$ (i.e., B receives \$1.00 from A). The sum of these payments is zero. But suppose A must put an additional \$1.00 in the "kitty" or "pay the house," then the sum of the payments among the players is not zero. This would be a *nonzero-sum* game.

A *strategy* is a player's predetermined method for making his choices during the game. Hence, a strategy is a set of decision rules.

Finally, a *payoff matrix* is a table which specifies how payments should be made at the completion of the game.

One final point before turning to the Theory of Games: this theory does not try to describe how a game should be played. It is concerned with the procedure and principles by which plays should be selected. It is, in effect, a decision theory applicable to competitive situations.

ZERO-SUM TWO-PERSON GAMES

Consider the following game for two players. Player A moves the ○ pieces in Fig. 18-1; player B moves the × pieces. The rules state that the pieces can be moved from one white square to any other white square adjoining it, provided that that square is not already occupied. Only one piece can be moved at a time and one piece must be moved each time. Players alternate choice of moves. The play is

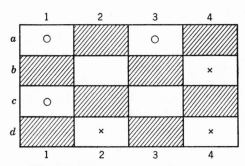

Fig. 18-1. Zero-sum two-person game.

over if a player has to move and cannot do so according to the rules of the game. He is then the losing player. The object of the game is to win in the least number of moves.

Assume that in this specific example player A makes a move from the given positions and that his choice is not transmitted to B. Player B, not knowing what A's choice was, may outline the following strategy: First choice of B: Move piece from $d4$ to $c3$. (A makes his second move.) Second choice of B: Move from $c3$ to $b2$. A glance at Fig. 18-1 will confirm that

1. These choices are possible regardless of A's two moves.
2. Player A loses the game after the second move of B.

In this case, then, we have a strategy for B which will assure his winning the game. In this example, it can be seen that one specific strategy for B will insure his winning the game irrespective of what the choices of A are going to be, provided A makes the first move. Therefore, in this case one can say that B has found a solution to the game. (Note that a better strategy does not exist for B in this case.)

To return to the example, if player B does not know who will have to make the first move, what will his best strategy be? For this example, we can outline a strategy for B as follows:

Move	Choice
1st	$d4$ to $c3$.
2nd	$c3$ to $b2$ or $d2$ to $c1$, or $b4$ to $a3$, and the play will be over and won by B. However, if none of these choices are possible, then move $c3$ to $d4$.
3rd	If impossible, play is over and won by A.
4th	Same as 2nd.
5th	Same as 3rd.
Etc.	

It can easily be seen that this is the best strategy for player B irrespective of who makes the first move. In a similar manner we can outline the best strategy for player A.

Once we have found the best strategy for both players, we have a complete *solution* for the game. Determination of the best strategies for the players constitutes the *solution* of the game.

These notions are accepted intuitively. We shall see that in three-person zero-sum games, for example, we will not be able to apply the same notions of what a solution is. Certain difficulties will arise, since we shall have to take into account the possibility of players forming coalitions. Even greater difficulties in defining a solution will occur in n-person nonzero-sum games.

For the moment, however, let us restrict ourselves to zero-sum two-person games, and let us accept the following definition: A game is solved if we can find the best strategies for each of the players.

RECTANGULAR (TWO-PERSON ZERO-SUM) GAMES (WITH SADDLE POINTS)

Consider the following game:

Player A has three possible plans: P, Q, R.

Player B has two possible plans: S, T.

The rules of the game state that the payments should be made according to the choices of plans:

Plans Chosen	Payment
P, S	A pays B \$2.00
P, T	B pays A \$2.00
Q, S	A pays B \$1.00
Q, T	B pays A \$3.00
R, S	B pays A \$1.00
R, T	B pays A \$2.00

What are the best strategies for players A and B in this game?

It is convenient to arrange rules of payments in matrix form. Let a positive number indicate a payment of B to A and a negative number a payment of A to B. We then have the "payoff matrix" shown in Table 18-1.

TABLE 18-1

		Player B	
	Plan	S	T
	P	-2	2
Player A	Q	-1	3
	R	1	2

Consider player B. Obviously plan T is not good for him. He always loses if he chooses this plan. Therefore, his best strategy is always to choose S and the worst that can happen is that he will lose $1.00 (when A chooses R).

Now consider player A. The most that he can get is when he chooses plan Q and B chooses T. But this is unlikely to happen * since by previous reasoning B will never choose T. Thus, the most that A can make (if B chooses S) is by choosing plan R, in which case he will make $1.00.

We thus have a best strategy for player A (namely plan R) and a best strategy for player B (namely plan S). We also know what the result of the choices of these strategies are: Player B pays player A $1.00.

We have, therefore, a complete solution of the game. Furthermore, for this solution, player A wins $1.00 and player B loses $1.00. For this example, $1.00 is referred to as the *value of the game.*

The game just presented is called a *rectangular game* since the payoff matrix is in rectangular form. In general, to obtain a solution of a rectangular game we shall want to find:

1. The best strategies for the two players.
2. The value of the game.

---

* We assume throughout this chapter that all players are intelligent. Hence, here, for example, player B would not choose plan T. If one's opponent does not act intelligently, one can obviously take advantage of such a fact.

The Minimax and Maximin Principle

Consider the payoff matrix of a rectangular game shown in Table 18-2. We shall first solve the game by means of the reasoning given

TABLE 18-2

		B	
	Plan	S	T
	P	−2	−4
A	Q	−1	3
	R	1	2

in the previous section. We shall then introduce a method of solution based on minimax principles. The reasoning in both cases is identical and, consequently, leads to the same solution.

METHOD 1. Player A will never choose plan P, since he can always do better by choosing plan Q or R. Player B realizes this and therefore cannot count on plan P at all. In that case, he obviously will never choose T, since he will always do better if he chooses S. A, in turn, realizes that B will choose S and therefore his best policy is R. Thus we have reached the solution:

> Best strategy for A: plan R.
> Best strategy for B: plan S.
> Value of game for A: \$1.00 (a gain).
> Value of game for B: −\$1.00 (a loss).

METHOD 2. Consider now the following reasoning:

Player A:

Under plan P the least (minimum) he can gain is −\$4.00.
Under plan Q the least (minimum) he can gain is −\$1.00.
Under plan R the least (minimum) he can gain is +\$1.00.

The highest (maximum) of the least (minimum) possible gains is \$1.00. We can then say that "max min for A" = \$1.00 (this corresponds to R, S choices).

Player B:

Under plan S his highest (maximum) loss is \$1.00.
Under plan T his highest (maximum) loss is \$3.00.

Therefore, the least (minimum) of his highest losses is \$1.00. We say that "min max for B" = \$1.00 (this corresponds again to R, S choices).

In mathematical notation, "max min for A" is denoted by

$$\max_{i} \min_{j} a_{ij}$$

where a_{ij} represents the element in the ith row and jth column of the payoff matrix. Similarly, "min max for B" is denoted by

$$\min_{j} \max_{i} a_{ij}$$

If, for a given game

$$\max_{i} \min_{j} a_{ij} = \min_{j} \max_{i} a_{ij} = g$$

then player A can win g, but can be prevented by player B from winning more than g.

In mathematical symbols, the payoff matrix for this example may be represented as $[a_{ij}]$, $i = 1, 2, 3; j = 1, 2$. Thus, in our example

$$a_{11} = -2 \qquad a_{12} = -4$$

$$a_{21} = -1 \qquad a_{22} = 3$$

$$a_{31} = 1 \qquad a_{32} = 2$$

and these results are given by

$$\max_{i} \min_{j} a_{ij} = a_{31} = 1$$

$$\min_{j} \max_{i} a_{ij} = a_{31} = 1$$

Therefore, the solution is given by choices of plans R and S (corresponding to a_{31}) by players A and B, respectively.

We note that Method 2 (the use of minimax and maximin principles) gives the same solution as that obtained by Method 1.

Saddle Points

Not every rectangular game leads to solutions involving a best single choice for both A and B. Consider, for example, the game whose payoff matrix is shown in Table 18-3: If A chooses P, B will obviously choose S. If A chooses Q, B will choose T. We note that there is not a definite best plan for A. The same can be said for B.

TABLE 18-3

	Plan	S	T
		B	
A	P	-2	1
	Q	2	-1

Using the min max principles, we find:

$$\text{max min for } A = -\$1.00 \text{ (Choice } Q, T)$$

$$\text{min max for } B = \$1.00 \text{ (Choice } P, T)$$

and, in this case, we have

$$\text{max min for } A \text{ is } not \text{ equal to min max for } B$$

i.e.,

$$\max_i \min_j a_{ij} \neq \min_j \max_i a_{ij}$$

We shall discuss such a game in the next section.

Games for which max min for A = min max for B are called games with a saddle point. In the example of the previous section, the saddle point consisted of the choices R, S.

In general: if

$$\max_i \min_j a_{ij} = \min_j \max_i a_{ij} = a_{i_0 j_0}$$

then

The best strategy for A is plan i_0.
The best strategy for B is plan j_0.
The value of the game (for A) is $a_{i_0 j_0}$.

The easiest technique in searching for a saddle point is to find a number that is *lowest in its row and highest in its column*. If such a number does not exist, then there is no saddle point. If one such number exists, it is the saddle point. The corresponding strategies are the best strategies and the number itself is the value of the game. If two or more such numbers exist, then there are two or more solutions. Each solution corresponds to a saddle point.

For example, consider a game which has the payoff matrix shown in Table 18-4. In this case, (III, III) is a saddle point, since 2 is lowest

TABLE 18-4

	Plan	B			
		I	II	III	IV
A	I	3	−5	0	6
	II	−4	−2	1	2
	III	5	4	2	3

in its row and highest in its column. Therefore

III is the best plan for A.
III is the best plan for B.
\$2.00 is the value of the game (A wins and B loses).

The payoff matrix shown in Table 18-5a has two saddle points [(P, S) and (P, U)], but the one shown in Table 18-5b has none.

TABLE 18-5

	S	T	U
P	1	2	1
Q	0	−4	−1
R	1	3	−2

(a)

	S	T	U
P	1	2	1
Q	0	−4	−1
R	2	1	2

(b)

Suppose we want to construct the payoff matrix for the following game and state whether the game has a saddle point: Each of two players simultaneously places a dime and a penny on the table. Player A collects all four coins if the similar coins are in the same column.

Otherwise player B collects all four coins. The payoff matrix is shown in Table 18-6, where D stands for dime, and P for penny. This game has no saddle point.

TABLE 18-6.   PAYOFF MATRIX (IN CENTS)

		B	
	Plan	PD	DP
A	PD	11	−11
	DP	−11	11

RECTANGULAR GAMES (WITHOUT SADDLE POINTS): MIXED STRATEGIES

Consider the game with the payoff matrix shown in Table 18-7. The payoff matrix has no saddle point; therefore in this case A and B

TABLE 18-7

		B	
	Plan	S	T
A	P	−3	7
	Q	6	1

do not have single best plans as their best strategies. Consequently, each player has to devise some *mixed strategy* in order to maximize his gain or minimize his loss.

Assume, for example, that A decides to play P half of the time and Q half of the time.* Now if B chooses S all the time, then the expected

---

* A would have to make his choices at random so that P is chosen with a frequency of $\frac{1}{2}$ and Q with a frequency of $\frac{1}{2}$. A suitable method for random choice in this case would be the flipping of an unbiased coin.

gain of A will be

$$\tfrac{1}{2}(-3) + \tfrac{1}{2}(6) = -1.5 + 3 = \$1.50$$

but if B chooses T all the time, A's expected gain will be

$$\tfrac{1}{2}(7) + \tfrac{1}{2}(1) = 3.5 + 0.5 = \$4.00$$

Assume, further, that B also has a mixed strategy. At random he chooses S half of the time and T half of the time. In this case A's expected gain will be

$$\tfrac{1}{2}[\tfrac{1}{2}(-3) + \tfrac{1}{2}(6)] + \tfrac{1}{2}[\tfrac{1}{2}(7) + \tfrac{1}{2}(1)] = \$2.75$$

In a similar manner we may calculate what A's expected gain will be for other mixed strategies. For example, if A plays P one-fourth of the time and Q three-fourths of the time, while B plays S one-third of the time and T two-thirds of the time, then A's expected gain will be

$$\tfrac{1}{3}[\tfrac{1}{4}(-3) + \tfrac{3}{4}(6)] + \tfrac{2}{3}[\tfrac{1}{4}(7) + \tfrac{3}{4}(1)] = \tfrac{1}{12}(-3 + 18 + 14 + 6)$$

$$= \tfrac{35}{12} = \$2.92$$

The question then arises: What is the best mixed strategy for the players? In the preceding examples we saw that A's gains varied from \$1.50 to \$4.00. We want to know whether he can insure some minimum gain and what that gain is. Similarly, can B insure that he will not lose more than some maximum amount?

The answer to these questions is in the affirmative. The mathematical theory of games gives us both the proof that there always are best strategies, as well as the means for finding them.

We shall discuss some of the mathematical results in the next two sections. Let us outline here how one actually finds the best strategies for the given game and what are the expected amounts to be gained or lost by the players.

Let A play P with the frequency x, and Q with a frequency $(1 - x)$. Then, if B plays S all the time, A's gain will be

$$g(A, S) = x(-3) + (1 - x)6 = 6 - 9x$$

If B plays T all the time, A's gain will be

$$g(A, T) = x(7) + (1 - x)1 = 1 + 6x$$

It can be shown mathematically that if A chooses x, so that $g(A, S) =$

$g(A, T)$, then this will lead to the best strategy for him. Thus

$$6 - 9x = 1 + 6x$$

$$5 = 15x$$

i.e.

$$x = \tfrac{1}{3}$$

We have the result

$$g(A) = \tfrac{1}{3}(-3) + \tfrac{2}{3}(6) = \$3.00$$

Thus, regardless of the frequency with which B plays either S or T, A's gain will be \$3.00. (If, for example, B plays S with a frequency $\tfrac{1}{4}$ and T with a frequency $\tfrac{3}{4}$, then A's expected gain will be

$$g(A, \tfrac{1}{3}, \tfrac{2}{3}) = \tfrac{1}{4}[\tfrac{1}{3}(-3) + \tfrac{2}{3}(6)] + \tfrac{3}{4}[\tfrac{1}{3}(7) + \tfrac{2}{3}(1)] = \$3.00$$

and similarly for any other choice of frequencies by B.) Therefore, by choice of frequencies $\tfrac{1}{3}$ and $\tfrac{2}{3}$, A can assure himself a gain of \$3.00.

The same method can be applied by player B. Let frequency of choice of S be denoted by y and that of T be denoted by $(1 - y)$. For best strategy we have

$$g(B, P) = y(-3) + (1 - y)7 = y(6) + (1 - y)1 = g(B, Q)$$

$$7 - 10y = 1 + 5y$$

$$6 = 15y$$

$$y = \tfrac{2}{5}$$

$$1 - y = \tfrac{3}{5}$$

$$g(B) = \tfrac{2}{5}(-3) + \tfrac{3}{5}(7) = \$3.00$$

Note that $g(A) = g(B)$, as expected for a zero-sum game. Thus, a complete solution of the given game is:

1. A should play P and Q with frequencies $\tfrac{1}{3}$ and $\tfrac{2}{3}$ respectively.
2. B should play S and T with frequencies $\tfrac{2}{5}$ and $\tfrac{3}{5}$ respectively.
3. The value of the game is \$3.00.

General Theorems for Rectangular Games

The payoffs for a rectangular game can always be given in "$m \times n$" matrix form, where player A has m possible plans and B has n possible plans, and the payoff matrix is $[a_{ij}]$. (See Table 18-8.)

TABLE 18-8

	Plan	I	II	$\cdots$	n
	I	a_{11}	a_{12}	$\cdots$	a_{1n}
	II	a_{21}	a_{22}	$\cdots$	a_{2n}
A	.	.	.	$\cdots$	.
	.	.	.	$\cdots$	.
	.	.	.	$\cdots$	.
	m	a_{m1}	a_{m2}	$\cdots$	a_{mn}

(The column group is labeled B.)

It can be shown mathematically that:

1. Each rectangular game has a specific value g. This value is unique.

2. There exists for player A a best strategy; namely, there exist frequencies $x_1, x_2, \cdots, x_m$, such that $x_1 + x_2 + \cdots + x_m = 1$ and such that if he plays plan I with frequency x_1, plan II with frequency $x_2, \cdots$, plan m with frequency x_m, then he can assure himself *at least* an expected gain of g, where g is the value of the game.

3. Similarly for player B, there exists a best strategy

$$Y = [y_1, y_2, \cdots, y_n], \qquad \sum_{j=1}^{n} y_j = 1$$

such that if he plays plans I, II, $\cdots$, n, with frequencies $y_1, y_2, \cdots, y_n$ respectively, he can assure himself *at most* a loss of g.

Note that, for a rectangular game where the matrix has a saddle point at (i_0, j_0), we have the following solution

$$x_i = \begin{cases} 0, & i \neq i_0 \\ 1, & i = i_0 \end{cases}$$

$$y_i = \begin{cases} 0, & j \neq j_0 \\ 1, & j = j_0 \end{cases}$$

$$g = a_{i_0 j_0}$$

General Solution of Rectangular Games

It can be shown that the unknowns x_1, x_2, $\cdots$, x_m, y_1, y_2, $\cdots$, y_n, and g can be found from the following relations

$$x_1 + x_2 + \cdots + x_m = 1, \qquad x_i \geqq 0 \tag{1}$$

$$y_1 + y_2 + \cdots + y_n = 1, \qquad y_j \geqq 0 \tag{2}$$

$$x_1 a_{1j} + x_2 a_{2j} + \cdots + x_m a_{mj} \geqq g \text{ for } j = 1, 2, \cdots, n \tag{3}$$

$$y_1 a_{i1} + y_2 a_{i2} + \cdots + y_n a_{in} \leqq g \text{ for } i = 1, 2, \cdots, m \tag{4}$$

Relation 3 actually represents n inequations, one inequation for each j. Similarly relation 4 represents m inequations. We thus have $m + n + 1$ unknowns with $m + n + 2$ relations (with the added restrictions $x_i \geqq 0$, $y_j \geqq 0$, since negative frequencies have no meaning). (Note that relations 3 and 4 may be equalities or inequalities.) The theorems given in the previous section assure us that there always exists a solution to these relations. They further assure that g is unique. However, a game may have several, or even an infinite number of, solutions for the x_i and y_j.

EXAMPLE: For the game represented by Table 18-7, the unknowns are x_1, x_2, y_1, y_2, and g. The relations are

$$x_1 + x_2 = 1, \qquad x_1 \geqq 0, \qquad x_2 \geqq 0 \tag{5}$$

$$y_1 + y_2 = 1, \qquad y_1 \geqq 0, \qquad y_2 \geqq 0 \tag{6}$$

$$x_1(-3) + x_2(6) \geqq g \tag{7}$$

$$x_1(7) + x_2(1) \geqq g \tag{8}$$

$$y_1(-3) + y_2(7) \leqq g \tag{9}$$

$$y_1(6) + y_2(1) \leqq g \tag{10}$$

Such problems can be solved either by "ordinary algebra," graphic devices, matrix algebra, or iteration. Each of these is considered in turn in the next four sections.

Algebraic Solutions

The algebraic method is a direct attempt to solve for the unknowns from relations 1, 2, 3, and 4. An important key to the solution is the previously stated fact that each rectangular game has a value, namely g, which exists and is unique. Therefore we try to find one such value

g that will satisfy the relations. If we find this g we know that it is the only g and proceed accordingly. Thus the first obvious step is to assume that relations 3 and 4 are equalities.

Let us see how this assumption leads to a solution for the example given in the last section. Here, one obtains the following system of equations

$$x_1 + x_2 = 1 \tag{11}$$

$$y_1 + y_2 = 1 \tag{12}$$

$$-3x_1 + 6x_2 = g \tag{13}$$

$$7x_1 + x_2 = g \tag{14}$$

$$-3y_1 + 7y_2 = g \tag{15}$$

$$6y_1 + y_2 = g \tag{16}$$

We have here five unknowns and six equations. We therefore solve using five equations only and check whether the sixth equation holds. We also check whether $x_1 \geqq 0$, $x_2 \geqq 0$, $y_1 \geqq 0$, $y_2 \geqq 0$. If the results check, then the solution is complete.

Equations 11 and 12 lead to $x_2 = 1 - x_1$, $y_2 = 1 - y_1$. Therefore eqs. 13, 14, and 15 become

$$-3x_1 + 6(1 - x_1) = g; \text{ hence } -9x_1 - g = -6 \text{ or } 9x_1 + g = 6 \tag{17}$$

$$7x_1 + (1 - x_1) = g; \text{ hence } 6x_1 + 1 = g \text{ or } 6x_1 - g = -1 \tag{18}$$

$$-3y_1 + 7(1 - y_1) = g; \text{ hence } -3y_1 + 7 - 7y_1 = g \text{ or } 10y_1 + g = 7 \tag{19}$$

Adding eqs. 17 and 18 we get $15x_1 = 5$, i.e., $x_1 = \frac{1}{3}$, so that, from eqs. 17, 18, and 11, we obtain

$$x_1 = \tfrac{1}{3}, \qquad x_2 = \tfrac{2}{3}, \qquad \text{and } g = 3$$

Substituting into eq. 19, we obtain $10y_1 = 7 - 3 = 4$, from which

$$y_1 = \tfrac{2}{5} \qquad \text{and} \qquad y_2 = \tfrac{3}{5}$$

Substituting into eq. 16, we have

$$6y_1 + y_2 = 6(\tfrac{2}{5}) + 1(\tfrac{3}{5}) = \tfrac{12}{5} + \tfrac{3}{5} = \tfrac{15}{5} = 3 = g$$

Then, since $\frac{1}{3} > 0$, $\frac{2}{8} > 0$, $\frac{2}{5} > 0$, and $\frac{3}{5} > 0$, we have the complete solution, namely

$$x_1 = \tfrac{1}{3}, \qquad x_2 = \tfrac{2}{3}, \qquad y_1 = \tfrac{2}{5}, \qquad y_2 = \tfrac{3}{5}, \qquad g = 3$$

On the other hand, if we try the same method for the game represented by Table 18-2 (which we have transformed into Table 18-9), we obtain

$$x_1 + x_2 + x_3 = 1 \tag{20}$$

$$y_1 + y_2 = 1 \tag{21}$$

$$x_1(-2) + x_2(-1) + x_3(1) = g \tag{22}$$

$$x_1(-4) + x_2(3) + x_3(2) = g \tag{23}$$

$$y_1(-2) + y_2(-4) = g \tag{24}$$

$$y_1(-1) + y_2(3) = g \tag{25}$$

$$y_1(1) + y_2(2) = g \tag{26}$$

We have here six unknowns x_1, x_2, x_3, y_1, y_2, and g and seven equations.

TABLE 18-9

			B	
	Frequency		y_1	y_2
	Plan		S	T
		x_1	P	-2	-4
A	x_2	Q	-1	3
	x_3	R	1	2

Consider, for example, eqs. 21, 24, and 25

$$y_2 = 1 - y_1$$

$$-2y_1 + (1 - y_1)(-4) = g, \qquad -2y_1 - 4 + 4y_1 = g, \qquad 2y_1 - 4 = g$$

$$-y_1 + (1 - y_1)3 = g; \text{ i.e., } -4y_1 + 3 = g$$

Therefore

$$2y_1 - 4 = -4y_1 + 3; \text{ i.e., } y_1 = \tfrac{7}{6}$$

which contradicts the restriction that $0 \leq y_1 \leq 1$. Thus if we assume the relations to be equalities, we do not have a solution.

A general procedure is then to assume one inequality and leave the other relations as equalities. If we again meet with a contradiction, we assume other inequalities until a solution is finally reached.

There is a theorem, however, that makes the computations easier. It states that if

$$x_1 a_{1j} + x_2 a_{2j} + \cdots + x_m a_{mj} > g, \text{ then } y_j = 0$$

and similarly if

$$y_1 a_{i1} + y_2 a_{i2} + \cdots + y_n a_{in} < g, \text{ then } x_i = 0$$

Applying this theorem to the example just cited, one proceeds as follows:

a. If $x_1(-2) + x_2(-1) + x_3(1) > g$, then $y_1 = 0$. Then eqs. 24, 25, and 26 lead to $y_2 = 0$, $g = 0$, so that $y_1 + y_2 = 0$ and, hence, is a contradiction, since $y_1 + y_2 = 1$.

b. Similarly, a contradiction is obtained if we assume $x_1(-4) + x_2(3) + x_3(2) > g$.

c. If $y_1(-2) + y_2(-4) < g$, then $x_1 = 0$ and eqs. 20, 22, and 23 will lead to a contradiction.

Proceeding in this manner, we finally find that only the following relations have a solution

$$x_1 + x_2 + x_3 = 1 \tag{20}$$

$$y_1 + y_2 = 1 \tag{21}$$

$$x_1(-2) + (x_2)(-1) + x_3(1) = g \tag{22}$$

$$x_1(-4) + x_2(3) + x_3(2) > g \tag{23a}$$

$$y_1(-2) + y_2(-4) < g \tag{24a}$$

$$y_1(-1) + y_2(3) < g \tag{25a}$$

$$y_1(1) + y_2(2) = g \tag{26}$$

Equation 23a implies $y_2 = 0$, so that $y_1 = 1$. Furthermore, eq. 24a implies $x_1 = 0$ and eq. 25a implies $x_2 = 0$, so that $x_3 = 1$. Therefore, the final solution is given by

$$x_1 = 0, \quad x_2 = 0, \quad x_3 = 1, \quad y_1 = 1, \quad y_2 = 0, \quad g = 1$$

This, incidentally, is an algebraic solution of a game with a saddle point. We note that the algebraic solution of a game is quite lengthy. This method becomes many times more involved when there are more plans for A and B.

Graphical Solution

A graphical solution may be used whenever one of the players has
only two possible plans from which to choose. We shall illustrate the

TABLE 18-10

		B		
Frequency		y_1	y_2	y_3
Plan		R	S	T
A	x_1	P	2	-2	3
	x_2	Q	-3	5	-1

method by the example shown in Table 18-10. The general relations
are

$$x_1 + x_2 = 1 \tag{27}$$

$$y_1 + y_2 + y_3 = 1 \tag{28}$$

$$2x_1 - 3x_2 \geq g \tag{29}$$

$$-2x_1 + 5x_2 \geq g \tag{30}$$

$$3x_1 - x_2 \geq g \tag{31}$$

$$2y_1 - 2y_2 + 3y_3 \leq g \tag{32}$$

$$-3y_1 + 5y_2 - y_3 \leq g \tag{33}$$

Rewriting and simplifying the equations involving the player who has
only the two possible plans (in this case, player A), we have

$$2x_1 - 3(1 - x_1) \geq g \quad \text{so that } 5x_1 - 3 \geq g \tag{34}$$

$$-2x_1 + 5(1 - x_1) \geq g \quad \text{so that } -7x_1 + 5 \geq g \tag{35}$$

$$3x_1 - (1 - x_1) \geq g \quad \text{so that } 4x_1 - 1 \geq g \tag{36}$$

Let us plot the line $g = 5x_1 - 3$ as is done in Fig. 18-2. This line
divides the plane into two regions. For any point (x_0, g) above the
line, we shall have: $g > g_0 = 5x_0 - 3$ and for a point below the line,
$g < g_0 = 5x_0 - 3$.

In our case we are interested in the inequality $5x_1 - 3 \geqq g$. There-fore, the required solution will be either on the line or below it. We

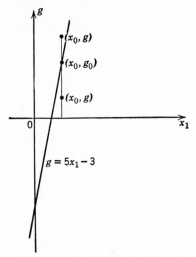

Fig. 18-2. Plot of line $g = 5x_1 - 3$.

plot all three lines in the interval $0 \leq x_1 \leq 1$ and note all the points below all three lines. (See Fig. 18-3.) We choose the point for which g is highest. In this example, the point will be found at the intersec-tion of $g = 5x_1 - 3$ and $g = -7x_1 + 5$, i.e.: $x_1 = \frac{2}{3}$, $x_2 = \frac{1}{3}$. Fur-thermore, $g = 5x_1 - 3 = \frac{10}{3} - 3 = \frac{1}{3}$.

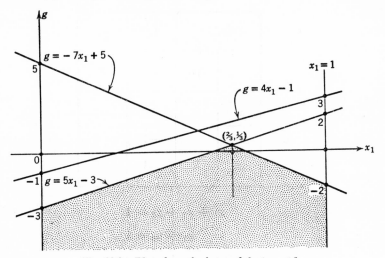

Fig. 18-3. Plots for g in interval $0 \leq x_1 \leq 1$.

Since eq. 31 leads to

$$3x_1 - x_2 = 3(\tfrac{2}{3}) - \tfrac{1}{3} = \tfrac{5}{3} > \tfrac{1}{3} = g$$

or

$$3x_1 - x_2 > g, \qquad \text{then } y_3 = 0$$

equations 28 and 32 lead to

$$y_1 + y_2 = 1, \qquad y_2 = 1 - y_1$$

i.e.,

$$2y_1 - 2(1 - y_1) = \tfrac{1}{3}, \qquad 4y_1 = 2 + \tfrac{1}{3} = \tfrac{7}{3}$$

or

$$y_1 = \tfrac{7}{12} \qquad \text{and} \qquad y_2 = \tfrac{5}{12}$$

and checking with eq. 33

$$-3(\tfrac{7}{12}) + 5(\tfrac{5}{12}) + 0 = \frac{25 - 21}{12} = \tfrac{4}{12} = \tfrac{1}{3} = g$$

Therefore, the solution is

$$x_1 = \tfrac{2}{3}, \qquad x_2 = \tfrac{1}{3}, \qquad y_1 = \tfrac{7}{12}, \qquad y_2 = \tfrac{5}{12}, \qquad y_3 = 0, \qquad g = \tfrac{1}{3}$$

Let us apply the graphical method to the game with a saddle point discussed earlier and represented by Table 18-11.

TABLE 18-11

			B	
	Frequency		y_1	y_2
		Plan	S	T
	x_1	P	-2	-4
A	x_2	Q	-1	3
	x_3	R	1	2

$$x_1 + x_2 + x_3 = 1 \tag{37}$$

$$y_1 + y_2 = 1 \tag{38}$$

$$-2x_1 - x_2 + x_3 \geq g \tag{39}$$

$$-4x_1 + 3x_2 + 2x_3 \geqq g \qquad (40)$$

$$-2y_1 - 4y_2 \leqq g \qquad (41)$$

$$-y_1 + 3y_2 \leqq g \qquad (42)$$

$$y_1 + 2y_2 \leqq g \qquad (43)$$

Equations 38, 41, 42, and 43 lead to

$$2y_1 - 4 \leqq g$$

$$-4y_1 + 3 \leqq g$$

$$-y_1 + 2 \leqq g$$

The corresponding lines in the interval $0 \leqq y_1 \leqq 1$ are plotted in Fig. 18-4. In this case we are interested in points above the line and

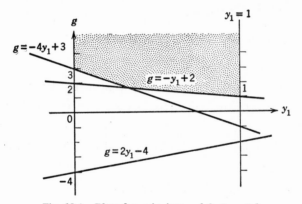

Fig. 18-4. Plots for g in interval $0 \leqq y_1 \leqq 1$.

we choose the lowest point of these points. This point is seen to be at $y_1 = 1$, so that $g = 1$, and $y_2 = 0$.

Equation 41 gives $-2y_1 - 4y_2 = -2 < 1 = g$. Therefore, $x_1 = 0$.
Equation 42 gives $-y_1 + 3y_2 = -1 < 1 = g$. Therefore, $x_2 = 0$.
Equation 43 gives $y_1 + 2y_2 = 1 = 1 = g$.

Since $x_1 + x_2 + x_3 = 1$ and $x_1 = 0$, $x_2 = 0$, it follows that $x_3 = 1$. Therefore, the final solution is

$$x_1 = 0, \qquad x_2 = 0, \qquad x_3 = 1, \qquad y_1 = 1, \qquad y_2 = 0, \qquad g = 1$$

Solution by Use of Matrices

(Note: This section is intended only for those readers who are familiar with matrix notations and operations.

NOTATION

$$A = [a_{ij}] = \begin{bmatrix} a_{11} & a_{12} \cdots a_{1n} \\ a_{21} & a_{22} \cdots a_{2n} \\ \cdot \\ \cdot \\ \cdot \\ a_{m1} & a_{m2} \cdots a_{mn} \end{bmatrix}$$

$B = [b_{ij}]$ = any square submatrix of A of order $r > 1$

$J_r = [1, 1, \cdots, 1]$, a $(1 \times r)$ matrix

C^T = the transpose of C

adj B = adjoint of B

$X = [x_1, x_2, \cdots, x_m]$, $\Sigma x_i = 1$, $x_i \geqq 0$

$Y = [y_1, y_2, \cdots, y_n]$, $\Sigma y_j = 1$, $y_j \geqq 0$

$\overline{X}$ = a $(1 \times r)$ matrix obtained from X by deleting those elements corresponding to the rows deleted from A to obtain B

$\overline{Y}$ = a $(1 \times r)$ matrix obtained from Y by deleting those elements corresponding to the columns deleted from A to obtain B

SOLUTION

1. Choose a square submatrix B of A of order $r(r \geqq 2)$ and calculate

$$\overline{X} = \frac{J_r \text{ adj } B}{J_r (\text{adj } B) J_r{}^T} = [x_{r_1}, x_{r_2}, \cdots, x_{r_r}]$$

$$\overline{Y} = \frac{J_r (\text{adj } B)^T}{J_r (\text{adj } B) J_r{}^T} = [y_{r_1}, y_{r_2}, \cdots, y_{r_r}]$$

2. If some $x_{r_i} < 0$, or some $y_{r_j} < 0$, then reject the chosen B and try another B.

3. If $x_{r_i} \geqq 0$ $(i = 1, 2, \cdots, r)$ and $y_{r_j} \geqq 0$ $(j = 1, 2, \cdots, r)$, calculate

$$g = \frac{|B|}{J_r (\text{adj } B) J_r{}^T}$$

and construct X and Y from $\overline{X}$ and $\overline{Y}$ by adding zeroes in the appropriate places.

Check whether

$$\sum_{i=1}^{m} x_i a_{ij} \geqq g \text{ for every } j = 1, 2, \cdots, n$$

and whether

$$\sum_{j=1}^{n} y_j a_{ij} \leqq g \text{ for every } i = 1, 2, \cdots, m$$

If one of the relations does not hold, try another B. If all relations hold, then X, Y, and g are the required solutions.

Example. Let the payoff matrix be that shown in Table 18-12. We have only three possible submatrices, and $J_2 = [1 \quad 1]$

TABLE 18-12

	y_1	y_2	y_3
x_1	2	-2	3
x_2	-3	5	-1

$$B_1 = \begin{bmatrix} -2 & 3 \\ 5 & -1 \end{bmatrix}, \quad B_2 = \begin{bmatrix} 2 & 3 \\ -3 & -1 \end{bmatrix}, \quad B_3 = \begin{bmatrix} 2 & -2 \\ -3 & 5 \end{bmatrix}$$

Consider B_1

$$\text{adj } B_1 = \begin{bmatrix} -1 & -3 \\ -5 & -2 \end{bmatrix}; \quad (\text{adj } B)^T = \begin{bmatrix} -1 & -5 \\ -3 & -2 \end{bmatrix}$$

$$\overline{X} = \frac{[1,1]\begin{bmatrix} -1 & -3 \\ -5 & -2 \end{bmatrix}}{[1,1]\begin{bmatrix} -1 & -3 \\ -5 & -2 \end{bmatrix}\begin{bmatrix} 1 \\ 1 \end{bmatrix}} = \frac{[-6, -5]}{[-6, -5]\begin{bmatrix} 1 \\ 1 \end{bmatrix}} = \frac{[-6, -5]}{-11} = \begin{bmatrix} \dfrac{6}{11}, \dfrac{5}{11} \end{bmatrix}$$

$$\overline{Y} = \frac{[1,1]\begin{bmatrix} -1 & -5 \\ -3 & -2 \end{bmatrix}}{-11} = \frac{[-4, -7]}{-11} = \begin{bmatrix} \dfrac{4}{11}, \dfrac{7}{11} \end{bmatrix}$$

Since $\frac{6}{11} > 0$, $\frac{5}{11} > 0$, $\frac{4}{11} > 0$, and $\frac{7}{11} > 0$ we continue.

$$X = [\tfrac{6}{11}, \tfrac{5}{11}], \qquad Y = [0, \tfrac{4}{11}, \tfrac{7}{11}]$$

or

$$x_1 = \tfrac{6}{11}, \; x_2 = \tfrac{5}{11}, \qquad y_1 = 0, \; y_2 = \tfrac{4}{11}, \; y_3 = \tfrac{7}{11}$$

$$g = \frac{\begin{bmatrix} -2 & 3 \\ 5 & -1 \end{bmatrix}}{-11} = \frac{2 - 15}{-11} = \frac{-13}{-11} = \frac{13}{11}$$

We now check the fundamental relations

$$2x_1 - 3x_2 = 2(\tfrac{6}{11}) - 3(\tfrac{5}{11}) = \tfrac{12}{11} - \tfrac{15}{11} = -\tfrac{3}{11} < \tfrac{13}{11}$$

This relation contradicts the requirement that $2x_1 - 3x_2 \geqq g$. So B_1 is not suitable.

Consider therefore B_2

$$\text{adj } B_2 = \begin{bmatrix} -1 & -3 \\ 3 & 2 \end{bmatrix}; \qquad (\text{adj } B_2)^T = \begin{bmatrix} -1 & 3 \\ -3 & 2 \end{bmatrix}$$

$$\bar{X} = \frac{[1, 1] \begin{bmatrix} -1 & -3 \\ 3 & 2 \end{bmatrix}}{[1, 1] \begin{bmatrix} -1 & -3 \\ 3 & 2 \end{bmatrix} \begin{bmatrix} 1 \\ 1 \end{bmatrix}} = \frac{[2, -1]}{[2, -1] \begin{bmatrix} 1 \\ 1 \end{bmatrix}} = \frac{[2, -1]}{1} = [2, -1]$$

Since $x_{r_2} = -1 < 0$, we reject B_2.

B_3 should give us the answer, since it is the only remaining submatrix and since we know that there must exist a solution

$$\text{adj } B_3 = \begin{bmatrix} 5 & 2 \\ 3 & 2 \end{bmatrix}; \qquad (\text{adj } B_3)^T = \begin{bmatrix} 5 & 3 \\ 2 & 2 \end{bmatrix}$$

$$\bar{X} = \frac{[1, 1] \begin{bmatrix} 5 & 2 \\ 3 & 2 \end{bmatrix}}{[1, 1] \begin{bmatrix} 5 & 2 \\ 3 & 2 \end{bmatrix} \begin{bmatrix} 1 \\ 1 \end{bmatrix}} = \frac{[8, 4]}{[8, 4] \begin{bmatrix} 1 \\ 1 \end{bmatrix}} = \frac{[8, 4]}{12} = \begin{bmatrix} \tfrac{2}{3}, \tfrac{1}{3} \end{bmatrix}$$

$$\bar{Y} = \frac{[1, 1] \begin{bmatrix} 5 & 3 \\ 2 & 2 \end{bmatrix}}{[1, 1] \begin{bmatrix} 5 & 2 \\ 3 & 2 \end{bmatrix} \begin{bmatrix} 1 \\ 1 \end{bmatrix}} = \frac{[7, 5]}{12} = \begin{bmatrix} \tfrac{7}{12}, \tfrac{5}{12} \end{bmatrix}$$

Since $\frac{2}{3} > 0$, $\frac{1}{3} > 0$, $\frac{7}{12} > 0$, $\frac{5}{12} > 0$, we continue.

$$X = [\tfrac{2}{3}, \tfrac{1}{3}], \qquad Y = [\tfrac{7}{12}, \tfrac{5}{12}, 0]$$

$$x_1 = \tfrac{2}{3}, \, x_2 = \tfrac{1}{3}, \qquad y_1 = \tfrac{7}{12}, \, y_2 = \tfrac{5}{12}, \, y_3 = 0$$

$$g = \frac{\begin{bmatrix} 2 & -2 \\ -3 & 5 \end{bmatrix}}{12} = \frac{10 - 6}{12} = \frac{4}{12} = \frac{1}{3}$$

$$2x_1 - 3x_2 = (2)(\tfrac{2}{3}) - (3)(\tfrac{1}{3}) = \tfrac{1}{3} = g$$

$$-2x_1 + 5x_2 = (-2)(\tfrac{2}{3}) + (5)(\tfrac{1}{3}) = \tfrac{1}{3} = g$$

$$3x_1 - x_2 = (3)(\tfrac{2}{3}) - \tfrac{1}{3} = \tfrac{5}{3} > g$$

$$2y_1 - 2y_2 + 3y_3 = (2)(\tfrac{7}{12}) - (2)(\tfrac{5}{12}) + (3)(0) = \tfrac{14}{12} - \tfrac{10}{12} = \tfrac{1}{3} = g$$

$$-3y_1 + 5y_2 - y_3 = (-3)(\tfrac{7}{12}) + (5)(\tfrac{5}{12}) - 0 = -\tfrac{21}{12} + \tfrac{25}{12} = \tfrac{1}{3} = g$$

The solution is, therefore

$$x_1 = \tfrac{2}{3}, \, x_2 = \tfrac{1}{3}, \qquad y_1 = \tfrac{7}{12}, \, y_2 = \tfrac{5}{12}, \, y_3 = 0, \qquad g = \tfrac{1}{3}$$

This checks with the solution of the same game obtained on page 538.

Iterative Methods

The iterative method is applicable when the graphical method cannot be applied and when the use of either the algebraic or matrix methods is not practical. It is a method that gives an approximate solution for the value of the game, and the method is such that one can approach the true value to any desired degree of accuracy. The method is not too satisfactory for finding optimum strategies as will be explained below.

We shall demonstrate the method by an example. Let the payoff matrix be that shown in Table 18-13. This matrix is equivalent to the matrix shown in Table 18-14.

We prepare Table 18-15 in 16 columns. Columns (1) and (16) are hypothetical move numbers. Columns (2), (3), (9), and (10) are actual choices. Note that:

Column (2) = Column (10) = A's choice

Column (3) = Column (9) = B's choice

Columns (4), (5), and (6) are payoffs to A corresponding to B's choice: column (3). Columns (11), (12), and (13) are payoffs to B corresponding to A's choice: column (10). Column (7) is A's best next choice

TABLE 18-13

	Plan	B		
	Plan	S	T	U
A	P	0	2	0
	Q	0	0	2
	R	3	0	0

TABLE 18-14

	Plan	A		
	Plan	P	Q	R
B	S	0	0	3
	T	2	0	0
	U	0	2	0

TABLE 18-15. PLANNING OF A AND B

	A's Planning						B's Planning						
Move	Choices		Payoff			Best Gain		Choices		Payoff			Least Loss		Move
n	A	B	P	Q	R	Plan	g/n	B	A	S	T	U	Plan	g/n	n
(1)	(2)	(3)	(4)	(5)	(6)	(7)	(8)	(9)	(10)	(11)	(12)	(13)	(14)	(15)	(16)
1	P	S	0	0	3	R	3/1	S	P	0	2	0	S	0/1	1
2	R	S	0	0	6	R	6/2	S	R	3	2	0	U	0/2	2
3	R	U	0	2	6	R	6/3	U	R	6	2	0	U	0/3	3
4	R	U	0	4	6	R	6/4	U	R	9	2	0	U	0/4	4
5	R	U	0	6	6	Q	6/5	U	R	12	2	0	U	0/5	5
6	Q	U	0	8	6	Q	8/6	U	Q	12	2	2	T	2/6	6
7	Q	T	2	8	6	Q	8/7	T	Q	12	2	4	T	2/7	7
8	Q	T	4	8	6	Q	8/8	T	Q	12	2	6	T	2/8	8
9	Q	T	6	8	6	Q	8/9	T	Q	12	2	8	T	2/9	9
10	Q	T	8	8	6	P	8/10	T	Q	12	2	10	T	2/10	10
11	P	T	10	8	6	P	10/11	T	P	12	4	10	T	4/11	11
12	P	T	12	8	6	P	12/12	T	P	12	6	10	T	6/12	12
13	P	T	14	8	6	P	14/13	T	P	12	8	10	T	8/13	13
14	P	T	16	8	6	P	16/14	T	P	12	10	10	T	10/14	14
15	P	T	18	8	6	P	18/15	T	P	12	12	10	U	10/15	15
16	P	U	18	10	6	P	18/16	U	P	12	14	10	U	10/16	16
17	P	U	18	12	6	P	18/17	U	P	12	16	10	U	10/17	17
18	P	U	18	14	6	P	18/18	U	P	12	18	10	U	10/18	18
19	P	U	18	16	6	P	18/19	U	P	12	20	10	U	10/19	19
20	P	U	18	18	6	P	18/20	U	P	12	22	10	U	10/20	20
21	P	U	18	20	6	Q	20/21	U	P	12	24	10	U	10/21	21
22	Q	U	18	22	6	Q	22/22	U	Q	12	24	12	S	12/22	22
23	Q	S	18	22	9	Q	22/23	S	Q	12	24	14	S	12/23	23
24	Q	S	18	22	12	Q	22/24	S	Q	12	24	16	S	12/24	24
25	Q	S	18	22	15	Q	22/25	S	Q	12	24	18	S	12/25	25
26	Q	S	18	22	18	Q	22/26	S	Q	12	24	20	S	12/26	26
27	Q	S	18	22	21	Q	22/27	S	Q	12	24	22	S	12/27	27

based on B's total choices: columns (4), (5), and (6). Column (14) is B's best next choice based on A's total choices: columns (11), (12), and (13). Note that

Column (7) in any move = Columns (2) and (10) in next move

Column (14) in any move = Columns (3) and (9) in next move

Column (8) is A's best total gain divided by the number of moves made. Column (15) is B's least total loss divided by the number of moves made. Columns (4), (5), and (6) in any move = columns (4), (5), and (6) in previous move plus result of B's present move. Columns (11), (12), and (13) in any move = columns (11), (12), and (13) in previous move plus result of A's present move. For example, for the tenth move

	P	Q	R		S	T	U	
(1)	(3)	(4)	(5)	(6)	(10)	(11)	(12)	(13)	(16)
9		6	8	6		12	2	8	9
	T = 2	0	0		Q = 0	0	2		
10		8	8	6		12	2	10	10

Whenever we have two equal choices choose the first in the order $P\,Q\,R$ or $S\,T\,U$.

Procedure

a. Start at choices P for A and S for B and fill in corresponding results in columns (1), (2), (3), (4), (5), (6), (9), (10), (11), (12), (13), and (16).

b. For A, R yields the highest gain. Therefore, put R in (7), and in move 2 put R in (2) and in (10). For B, either S or U is the best move; choose first, namely S. Then put S in (14) of move 1, and in (3) and (9) of move 2.

c. The highest total for A is now 3. Therefore, in (8) put 3/1. The lowest total for B is now 0. Therefore, in (15) put 0/1.

d. Add results of move 2 to move 1

(1)	(2)	(3)	(4)	(5)	(6)	(7)	(8)	(9)	(10)	(11)	(12)	(13)	(14)	(15)	(16)
1	P	S	0	0	3	R	3/1	S	P	0	2	0	S	0/1	1
		S = 0	0	3					R = 3	0	0				
2	R	S	0	0	6			S	R	3	2	0			

e. Repeat step b for move 2.

f. Repeat step c for move 2.

g. Repeat step d for move 2 and obtain data for move 3, etc.

We find the following results:

$$A\text{'s lowest gain is } 0.80 \text{ (move 10)}$$

$$B\text{'s highest loss is } 0.71 \text{ (move 14)}$$

Therefore

$$0.71 \leqq g \leqq 0.80$$

A played:	P	12 times	B played:	S	7 times
	Q	11 times		T	9 times
	R	4 times		U	11 times
		Total 27 times			Total 27 times

Therefore

$$x_1 \sim \tfrac{12}{27} = 0.44 \qquad y_1 \sim \tfrac{7}{27} = 0.26$$

$$x_2 \sim \tfrac{11}{27} = 0.41 \qquad y_2 \sim \tfrac{9}{27} = 0.33$$

$$x_3 \sim \tfrac{4}{27} = 0.15 \qquad y_3 \sim \tfrac{11}{27} = 0.41$$

These are approximate results and are based on 27 moves only. Higher accuracy may be obtained if we continue recording more moves.

The true solutions of the game may be found (with relative ease) by:

a. Algebraic method: take all relations as equalities.

b. Matrix method: take $B = \begin{bmatrix} 0 & 2 & 0 \\ 0 & 0 & 2 \\ 3 & 0 & 0 \end{bmatrix}$.

The results are

$$x_1 = 0.375 \qquad y_1 = 0.250$$

$$x_2 = 0.375 \qquad y_2 = 0.375$$

$$x_3 = 0.250 \qquad y_3 = 0.375$$

$$g = 0.75$$

It should be pointed out that while this method may be used to obtain the value of the game to any desired degree of accuracy, it may not be very useful in determining the optimum strategies. For further discussion of this point, see ref. 22, Chapter 4.

ZERO-SUM *n*-PERSON GAMES

Coalitions

The characteristics of an n-person zero-sum game are the values of the game for the various coalitions that can be formed by the players. If, for example, the players are A, B, C, and D, the coalitions shown in Table 18-16 can be formed.

TABLE 18-16. VARIOUS COALITIONS

	Group I	Versus	Group II
1	A, B, C		D
2	A, B, D		C
3	A, C, D		B
4	B, C, D		A
5	A, B		C, D
6	A, C		B, D
7	A, D		B, C

If the value of the game for A, B, C is g, then the value of the game for D is $-g$, since the game is zero-sum. Thus, in a four-person game we would have seven values, or characteristics, for the game.

Each value actually follows a solution of a rectangular game when the two coalitions are the two opponents. Let us find the characteristics of the following three-person zero-sum game:

Player A has two possible plans: P_1, P_2

Player B has two possible plans: Q_1, Q_2

Player C has two possible plans: R_1, R_2

The payoff is in terms of the choice of plans shown in Table 18-17.

TABLE 18-17. PAYOFF MATRIX

Choice			Payoff		
A	B	C	A	B	C
P_1	Q_1	R_1	2	1	-3
P_1	Q_1	R_2	-1	1	0
P_1	Q_2	R_1	-1	-2	3
P_1	Q_2	R_2	0	2	-2
P_2	Q_1	R_1	3	-2	-1
P_2	Q_1	R_2	-2	0	2
P_2	Q_2	R_1	0	-1	1
P_2	Q_2	R_2	-1	1	0

Thus we have three possible coalitions:

1.	A	*versus*	B, C
2.	B	*versus*	A, C
3.	C	*versus*	A, B

Let us solve each of the corresponding rectangular games.

1. A VERSUS B, C. The payoff matrix in A's terms is shown in Table 18-18. This matrix has a saddle point. Therefore, we have the

TABLE 18-18. A VERSUS B, C

		B, C			
	Plan	Q_1, R_1	Q_1, R_2	Q_2, R_1	Q_2, R_2
A	P_1	2	-1	-1	0
	P_2	3	-2	0	-1

solution for A versus B, C:
 A's best plan is P_1.
 B's and C's best combination of plans is Q_1, R_2.
 The value of the game for A is $g(A) = -1$.
 The value of the game for B, C is $g(BC) = 1$.
2. B VERSUS A, C. By inspection of Table 18-19 we find that A, C

TABLE 18-19. B VERSUS A, C

		A, C			
	Plan	P_1, R_1	P_1, R_2	P_2, R_1	P_2, R_2
B	Q_1	1	1	-2	0
	Q_2	-2	2	-1	1

will never play combination P_1, R_2 or P_2, R_2. The matrix is therefore the one shown in Table 18-20.

TABLE 18-20

			A, C	
			y	$1 - y$
		Plan	P_1, R_1	P_2, R_1
B	x	Q_1	1	-2
	$1 - x$	Q_2	-2	-1

Solving algebraically

$$x - 2(1 - x) = -2x - (1 - x)$$

Therefore, $x - 2 + 2x = -2x - 1 + x$; i.e., $x = \frac{1}{4}$

Therefore, $g(B) = \frac{1}{4} - 2(1 - \frac{1}{4}) = \frac{1}{4} - \frac{6}{4} = -\frac{5}{4}$

Similarly

$$y - 2(1 - y) = -2y - (1 - y);$$

i.e.

$$y - 2 + 2y = -2y - 1 + y, \text{ so that } y = \frac{1}{4}$$

The solution for B versus A, C is thus:

B's best strategy is to play plan Q_1 with a frequency of $\frac{1}{4}$ and plan Q_2 with a frequency of $\frac{3}{4}$.

A's and C's best strategy is for C to play R_1, and for A to play P_1 with a frequency of $\frac{1}{4}$ and P_2 with a frequency of $\frac{3}{4}$.

The value of the game for B is $g(B) = -1.25$.

The value of the game for A, C is $g(AC) = 1.25$.

3. C VERSUS A, B. By inspection of Table 18-21 we find that A, B will never play the combinations P_2, Q_1 or P_2, Q_2. Therefore

$$-3x + 0(1 - x) = 3x - 2(1 - x)$$

$$-3x = 3x - 2 + 2x, \text{ or } x = \frac{1}{4}$$

$$g(C) = -3(\frac{1}{4}) = -\frac{3}{4}$$

$$-3y + 3(1 - y) = 0 - 2(1 - y)$$

$$-3y + 3 - 3y = -2 + 2y, \text{ so that } y = \frac{5}{8}$$

TABLE 18-21. C versus A, B

		Plan	P_1, Q_1	P_1, Q_2	P_2, Q_1	P_2, Q_2
			y	$1 - y$	0	0
C	x	R_1	-3	3	-1	1
	$1 - x$	R_2	0	-2	2	0

The solution of C versus A, B is thus:

C's best strategy is to play R_1 with a frequency of $\frac{1}{4}$ and R_2 with a frequency of $\frac{3}{4}$.

A's and B's best strategy is for A to play P_1, and for B to play Q_1 with a frequency of $\frac{5}{8}$ and Q_2 with a frequency $\frac{3}{8}$.

The value of the game for C is $g(C) = -0.75$.

The value of the game for A, B is $g(AB) = 0.75$.

The characteristics of the game are therefore

$$g(A) = -1.00 \qquad g(BC) = 1.00$$

$$g(B) = -1.25 \qquad g(AC) = 1.25$$

$$g(C) = -0.75 \qquad g(AB) = 0.75$$

We shall not endeavor to outline a best strategy for players when no coalitions are formed. Our study has been based on the assumption that a player plans his strategy against the best his opponent can do. In this case the opponent of A, say, is the coalition B, C and we therefore have to study the best strategy for the coalition; and this we have done.

The discussion that follows is based on the classical approach of von Neumann and Morgenstern.[18] In a later section, we shall give their definition of a solution of an n-person zero-sum game where $n \geqq 3$.

Imputations

Consider the payoff matrix shown in Table 18-17. If A, B, and C choose P_1, Q_1 and R_1 respectively, then the payoff to the players will be

2, 1, and −3 respectively. C gains −3 (i.e., loses three units) and A and B gain 2 and 1 respectively.

Is it reasonable to expect that C will be willing to accept this result as his general payoff? Obviously not! We know, for a fact, that even when he plays alone against A and B in coalition, he can so choose his plans that he will expect to lose no more than 0.75 (see page 550). Similarly, A and B will never agree to any general payoff that will make them pay more than 1.00 and 1.25 respectively.

Thinking in this manner, a payment such as, say, $A = 0.50$, $B = −0.25$, and $C = −0.25$ could occur. In this case no player's payoff is less than what his value of the game is. Here $0.50 > −1.00$, $−0.25 > −1.25$, and $−0.25 > −0.75$. We call such a general payoff an *imputation*.

In mathematical symbols for an n-person game, let $g_1, g_2, g_3, \cdots, g_n$ be the value of the game for players $1, 2, \cdots, n$ respectively, when each plays alone against a coalition of all the others. Then $[x_1, x_2, \cdots, x_n]$ is an imputation, if

$$x_i \geqq g_i, \quad \text{for } i = 1, 2, \cdots, n$$

and $\qquad \Sigma x_i = 0 \qquad$ (since the game is zero-sum)

For the example given in the previous section, the following are imputations

(1) $[−0.75, 0.25, 0.50]$ (3) $[0.30, −0.80, 0.50]$

(2) $[2.00, −1.25, −0.75]$ (4) $[−0.15, 0.85, −0.70]$

but not these

(5) $[0.50, 0.50, −1.00]$ (since $−1.00 < −0.75$)

(6) $[0.26, −1.26, 1.00]$ (since $−1.26 < −1.25$)

Players B and C (not in coalition) will prefer (1) to (2) or (4) to (2). Players A and B (not in coalition) will prefer (4) to (1).

We use the word *dominance* to signify this preference. We say (1) *dominates* (2) with respect to players B and C. (4) dominates (1) with respect to players A and B.

The relation of dominance is used only for two players or more, and is written symbolically

$$[−0.75, 0.25, 0.50] \underset{B,C}{>} [2.00, −1.25, −0.75]$$

$$[−0.15, 0.85, −0.70] \underset{A,B}{>} [−0.75, 0.25, 0.50]$$

In general, for imputations

$$[y_1, y_2, \cdots, y_n] \underset{i=i_1, \; i_2, \; \cdots, \; i_r}{>} [x_1, x_2, \cdots, x_n]$$

provided

$$y_{i_k} > x_{i_k} \quad \text{for } k = 1, 2, \cdots, r$$

We also speak of one imputation dominating another. In this case we mean that there exists a group of players (two or more) for which the dominance exists. Thus (3) > (4) (the group is players A, C). But no relation of dominance exists between imputations (1) and (3), since no group of players exists for which dominance holds.

Definition of a Solution

We are now in a position to give the von Neumann and Morgenstern definition of an n-person zero-sum game. A solution of a given n-person game is a set of imputations such that:

1. No one imputation in the set dominates another imputation in the set.
2. Any other imputation is dominated by one of the imputations of the set.

For the example we have been discussing in this chapter, the solution will consist of the following set of three imputations

$$K = [0.50, \; 0.25, \; -0.75]$$
$$L = [0.50, \; -1.25, \; 0.75]$$
$$M = [-1.00, \; 0.25, \; 0.75]$$

inasmuch as they meet the two foregoing requirements. Compare them, for instance, with the imputations given in the preceding section

$$L > (1) \quad \text{with respect to } A, \; C$$
$$M > (2) \quad \text{with respect to } B, \; C$$
$$L > (3) \quad \text{with respect to } A, \; C$$
$$L > (4) \quad \text{with respect to } A, \; C$$

The following results can be shown to be true:

1. Every three-person game has a solution. The solution may consist of:

   a. A unique finite set of three imputations (as shown).
   b. An infinite set of imputations; there are infinitely many collections of such sets.

2. Every four-person game has a solution.

GAMES WITHOUT ZERO-SUM RESTRICTION

Imputations

The game with no zero-sum restriction is such that total payments to players at the end of a play need not necessarily be zero. Such games may represent economic situations, where the end result of, e.g., two competing companies need not end in one company's gain being exactly equal to the other company's loss. It is easiest to conceptualize n-person games with no zero-sum restrictions, as $n + 1$ zero-sum games, where the $n + 1$ player is a fictitious player, whose payoff is such as to cause the sum of all payments to be zero. In the case of the two competing companies, nature may be assumed to be the third player, thus making the game a zero-sum game. It should be noted, however, that the introduction of the $n + 1$ player to the given n-person game does not reduce the solution to one of an $n + 1$ person zero-sum game, since the $n + 1$ player is not free to join various possible coalitions. We therefore treat player $n + 1$ only from the point of view of his highest possible loss.

These considerations lead us to the following definitions of an imputation:

Let $g_1, g_2, \cdots, g_n$ be the value of the game for players $1, 2, \cdots, n$ respectively.

Let g_{n+1} be the value of the game for the fictitious player $n + 1$. Recall that the value of the game g for players $1, 2, \cdots, n$ going in coalition is

$$G = g(1, 2, \cdots, n) = -g_{n+1}$$

We define $[x_1, x_2, \cdots, x_n]$ as an imputation if

$$x_i \geqq g_i \qquad \text{for } i = 1, 2, \cdots, n$$

and

$$\sum_{i=1}^{n} x_i = G$$

For example: For a two-person game, let

$$g_1 = -1, \qquad g_2 = 0, \qquad g_{n+1} = g_3 = -3$$

Then $G = -g_3 = 3$ and the following are imputations

$$[1, 2], \qquad [-1, 4], \qquad [3, 0]$$

but not the following

$$[4, -1] \qquad \text{since } -1 < g_2 = 0$$

$$[1, 1] \qquad \text{since } 1 + 1 = 2 < G = 3$$

Note that this definition does not contradict the definition given for zero-sum games. For those games we have $G = 0$. The notion of dominance, too, is not affected by the new definition, as may be readily verified.

Solution of n-Person Games

The definition of a solution of a given n-person game with no zero-sum restriction is the same as for zero-sum games, namely:

A solution is a set of imputations (defined in this section) such that:

1. No one imputation in the set dominates another imputation in the set.

2. Any other imputation is dominated by one of the imputations of the set.

TABLE 18-22.   Two-Person Nonzero-Sum Game

Plan		Payoff	
A	B	A	B
P_1	Q_1	3	-1
P_1	Q_2	-1	1
P_2	Q_1	1	0
P_2	Q_2	-2	-1

EXAMPLE I.   Consider the two-person nonzero-sum game shown in Table 18-22. For player A the payoff matrix is given in the following diagram.

		Q_1	Q_2
A	P_1	3	-1
	P_2	1	-2

This matrix has a saddle point and we have

$$g(A) = -1$$

For player B the payoff matrix is given in the following diagram.

			P_1	P_2
B	x	Q_1	-1	0
	$1 - x$	Q_2	1	-1

The game has no saddle point. Solving we have

$$x(-1) + (1 - x)(1) = x(0) + (1 - x)(-1)$$

$$-x + 1 - x = -1 + x, \qquad 2 = 3x, \qquad x = \tfrac{2}{3}$$

Therefore $\qquad g(B) = \tfrac{2}{3}(-1) + (\tfrac{1}{3})1 = -\tfrac{2}{3} + \tfrac{1}{3} = -\tfrac{1}{3}$

$$g(B) = -\tfrac{1}{3}$$

For the $n + 1$ player, the payoff matrix will be:

	P_1, Q_1	P_1, Q_2	P_2, Q_1	P_2, Q_2
C	-2	0	-1	3

This matrix again has a saddle point. Therefore

$$g(C) = -2, \qquad G = 2$$

Thus the solution of the game is given by any imputation $[x_1, x_2]$ such that

$$x_1 \geqq -1$$

$$x_2 \geqq -\tfrac{1}{3}$$

$$x_1 + x_2 = 2$$

EXAMPLE II. Let the values of the game for a three-person non-zero-sum game be

$$g(A) = 0, \qquad g(B) = -1, \qquad g(C) = -2, \qquad G = 1$$

A solution of the game can be found from geometrical considerations of Fig. 18-5, which is self-explanatory after a close study.

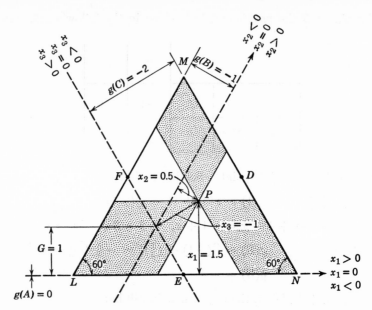

Fig. 18-5. Drawing for three-person nonzero-sum game.

Any point in the triangle LMN is an imputation, e.g.,

$$P = [1.5, 0.5, -1]$$

is an imputation since

$$x_1 = 1.5 > 0 = g(A)$$

$$x_2 = 0.5 > -1 = g(B)$$

$$x_3 = -1 > -2 = g(C)$$

$$\Sigma x_i = x_1 + x_2 + x_3 = 1.5 + 0.5 - 1 = 1 = G$$

Note that any point (= imputation) in the dotted area is dominated by P, and that any point in the undotted area dominates P.

A solution of the game is given by points D, E, and F

$$D = [2, 1, -2], \qquad E = [0, 1, 0], \qquad F = [2, -1, 0]$$

It can be readily verified that these imputations do not dominate one another, and that every other imputation is dominated by one of the imputations D, E, or F.

CONCLUSION

In the last few years a number of books have appeared on the subject of the theory of games.

McKinsey, in his *Introduction to the Theory of Games*,[13] offers an excellent mathematical treatment of the general theory, with major emphasis on two-person games. He also discusses the relationship of the theory of games to linear programming and statistical inference. This work contains a rather complete and up-to-date bibliography of game theory. Additionally, in the closing chapter (18) McKinsey discusses a number of the unsolved problems in this field.

Blackwell and Girshick [1] have written a text in this field "intended primarily as a textbook in decision theory for first-year graduate students in statistics" and requiring more mathematical maturity than the previously cited work of von Neumann and Morgenstern.* Although the discussion of game theory is only a means to an end, namely, statistical decision theory, their work represents an important step forward in enabling one to apply these principles to industrial problems. (This work also contains an excellent bibliography.)

Some of the most important basic research developments in the field of game theory are presented in the two volumes edited by Kuhn and Tucker.[7-8] Additional contributions have been made through the many reports issued from the RAND Corporation by Bellman, Bohnenblust, Dresher, Harris, Helmer, Karlin, Shapley, Snow, and others. The important formal relationship between linear programming and the theory of games is shown by Dantzig.[5]

Very little has been accomplished by way of applying the theory. Military applications have been referred to but have not been made public. Papers, such as McDonald's,[9] Shubik's,[20] and Caywood and Thomas',[3] do not deal with actual industrial applications but rather explore the possibility of so applying it.

In conclusion, it is worth quoting Williams'[22] succinct appraisal of the theory of games:

> While there are specific applications today, despite the current limitations of the theory, perhaps its greatest contribution so far has been an intangible one: the general orientation given to people who are faced with overcomplex problems. Even though these problems are not strictly solvable —certainly at the moment and probably for the indefinite future—it helps to have a framework in which to work on them. The concept of a strategy,

---

* An early elementary nonmathematical exposition of von Neumann's theory is given by McDonald.[11] Next in order of mathematical sophistication is the very witty and lucid work of Williams.[22]

the distinctions among players, the role of chance events, the notion of matrix representations of the payoffs, the concepts of pure and mixed strategies, and so on give valuable orientation to persons who must think about complicated conflict situations. (p. 217)

BIBLIOGRAPHY

1. Blackwell, D., and Girshick, M. A., *Theory of Games and Statistical Decisions*, John Wiley & Sons, New York, 1954.
2. Brown, G. W., "Iterative Solution of Games by Fictitious Play," Chap. XXIV in T. C. Koopmans (ed.), *Activity Analysis of Production and Allocation*, Cowles Commission Monograph No. 13, John Wiley & Sons, New York, 1951.
3. Caywood, T. E., and Thomas, C. J., "Applications of Game Theory in Fighter Versus Bomber Combat," *J. Opns. Res. Soc. Am.*, *3*, no. 4, 402–411 (1955).
4. Cushen, W. E., "Operational Gaming," in J. F. McCloskey and J. M. Coppinger (eds.), *Operations Research for Management II*, The Johns Hopkins Press, Baltimore, 1956.
5. Dantzig, G. B., "A Proof of the Equivalence of the Programming Problem and the Game Problem," Chap. XX in ref. 2.
6. Dresher, M., "Games of Strategy," *Math. Mag.*, *25*, 93–99 (1951).
7. Kuhn, H. W., and Tucker, A. W. (eds.), *Contributions to the Theory of Games I*, Annals of Mathematics Study No. 24, Princeton University Press, Princeton, 1950.
8. ———, *Contributions to the Theory of Games II*, Annals of Mathematics Study No. 28, Princeton University Press, Princeton, 1953.
9. McDonald, John, "Applications of Game Theory in Business and Industry," Games Symposium of the American Association for the Advancement of Science, St. Louis, Dec. 29, 1952.
10. ———, "Poker: An American Game," *Fortune, 37*, 128–131 and 181–187 (1948).
11. ———, *Strategy in Poker, Business, and War*, W. W. Norton and Co., New York, 1950.
12. ———, "The Theory of Strategy," *Fortune, 38*, 100–110 (1949).
13. McKinsey, J. C. C., *Introduction to the Theory of Games*, McGraw-Hill Book Co., New York, 1952.
14. Morgenstern, O., "The Theory of Games," *Sci. Amer.*, *180*, 22–25, (1949).
15. Nash, J. F., "Equilibrium Points in n-Person Games," *Proc. Nat. Acad. Sci.*, *36*, 48–49 (1950).
16. ———, "Non-Cooperative Games," *Ann. Math.*, *54*, 286–295 (1951).
17. Neumann, J. von, "Zur Theorie der Gesellshaftsspiele," *Math. Ann.*, *100*, 295–320 (1928).
18. ———, and Morgenstern, O., *Theory of Games and Economic Behavior*, Princeton University Press, Princeton, 3rd ed., 1953.
19. Paxson, E. W., "Recent Developments in the Mathematical Theory of Games," *Econometrica*, 17, 72–73 (1949).
20. Shubik, Martin, "The Uses of Game Theory in Management Science," *Mgmt. Sci.*, *2*, no. 1, 40–54 (1955).
21. Stone, R., "The Theory of Games," *Econ. J.*, *58*, 185–201 (1948).
22. Williams, J. D., *The Compleat Strategyst*, McGraw-Hill Book Co., New York, 1954.

Chapter 19

Bidding Models

INTRODUCTION

Bidding for the rights to property or for the opportunity to render service is a relatively pure type of competition. Opposing bidders compete for rights or opportunities under rules established by the government and/or the party who puts the rights or opportunities up for bid. Most businesses are involved in bidding in one form or another: bidding for contracts, for concessions, for licenses to use a patent, etc. In fact, pricing of products or services can be conceived of as bidding for customers' dollars.

This aspect of competitive behavior has not been given much attention by Operations Researchers. Potentialities in this area have not generally been recognized. Unfortunately, details of the successful applications of O.R. to the development of bidding strategies cannot be made public for reasons of industrial security. Consequently, any discussion of such strategies must either be abstract or must conceal the real problem by paraphrasing it.

Some of the simpler bidding problems can be solved by game theory techniques. Situations where the number of bidders becomes large and may, in fact, be unknown cannot as yet be handled in this manner. These situations can be attacked by analytic methods, some of which will be discussed in this chapter. Even the simpler bidding problems are more easily handled by analytic methods introduced here than by the matrix approach of standard game theory.

There are two kinds of competitive bidding situations that occur. One is closed bidding in which two or more bidders submit independent

560 Introduction to Operations Research

bids for the rights to property or to render service. In most cases only one bid per competitor is allowed and the judge accepts the highest or lowest bid as dictated by the rules. The other kind of bidding is auction, or open, bidding in which two or more bidders continue to bid openly on an item of value until nobody is willing to increase the bid. The last bid is then considered the winning bid.

Two relatively simple bidding situations will be considered by way of introduction to the construction of closed and auction bidding models and then a more complicated and practical situation involving closed bids by a number of bidders on a contract will be discussed.

AUCTION BIDDING: TWO BIDDERS AND TWO ITEMS

First, let us consider the simple situation where two items of known values, V_1 and V_2, are to be auctioned, one at a time. Let us assume there are only two bidders, A and B, who have S_A and S_B dollars, respectively, available for bidding. Assume, also, that S_A and S_B are each smaller than $V_1 + V_2$ and $\frac{1}{2} < (S_A/S_B) < 2$. We assume also that A knows the amount of money B has available.* Bidder A wishes to know at what point he should stop bidding for the first item.

To solve this problem, A must first decide what his objective should be in the bidding. The most obvious objective is to maximize his return. It is also possible that A may have as his objective the minimization of B's return. This objective can be stated by A as maximizing the net *difference* between A's return and B's return. *It is interesting to note that these two objectives will lead to different optimum policies.* In this first example we will consider A's objective to be the maximization of the *difference*, $R_A - R_B$, where R_A is A's return and R_B is B's return.

Maximizing Difference in Return

Suppose B has bid X dollars on the first of the two items up for sale and the smallest increment of bid is Δ. A must decide whether he should bid $X + \Delta$ or let B win with the bid X. A reasons as follows:

1. If A lets B win the first item for X dollars, B will then have $S_B - X$ dollars remaining for the second item. Since $S_A > S_B - X$,†

---

* Since we are determining an optimum strategy for A, we need not be concerned as to whether B has knowledge of S_A.

† This follows from the assumptions that $\frac{1}{2} < S_A/S_B < 2$ and A and B are both intelligent players.

then A is certain to be able to win the second item for $S_B - X + \Delta$. Then, if A lets B win the first item for X

$$R_B = V_1 - X \tag{1}$$

$$R_A = V_2 - (S_B - X + \Delta) \tag{2}$$

The difference between A's return and B's return is

$$(V_2 - S_B + X - \Delta) - (V_1 - X)$$

2. If A bids $X + \Delta$ and B lets him win at this bid

$$R_A = V_1 - (X + \Delta) \tag{3}$$

$$R_B = V_2 - [S_A - (X + \Delta) + \Delta] \tag{4}$$

Since A will have only $S_A - (X + \Delta)$ after the first sale, B will win the second bid for $S_A - (X + \Delta) + \Delta$, and the difference between A's return and B's return is

$$R_A - R_B = [V_1 - (X + \Delta)] - (V_2 - S_A + X) \tag{5}$$

Thus A will let B have the first item for X dollars if the difference between A's return and B's return is greater than the difference which will result if A goes one increment higher and bids $X + \Delta$. The condition that A bids $X + \Delta$ is, then

$$(V_2 - S_B + X - \Delta) - (V_1 - X) \leqq (V_1 - X - \Delta)$$
$$- (V_2 - S_A + X) \tag{6}$$

or $\qquad\qquad 4X \leqq 2V_1 - 2V_2 + S_A + S_B$

That is, A bids $X + \Delta$ if

$$X \leqq \frac{2(V_1 - V_2) + (S_A + S_B)}{4} \tag{7}$$

In this situation, if B is intelligent and bids correctly, A will be forced up to the value of X given by

$$X = \frac{2(V_1 - V_2) + (S_A + S_B)}{4} \tag{8}$$

The difference between A's return and B's return is then found by substituting the value of X in eq. 8 into eq. 5, which gives

$$R_A - R_B = \frac{S_A - S_B}{2} - \Delta \tag{9}$$

Thus, as $\Delta \rightarrow 0$, the difference in returns is independent of the values being bid on and depends only on the initial capital difference between the two bidders. A's individual return will be

$$R_A = \frac{V_1 + V_2}{2} - \frac{(S_A + S_B)}{4} - \Delta \qquad (10)$$

To illustrate these results, suppose A has \$100 and B has \$110 available for bidding, and that A and B each know how much the other has available. Now suppose B has bid \$60 on the first of the two items. A must then decide whether or not to bid \$61.

According to inequation 7, A should bid \$61 if

$$\$60 \leq \frac{2(V_1 - V_2) + (\$100 + \$110)}{4}$$

Let us assume that A values item 1 at \$75 and item 2 at \$100. Then

$$\frac{2(\$75 - \$100) + (\$100 + \$110)}{4} = \$40 < \$60$$

Therefore, A should not bid more than \$40 for item 1. Consequently, A should let B have item 1 for \$60 and he is assured of getting item 2 for no more than (\$110 − \$60 + \$1), or \$51.

According to A's evaluation of the items, then, B's net gain would be (\$75 − \$60) or \$15. A's net gain would be (\$100 − \$51), or \$49. A would then come out better than B by the amount (\$49 − \$15), or \$34.

If, however, A bid \$61 for item 1 and won, his net gain would be (\$75 − \$61), or \$14, and B could get item 2 for (\$100 − \$61 + \$1), or \$40. B's net gain would be (\$100 − \$40), or \$60, and his advantage over A would be (\$60 − \$14), or \$46.

It should be noted that, if B places different values on the items than A does, the relative advantage of the alternatives would not be the same for him.

Maximizing Expected Return

Let us now consider the case where A has as his objective the maximization of his own expected return. A will now bid $X + \Delta$ for the first item when his expected return is greater than or equal to his expected return if he lets B win the first item for X; i.e., when

$$V_1 - (X + \Delta) \geq V_2 - (S_B - X + \Delta) \qquad (11)$$

or, equivalently, when

$$X \leq \frac{V_1 - V_2 + S_B}{2} \qquad (12)$$

Similarly B, in bidding to maximize his expected return, will bid $X + \Delta$ if

$$X \leqq \frac{V_1 - V_2 + S_A}{2} \qquad (13)$$

If A and B bid correctly, the final bid will be Δ plus the smaller of either

$$\frac{V_1 - V_2 + S_B}{2} \qquad \text{or} \qquad \frac{V_1 - V_2 + S_A}{2}$$

If $S_A > S_B$, A's return under this objective is found by substituting $(V_1 - V_2 + S_B)/2$ for X in the left side of inequation 11. This yields

$$R_A = \frac{V_1 + V_2 - S_B}{2} - \Delta, \qquad (S_A \geqq S_B) \qquad (14)$$

If $S_A < S_B$, A's return is found by substituting $(V_1 - V_2 + S_A)/2$ for X in the left side of inequation 11. This yields

$$R_A = \frac{V_1 + V_2 - S_A}{2} - \Delta, \qquad (S_A \leqq S_B) \qquad (15)$$

Note that A's return (as given by either eq. 14 or 15) using the objective of maximizing his return is always greater than his return (as given by eq. 9) when the objective is to maximize the difference between A's return and B's return.

Now let us consider the same situation as was described in the last section, except that A's objective is to maximize his own expected return; i.e., he has no direct concern with how B makes out. It was shown in the previous discussion that if B got item 1 for $60 and A obtained item 2 for $51, A's return was ($100 − $51), or $49. If A had taken item 1 for $61 his return would have been ($75 − $61), or $14. The best choice is clear in terms of maximum return, and, in this case, the decision is the same as it was before.

Using inequation 12, we can determine that A should not bid more than $42.50 for item 1, since

$$\frac{\$75 - \$100 + \$110}{2} = \$42.50$$

On the other hand, if maximization of difference in return is the objective, A should not bid more than $40.

CLOSED BIDDING: TWO BIDDERS AND TWO ITEMS

This situation is similar to the previous one except that the two items of value, V_1 and V_2, are to be bid on simultaneously by two bidders, A and B, each of whom submits two closed bids. To make this example very simple, we will suppose that A and B each have S dollars available for both items and $S < (V_1 + V_2)$. In the event of a tie, we shall assume that a coin flip decides the winner.

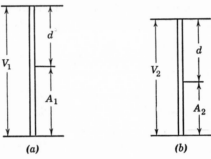

(a)   *(b)*

Fig. 19-1.   (*a*) Item 1.   (*b*) Item 2.

The correct strategy can be found by examining Fig. 19-1. A's optimum bids for items 1 and 2, A_1 and A_2 respectively, are found by setting bids A_1 and A_2 such that the profit will be the same for both items if the bids are successful. Therefore, if we let d represent the total profit associated with a successful bid

$$d = \frac{V_1 + V_2 - S}{2} \tag{16}$$

Hence

$$A_1 = V_1 - d = \frac{V_1 - V_2 + S}{2}, \qquad (V_1 - V_2 + S \geqq 0) \tag{17}$$

$$A_2 = V_2 - d = \frac{V_2 - V_1 + S}{2}, \qquad (V_2 - V_1 + S \geqq 0) \tag{18}$$

If either eq. 17 or 18 results in A_1 or A_2 being negative, the solution is then given by changing the "negative" bid to zero and bidding all available funds on the other item.

This is also B's optimum strategy. If A and B both adopt the optimum strategy, their bids will be equal and the results will be determined by coin flipping. The expected return for both A and B will then be equal to d, as given in eq. 16.

Now if B deviates from this strategy by bidding, for example, $V_1 - d + \delta$ for item 1 and $V_2 - d - \delta$ for item 2, A will win item 2 and B will win item 1. But the gains will be different.

$$B\text{'s return} = V_1 - (V_1 - d + \delta) = d - \delta \qquad (19)$$

$$A\text{'s return} = V_2 - (V_2 - d) = d \qquad (20)$$

A's return is greater than B's by the amount δ. Thus by adopting the optimum strategy A_1 and A_2, A obtains a return of *at least* d and prevents B's return from exceeding d.

Suppose, for example, that in the previous illustration both A and B had \$100 available. Then, according to eq. 17, the amount A should bid on item 1 would be

$$A_1 = \frac{\$75 - \$100 + \$100}{2} = \$37.50$$

and the amount he should bid on item 2 would be

$$A_2 = \frac{\$100 - \$75 + \$100}{2} = \$62.50$$

His profit in both cases (should he win) would be \$37.50; i.e., (\$75 − \$37.50) and (\$100 − \$62.50). The same strategy is best for both B and A. Then, if both knew this, the acquisition of items would depend on the toss of a coin and be a matter of chance.

If the initial amounts become different and the number of items increases, the problem becomes more complicated, but best strategies can still be found by analytic means.

CLOSED BIDDING: NUMBER OF BIDDERS, LARGE AND NOT KNOWN EXACTLY

Let us now discuss an example closer to reality. Consider a case where a government agency invites a large number of companies within the same industry to bid for contracts. Each company interested in obtaining a contract must submit a closed bid and the company submitting the lowest bid gets the contract. In this situation, the number of competitors who will actually submit bids on each contract may be unknown. We shall first discuss the problem of bidding on one contract and then extend this to the case where several contracts are bid for simultaneously.

For a company to adopt any strategy, it is essential that its objective in the bidding be clearly defined. In this case, there are many possible objectives and different strategies will result from different objectives.

1. The most likely objective is to maximize total expected profit.
2. A second objective may be to gain at least a certain percentage of investment.
3. Another possibility is to minimize expected losses.
4. An objective which generally is found in a true competitive situation is to minimize profits of competitors. A competitor making a great deal of money will generally become a stronger competitor and, in the long run, hurt one's company.
5. It may be important to obtain the contract, even at a loss, in order to keep production going.

These, and other objectives, as well as combinations of objectives, are found in bidding problems. Each problem will have a different solution depending on the objectives of the bidding company. In the example being discussed, we shall assume that the company's sole objective is to maximize total expected profit. This is certainly one of the most common objectives and one of the simplest to handle in a bidding situation of this type.

The General Model

Let C = the estimated cost of fulfilling the contract. The actual cost determined after completion of the job will, of course, differ from

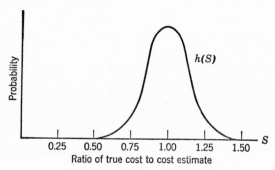

Fig. 19-2.   Reliability of cost estimate.

the estimated cost. It is important, therefore, to determine the bias and variability of the cost estimate. This can be done by studying past data on estimates and actual costs. The distribution of the true cost as a fraction of the estimated cost can then be obtained. (See Fig. 19-2.)

Let $h(S)\,dS$ = the probability of the ratio of the true cost to the estimated cost being between S and $S + dS$.

Let x = the amount bid for the contract. Then if a bid of x wins, the profit will ultimately be $x - SC$.

Now let $P(x)$ = the probability that a bid of x will be lowest and win the contract. Then the expected profit $E(x)$ if a bid of x is made will be

$$E(x) = \int_0^\infty P(x)(x - SC)h(S)\,dS \tag{21}$$

The value of x for which this expected profit is maximum is the value of x which should be bid. Since $P(x)$ is independent of S and

$$\int_0^\infty h(S)\,dS = 1$$

eq. 21 becomes

$$E(x) = P(x)(x - C') \tag{22}$$

where

$$C' = C \int_0^\infty Sh(S)\,dS = \text{estimated cost corrected for bias}$$

In general, $E(x)$ will look something like the curve in Fig. 19-3. That bid which maximizes expected profit is then easily found from the maximum of the expected profit curve.

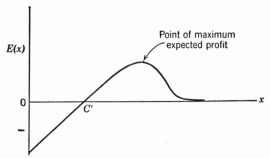

Fig. 19-3. **Expected profit versus amount bid.**

Once the expected profit curve is determined it is relatively simple to find the bid which maximizes profit. The difficulty in determining the expected profit lies in determining $P(x)$, the probability of winning as a function of the amount bid.

Probability of Winning

One way of determining the probability of winning with a given bid lies in studying previous bidding data. Presumably the results of previous bidding on contracts are always announced and from these announced bids the "bidding patterns" of potential competitors may be studied. Suppose we are studying competitor A. On every previous contract on which A bid and on which our company made a cost estimate, we take the ratio of A's bid to our cost estimate. If there are enough previous contracts on which A has bid, a pattern of A's bidding behavior relative to our cost estimates will emerge. These patterns can be made for all potential competitors. A few examples are shown in Fig. 19-4.

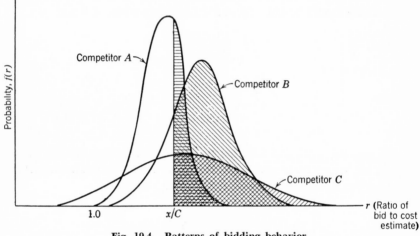

Fig. 19-4. Patterns of bidding behavior.

Now if we know exactly which competitors are going to submit bids, the probability of winning for a given bid is relatively easy to compute. Assuming that each competitor is likely to bid as he has done in the past, which is the best assumption in the absence of additional information, the probability of being lower than competitor A by bidding x is the area to the right of the ratio x/C on A's bidding distribution curve. Similarly, the probability of being lower than B is the area to the right of the ratio x/C on B's distribution curve. The probability of being the lowest bidder with a bid of x, when the competitors are known, is simply the product of the probabilities of defeating each of the known competitors.

If it is not known exactly how many competitors will submit bids, the problem becomes more difficult. In this case, it is necessary to use the concept of an "average" bidder. The bidding distribution of the "average" bidder is found by combining all previous ratios of an opposition bid to our cost estimate and obtaining one distribution function. See Fig. 19-5.

Let $f(r)$ = the probability density function of the ratio of the average bidder's bid to our cost estimate. Then the probability of a bid x being lower than one average bidder equals $\int_{x/C}^{\infty} f(r)\, dr$. The probability of being lower than k average bidders is then $\left[\int_{x/C}^{\infty} f(r)\, dr\right]^k$.

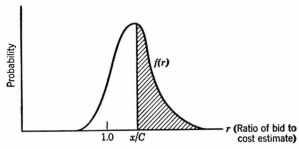

Fig. 19-5. **Bidding pattern of average bidder.**

Now let us assume that we can determine the probability of k bidders submitting bids. Then, if this probability is $g(k)$, the probability $P(x)$ of a bid x being the lowest bid becomes

$$P(x) = \sum_{k=0}^{\infty} \left\{ g(k) \left[\int_{x/C}^{\infty} f(r)\, dr \right]^k \right\} \tag{23}$$

Now $f(r)$ can be found by fitting a curve to the available data. A gamma distribution will frequently furnish a good fit to data of this sort. Where this is so

$$f(r) = \frac{a^{(b+1)}}{b!}\, r^b e^{-ar} \tag{24}$$

where a and b are constants obtained from the curve fitting the frequency data to the gamma distribution.

It is also reasonable to assume that the number of bidders might have a Poisson distribution. That is, if λ is the estimated number of bidders, then

$$g(k) = \frac{\lambda^k e^{-\lambda}}{k!} \tag{25}$$

Both of these distributions can be tested to determine whether they agree with the past data. Assuming that we have a good way of estimating λ, we find

$$P(x) = e^{-\lambda} \sum_{k=0}^{\infty} \left\{ \frac{1}{k!} \left[\lambda \left(\int_{x/C}^{\infty} \frac{a^{b+1}}{b!} r^b e^{-ar} \, dr \right) \right]^k \right\} \tag{26}$$

$$= e^{-\lambda} \exp \left[\lambda \left(\int_{x/C}^{\infty} \frac{a^{b+1}}{b!} r^b e^{-ar} \, dr \right) \right] \tag{27}$$

$$= \exp \left\{ -\lambda \left[1 - \sum_{i=0}^{b} \frac{1}{i!} \left(\frac{ax}{C} \right)^i e^{-\frac{ax}{C}} \right] \right\} \tag{28}$$

The summation is nothing more than the cumulative of the Poisson distribution which is easily found from tables.

Determination of Optimum Bid

The expected profit E.P. now becomes

$$\text{E.P.} = (x - C')P(x) = (x - C') \exp \left\{ -\lambda \left[1 - \sum_{i=0}^{b} \frac{1}{i!} \left(\frac{ax}{C} \right)^i e^{-\frac{ax}{C}} \right] \right\}$$
$$\tag{29}$$

where C' is as defined after eq. 22.

A graph of expected return plotted against amount bid can now be prepared and the optimum value for x is easily determined (Fig. 19-3).

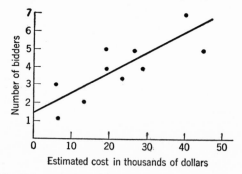

Fig. 19-6. **Number of bidders versus estimated cost.**

An analytic solution for the maximum can be computed but is not available in closed form. The important parameters in this method of determining the optimum bid are the estimated cost and the expected number of bidders. The estimated cost has been discussed previously. There are several possible methods of getting an estimated number of bidders.

In many cases information is available to a company about the intentions of its competitors. This information combined with the experience of the executives of the company may give a good estimate of the number of bidders.

The size of the contract may have some correlation with the number of bidders. Thus, a regression of the number of bidders can be plotted against our cost estimates on previous bids. If this is significant, our cost estimate can be used to estimate the number of bidders from the regression equation.

For example, a study of the number of bidders versus cost estimates might be that of Fig. 19-6. A linear regression is made on the data and the line in the figure gives a satisfactory fit. This line is then used to estimate the number of bidders from a knowledge of the estimated cost.

Simultaneous Bidding on More Than One Contract

A case of considerable interest arises when the government is accepting bids on more than one contract simultaneously. Each company must then decide on which contracts it should bid and how much it should bid for each contract. The problem may be further complicated by restrictions placed on each company's bidding. These restrictions may be self-imposed or imposed by the government. Examples of a few possible restrictions are as follows:

1. The company cannot bid for contracts such that the total cost estimates of the contracts bid on exceed a fixed amount.

2. The company cannot obtain more than a fixed number of contracts.

3. The company must have a certain confidence of obtaining at least a fixed number of contracts.

4. The company's total amount bid cannot exceed a fixed amount.

It is apparent that each restriction or combination of restrictions will lead to different sets of bids. The technique of solving the problem will depend on the particular restrictions. To illustrate the general ideas underlying the solution of these problems, we will assume restriction 4 and solve the problem of bidding on n simultaneous contracts. This restriction may arise in several ways. The government may not wish any single company to obtain too much of the business and may place an upper limit L on the total amount each company may bid. Or perhaps because of financing difficulties or capacity limitations the restriction may be self-imposed by the management. Thus, if x_i is the company's bid on the ith contract, we wish to maximize total expected profit subject to

$$x_1 + x_2 + \cdots + x_i + \cdots + x_n \leq L \qquad (30)$$

To solve this problem, we proceed by treating *each* contract as shown in the preceding section to obtain the expected return curve. A graphical interpretation of this knowledge is shown in Fig. 19-7 for three contracts.

For each contract, construct a table with three columns; see Table 19-1. The first column is the *amount of the bid*. The amount of bid column should increase in even increments of reasonable size from the estimated cost of the contract to the point where the expected profit

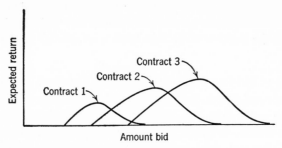

Fig. 19-7.   Expected return curves.

becomes zero. The second column lists the *expected profit on the contract for the amount bid*. The third column gives the *change in expected profit by adding an increment of bid*. The tables will look like Table 19-1.

Let us assume the situation represented in Table 19-1 (in which we are interested in three contracts) and let us further assume that our

TABLE 19-1.   How to Obtain Optimum Set of Bids Within
Restrictions

	Contract 1			Contract 2			Contract 3	
Amount Bid	Expected Profit	Change in Expected Profit	Amount Bid	Expected Profit	Change in Expected Profit	Amount Bid	Expected Profit	Change in Expected Profit
$100,000	0		$100,000			$100,000		
105,000	$ 3,000	+$3000	105,000			105,000		
110,000	5,500	+ 2500	110,000			110,000		
115,000	7,500	+ 2000	115,000			115,000		
120,000	9,000	+ 1500	120,000	0		120,000		
125,000	9,900	+ 900	125,000	$2000	+$2000	125,000		
130,000	10,200	+ 300	130,000	3700	+ 1700	130,000		
135,000	9,900	− 300	135,000	5100	+ 1400	135,000		
140,000	9,000	− 900	140,000	6100	+ 1000	140,000		
145,000	7,500	− 1500	145,000	6700	+ 600	145,000		
150,000	5,500	− 2000	150,000	6800	+ 100	150,000	0	
155,000	3,100	− 2400	155,000	6400	− 400	155,000	$ 3,000	+$3000
160,000	300	− 2800	160,000	5600	− 800	160,000	5,500	+ 2500
165,000	0	− 300	165,000	4400	− 1200	165,000	7,500	+ 2000
170,000	0		170,000	2900	− 1500	170,000	9,000	+ 1500
175,000	0		175,000	1100	− 1800	175,000	10,000	+ 1000
180,000	0		180,000	0	− 1100	180,000	10,400	+ 400
185,000	0		185,000	0		185,000	10,200	− 200
190,000	0		190,000	0		190,000	9,400	− 800
195,000	0		195,000	0		195,000	8,000	− 1400
200,000	0		200,000	0		200,000	6,000	− 2000
205,000	0		205,000	0		205,000	3,500	− 2500
210,000	0		210,000	0		210,000	500	− 3000
215,000	0		215,000	0		215,000	0	− 500

upper bidding limit has been set at $440,000. The first step is to place our bids at the optimum point for each contract. In this case that means bids of $130,000 for contract 1, $150,000 for contract 2, and $180,000 for contract 3. The sum of these bids is $460,000. This means we must reduce the sum of the bids by $20,000. Examination of the incremental changes in expected profit given in the third column enables us to determine which bids should be reduced so as to get within the allowed limit. We see that the first $5000 reduction in bid should be made on contract 2, since this reduces expected profit by only $100 while $5000 reductions on contracts 1 and 3 result in profit deductions of $300 and $400 respectively.

Proceeding in this manner, we eventually obtain the optimum set of bids permitted with the restriction. The optimum set of bids for Table 19-1 is $125,000 for contract 1, $140,000 for contract 2, and $175,000 for contract 3.

Essentially the problem considered is one of nonlinear programming since the expected profits on each contract are nonlinear functions of the amount bid. The method of solution is relatively simple and quick, even when bidding on a large number of contracts.

PART
IX

TESTING, CONTROL,

AND

IMPLEMENTATION

In Parts IV through VIII we have discussed various models which have proved useful in conducting O.R. studies. We now turn to the problems of 1. testing the adequacy of models and the solutions derived from them, 2. designing procedures for controlling the solution where it is used, and 3. implementing the solution (i.e., putting it to work). The fact that model-construction is considered first and testing, control, and implementation second does not imply that researchers must follow this pattern. Model construction and testing may, and frequently do, go on simultaneously. Consideration of how the solution can and will be used may affect the form and complexity of the model which is developed and the solution derived from it.

Even a solution which is tried and true remains optimal only as long as the system for which it was developed does not change in any significant way. Few systems studied by O.R. remain this stable. Consequently, a control system is required for solutions which are used over a period of time so that significant changes can be detected and adjustments in the solution which are required by these changes can be made.

Finally, the solution must be translated into action. This implementation phase of the research can "make or break" a project. Consequently, it should be as carefully planned and controlled as possible.

Chapter 20

Data for Model Testing

INTRODUCTION

In this chapter we are concerned with problems associated with gathering the evidence to test the models which have been discussed in other parts of this book. This topic is so large that it would be foolish to attempt to accomplish any sort of adequate coverage in one chapter. Instead, we will cite relevant literature.

The type of evidence one uses to test a model depends very much on the kind of test one has in mind. In testing a model we ask, "What are the possible ways in which a model can fail to represent reality adequately and hence lose some of its potential usefulness?" This is itself an intricate question, the answer to which depends on the concept of an objective test. For present purposes, we can suggest four ways in which one may question the adequacy of a model:

1. The model may assert a dependence of the effectiveness of the system (the dependent variable) on one or more (independent) variables which, as a matter of fact, do *not* affect the system's effectiveness. That is, the model may fail by including variables which are not pertinent. For example, the model may express the average number of sales calls required to convert a prospect into an account as a function of the size of the account. In at least one situation these two variables were found to have no relationship.

2. The model may *fail to include* a variable which does have a significant effect on the system's effectiveness. For instance, a model may not express the dependence of the total cost of production on

costs of changes in the size of the work force in a situation where these costs are critical.

3. The model may inaccurately express the actual relationship which exists between the measure of effectiveness (E) and one or more of the *pertinent* independent variables (x_i, y_i). For example, the model may assert that the total cost of an industrial operation increases linearly with the length of delays in shipment. (That is, the model may express the total cost of a delay as nc_d, where n is the number of days' delay and c_d is the cost of delay per day.) But in reality, the total cost of a delay may be $(c_d)^n$.

4. Finally, even if the model is an accurate picture of reality in the sense of conforming to the foregoing three conditions, it may still fail to yield good results if the parameters contained in it are not evaluated properly; i.e., "wrong numbers" may be substituted for the symbols representing the parameters.

Item 4 is really a general case of items 1 and 2, because the inclusion or exclusion of a variable depends on the values of the parameters in the model.

In testing the model, we can begin by testing it as a whole, i.e., by determining the accuracy of its prospective or retrospective predictions of the system's effectiveness. If this procedure informs us that the model is not adequate, then we will have to do further testing to find out which of the four types of deficiency mentioned here is present. We can, of course, test for these deficiencies first, and then test the model as a whole. As a matter of fact, the procedure actually followed will ordinarily depend on the amount of confidence we have in the model. If we believe the model is a good one, we are likely to begin by testing it as a whole. If we are less confident, we are likely to test those aspects concerning which we have the most doubt. If we do test it as a whole, the only relevant evidence may be a comparison of the model's predictions with actual events.

We want now to consider the kinds of data that are available to make the necessary tests, and the manner in which the data are to be collected.

"UNDESIGNED" DATA AND RESULTS

There is a significant aspect of all testing procedures which is unplanned; i.e., there are eventualities which unexpectedly confront the researcher. This is ordinarily true, of course, despite the most meticulous planning. One may construct a model that appears to describe a process adequately only to discover, on testing, that an important aspect has been omitted. For example, a production model may adequately balance inventory-carrying costs and setup costs, but it may ignore the very important cost of changing the size of the labor force. Or, a model may assume that raw-material deliveries can be made at any time, when actually the supplier's policy is to deliver only twice a month.

Such evidence of an omission usually arises because of poor communication between sponsor and research team, though this remark only indicates what the problem is, of course, and not the answer. Some of the case histories given in this book are examples of successful attempts by research teams to find adequate channels of communication.

There are thus some types of evidence relevant to a model that seem at first to be so simple in nature that no design for their collection is required. However, the history of science is replete with examples of so-called simple evidence that turned out to be very complicated. Experience seems to dictate the maxim that *all* evidence is complicated and techniques for its collection should be designed unless the contrary can be wholly justified; simplicity of evidence must not be accepted on intuitive grounds.

The design of the process of collecting evidence consists of the following parts: definition (including measurement), sampling (including experimental designs), data-reduction, use of the data in the test, examination of the result, and possible redesign of the evidence.

SCIENTIFIC DEFINITIONS

Scientific defining consists of specifying the best *conceivable* (not necessarily obtainable) conditions under which, and procedures by which, values of the variable can be obtained. "Best conceivable" is, of course, a relative concept; it means the best that *we can* conceive, *not* the best that can ever be conceived.

At first glance, such a step might seem like a very impractical one. Why bother to specify procedures we may not be able to carry out? The answer lies in the fact that concern with *ideal* (or *optimum*) observational conditions and procedures is neither idle dreaming nor wishful thinking; it is quite important if we want to know how good are the results we eventually obtain. Further, and more important, the ideal conditions and procedures act as a *standard* by means of which we can evaluate the attainable observational conditions and operations, determine their shortcomings, and make any necessary adjustments in the resultant data. The use of *idealized operational* (*i.e.*, *scientific*) *definitions* * for the adjustment of actual data is common to all the sciences. Consider a familiar physical example: the determination of the acceleration of a freely falling body. The idealized operations for measuring such an acceleration might require (among other things) a perfect vacuum in which the bodies could fall with complete freedom. Actually, the physicist can never create a perfect vacuum, but he can conduct his experiment in such a way as to estimate how a body *would* fall if it were in a perfect vacuum. He determines how acceleration is affected by variations in atmospheric pressure. He uses mathematical functions to relate changes in atmospheric pressure to changes in acceleration. Then, by extrapolation, he determines what would occur in a complete vacuum, and thereby infers the acceleration of an ideally freely falling body.

The two most common types of quantitative variables are the *enumerative* and the *metric*. The enumerative variable requires counting for its evaluation whereas the metric variable requires measurement.

Scientific Definitions of Enumerative Variables

Counting is frequently and mistakenly thought to be a very simple (if not the simplest) type of quantification. If, for example, one were repeatedly to count the number of occurrences of the letter "e" on this page, one would ordinarily find considerable variation among the counts. The census taker and the inventory taker can attest to the difficulties in this operation. It is true that it is simple merely to count, but *it is not simple to count accurately.*

There are two types of errors which can arise in the counting operation: *overenumeration* and *underenumeration*. Overenumeration results either from counting the same unit more than once or from counting units which should not be counted at all. Underenumeration, on the other hand, results from the failure to count a unit which should be counted. Furthermore, these errors can occur because of a failure to match elements with *consecutive* integers (e.g., overenumeration because of skipping numbers and underenumeration through duplication of numbers).

The counting process involves two basic steps: 1. identification of the units to be counted, and 2. matching these units with consecutive integers. The errors in counting are all traceable to inadequacy in one or both of these steps.

It is desirable to design the best conceivable counting procedure, even if we cannot carry out the design in practice. This involves

---

* For a detailed discussion of scientific defining, see Ackoff,[1] p. 305, and Hempel.[20]

specifying the standard environment in which, and the standard operations by which, the count can ideally be made, as well as providing an explicit definition of the elements to be counted. Once this standard is specified, it will be possible to use it to evaluate alternative practically-realizable counting procedures, and to select the best of these. The standard also provides a basis for estimating the error that is likely to occur in the practical counting procedure which is eventually used.

Scientific Definitions of Properties

The idealized design of a procedure for measuring properties depends primarily on the type of property involved. In the case of counting, the idea is to include those objects in the count which have a certain property, and to exclude the rest. Now, however, we are to be concerned with the degree to which an object has a certain property. That is, we pass from the "yes-no" type of decision to the "how much" type.

Scientific definitions of properties involve specifying the following characteristics of the idealized measuring procedure:

1. Identification of the thing, event, or class of things or events which should be observed.

2. Specification of the environment in which the observations should be made.

3. Specification of the changes in the environment which should be made, if any, during the observation period.

4. Specification of the operations to be performed and the instruments and measure to be used by the observer.

5. Specification of the readings (data) to be made.

6. Specification of the analysis of the data.

The formal description of the measure * to be used states what logical and mathematical operations we want to be able to perform on the data to be obtained in evaluating a variable. The scientific definition (observational standard) states how, ideally, we would go about collecting pertinent data. The operational specification of the data-collection process states how we actually intend to collect and adjust the data. Errors can arise in each of these three stages of planning relative to testing the model. Despite the fact that consumers of O.R. are more inclined to challenge the data used in testing the model than the model itself, many researchers tend to skimp on research

---

* For a more complete discussion of the theory of measurement see refs. 3, 4, 31, 32, 37, 38, and 39.

planning where data collection is involved. Fellow professionals are more likely to challenge the model itself. But if research results are to be "sold" and put to use, the researcher must be prepared to defend his data as well as he usually can defend his model.

The defense of data involves not only demonstrating its pertinence by reference to definitions but also demonstrating its approximation to representativeness by reference to the sampling procedure used.

SAMPLING

In evaluating variables, we are either involved in measuring the property of a single unit or in counting the members of, or measuring the properties of, a class of units (a population). The definition of a property of a single unit specifies the conditions under which the observation should be made. If these conditions can be met and observations can be made without error, only one observation is required. But if the conditions are not met, observations are subject to error which can only be estimated if two or more observations are made. How many observations to make, and where, are sampling questions. Since the standard conditions specified in the definition can seldom be met in practice, we must choose an experimental design which allows us, by techniques such as the analyses of variance and covariance, to assess the magnitude of the deviations and ascribe them to specific environmental factors; or we must make our observations on a subset (of the population) which allows us to draw inferences which are valid for the whole population with the least possible bias. The subject of sampling is concerned with the selection of appropriate subsets.

If we are evaluating a property of a population or counting its membership, it is frequently impossible or impractical to observe every member of the class (e.g., every nut and bolt made in a factory). Consequently, once again sampling is required.

The aim of sampling, in general, is a very simple and well-recognized one. We simply want to use the minimum amount of time and effort in getting the required information. The problem of sampling design can be posed in the usual form of all problems presented in this book: a balance of economic forces. If we spend a lot of time and money in gathering data, our decisions in the main will be more precise and less subject to error. But we will have paid for this precision in terms of delay and cost. What is the proper balance? Some academic faculties are prone to appoint committees to investigate painstakingly first and then to make recommendations. Some executives in business are prone to make snap judgments of actions to be taken, fast and forcefully.

Somewhere in between these extremes lies the rational economic balance of the risks of erroneous decisions and the costs of gathering data.

Before discussing the scientific theory of sampling, let us mention some unscientific approaches to the problem. When a woman shops for corn, she may pick out a few ears to see if they are fresh. She selects what seems to her to be typical ears in the "population." No operational rules are set down, other than the use of judgment. Judgment sampling is by far the most common type of sampling, because it is cheap, simple, and quick. We use judgment sampling every hour of the day: in selecting eating places, neckties, and shoes. But, though judgment sampling is simple to apply it is very difficult to evaluate. Normally we do not know how a person's judgment will operate in selecting items, so that we have no adequate way of determining what kind of a sample he has drawn. Some people tend to pick items which they feel to be close to the average item of the population, no doubt because this seems to them a way of getting "representative" samples. For example, a railroad selected a "typical week" in October as "representative" of its traffic conditions. Another company selected a "typical area" for a consumer study. This kind of judgment sampling is called "purposive." It is a procedure that may yield a very poor sample in terms of information about the population, especially if we are interested in *variances* as well as population means. In general, in judgment and purposive sampling we cannot determine *the probability that an element will be selected from the population*, and it is this, as we shall see, which is the basic requirement for measuring the reliability of the estimates we derive from the data obtained from a sample.

In the main, we can describe sampling as the selection of items from a population. The "population" of objects, events, environments, and stimuli to be sampled should be specified in the definition of the variable being evaluated. The population represents all the possible data of the relevant kind that can be collected.

Evaluation of Samples and Sample Estimates

The decision which we must make in designing a sampling procedure is concerned with the method of drawing the sample and the method of making estimates about the population from the sample. If a prescribed method is carried out correctly, then we have two opposing considerations:

1. The probability that the estimate made on the basis of the sample will actually deviate from the true population value by an amount greater than some amount x.

2. The cost of taking the sample.

In the main, the probability of deviations will decrease with an increase in the sample size, but the cost of taking the sample will increase with an increase in sample size.

The probability of deviations of the estimated values from the true value is partially contained in the measure of the dispersion (or spread or variability) of estimates yielded by the sampling procedure. This dispersion is usually measured by the *variance* (or standard error) of the estimate. The variance is the mean squared deviation of the estimated values from the true values. The *standard deviation* and *range* are other common measures of dispersion.

Another important characteristic of a sampling procedure (which relates to the probability of deviations of the estimated value from the true value) is its "bias." Bias is the deviation of the *expected value* of an estimating procedure from the *true value*. The expected value, in turn, is the average estimate that would ultimately be approached in *the long run*, i.e., if the procedure were repeated indefinitely. Bias is an extremely unfortunate name for this property of estimates, especially in a world in which there is the strongest possible opprobrium for being prejudiced. Actually, a method of estimating may introduce some bias and yet be highly desirable in terms of cost and over-all error. For example, *ratio* estimates are biased but in some cases have so much smaller variance than unbiased *linear* estimates that the probability of deviating from the true value by a specified amount is less if a ratio estimate is used.

If we know the bias and the variance of a sampling and estimating procedure, we can usually determine the probability of obtaining specific deviations, provided the sampling and estimating instructions are carried out correctly. This proviso is significant. In many applications of sampling it is ignored, and the resulting sampling-estimating plan does not yield an optimum. Very often, errors in not carrying out the sampling correctly, and errors in computation, increase with an increase in the sample size n. Hence, a more general model for sampling consists of the following components:

Cost of sampling = (1) cost due to bias and variance

+ (2) cost of examining n items

+ (3) costs of failure to meet sampling
specifications

If (3) increases with n, it may turn out that even a 100% count entails very large errors, and is one of the worst possible sampling designs. The U.S. Census Bureau, for example, used a Post Enumeration (sample) Survey to estimate errors of the 1950 Decennial Census which aspired to be a complete count.

Types of Sampling Designs

In *unrestricted random sampling* every possible sample has the same chance of being chosen. Restricted random sampling represents methods where each possible sample does not have an equal probability of being drawn. But in each case where random sampling is used scientifically, the probability of selecting any sample is known.

In a book of this sort it is not appropriate to cover in detail all of the methods of sampling. The best that can be done here is to describe briefly some of the sampling procedures which have been very useful in O.R. It should be emphasized, however, that this treatment is no substitute for an extended exposure to sampling theory and methods.* These methods should be part of the equipment not only of every operations researcher but of every scientist.

The various schemes for sampling are all based on very simple, practical considerations. These are:

1. Items of the population may fall into recognizable groups (e.g., in terms of location, or dollar amounts on an invoice, etc.). If this is the case, it is reasonable to think in terms of sampling from these groups, because in general we reduce the variance of the estimates and (more important) we can be selective in the amount of sampling that is done in each group. Invoices with large dollar amounts are more important than ones with small dollar amounts; hence we should take a larger sample of the more important items.

2. Items of a population often fall into clusters (e.g., a shipment shown on an invoice; people in a house, block, or town; items in a warehouse, etc.). If we go to look at some item in a cluster, we might just as well look at the rest of the items. Hence the cluster becomes the basis of sampling, not the original items. The use of clusters may increase the variance of the estimates but greatly decrease the costs of gathering the sample: the usual economic balancing problem.

3. We do not have to plan completely in advance. We can let the sample information that comes in dictate how the next steps are to be taken.

The following is a general classification of the principal types of sampling designs:

* For comprehensive surveys of contemporary sampling theory see refs. 1, 7, 11, 19, 35, and 50.

I. *Fixed Sampling Design:* the sampling design is fixed and not subject to change in terms of sample data.

A. *Unrestricted Random Sampling:* a random sample * is selected from the whole population by either

1. *Simple Random Sampling:* assigning a different number to each element in the population and using random numbers to select the sample, or
2. *Systematic Random Sampling:* where a population is ordered, selecting a starting place at random and then selecting subsequent elements at a fixed interval from the first and subsequent selections.

B. *Restricted Random Sampling:* the population is divided into subgroups (and possible subsubgroups, etc.) and either some of these are selected and/or random samples from some or all of these are selected.

1. *Multistage Random Sampling:* random samples are drawn from subgroups which have themselves been selected with

a. equal probability, or with
b. probability proportionate to the relative size of the subgroup, or some other criterion.

2. *Stratified Random Sampling:* a random sample is drawn from every subgroup of the population. The size of the sample from the subgroups may be

a. independent of the size of the subgroups (i.e., samples of equal size),
b. proportionate to the relative size of the subgroup, or
c. proportionate to the relative size of the subgroup and the dispersion of the elements within it (*Optimum Allocation*).

3. *Cluster Sampling:* a random sample of subgroups is selected, all elements of which are included in the final sample.
4. *Stratified Cluster Sampling:* a combination of B2 and B3, where more than two stages of sampling are involved.

II. *Sequential Sampling:* † a small random sample is selected and analyzed, on the basis of which a decision is made as to whether or not to continue sampling and if so, how. The samples may be either

A. in groups, as in *Double* or *Multiple Sampling*, or
B. single items taken one at a time.

The aspect of sampling called "experimental design" usually refers to a sampling plan based on the variables in the model which is to be tested. Instead of keeping everything fixed except one variable, it is possible to design data-collection systems at "optimally" located

* Tables of random numbers can be found in refs. 22, 26, 40, and 41. Details on the generation of such numbers can be found in ref. 25.
† For details on sequential sampling see refs. 5, 34, 43, and 45.

points of some of the variables of the model. This sampling method assumes that the variables of the model can be manipulated in reality —or at least in a realistic model. Thus a company that services a number of its customers with a device owned by the company and rented by the customer might be able to change the properties of these devices in a systematic way, in order to test a model for optimal service at minimal cost. For information on various types of experimental designs, see references 8, 13, 17, and 27. Special mention should be made of the experimental search methods of Box,[2] which are designed to locate the maximum of a function by an optimal search pattern. The relevance of this to O.R. is clear, since many O.R. models are designed to find the optimal (minimal or maximal) point of some function.

Reduction of Data

The observations made on the sampled items or in a sample of situations provide the raw data on the basis of which variables are assigned values and, hence, provide the basis for testing all or part of the model. In many cases the data require collation, editing, coding, punching, etc. We are not going to consider these phases of data processing here. (Discussion of these can be found in Chapter X of Ackoff.[1]) Our concern here is with the *form* into which the data must be transformed to be useful in the testing process.

In general, the ultimate form to which the data must be reduced will be either an estimate of the value of a parameter or an inferential "statistic" which describes a relationship between two or more variables. For example, in testing a lot-size model we must first evaluate the cost variables in order to compute the total cost "predicted" by the model. Once these predictions are obtained they are compared with observed values in order to derive a "statistic" which can be used to determine whether or not the model predicts well.

Let us consider the problem of estimation first. For the sake of simplified exposition, we are treating sampling and estimation separately, but in designing research it is necessary to consider these simultaneously. The cost associated with a sampling plan involves the cost of analyzing the data, and this latter cost cannot be determined without some specification of the estimating procedure.

An estimation procedure that is "best" for one sampling plan is not necessarily best for another. Consequently, the expression "best estimate" is always relative to the type of sample involved.

A "best" estimate relative to a sampling procedure is one which minimizes the expected costs of error (over- and underestimation). At present, however, we do not have tools available for generating such "best" procedures. Most of the estimation procedures currently considered to be best are based on the assumption that costs of over- and underestimation are (approximately) proportionate to the square of the amount of over- or underestimation. This assumption seems reasonable in many cases; i.e., it seems four times as serious to err by two units as to err by one, nine times as serious to err by three units as to err by one, etc. One "advantage" of this assumption is that minimization of the square of errors (the principle of "least squares" *) is relatively simple to handle mathematically. Further, minimizing the squares may minimize other functions of the error as well. Nevertheless, the possible arbitrariness of the assumption should be kept in mind.†

Estimates of the variability of estimates are very important in O.R. The value of a model cannot be completely determined unless we know how variable are its estimates of effectiveness. In fact, unless we have some idea of the reliability of the estimate of effectiveness we should not use the model. We should have some notion of how likely it is that an estimated improvement will actually be an improvement and not a loss. (One of the serious shortcomings of linear programming is the difficulty of generating an estimate of the reliability of the optima it yields.) A determination of the reliability of effectiveness estimates can be made in one of two ways:

1. If we have a model of the form $E = f(x, y)$ and the variances of the estimates of x and y are known, then, for certain types of functions, it is possible to determine analytically what is the variance of the estimate of E.

2. By comparing theoretically computed estimates of effectiveness with actual effectiveness, the variance of the difference can be computed by standard estimating procedures.

The actual manner in which the data are reduced and the specific estimates that are used depend on which of the questions about the model (see p. 577 of this chapter) one is attempting to answer. Statistical tests of the significance or nonsignificance of a variable can be

---

* Least squares and other estimates of population characteristics which are suitable for various sampling plans are discussed in detail in ref. 12, Chaps. 8 and 9.

† R. A. Fisher [16] has suggested that estimates should provide "maximum information" and that they should maximize the likelihood of the observed events (the principle of "maximum likelihood"). In most practical cases, however, there is little difference between least squares estimates and maximum likelihood estimates and a third type called "minimax estimates" (estimates which minimize the maximum risk that could occur).

found in references 12, 16, 18, 21, 23, 28, 29, 33, 48, and 49. These tests may enable one to determine such matters as:

   a. whether a variable should or should not be included,
   b. whether the form of an analytic function is linear or some other type,
   c. whether the form of a probability function is normal or some other type,
   d. whether the model has failed to include a variable that ought to have been included.

In the next chapter, we shall consider some of the methodological problems associated with these tests.

CHECKING THE EVIDENCE— TESTING THE SOLUTION

We have discussed how various aspects of the model can be tested by the evidence. In concluding this discussion, mention should be made of tests of the whole model against past experience (retrospective tests). In Chapter 21 we shall describe tests of the model against current experience for repetitive decisions.

Does the Solution Yield Better Performance?

An O.R. solution to a problem is supposed to yield an improvement over current practices or show that no improvement is possible. Acceptance of the solution by the decision-makers is much more likely to depend on its tested performance than on its underlying logic, or the validity of aspects of the model.

In a retrospective test, the past has to be reconstructed. This means that the values of the uncontrolled independent variables (e.g., demand and setup costs in production planning) have to be determined. Values of all of these variables are seldom readily available, and, if available at all, they tend to be hidden in records. Experience with such records breeds a healthy skepticism since one learns that numbers seldom mean what they first appear to mean. It is necessary in many cases, therefore, to reconstruct the procedure by which they were generated—in effect, to reconstruct the (usually implicit) operational model from which the records were made. Once this is done, they can be compared with observational standards and the required adjustments can be made. For example, figures provided by a sales department as representing past orders may on inspection represent past shipments. Not only is there likely to be an unsystematic time displacement of shipments but there may have been orders which were lost because of the inability to ship promptly. The adjustment of shipments to orders received may be a complex one and require considerable study.

In many cases the past data available cover such a short period of time that it is best to use all of these data. In such a case no sampling of time is required. Here the researchers will usually run into the fact that management seldom considers any short period of time to be normal or typical. In fact, one rapidly concludes that nothing is so atypical as a typical year.

When abundant historical data are available, it is important in sampling the past to obtain the maximum assurance of representativeness through stratified sampling of the characteristics that management used in judging whether a year was typical or not. For example, managers will usually distinguish between a good year and a bad year, a year in which raw material was plentiful and one in which the supply was low. The convincingness of the test of the solution depends on how well all such periods are represented.

The test itself usually consists of a comparison of actual effectiveness obtained with what would have been obtained if the solution had been used. A "straight" comparison is usually not enough. For example, in comparing production costs in the case study presented in Chapter 2, possible errors in estimates of the values of variables in the model had to be taken into account. This can be done in several ways:

1. Suppose the model is of the form $E = f(x, y)$. If the variability of the estimates of x and y is known, then it is possible, in many cases, to compute the variability of the estimates of E. If the variability of the estimates of E is known, it is possible to determine whether or not the differences in effectiveness observed in the test can be due to chance or not.

2. By testing the total model in the manner described, one can empirically generate an estimate of the variability of the estimates of E. This estimate can then be used as described in item 1.

3. When it is not practical to obtain estimates of the variability of E (as in the case presented in Chapter 2), one can ask: By how much would the estimates of variable values have to be in error before the apparent improvement yielded by the solution over past practices would be a loss? For example, in Chapter 2 it was reported that both of the cost terms (fixed and variable cost per run) would have had to be underestimated by 10% before the solution would have resulted in a loss to the company. In this case, good reason existed for believing

that errors of estimating cost could not possibly be of this magnitude. These reasons, of course, had to be made explicit and had to be supported by evidence. In this instance, evidence consisted of demonstrating that if these cost estimates were in error by 10% in the same direction, then, even using the previous planning procedures, no profit could have been realized by the company. But as a matter of fact a profit was realized; therefore, the cost estimates could not be in error by the critical amount.

In retrospective tests, not only must one carefully sample past time (as explained in the preceding discussion), but other types of sampling may also be critical. For example, it may not be practical to compute retrospective reductions in production costs for each of several thousand parts. A sample of parts may have to be selected. If many plants, customers, etc., are involved, samples of these may also be necessary. Unless these samples are scientifically designed, inferences from the sample to the total population cannot be drawn with confidence.

Briefly, then, in testing a solution retrospectively, it is necessary not only to compare actual and hypothetically optimum past performances but to determine the significance of the retrospectively observed differences by one of the methods described.

Sometimes the test of the solution can be made by waiting for data to accumulate. The same problems of adjustment of data and sampling arise (since one can seldom handle the total system). A greater degree of control of data collection is usually possible, but there is also usually a compensating loss in ability to test over a variety of business conditions. That is, in this type of testing, observed differences are likely to be more reliable, but for a narrower range of conditions, than in retrospective testing.

Where possible, it is desirable to test both ways. This gives a greater confidence in continued gains to be obtained by use of the solution. Extrapolation from the past to the future is so frequently "ticklish" and difficult to "sell."

CONCLUSION

We have just considered procedures for testing the adequacy of models and the solutions derived from them. The fact that we considered the construction of models first and testing procedures second does not imply that researchers must follow this pattern. Some researchers feel that the best way to begin research is to see what data are available, since they think that only in this way can they "theorize" about a situation in a practical fashion. Others feel that there is no point in gathering data until there is a model, since they argue that only in this way can they know what data to gather.

The growth of science has shown that these differences of opinion really do no more than account for the way researchers behave in terms of their personal traits, and have little to do with the question of *the* proper method. One reason for research teams as opposed to individuals is that teamwork controls excessive preoccupation with data or with models on the part of the researchers. The research procedure is a dynamic interaction of evidence (data) and models (theory), and which comes first is a relatively minor problem. But "dynamic interactions" are difficult to write into a systematic book of this kind. They are more easily expressed in the actual case histories. In order to give a systematic account of O.R. procedures, we have had to present the material in sequence, and have somewhat arbitrarily treated model-construction first and testing second.

One might argue (and many people do) that a "sufficiently well-established" model does not need to be tested. Or one might modify this position somewhat and argue that the researcher makes certain assumptions about a situation, and as long as these assumptions are made explicit there is no need, *as far as research is concerned*, for further justification. Both of these viewpoints, in effect, argue against gathering evidence. For "evidence" is a name for information that is potentially capable of making us change our minds. If the researcher is content with his model, evidence is superfluous for him, though it may be very important for anyone who wants to utilize the results.

These viewpoints, characteristic of a classical philosophy of science called rationalism, appear to be unsatisfactory when research is taken within a comprehensive frame of reference. Separation of the theoretical and experimental aspects of research may be desirable from time to time. But permanent separation of the two leads to a tragic divorce; the model builder may build his models so that they cannot be adequately tested. In any event, if O.R. is the study of executive-type decisions, it must regard the procedures of testing a model to be as critical as the procedure of model-building. There is no point in optimizing in theory but becoming haphazard in testing.

BIBLIOGRAPHY

1. Ackoff, R. L., *The Design of Social Research,* University of Chicago Press, Chicago, 1953.
2. Box, G. E. P., "The Exploration and Exploitation of Response Surfaces," Technical Report No. 4, Philadelphia Ordnance District, Dept. of the Army with Institute of Statistics, North Carolina State College, Raleigh, 1954.
3. Campbell, N. R., *An Account of the Principles of Measurements and Calculations,* Longmans, Green & Co., New York, 1928.
4. Churchman, C. W., "A Materialist Theory of Measurement," in R. W. Sellars, V. J. McGill, and Marvin Farber (eds.), *Philosophy for the Future,* The Macmillan Co., New York, 1949.
5. ———, *Statistical Manual: Methods of Making Experimental Inferences,* Pittman-Dunn Laboratory, Frankford Arsenal, Philadelphia, 1951.
6. ———, *Theory of Experimental Inference,* The Macmillan Co., New York, 1948.
7. Cochran, W. G., *Sampling Techniques,* John Wiley & Sons, New York, 1953.
8. ———, and Cox, G. M., *Experimental Designs,* John Wiley & Sons, New York, 1950.
9. Coombs, C. H., Raiffa, H., and Thrall, R. M., "Some Views on Mathematical Models and Measurement Theory," in R. M. Thrall, C. H. Coombs, and R. L. Davis (eds.), *Decision Processes,* John Wiley & Sons, New York, 1954.
10. Cramér, Harald, *Mathematical Methods of Statistics,* Princeton University Press, Princeton, 1945.
11. Deming, W. E., *Some Theory of Sampling,* John Wiley & Sons, New York, 1950.
12. Dixon, W. J., and Massey, F. J., Jr., *Introduction to Statistical Analysis,* McGraw-Hill Book Co., New York, 1951.
13. Federer, W. T., *Experimental Design,* The Macmillan Co., New York, 1955.
14. Feller, W., *An Introduction to Probability Theory and Its Applications,* John Wiley & Sons, New York, 1950.
15. Ferris, C. D., Grubbs, F. E., and Weaver, C. L., "Operating Characteristics for the Common Tests of Significance," *Ann. math. Statist., 17,* 178–197 (1946).
16. Fisher, R. A., *Statistical Methods for Research Workers,* Oliver & Boyd, London, 1948.
17. ———, *The Design of Experiments,* Oliver & Boyd, London, 1949.
18. Hald, A., *Statistical Theory with Engineering Applications,* John Wiley & Sons, New York, 1952.
19. Hansen, M. H., Hurwitz, W. N., and Madow, W. G., *Sampling Survey Methods and Theory,* John Wiley & Sons, New York, 1953.
20. Hempel, C. G., "Fundamentals of Concept Formation in Empirical Science," in *International Encyclopedia of Unified Science* (Part III), University of Chicago Press, Chicago, 1952.
21. Hoel, P. G., *Introduction to Mathematical Statistics,* John Wiley & Sons, New York, 2nd ed., 1954.
22. Horton, H. B., *Random Decimal Digits,* Interstate Commerce Commission, Washington, 1949.
23. Johnson, P. O., *Statistical Methods in Research,* Prentice-Hall, New York, 1949.
24. Kendall, M. G., *Advanced Theory of Statistics,* Chas. Griffin & Co., London, 2 vols., 1947.

25. Kendall, M. G., and Smith, B. B., "Randomness and Random Sampling of Numbers," *J. R. statist. Soc.*, *101*, 147–166 (1938).
26. ———, "Tables of Random Sampling Numbers," in *Tracts for Computers*, no. 24, Cambridge University Press, Cambridge, 1940.
27. Mann, H. B., *Analysis and Design of Experiments*, Dover Publications, New York, 1949.
28. Massey, F. J., Jr., "The Kolmogorov-Smirnov Test for Goodness of Fit," *J. Amer. statist. Ass.*, *46*, 68–78 (1951).
29. Mode, E. B., *The Elements of Statistics*, Prentice-Hall, New York, 1941.
30. Mood, A. M., *Introduction to the Theory of Statistics*, McGraw-Hill Book Co., New York, 1950.
31. Nagel, Ernest, "Measurement," *Erkenntniss*, *2*, 313–333 (1931).
32. ———, *On the Logic of Measurement*, Thesis, Columbia University, New York, 1930.
33. Snedecor, G. W., *Statistical Methods*, Iowa State College Press, Ames, 4th ed., 1946.
34. Statistical Research Group, *Sequential Analysis of Statistical Data: Application*, Columbia University Press, New York, 1946.
35. Stephan, F. F., "History of the Uses of Modern Sampling," *J. Amer. statist. Ass.*, *43*, 12–39 (1948).
36. ———, "Sampling," *Amer. J. Sociology*, *55*, 371–375 (1950).
37. ———, "Mathematics, Measurement, and Psychophysics," in S. S. Stevens (ed.), *Handbook of Experimental Psychology*, John Wiley & Sons, New York, 1951.
38. Stevens, S. S., "On the Problem of Scales for the Measurement of Psychological Magnitudes," *J. univ. Sci.*, *9*, 94–99 (1939).
39. ———, "On the Theory of Scales of Measurement," *Science*, *103*, 677-680 (1946).
40. The RAND Corporation, *A Million Random Digits*, The Free Press, Glencoe, 1955.
41. Tippett, L. H. C., *Tables of Random Sampling Numbers*, in *Tracts for Computers*, no. 15, Cambridge University Press, Cambridge, 1927.
42. Wald, Abraham, "Contributions to the Theory of Statistical Estimation and Testing Hypotheses," *Ann. math. Statist.*, *10*, 299–326 (1939).
43. ———, "Foundations of a General Theory of Sequential Decision Functions," *Econometrica*, *15*, 279–313 (1947).
44. ———, "On the Principles of Statistical Inference," in *Notre Dame Mathematical Lectures*, no. 1, Notre Dame University, Notre Dame, 1942.
45. ———, *Sequential Analysis*, John Wiley & Sons, New York, 1947.
46. ———, "Statistical Decision Functions," *Ann. Math.*, *20*, 165–205 (1949).
47. ———, "Statistical Decision Functions which Minimize the Maximum Risk," *Ann. Math.*, *46*, 265–280 (1945).
48. Walker, H. M., *Elementary Statistical Methods*, Henry Holt & Co., New York, 1943.
49. Wilks, S. S., *Elementary Statistical Analysis*, Princeton University Press, Princeton, 1949.
50. Yates, Frank, *Sampling Methods for Censuses and Surveys*, Chas. Griffin & Co., London, 1949.

Chapter 21

Controlling
and Implementing
the Solution

INTRODUCTION

Many, if not most, O.R. projects deal with management decisions that are recurrent. An inventory problem, for example, usually involves the development of a "decision rule" which is a solution that can be applied repetitively as the need occurs and the situation changes. Production quantities may be determined each week or month. Hence the solution must be used over and over again. But the systems which are dealt with in O.R. are seldom stable. Their structure is subject to change. Relationships between the variables which define the system (the system's *parameters*) and the value of the parameters themselves are usually subject to change.

In such situations the relationships and parameters used in the decision rule must be adjusted for changes in the system as they occur. Costs may change, the distribution of demand may change in some or all of its characteristics, and the relationships between variables may change over time. Hence the values of the relationships and parameters should be periodically re-evaluated and the assumptions involved in the model (from which the decision rule is derived) should be re-examined periodically. That is, the solution must be *controlled* lest it lose some of its effectiveness because of changes in the system.

Once a solution has been tested and, if it is to be used repetitively, a control procedure has been designed, it must be put into operation. That is, the solution must be implemented if the O.R. project is to be fully consummated. The objective of O.R. is to improve operations, not merely to submit a report. Hence, a plan for implementation should be developed and carried out.

Complete methodologies have not yet been developed for optimizing either the control or implementation procedures. Enough is known, however, to design procedures which are more likely to lead to success than either leaving these phases of the project to chance or relying on others (management or operating personnel) to take care of them.

Because of our inability to design an optimum control procedure, there is considerable room for ingenuity in this phase of the research. Such ingenuity is likely to spring from an intimate knowledge of statistical methods, techniques, and tools, particularly those related to the subject of statistical quality control. A knowledge of the general philosophy and logic of statistical quality control * as well as of its techniques and tools † is very helpful, if not essential, in designing effective control systems.

CONTROLLING THE SOLUTION

The effectiveness of a solution in an O.R. problem may be reduced by changes in either values of the parameters of the system or the relationships between them, or both. (See p. 577, Chapter 20.) A previously insignificant parameter may become significant, or, conversely, a previously significant parameter may become insignificant. Changes in the values and functional relations of the parameters which remain significant may also affect the effectiveness of the solution. It is important to recall that if certain parameters have values near zero, some of the variables of the system will no longer play a significant role.

Let us consider examples of these possibilities. First, a previously irrelevant variable may become relevant. For example, the model of a production and inventory control problem may not include in-process inventory cost (as was the case in Chapter 2) because the production-cycle time is very short and the associated costs are very small. But a change in the product mix or volume of business may considerably extend this production cycle. In-process inventory cost may thereby become significantly large. On the other hand, in a system in which in-process inventory costs are significant, a reduction in the production cycle may make this variable insignificant. In a purchasing-quantity problem the possible purchase quantities may all fall within one price range, and hence price breaks can be ignored.

* See refs. 3 and 24.
† See refs. 5, 6, 9, 13, 15, 22, 23, and 25.

But if either the volume of business or the suppliers' pricing policies change, these price breaks may become very significant.

Second, the value of a parameter which appears in the decision rule may change significantly. For example, it is not at all unlikely that demand, arrival rates, available facilities, costs, etc., will change. Such changes require modification of the values used in the solution. In other words, the values of the parameters should be re-estimated periodically.

Third, the functional relationships in the solution may change. For example, the cost of a shortage may be a linear function of time in a period in which demand exceeds supply, or it may even be a constant (independent of the duration of the shortage). In a period in which supply exceeds demand, however, the cost of a shortage may rise at an increasing rate with the duration of the shortage.

Not every change in a parameter or relationship is *significant*. In general terms, a change is significant if

1. adjustment of the solution for the change results in an improvement in effectiveness, and

2. the cost of making the adjustment and carrying it out does not offset the improvement in effectiveness.

Design of a control system, then, consists of three steps:

1. Listing the variables, parameters, and relationships that either are included in the solution or should be if their values were to change.

2. Development of a procedure for detecting significant changes in each of the parameters and relationships listed.

3. Specification of action to be taken or adjustments to be made in the solution when a significant change occurs.

The last two steps are interrelated because determination of the significance of a change (step 2) depends on the cost of making the adjustment specified in step 3.

It is convenient to treat the control of parameters and relationships separately since the requirements are not exactly the same. The control of parameters is considered first.

Control of Parameters

The first step in designing a control procedure involves listing all the variables and relationships which, if they were to change in value, might affect the effectiveness of the solution. It is obvious that this list should include all variables and relationships which appear in the solution. What is not so obvious is that the list should also contain variables which are not comprised in the solution but which should be included under different (but possible) conditions. In a preceding example, in-process inventory was such a variable. Composition of this list should be based on the analysis of the system which preceded construction of the model from which the solution was derived. A re-examination of each variable that was discarded at that time is required to determine if it can become relevant under a different set of conditions or if its value will change by some significant amount.

It is usually convenient to "break" some parameters into their "observable" components. For example, setup cost can be broken into man-hours per setup and cost per man-hour, and inventory-carrying cost can be broken into storage cost, cost of money, taxes, etc. By so doing it is generally simpler to find the cause of a change when it occurs and this, as we shall see, is an essential part of control.

The parameters which are listed should be classified into two types:

1. Variables whose values during the period covered by a decision can be known in advance, such as the number of models in a line, the number of work days in an accounting period, and the price for which an item is to be sold. Control of such measures consists either (a) of establishing communication lines between those who know these values and those who use the decision rules or (b) of providing the latter with source material (such as a calendar in the case of the number of work days per accounting period).

2. Measures whose values cannot be known in advance, such as number of units sold, number of hours worked, and arrival rate of trucks. These values must be estimated in advance.

It is usually easy to design control procedures for the first class of measures but it is not always easy to put the procedure into operation. It is generally difficult, however, to design control procedures for the second class. Consequently, this discussion is directed toward controlling measures whose values must be estimated.

The problem of controlling a measure whose value must be estimated consists of determining (on the basis of known or estimated past values) either whether an estimated value used in the past should be changed for future use or whether the estimating procedure itself should be changed. For example, an average setup cost computed from the past may be used in present decisions. Control in this case consists of determining whether a significant change has occurred in the true value of this average and, if so, what value to use in the future. If, on the other hand, the measure is "number of units required per month" and its value is forecasted each month, then assumptions implicit in the model concerning characteristics of these forecasts must be checked. For instance, the forecast may be assumed to be unbiased; i.e., the expected value of the deviations of the forecast from the true values is assumed to be equal to zero. Then the amount of bias should be checked to determine whether a significant change in it has occurred and, if so, how much. This in turn will lead to adjusting the forecasted values used. Note that in this latter case control is applied to estimates rather than true values.

Essential to the control of any measure, then, is the determination of whether its true value or one or more of the characteristics of its estimate have changed. This determination consists of testing the hypothesis that no change has occurred in the variable or the characteristics of its estimate (which are themselves variables).

Errors in Detecting Changes. Determination of whether or not such a change has occurred is subject to two types of error:

Type I—asserting that a change has occurred when it has not, and

Type II—asserting that a change has not occurred when it has.

An understanding of the two types of error is essential to comprehend what is involved in controlling a variable.

The first type of error is expressed in the significance level α at which the hypothesis of no change (the *null hypothesis* H_0) is tested. If, for example, a 5% significance level is used in testing the hypothesis, we would assert that a change has occurred when it actually has not in 5% of the cases. One of the problems in setting up a control procedure, then, is to determine the significance level (i.e., the acceptable type I error) at which the test of the null hypothesis is to be made.

The type II error is more complicated because the seriousness of the assertion that a change has not occurred when it has depends on the amount by which it actually has changed. Hence, the type II error is not a single value but is represented by a set of probabilities assigned to the various amounts of change which can occur. These probabilities are a function of the type of statistical test which is used to determine whether or not a change has occurred. The probabilities associated with various type II errors can be conveniently shown in what is called an operating characteristic (O.C.) curve. Such a curve is shown in Fig. 21-1. This figure shows such an O.C. curve for one particular statistical testing procedure, the "2-sided z test." The horizontal axis represents various "true" possibilities (in standard units) which we are willing to consider as alternatives to the hypothesis that no change has occurred. To make use of this curve, the hypothesis has to be stated in the form that a true average (say, of demand) is equal to a (i.e., $H_0: \mu = a$), where a represents the value being used in the solution. The alternative values λ which μ could have are represented along the horizontal axis. The units of λ are given in terms of the true standard deviation of the population (i.e., σ units). Deviations from a can be both positive and negative.

One unit away from the zero point on the scale represents the event in which the true mean value μ is now one standard deviation σ away

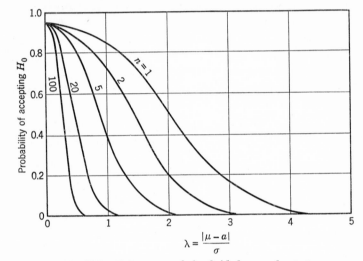

$$\lambda = \frac{|\mu - a|}{\sigma}$$

Fig. 21-1. O.C. curves of the 2-sided normal z test.

from the value a being used in the solution. For example, suppose we want to test the hypothesis that the true average demand per month is \$125,000. Then, if the true standard deviation of the readings of a set of data on demand per month is \$11,200, one unit along the base line represents a possible true situation in which the true average demand for a specific month actually lies between \$113,800 and \$136,200. Two units would represent the possibility that the true average lies between \$102,600 and \$147,400, etc.

The curves drawn in Fig. 21-1 represent the probabilities that we will accept the hypothesis of no change H_0 for each possible value that the true mean may have. When H_0 is actually true (and hence $\mu = a$), and if we use an 0.05 significance level, the curve passes through the 0.95 probability point at $\lambda = 0$. This means that, when H_0 is true, the probability is 0.95 that H_0 will be accepted, and hence the probability is $1 - 0.95$, or 0.05, that it will be rejected when it is true. As we move to the right, and consider possible type II errors, the probability of acceptance begins to drop. We observe that the behavior of this curve depends upon how large the sample is. If, for example, we conduct the test with only two observations,* then the probability of acceptance is about 0.72 when we move out one σ unit, whereas if we use 20 observations the probability of acceptance is about 0.04. The larger the sample, the less probable it is that we will accept H_0 when a very large change has occurred. Figure 21-1 shows how the O.C. curve drops much more sharply for larger samples. For the very small samples of one or two observations, the probability of accepting the null hypothesis when it is false is still quite high even when we go out as far as two σ units.†

DETECTION OF AND ADJUSTMENT FOR SIGNIFICANT CHANGES. Ideally, in the design of a control system for a variable, six interdependent decisions should be made if possible. (In some situations there may be no choice with regard to one or more of these decisions.) The decisions are as follows:

1. The frequency of (i.e., period between) control checks.
2. The number of observations per control check, if more than one is possible.
3. The way items should be selected for observation (i.e., the sampling design) if more than one observation is specified.
4. The statistical testing procedure to be used to determine whether or not a value has changed.
5. The specific decision rule based on the test.
6. The action to be taken if the test indicates that a parameter's value has changed.

Again, ideally, these decisions should be made in such a way as to minimize the sum of the following costs:

1. The cost of taking the observations.
2. The cost of performing the test.
3. The expected cost of a type I error (i.e., the cost of changing a value when it is not warranted).
4. The expected cost of type II errors (i.e., the cost of not changing a value when it is warranted).

In some cases we may be more concerned with minimizing the maximum cost or some other cost characteristic other than the expected cost. Exploration of these possibilities would be too lengthy for a book of this type. Consequently, attention is directed to one cost

---

* The O.C. curve shown is based on the assumption that the observations which are made are a random sample of the population of possible observations, that the population is normal, and that the specific statistical test mentioned above is used.

† For further discussion of the two types of error see refs. 3, 26, 27, and 28.

function, the expected cost, because it is the most frequently used decision criterion in designing such control procedures.*

Unfortunately, at the present time the six decisions listed cannot be made in such a way as to assure minimization of the sum of the four costs. The design of an optimizing procedure can be specified in general terms; i.e., a model can be constructed which expresses the total expected cost as an abstract (but not as a concrete) function of the six decisions. In addition, some of the expressions which would appear in the model cannot be evaluated. In most situations, for example, the expected costs associated with type I and type II errors cannot be determined. Furthermore, the required O.C. curves or equations (power functions) from which they are derived are not available.

Some brief remarks on the problems involved can be made here; for further reading see references 3, 21, 27, and 28. It can be seen that the theory of inference has become a part of the total theory of decision making, in which values, in the sense of what outcomes are found *desirable*, enter in as critical determinants of behavior. The modern trend seems to be away from "intuitive" bases for reasoning and towards economically oriented bases. Indeed, one may *want* to use a "biased" method of testing simply because it does the most desirable thing *in toto*.

In addition to the O.C. curves, we also talk of "cost" curves, which portray the cost of accepting a hypothesis under various conditions. The estimates of cost can only be obtained by associating some course of action with each hypothesis. In effect, the verbal or symbolic hypothesis is only a convenient intermediary between evidence (the observations) and action.

To illustrate this point, consider two cost curves relative to two possible actions. The first action might be to accept a lot of material. The second action might be to reject the lot. The "situations" in which these actions take place can be represented by the true but unknown proportion defective p in the lot. Thus, for the first course of action, the cost of acceptance is virtually zero up to, say, 1% defective, and then begins to rise, and rises rather sharply at 3% because of customer reactions. The cost of rejection implies lost material, for example, and is therefore linear with respect to p. It can be seen that, with respect to acceptance, there is an area of indifference between 0% and 1% defective, so that the correct verbal hypothesis is

$$H_0 : p \leq 0.01$$

$$H_1 : p > 0.01$$

* For discussion of decision criteria in statistical testing see refs. 3, 26, 27, and 28.

Suppose there are two distinct methods for testing the lot. Which is better? The obvious suggestion is to multiply the probability of accepting H_0 by the cost of accepting H_0, plus the probability of accepting H_1 times the cost of accepting H_1, for each value of p. We thus derive a "risk" function for each method; i.e., the risk equals the cost for a given value of p times the probability of acceptance.

In order to evaluate the methods in terms of the risk function, it is necessary to know how often various values of p may occur. For example, it may happen that no lots with p values over 3% ever occur. If this is the case, then the behavior of the risk function for $p > 0.03$ should be ignored in judging methods.

Thus the judgment of a method of testing hypotheses depends on some statement about the a priori values of the parameters like p in the illustration given above. This is one of the critical problems of modern statistical decision theory. One attitude, based on the classical "principle of insufficient reason," says that if no knowledge about p exists, then one should assume that any value is as likely to occur as any other. This would mean that, in judging methods of testing hypotheses, one should take the total area under the risk curve as the measure of the inefficiency of the method (that method with the smallest total risk is best). Another attitude says that if no prior information exists, one should consider the situation as though one were playing a game. The experimenter's method of testing is like a strategy in a game. "Nature" is the opponent, and Nature's strategy consists of some particular value of the parameters. If Nature is a conscious opponent, she will "choose" that value of p which will produce the greatest expected loss for the experimenter. Hence the experimenter should play so as to minimize the effect of Nature's strategy, i.e., to minimize maximum risk.

To illustrate this point, we can set up a game theory matrix. We assume that the experimenter has only two choices, Method I and Method II. These are his strategies. We assume, further, that p can only take on the values 1, 2, 3, or 4%. These are Nature's possible strategies. The matrix, therefore, is

| | Nature | | | |
Experimenter	$p = 1\%$	$p = 2\%$	$p = 3\%$	$p = 4\%$
Method I	100	250	255	225
Method II	50	175	325	175

The values in the matrix are the "payoffs," which, for this problem, are always positive payoffs on the part of the experimenter to Nature (they are "penalty" costs and not actual over-all losses). The experimenter may be prone to choose Method II, since it has the minimum loss (50). But if he does choose this method, Nature (assuming her to be vindictive) will choose $p = 3\%$, with a consequent serious loss to the experimenter. If he chooses Method I, Nature will still choose $p = 3\%$ and both players will do as well as possible [the cell (Method I, $p = 3\%$) is a saddle point]. Hence the experimenter chooses Method I.

Methodologically, the interesting point is that to determine finally what method is best, one has to make certain assumptions about the parameters which are being tested. But if one knows the probability distribution of p, as in the illustration above, why should one test hypotheses about p? The answer lies in recognizing the "cycularity" of all scientific research, including hypothesis-testing. One assumes a basis for evaluating methods of testing hypotheses; the tested hypotheses can be used eventually to test the assumption for evaluating methods (e.g., the tests will begin to provide information concerning the distribution of true percentage defectives in lots). The cycularity of research only becomes a vicious circle if one does not make any progress as a result of the effort.

Despite these critical problems, various degrees of approximation to an optimum design of a control system are possible. These depend on the specific circumstances of the study. We cannot specify one procedure for designing control systems that approximates an optimum in all situations. Instead, we can make some general remarks on control, and subsequently illustrate these by specific case studies. Further details on control methods are given in references 6, 9, 13, 15, 17, 18, 22, 23, and 24.

1. When the testing in the control procedure indicates that a value has changed significantly, a new value should not be substituted automatically. An attempt to find the cause of the change (i.e., the "assignable cause") should be made. If such a cause is found then it may be a cause that will not continue and hence the substitution should not be made. For example, the mean of a distribution of "demand per month" may appear to go out of control in a month in which an "improbably" high demand occurs. The reason may be that a price increase has been announced to take effect on the following month and buyers are trying to stock up before the increase. In such a case, return to "normal" fluctuations can be predicted and no change need be made. Furthermore, a discovery of an assignable cause may indicate a variable which should be included as part of the model and solution. In the illustration just used, for example, the production

planners who apply the decision rule should receive early notification of future price changes so that they can adjust the estimated demand accordingly. The assignable cause which is found may not be an intermittent one but may represent a relatively constant change in the system. The introduction of automatic production equipment, for instance, may significantly affect setup and direct labor costs.

2. If no assignable cause can be found then the new value should be substituted for the old, but particular attention should be given to the value in the immediately succeeding periods to see if and how its value "settles down," and also to search for any clues to the cause(s) for the change.

3. The frequency with which a value should be checked (i.e., the control interval) can be determined by the time period between successive applications of the decision rule. If, for example, production is planned each month, then the value should be checked once a month.

4. In some cases there is only one occurrence of the event to be observed during the control period. For instance, monthly requirements can only be determined once a month; then, if the control period is 1 month, there is no question as to sample size.

5. If larger samples can be drawn, the use of a statistical control procedure may assume that the observations which can be made in any time interval are a random sample of the observations generated in all such time intervals.* It is important to check this assumption of temporal randomness. In so doing we may also improve the accuracy of the estimates used in the solution.

6. Up to this point we have been concerned with controlling individual values. In practice, however, simultaneous changes may occur in several measures. Two changes, each of which is insignificant if it occurs alone, may be significant when they occur at the same time. The possible combinations of changes are usually so numerous that the operations researchers cannot feasibly plan for every possible combination. This means that these situations must be analyzed as they arise. Part of the control methods described are needed to determine what changes have occurred but the significance of simultaneous changes usually must be decided as the changes arise. To provide such treatment control responsibility should be assigned to personnel (the O.R. team or others) who thoroughly understand how the solu-

---

* This is not the same as assuming that the observations made in any particular time interval are a random sample of possible observations in that same interval. Both assumptions are made if a sample of observations is taken within the control interval but the one mentioned in this note is supported by the use of random sampling procedures.

tion or decision rule was developed. Such knowledge is necessary for determining the significance of simultaneous changes and how to adjust for them.

Before turning to illustrations, let us consider the other aspect of control, mentioned above.

Controlling Relationships

Every probability distribution asserts a relationship between the probability of an event and the values of other variables. In the case of distributions which appear in the model and solution, as, for example, the distribution of demand, the parameters which define the distribution must be controlled (e.g., the mean and variance) as well as the form of the distribution (e.g., normal or Poisson). Both aspects of the distribution should be subjected to control.

Control over the parameters of a distribution (e.g., the mean and variance) is accomplished in the same way as it is for any other measure and hence needs no separate discussion. There are, however, no "standard" procedures for controlling the form of a distribution. Such control may be obtained by periodically testing the "goodness of fit" in the manner given by standard statistics texts. The frequency with which such tests should be conducted depends on the rate at which data are generated. The visual plotting of data, as they become available, can frequently indicate when a check should be made. For instance, in the case of a normal distribution, periodic plots of the data can be made on normal probability paper on which the assumed distribution is also plotted. Examination of these charts can provide clues to changes in the parameters of the distribution as well as to the form.*

The control of relationships which do not take the form of probability distributions also involves control over the form of the function which relates the variables and the values of the variables. Suppose the model contains the expression nc, where n is the number of units per production run and c is the direct labor cost per unit. The expression nc is taken as the cost of direct labor per run. A multiplication relationship is asserted between n and c. Control of this expression has two parts.

First, the goodness of the fit of the straight line nc to the most recently observed data on direct labor cost per run should be periodically checked. An increase in run size may, for example, increase the efficiency of labor so that the unit cost decreases as n increases. This would show up on a visual plot of total cost against n.

* For details on tests for normality see refs. 6 and 8.

Second, the deviations of the observed direct labor cost per run from the theoretical cost nc should be plotted against time and tested for randomness. If the observed time series is not random then the value of the direct labor cost per run is dependent on time and, hence, time should be introduced as a variable in the relationship. The reason for this time dependence (e.g., increased experience of machine operators) should be determined so that control over the causal system can be maintained.

Every O.R. project has unique characteristics which create unique control problems but which also offer challenging opportunities for the development of unusual control procedures. There is a good deal of room for scientific creativity in this phase of the research. This is illustrated in the three cases which follow. In each of these cases control procedures were developed which are well adapted to the uniqueness of the problem.

Examples of Control Systems

CASE 1.* In a production and inventory control project performed for the Mullins Manufacturing Company, the monthly sales forecast of certain kitchen sinks was computed as one-third the average quarterly sales (based on the last four quarters). Though this forecast was found to be better than a number of alternatives which were tested, it had poor reliability (its variance was large) and hence it was considered to be relatively unstable. It was possible to show by retrospective testing that if the solution were applied without critically evaluating the forecast each time a production schedule was prepared, serious shortages would result. A control system was set up for this variable as follows:

A study of several years of past data revealed that a shortage never occurred in a month for which the ratio of beginning inventory to sales for that month was greater than 0.14. That is, this ratio was an indication of the amount of production lead time required, in practice, to fill inventory before a shortage occurred.

Since production for a given month is planned before that month's sales are known, the forecast itself must be used in computing this ratio. Inventory at the beginning of the month planned must also be estimated. Unfavorable estimated ratios of beginning inventories to sales for a planned month thus indicate poor previous forecasts for which corrections should be made. That is, if the estimated ratio is less than 0.14, more than the normal production quantity (computed by an order quantity equation) is required, and it is given a high priority.

* A complete description of this project can be found in refs. 11, 12, and 16.

If, on the other hand, the estimated ratio is greater than 1.14, no production should be required for the planned month. A simple chart was prepared to assist the planner. It is shown in Fig. 21-2.

Each month, for each item, a point was plotted which represents the forecast inventory-to-sales ratio. This point can fall into any one of the five areas shown. Note the area marked "No-go—Recompute."

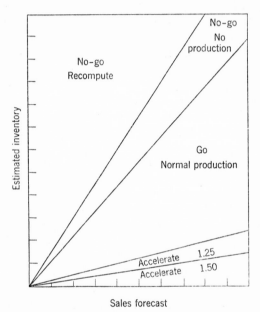

Sales forecast

Fig. 21-2. Production control chart for a given month.

This indicates that a permanent change in the forecasting method is probably required. A study of the economics of change of operations indicated that a finer set of instructions than those given on the chart was not justified. Use of this control chart, together with the production quantity decision rule derived from a model of the process, has yielded a considerable reduction of inventory and at the same time has virtually eliminated shortages.

CASE 2.* In another study done at the Lamp Division of the General Electric Company, a considerable reduction in the number of sales calls required per account per year was indicated. Retrospective testing indicated no short-range effect (over 2 years) on sales volume by such reductions. However, sufficient data were not available for determining whether or not there might be any significant long-range

---

* A complete description of this project can be found in refs. 1 and 4.

effects. Consequently, a procedure had to be developed to determine if and when such long-range effects occurred.

The procedure developed consists of conducting periodic multiple regression analyses between current sales volume by account and past changes in the annual number of calls made on the account. For example, at the end of 1955 the regression of 1955 sales volume (by account) was determined on changes in the number of calls from: *a.* 1952 to 1953, *b.* 1953 to 1954, and *c.* 1954 to 1955. At the end of 1956, another variable will be added: *d.* changes in calls from 1955 to 1956. This will continue until a period of 10 years has been covered. If decreases in sales volume in any one year are found to be significantly related to call-reductions in any one or combination of years, then a change in policy can be made.

In order to make these periodic control checks as powerful as possible, it was necessary to arrange for the collection of better sales-call data than were previously available. New sales report forms were designed and put into use for this purpose.

CASE 3.* The company that sponsored this project is a chemical producer with average annual gross sales of approximately 55 million dollars. Its production is centered in seven plants spread around the country. The company employs approximately 2500 persons. Their products are numerous and varied and involve bacteriological as well as chemical processing.

This particular project involved the control of the production and inventory of three products which are designated here as A, B, and C. These products are processed in one plant and all begin in the same fermentation process. Differentiation between them occurs at later stages of the approximately 50-step process.

After an intensive study of the system the O.R. team developed a production-planning procedure. In this procedure it was important to take into account the interval between the time of scheduling (t_0) and the time at which the product scheduled at t_0 became available (t_1). The interval (t_0, t_1) had been established as being 10 days.

The planning procedure was as follows:

1. At the time of planning (t_0) the amount of each product in stock (S_{OA}, S_{OB}, and S_{OC}) is determined.

2. The highest 10-day sale of each product in the preceding nine 10-day periods (X_A, X_B, and X_C) is determined. Then the estimates of sales for the intervals (t_0, t_1) and (t_1, t_2) are fX_A, fX_B, and fX_C, where f is a safety factor defined as the smallest value which, when

---

* A complete description of this project can be found in ref. 2.

used in this planning procedure, yields no shortages. Analysis of past data showed that the value of f was 2.0.

3. Then, the amounts of stock, S_1, desired at t_1 are also fX_A, fX_B, and fX_C.

4. The quantity of product A, Q_A, to be produced during (t_0, t_1) is found from the equation

$$Q_A = fX_A - (S_{OA} + a_{OA} - fX_A) = 2fX_A - S_{OA} - a_{OA}$$

where a_{OA} is the amount of product A to be added to stock in the interval (t_0, t_1). Q_B and Q_C are similarly determined.

Suppose, for example, that 25 units of a product are in stock at t_0 (i.e., $S_0 = 25$), and that 75 units were planned for production during the last period and will become available during (t_0, t_1) (i.e., $a_0 = 75$). Suppose further that the highest sale in the previous nine 10-day periods is 35 units (i.e., $X = 35$). Assume that a safety factor of 2 is used (i.e., $f = 2$). Then the number of units to be produced (Q) is determined as follows:

$$Q = (2)(2)(35) - (25) - (75) = 40$$

To aid in planning production, a table was prepared to show the yields of the three products for various levels of fermentation in a 10-day period. Because of the nature of the process, when A is scheduled certain amounts of B and C become available. By using this table, the expected yield of the products could be determined, knowing only the flow of materials from each fermentor. A work sheet was also prepared to aid in planning for each 10-day period.

In the first retrospective test of this simple planning procedure, no attempt was made to limit the change in number of fermentors set up from one scheduling period to the next scheduling period. The results of applying this procedure retrospectively to the period beginning January 1950, and ending December 1952, were as follows: no shortages occurred; the average inventory of A was decreased by 58%; the average inventory of B was decreased by 63%; and the average inventory of C was decreased by 56% as compared to actual average inventories of the 3-year period being studied. Also, these reductions were reflected in the reduced total number of fermentors required. In the 3-year period a reduction of 17% of fermentors required was obtained. Thus, both inventory costs and production costs would have been reduced by this method.

Other studies had shown that the carrying cost of money invested in finished products, storage, supervision, obsolescence, deterioration, etc., amounted to about 2% of the cost of the finished product per month. On the basis of the 2% per month figure, an approximate cost of inventories for the 3-year period was computed. In this retrospective trial of the planning procedure the average monthly cost of inventories was reduced by 42%.

These results were very encouraging. But in this retrospective test the level of production was subjected to frequent and severe fluctuations. This required frequent changes in the number of work crews employed. Such changes were unacceptable to the company because of the labor problems that would have arisen out of hiring and laying off men as production fluctuated.

The company has a plant seniority system in which any one personnel change in the plant making the product may require five different personnel changes in other plants. In this system, if a man is needed in that particular plant he can be drawn from another job that, in turn, can pick a man from a lower ranking job, according to the company's seniority system. This system requires in all a possible shift of five different people, because of the five different levels of seniority. Such an arrangement can result in increased training costs and in delays in the increase of production. For these reasons, an acceptable production-planning procedure had to be accompanied by labor stabilization; i.e., it must require only a minimum number of transfers either into or out of the plant involved. Data were obtained to show the labor force that would be needed within the plant to handle various production levels.

The average fermentation rate of all production plans examined was at a level requiring three crews. This raised the question: If three crews had been employed during these 3 years (1950–1952), and if production had varied from the minimum to the maximum for the three crews, what inventories would have developed, and what shortages would have existed? The same basic planning method was then reapplied to the 3-year period, with the imposed limitations of a three-crew operation. In this retrospective run all sales demands were met over the 3-year period, and inventories were reduced as follows: A, 39%, B, 57%, and C, 57%, or a decrease in inventory costs of about 40%. Also, the number of fermentors needed to be set up could have been reduced by as much as 18%.

This planning procedure in its revised form was subsequently applied prospectively on paper to the first 8 months in 1953. All sales demands were met and no shortages were incurred.

As indicated in the preceding the planning procedure described was tested by applying it retrospectively to the last 3 years of operation.

The results spoke for themselves, but they raised two serious questions:

1. Why does this planning procedure work?
2. What assurance is there that it will continue to work? Or, more constructively, how and when can modifications be made in the procedure to keep it working effectively?

This planning procedure is designed around two basic characteristics of sales:

1. In general, the amount sold in any one planning period did not exceed twice the largest sale in any of the planning periods in the preceding 3 months.
2. The average 10-day sales requirements could be met by a three-crew operation, with no recycling.

To assure the continued usefulness of this planning procedure, it is necessary to check these two characteristics to detect changes in them. Furthermore, it is necessary to have methods of determining when and how to change the planning procedure, if these characteristics change. First, let us consider the scheduling factor.

The following ratio for each product was plotted for a period of the past 41 months: actual sales of the month to the highest monthly sales in the preceding 3 months. The results for A are shown in Fig. 21-3. The results for the other products were quite similar.

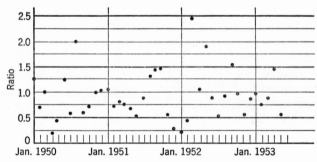

Fig. 21-3. Control chart for A's planning safety factor (ratio of actual sales to highest monthly sales in preceding 3 months).

It will be noted that the ratios tend to fall in the range from 0.5 to 1.5 with an estimated mean of 1.0. As indicated in the preceding discussion, studies showed that a planning factor of 2 is needed for ratios that fall in this range to avoid shortages during the period studied.

For example, when a factor of 1.75 is used, shortages do occur.* Figure 21-3 can be used for control purposes. As long as the ratios fall within these bands, it will be safe in general to use a safety factor of 2.

If a point fell outside the control limits the production planners were instructed to look first for an assignable cause. For example, the observed ratio of almost 2.5 shown in Fig. 21-3 was due to a price increase which was announced by the company, to go into effect the following month. In this particular plot an assignable cause was found for each point that went out of control. Each different type of assignable cause that was revealed in turn revealed a relevant variable which was not included in the model and should be, if there were no problem of implementation. In this case, however, it was simpler to specify changes in the system to be looked for (such as price changes) and the necessary corrective action. Since it was found that the scheduling procedure prevented shortages even in the "out of control above" periods, but just did so in several cases, the adjustment rule developed was to increase the safety factor f from 2.0 to 2.5 if two consecutive points went "out of control above" and there was no reason to expect them to come back in control. The planners were instructed, in such an eventuality, to prepare a new control chart with limits at 1.0 and 2.0.

Both of the occurrences of a sequence of points below the 0.5 limit were due to assignable and predictable causes. Analysis showed that excessive inventories would not have resulted from them if the scheduling procedure had been used. The rule of adjustment developed, then, was that if three points fell below 0.5 and there was no reason to expect them to go back in control, the safety factor f should be changed to 1.5 and the limits should be drawn at 0 and 1.0.

Now let us consider the question of crew level. Let O_h represent the highest monthly sales in the preceding 3 months. Then, according to the scheduling procedure, $2(O_h/3)$ or $\frac{2}{3}O_h$ will be scheduled for availability during the first 10-day period. At the end of each month, the ratio of average monthly inventory to the total monthly sales can be computed, where the average monthly inventory is the sum of the inventory at the start of each planning period divided by three. This may be compared with upper and lower limits expected for this ratio, on the assumption that the safety factor (2) remains in control. The calculation of approximations to these limits is made as follows:

In accordance with use of a safety factor of 2, actual sales for a month should not be more than $1.50O_h$ nor less than $0.50O_h$; i.e., not more than $\frac{1}{2}O_h$ nor less than $\frac{1}{6}O_h$ for a 10-day period. Planning is for

* By such computations it was possible to show the company how much it would cost to avoid various numbers of shortages.

10-day periods, and planners take into account actual sales as they become known. Using the limits associated with a safety factor of 2 (i.e., 0.5 and 1.5), the upper limit and lower limit for the ratio of average inventory to actual monthly sales are found to be approximately 2.33 and 0.63 respectively. These latter approximate limits are computed as follows: If O_h represents the highest sale in the preceding 3 months, then, on the assumption of equal sales during each 10-day period of the month, $\frac{1}{3}O_h$ may be taken as the highest sale in any of the preceding nine 10-day periods. Planning is then directed toward producing $\frac{2}{3}O_h$ for the first period in the new month.

Table 21-1 shows what happens when the lowest value in the expected range of sales is obtained. Similarly, Table 21-2 shows what

TABLE 21-1. UPPER LIMIT CALCULATIONS

10-Day Period	Inventory (Production + "Left-over")	Expected Sales
1	$\frac{2}{3}O_h$	$\frac{1}{3}(0.5O_h)$
2	$\frac{2}{3}O_h + \frac{2}{3}O_h - \frac{1}{6}O_h = \frac{7}{6}O_h$	$\frac{1}{3}(0.5O_h)$
3	$\frac{2}{3}O_h + \frac{7}{6}O_h - \frac{1}{6}O_h = \frac{5}{3}O_h$	$\frac{1}{3}(0.5O_h)$
Total	$\frac{7}{2}O_h$	$\frac{1}{2}O_h$

Average inventory $\frac{7}{2}O_h/3 = \frac{7}{6}O_h$.
Average inventory to total monthly sales = $(\frac{7}{6}O_h)/(\frac{1}{2}O_h) = 2.33$.

happens when the highest value in the expected range of sales is obtained.

TABLE 21-2. LOWER LIMIT CALCULATIONS

10-Day Period	Inventory (Production + "Left-Over")	Expected Sales
1	$\frac{2}{3}O_h$	$\frac{1}{3}(1.5O_h)$
2	$\frac{2}{3}O_h + \frac{2}{3}O_h - \frac{1}{2}O_h = \frac{5}{6}O_h$	$\frac{1}{3}(1.5O_h)$
3 *	$O_h + \frac{5}{6}O_h - \frac{1}{2}O_h = \frac{4}{3}O_h$	$\frac{1}{3}(1.5O_h)$
Total	$\frac{17}{6}O_h$	$\frac{3}{2}O_h$

Average inventory $17O_h/(6 \times 3) = \frac{17}{18}O_h$.
Average inventory to total monthly sales = $(\frac{17}{18}O_h)/(\frac{3}{2}O_h) = \frac{17}{27} = 0.63$.

* At the beginning of the second period (when one plans for production of goods that become available during the third period), the first period's sales are known. In this case it is assumed to be $\frac{1}{3}(1.5O_h)$. The forecast demand for the third period, then, is $2[\frac{1}{3}(1.5O_h)] = O_h$.

The ratios of average total monthly inventory (over-all product types) to total monthly sales are plotted in Fig. 21.4. The upper and lower control limits (2.33 and 0.63) are also shown. When a plotted ratio goes over the upper limit, it indicates inventory may be becoming too large and when it goes under the lower limit it indicates that inventory may be becoming too small.

The general conformity of these data to theoretical expectations indicates why the retrospective tests which maintained a three-crew-level operation were so successful. None of the inventory to sales ratios for the retrospective trial of the new planning procedure fell outside the control limits as did the ratios yielded by actual performance as shown in Fig. 21-4. Furthermore, analysis of actual inventories

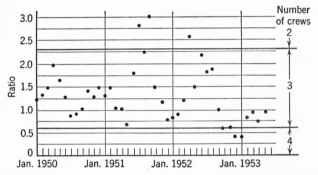

Fig. 21-4. Control chart for crew operation (ratio of average monthly inventory to total monthly sales).

at the out-of-control points revealed critically low or high inventories or shortages. Since the cost of changing the level of operation is quite high, a relatively high degree of assurance of a "real" change is required before a change is recommended. Instructions are to change the crew level only after three consecutive points are out of control in the same direction.

The graphic device, Fig. 21-4, cannot be used alone. Sales forecasts must be taken into consideration when deciding whether crew levels should be changed. The device does, however, show clearly when operations at a three-crew level begin to build too large or too small inventories. It is important to note, however, that its use assumes that the planning factor is in control. If the planning factor is not in control, the inventory sales ratio will probably also go out of control, but the trouble may be with the planning factor and not the crew level.

These two control devices require supplementation by good judgment and knowledge of general and special business conditions. They cannot be applied automatically.

IMPLEMENTATION

Once the solution has been derived and tested, it is ready to be put to work. Conversion of the solution into operation may not appear to be of direct concern to the research team but it should be for two reasons:

1. No matter how much care has been taken in deriving a decision rule and testing it, shortcomings may still appear when it is put into operation or ways of improving the solution may become apparent. If adjustment of the decision rule to take care of unforeseen operating problems is left in the hands of those who do not understand how it was derived, the adjustment may seriously eat into its effectiveness. Operating personnel may, for example, see no harm in making what appears to them to be a slight change, but such a change may be critical.

2. Carrying out the solution may not be as obvious a procedure in the context of complex operations as it initially appears to be to the researchers. The solution must be translated into a procedure that is workable if its potential is to be fully realized. The procedure must be as accurate a translation of the solution as is practically feasible and only the researchers can minimize the loss in the solution's effectiveness that is incurred in this translation.

The nature of the implementation problem depends on whether the solution pertains to a one-time or repetitive decision. In the case of one-time decisions the problem is simpler but by no means disappears. This discussion will be directed primarily toward the repetitive decision because of its greater complexity.

The problem of implementation cannot be separated from problems of organizing and administering the research but, although these phases of the problem are considered in the case presented in the foregoing, detailed discussion of them is not provided until the next chapter. Here we concern ourselves only with the translation of the solution into an operating procedure.

It must be admitted that at the current stage of development of O.R. no well-formulated methodology of implementation is available. O.R. has been preoccupied with the development of techniques and tools, but it is beginning to catch up with the implementation problem. The methodology that can be recorded now is rather obvious, but this does not mean that its application is automatic. Doing even the obvious is considerably better than leaving implementation completely in the hands of operating or even management personnel.

Translation of the solution into the operating procedure involves answering three questions and proceeding accordingly. The three questions are:

1. Who should do what?
2. When?
3. What information and facilities are required to do it?

On the basis of the answers to these questions the operating procedure can be designed and any necessary training and transition can be planned and executed.

Implementation of a solution involves people taking action. These people must be identified and the required action must be specified. The details cannot be enumerated without a thorough knowledge of the operations and the division of responsibility in the organization under study. The analysis of the organization (discussed in Chapter 4) provides much of the needed information and the rest should be provided by management and operating people working with the research team. This and the other phases of implementation require continuous co-operation and communication between management, operators, and researchers. The question of how to organize for such co-operation is discussed in the next chapter.

Each person who is given responsibility for initiating action in carrying out the solution or using the decision rule should be instructed as to when they are to take action. The tools required to do the job should be made available to those who need them and these people should be trained in their use. The tools should not be too complex for the operating personnel to use. It may be necessary, for example, to convert even a simple equation into a nomograph (as was done in the case reported in Chapter 2) or tables. In some cases the tools may require simplification even if such simplification results in a loss of some of the original solution's power. The solution or decision rule is generally used by personnel whose mathematical sophistication is less than we desire. Consequently, if we want to assure use of our recommended decision rules, we must frequently simplify them before handing them over to executives and operating personnel. In many cases this means that we must either translate elegant solutions into approximations that are easy to use or side-step the elegance and move directly to a "quick-and-dirty" decision rule.

It should be realized that in one sense almost every solution in O.R. is an approximation and is "quick and dirty" to some degree. This follows from the fact that in constructing every model some simplifying assumptions are made. Reality is too difficult to represent in all its complexity. These simplifying assumptions reduce the generality of the model and solutions derived from it. But this is only a polite way of saying that quickness and dirtiness are involved. It is well for the operations researcher to realize that an approximate solution which is used may be a great deal better than a more exact solution which is not.

The case which follows illustrates the importance and complexity of the implementation phase of O.R.

Case Study in Implementation

In Chapter 4 a case was described involving a company which produces a major piece of equipment used in trucks, boats, and construction equipment. It will be recalled that analysis of the company's production organization revealed that development of a decision rule to govern purchase and production quantities would not solve the company's problems. It would not do so because it was found that such rules could not be implemented effectively. The difficulties arose because of the length of time required to process sales orders and the lack of information required for use of the decision rules. An analysis of the system led to a set of recommendations which were directed toward implementing the decision rules which were developed:

1. Reduction of the number of different groups handling the order so as to remove duplication of effort.

2. Provision of adequate reference files for groups handling the order to facilitate handling the bulk of the orders as standard.

3. Physical relocation of the groups handling the order to replace written communication with oral communication.

4. Redesign of the forms used in the order-processing procedure so as to include all, and only, the pertinent information.

5. Establishment of effective controls on the release of engineering changes in the product and the dissemination of this information.

It was felt that these changes in the order-processing procedure would reduce the average time required to process an order from 3 weeks to 1 week in addition to making possible the use of economic purchase- and production-lot equations.

The recommended production and inventory control system was designed so as to utilize an IBM 650 digital computer. The general procedure which was to be used in this system was as follows:

1. Policy information would be supplied to the Tabulating Department by the Material Control Department.

2. Routine decisions would be performed on the IBM 650 digital computer.

3. As a result of the information issued from the Tabulating Department, production and purchasing decisions would be made by the Material Control Department.

It was felt that this system would provide means for effectively controlling the level of inventory and for decreasing shortages and the need for expediting.

As a result of the new order-processing procedure and production and inventory control system, parts requirements would be known, on the average, 1 week after receipt of the customer's order by the company. By utilizing the computer, a current inventory balance would be known at all times. In addition, the controls recommended in the new system would yield a means for determining future inventory requirements.

The decision rules and the implementation recommendations were submitted to the company's management after 6 months of study by the O.R. team. At this time, management gave its full approval for the implementation of the recommendations into the company's operations. The following 12 months were spent on the implementation itself. During this phase of the study, the company enjoyed a substantial increase in business which complicated the implementation by generating new problems. If these problems had not been faced by the research team much of the power of the decision rules would have been lost.

In the design of the implementation program a number of factors were considered important. The major factors were:

METHOD OF COMMUNICATION TO MANAGEMENT. During the implementation periodic verbal reports were given to management together with the appropriate visual aids. These reports gave the status of the implementation, emphasizing not only the progress that had been made but also the areas in which management decisions were needed and where management could put more emphasis. These reports were concise so that management would not be burdened with more details than were necessary for their understanding of the status of the work.

METHOD OF COMMUNICATION TO SUPERVISORS. Shortly after management had given approval for the implementation, a meeting was held for all supervisors. At this meeting, the major changes which were to take place in the company were presented together with the reasons for conducting the study and the benefits which would accrue from the study. After an introduction by a member of management, members of the O.R. team gave this presentation. Further meetings with the supervisors regarding their particular areas of work were held when necessary in the progressive stages of implementation.

METHOD OF COMMUNICATION TO NONSUPERVISORY PERSONNEL. The nonsupervisory personnel in areas affected by the implementation were given group presentations similar to the one given to the supervisors. The pertinent details for the specific area in which they were concerned were discussed. After these presentations individual training sessions were held with these people in which the details of their roles were explained, their questions were encouraged, and their problems were discussed thoroughly.

During these meetings stress was placed on "data discipline," or the timely and accurate preparation of information which flows through the communication system. No system which involves paper work, no matter how well designed, is any better than the accuracy of the paper work which is fed into the system. For example, inspection tickets must specify the correct part identification as well as the correct number of units inspected, passed, and rejected. If this information is incorrect, inventory balances will be misleading and new lots of parts may be ordered when they are not needed or shortages will occur which could have been prevented.

OVER-ALL POINT OF VIEW. During the implementation stages of the study, as well as in the earlier stages, the O.R. team kept in mind the over-all point of view. One tool which the team found effective in this study was a time chart. The implementation phase of the project was divided into its logical subdivisions. For each subdivision, a tentative schedule was set up together with the progress to date. Periodically, the progress-to-date line was reviewed. By this means the team was able to evaluate the progress in each of the areas of the study and, at the same time, not lose sight of the general objectives.

During the implementation phase of the study, the team continued to make refinements on the new production and inventory control systems. Often the original recommendations were modified in the light of what was learned at this stage. By keeping the over-all point of view, the team was in a position to evaluate the effect of any modification on the entire system.

An implementation problem such as this one which encompassed nearly all of the company's operations was, by necessity, a long-drawn-out procedure. There were times when people became somewhat discouraged at the apparent lack of progress and the delay before seeing the full benefits accruing from the changes. It was a major task of the O.R. team to know the company personnel well enough to sense this type of attitude and arrange to make informal visits to discuss the situation, bringing the necessary words of encouragement.

Taking into account the personalities involved was perhaps the most crucial part of this implementation program. Knowing how and when to approach the company personnel was the key to the success of the implementation.

CONCLUSION

There is a tendency among researchers to lose patience with a problem once they have solved it on paper. They are anxious to get on to the next problem and leave the "dirty" work of control and implementation to others. This impatience more than anything else is responsible for the fact that so many paper solutions are either never put into effect or, if put into effect, yield such disappointing results. Not only must the operations researcher realize that control and implementation are important to the success of the project but also that these phases of a project present a real challenge to scientific method. In implementation we deal with the most difficult subject matter confronted by science, people, and social groups.

As illustrated in the preceding case the design of a control system and implementation procedure is only part of attaining control and putting the results to work. Organization, training, and administration play an important role in these phases of the research as well as in the preceding phases. Management, those who carry out management decisions, and the researchers are part of a team whose success depends on how well their individual and combined efforts are organized, how well they have been trained for their respective jobs, and how well the research is administered. These are the subject of the next chapter.

BIBLIOGRAPHY

1. Ackoff, R. L., "Allocation of Sales Effort" in *Proceedings of the Conference on "What Is Operations Research Accomplishing in Industry?,"* Case Institute of Technology, Cleveland, 1955.
2. ———, "Production and Inventory Control in a Chemical Process," *J. Opns. Res. Soc. Am.,* 3, 319–338 (1955).
3. Churchman, C. W., *Theory of Experimental Inference,* The Macmillan Co., New York, 1948.
4. Davidson, W. E., "Operations Research in the Lamp Division of the General Electric Company," in *Proceedings of the Conference on "What Is Operations Research Accomplishing in Industry?,"* Case Institute of Technology, Cleveland, 1955.
5. Dixon, W. J., and Massey, F. J., Jr., *Introduction to Statistical Analysis,* McGraw-Hill Book Co., New York, 1951.
6. Duncan, A. J., *Quality Control and Industrial Statistics,* Richard D. Irwin. Chicago, 1952.

7. Ferris, C. D., Grubbs, F. E., and Weaver, C. L., "Operating Characteristics for the Common Tests of Significance," *Ann. math. Statist.*, *17*, 178–197 (1946).

8. Geary, R. C., and Pearson, E. S., *Tests of Normality*, Biometrika Office, London, 1938.

9. Grant, E. L., *Statistical Quality Control*, McGraw-Hill Book Co., New York, 2nd ed., 1952.

10. Hald, A., *Statistical Theory with Engineering Applications*, John Wiley & Sons, New York, 1952.

11. Hare, V. C., Jr., and Hugli, W. C., "Applications of Operations Research to Production Scheduling and Inventory Control, II," *Proceedings of the Conference on "What Is Operations Research Accomplishing in Industry?,"* Case Institute of Technology, Cleveland, 1955.

12. Hickox, C. H., "The Role of the Company Technician in Operations Research," in *Proceedings of the Conference on "What Is Operations Research Accomplishing in Industry?,"* Case Institute of Technology, Cleveland, 1955.

13. Juran, J. M. (ed.), *Quality Control Handbook*, McGraw-Hill Book Co., New York, 1946.

14. Kendall, M. G., and Smith B. B., "Randomness and Random Sampling of Numbers," *J. R. statist. Soc.*, *101*, 147–166 (1938).

15. Kennedy, C. W., *Quality Control Methods*, Prentice-Hall, New York, 1948.

16. Knecht, F. W., Jr., "Applications of Operations Research to Production Scheduling and Inventory Control, I," in *Proceedings of the Conference on "What Is Operations Research Accomplishing in Industry?,"* Case Institute of Technology, Cleveland, 1955.

17. Littauer, S. B., "Social Aspects of Scientific Method in Industrial Production," *Phil. Sci.*, *21*, 93–100 (1954).

18. ———, "Technological Stability in Industrial Operations," *Trans. N. Y. Acad. Sci.*, Ser. II, *13*, no. 2, 66–72 (1950).

19. ———, "The Development of Statistical Quality Control in the United States," *Amer. Statistician*, *4*, 14–20 (1950).

20. Mosteller, Frederick, "On Some Useful 'Inefficient' Statistics," *Ann. math. Statist.*, *17*, 377–408 (1946).

21. Neyman, Jerzy, and Pearson, E. S., "On the Problem of the Most Efficient Tests of Statistical Hypotheses," *Phil. Trans.*, Ser. A, *231*, 289–337 (1933).

22. Peach, Paul, *An Introduction to Industrial Statistics and Quality Control*, Edwards & Broughton Co., Raleigh, 2nd ed., 1947.

23. Rutherford, J. G., *Quality Control in Industry—Methods and Systems*, Pitman Publishing Corp., New York, 1948.

24. Shewhart, W. A., *Statistical Methods from the Viewpoint of Quality Control*, U. S. Department of Agriculture, Washington, 1939.

25. Tippett, L. H. C., *Technological Applications of Statistics*, John Wiley & Sons, New York, 1950.

26. Wald, Abraham, "Contributions to the Theory of Statistical Estimation and Testing Hypotheses," *Ann. math. Statist.*, *10*, 299–326 (1939).

27. ———, "On the Principles of Statistical Inference," in *Notre Dame Mathematical Lectures*, no. 1, Notre Dame University, Notre Dame, 1942.

28. ———, "Statistical Decision Functions," *Ann. math. Statist.*, *20*, 165–205 (1949).

PART X

ADMINISTRATION

OF OPERATIONS

RESEARCH

The organization that wishes to build an O.R. facility has three major administrative problems:

1. Selecting personnel from within or without the organization.
2. Training of personnel selected (except in the rare case where a trained team can be hired).
3. Organizing the team and its work.

These three problems are discussed in Chapter 22. It is the third problem that was anticipated in the discussion of implementation in Chapter 21.

Selection, Training,

and Organization

for Operations Research

INTRODUCTION

The day is probably coming when the statement that someone is an operations researcher will have as clearly recognized a meaning as the statement today that someone is, for example, a theoretical physicist. The label will carry with it an analogous rough identification of the training that the individual has had and what he can do. But until that day comes, selection and training will be major problems for any organization that wants to start O.R. activity.

The creation of the Operations Research Society of America and the Institute of Management Sciences and the very rapid growth of the literature in the field (particularly through the publication of the periodicals *Operations Research* * and *Management Science*) during the past few years have reduced one problem. Research personnel in many fields have heard of, and have become interested in, O.R. As a result, those charged with the selection of students and employees are relieved in part of the problem of explaining O.R. "from scratch" and are now able to exercise more choice than was available a scant few years ago. But the problem of whom to select and how to train them still remains.

It is extremely difficult, even in well-established fields, to provide good operational principles for the selection, training, and organization of professional personnel. The best that can be done in a new field is to provide rules of thumb based on the limited experience of

* Formerly *Journal of the Operations Research Society of America.*

those who have been in practice. Since such experience differs among practitioners, the guidance offered also differs. Consequently, no claim for authoritativeness is made for the content of this chapter.

Considerably more attention has been given to the organization of large independent O.R. groups working on military problems than to small groups working in and for industry. For an excellent presentation on large groups see McCloskey.[6] Most of the large groups' thinking is not applicable to industry. However, a good deal of thought has been given to industrial research and research teams in general,[1, 2, 4, 5] and some of this is applicable to the problems considered here. The principal problem confronting industries interested in O.R. is the question: How do we get started? In general there are three ways of getting started:

1. Start a group using only company personnel and, if none of the company personnel have been trained in O.R., hire into the company an experienced Operations Researcher.

2. Form a group consisting of company personnel *and* personnel from an O.R. agency hired on a contract or consulting basis until company personnel are able to carry on independently.

3. Engage an O.R. agency to perform the entire O.R. job for the company, using no company personnel.

The last alternative has advantages where a problem urgently requires solution. But it leaves the company with no capacity for performing its own O.R. Consequently, this discussion will be restricted to the first two of the alternatives listed.

SELECTION OF PERSONNEL

Here we are concerned primarily with professional characteristics rather than personality. The problem of selection involves personality, but not in any unique way with perhaps one exception. The ability to communicate with nonprofessionals is essential. The operations researcher in industry must be capable of making effective lay presentations of technical matters. He must be able to learn company and industry jargon, not only to speak it but to understand it when spoken by others. Most important, he must have a respect for the skills that make a good manager, foreman, and worker and he must not be inclined to speak down to those who are not technically trained.

The team should contain a minimum of one person who is thoroughly familiar with the industrial organization's over-all operations and one who is a well-trained and experienced scientist or engineer. A single person may combine these two, and in many cases O.R. has begun successfully with such a one-man operation. There are considerable advantages to having at least two persons start off, however, for they can not only think together but think "against each other" fruitfully, and with different scientific tools. This can yield results that are greater than the sum of the parts. Furthermore, there is evidence that a two-man team tends to expand its usefulness more rapidly than does one man.

The usefulness of the person who knows the company's operations is directly proportionate to the breadth of his knowledge. Depth of knowledge of any one phase of operations is not as important as breadth because O.R. is so vitally concerned with interrelationships. (Specialized knowledge can be obtained by enlisting, whenever necessary, the aid of those in the company who are best equipped with this knowledge.) This person should also be inclined toward quantitative thinking, but need not be highly trained in mathematics or its application. Most important, he should not be afraid of numbers and symbols and should be willing to extend his knowledge in this area. He need not be a scientist or engineer. Effective teams have included accountants, people from marketing, the legal department, purchasing, and administration.

If this person is an engineer, then the second member of the team should, if possible, be one trained in science. Conversely, if he is a scientist, the second person should, if possible, be an engineer. This provides a desirable balance between theory and application.

The scientist who is intent upon the pursuit of knowledge for its own sake is a poor risk. So is the scientist who is wedded to the laboratory; the complicated data of the real world are in too great contrast to the controlled conditions of the laboratory. The perfectionist, who is more intent upon the "completeness" of the end result than he is upon meeting a deadline is also a poor risk. The scientist or engineer who has worked in two or three related fields of specialization, ostensibly because he has not been satisfied with the "answers" to be found in any one, is a good risk.

The members of the team should be "method-oriented." That is, they should be researchers who are more interested in the way research is conducted than in the specific subject matter studied. They should be persons interested in formulating problems, constructing models, and devising methods for testing models and measuring so-called intangibles. They should not be persons who are committed to a single bag of scientific or engineering tools or handbooks. They must be flexible and inquiring with regard to the possibility of research in areas hitherto thought to be incapable of being studied scientifically.

At least one member of the team should be capable of reading and understanding the growing literature in the field of O.R., specifically, the references cited in this book. He should also be given the opportunity to do this without constant interruption from other job duties.

In a two-man team, it is desirable that one of the members be "data-oriented" and the other "theory-oriented." Most scientists and engineers tend to be one or the other. Few are balanced between these two tendencies. A team whose members are all data-oriented or all theory-oriented will be unbalanced. Data-oriented researchers will tend to ignore the model construction phase of research, and theory-oriented researchers will tend to ignore the data to preserve their models. Only through interchange between these types can an inclusive approach be obtained.

Inasmuch as the problem of internal communication is most easily solved when there is mutual respect among the representatives of the several fields, one should be wary of, for example, the physical scientist who frowns on the notion of working with engineers, shudders at the thought of associating with economists, and howls at the idea of working with a psychologist or sociologist. Such a one is too narrowly specialized to appreciate the contributions that have been made by specialists outside his own field.

If the team is to be expanded either initially or subsequently, the following listing can be used as a guide:

One company man.
One scientist (physical).
One engineer.
One mathematician and/or statistician.
One scientist (behavioral: biology, psychology, or social science).
One logician or specialist in scientific methodology.

Expansion beyond this should be designed to obtain as wide a representation of the fields of science and engineering as possible, consistent with the personality considerations associated with good teamwork.

If none of the team members has had training or experience in O.R. and an experienced person is not hired, then such experience should be brought into the team either in the form of consultation or contracted participation. There are a number of management consulting firms, research institutes, and educational institutions that can and do provide such assistance. Systematic exposure to an experienced operations researcher on the job is one of the most effective ways of training newcomers to O.R., and it assures the sponsor that effective tools are not being overlooked.

The desirability of the mixed team is not arbitrary. It is based on a sound scientific observation: many processes appear in many manifestations and hence have been studied independently by many sciences. By bringing to bear the widest range of methods developed for studying a particular system, most effective results can be obtained. A very good illustration of this point is the phenomenal development of knowledge concerning communication and control systems that resulted from bringing together scientists and engineers from many diverse fields to form the discipline now known as cybernetics. It was learned that physicists, chemists, biologists, psychologists, social scientists, electrical engineers, philosophers, and many others were all studying communication and control as it appeared in different phenomena. By bringing them together, a "common language" emerged and knowledge was pooled to yield one of the most monumental advances in contemporary science.

Different researchers with the same training do not supplement each other in the same way as do researchers from diverse fields. Furthermore, the types of problems to which O.R. should be applied require for their successful solution many specialists, since so many different types of activity become involved in the over-all approach that is characteristic of the field. The case study presented in Chapter 3 by Professor Mitten illustrates this point dramatically. The three persons combined into a team for that study cannot help but seem strange at first glance, but further reading will show the sound logic behind the selection. There is a far greater danger from having too little diversity of specialists than from having too much.

It might be helpful to describe briefly some of the teams formed by companies with which Case Institute of Technology has co-operated in initial O.R. efforts.

A machine tool manufacturer designated a financial analyst who was assistant to the treasurer to work along with two operations researchers brought in from an outside agency. Specialists in the company were involved from time to time, but the financial analyst was the company's key man about whom the entire effort was constructed. He had a wide knowledge of company operations and easy access to all departments.

A chemical company designated the head of its quality control section to lead its O.R. effort. He had a doctoral degree in physical chemistry. In his section were quality control personnel and statisticians whom he used, but he was reinforced by a member of the accounting department who had been trained in chemistry as well.

A kitchen equipment manufacturing company designated one of the assistants to the vice president in charge of long-range planning as director of its O.R. effort. He had no advanced training in science or engineering but had long experience with the company in analysis of its operations. He was supplemented by a young graduate engineer and assisted by the director of marketing research.

A lamp manufacturing company created a three-man team consisting of its chief auditor, the research assistant to the manager of sales operations, and a member of the market research staff.

An oil company built its team about a man trained in business administration and a mechanical engineer employed in the research section of its manufacturing division.

A pharmaceutical company formed a team by hiring an expert statistician and supplementing him with an industrial engineer who had been in the company's employ for several years.

An automobile parts manufacturer formed a team by combining its director of planning for one of its phases of manufacturing and the head of its quality control effort.

A steel manufacturing company's team consisted of a high-ranking member of its accounting staff and the head of its quality control section.

These examples could be multiplied many times. It should be apparent, however, that starting is not as difficult as it might seem. But training the personnel selected so that they can do an effective job is not an easy task. The success of any such training effort will naturally depend on the quality of the personnel selected to do the work. In each of the cases mentioned a good, functioning O.R. group was developed.

TRAINING

Training in O.R. can be obtained either through an apprenticeship or formal training conducted by an educational institution. The trainee or hired operations researcher must also learn about the organization by which he is employed if he is not already familiar with it. Let us consider the latter case first.

Learning about the organization takes time. During this time a mutual respect must develop between the specialist who knows nothing about the organization but has techniques which may help it, and the expert who knows the organization inside out but lacks the tools to tackle the problems he recognizes as important.

This aspect of organizational training may be speeded up by formal orientation. The new man should be told as much as possible about the organization and he should have the opportunity to move about, meet key people, and observe what goes on in the various parts of the organization. If the company is dispersed geographically, the training should involve visits to the decentralized units.

These remarks may appear obvious but all too frequently a new specialist is thrown into a problem by management before this orientation has been completed, just as at one time a salesman was given merely an order book and a price list and told to go get orders.

On-the-Job Training

The company can approach its early O.R. problems by use of teams composed of untrained company personnel and specialists from an outside O.R. agency. The trainees should be relieved of enough of their other company responsibilities to be able to devote all the time required to the project.

Time should be allowed for the trainees to do the reading suggested by the experienced operations researchers and to discuss their reading. Time should also be allowed for attendance at conferences conducted by institutions and professional societies. An increasing number of such conferences is being held each year.

As the trainees gain experience, less and less reliance need be placed on outside specialists. The specialists can be used as consultants during the final period of transition of the trainees to specialists. Even after training is completed, occasional use of consultants can keep the company's operations researchers up to date.

Special training programs can be used to supplement on-the-job training. Arrangements can be and have been made for an educational institution to give O.R. courses at the company for the technical personnel designated as trainees. It is also possible to have nontechnical courses given for company management. Such courses can be designed to inform management about the possibilities of O.R.: the general nature of its methods, the problems it has handled and can handle, and the associated requirements. A course of this nature can produce an informed and interested management cadre that can actively participate in the development of O.R. in the company.

If such specially designed courses are not feasible, attendance at "short courses" in O.R. can be substituted. Massachusetts Institute of Technology gives such a 2-week course [8] and Case Institute of Technology holds a similar course twice each year. These courses are intensive programs designed for trainees from industry. They do not produce "finished" practitioners but they do provide a basis on which the trainee can build by reading and experience. Related courses in applied mathematics and computers are given by a number of educational institutions.

Another way of obtaining training-by-doing is to have the company trainee serve an apprenticeship with an outside O.R. group. Arrangements for such training can be made with some groups associated with educational institutions.

Curricular Programs in O.R.

An increasing number of educational programs in O.R. is appearing on the horizon. Case Institute of Technology has a fully developed curriculum in O.R. (leading to the M.S. and Ph.D. degrees) and The Johns Hopkins University began a similar program in September 1955. Massachusetts Institute of Technology accepts theses in O.R. and Columbia University has a curriculum in Operations Engineering which is essentially an O.R. curriculum. Such schools as the University of Pennsylvania, the American University, Illinois Institute of Technology, Carnegie Institute of Technology, Pennsylvania State University, George Washington University, Ohio State University, Rensselaer, and the University of California (Los Angeles) are offering courses and/or degree programs that include O.R.*

As yet these institutions are turning out only a handful of trained professionals each year. These are not nearly enough to fill the need, but these men will produce others in the years to come as the number of educational programs involved increases in number. Industrial organizations can subsidize such programs by endowing fellowships for students in O.R. Such students are under no obligation to accept employment by the endower. But similar endowments in other fields by industries have "paid off" and undoubtedly will in this area.

ORGANIZATION

The following questions are the most common ones regarding the organization of O.R. teams in the company:

1. Where should the team be located in the company?
2. How should it be administered?
3. What types of problems should it begin with and proceed to?

Let us consider each of these in turn.

---

* For a discussion of a corresponding effort in Great Britain, see ref. 3. For discussion of educational programs in O.R., see refs. 9 and 11.

To whom should the O.R. group report? There are two principal schools of thought on this question. One insists that no one lower than the highest operating executive of the company should be considered. The other believes that the O.R. group should stay away from the top few echelons and get down where the "real" work is being done, because here is where the data are generated and here is where the "real" problems have their impact. A compromise position is to attack the group as far down the ladder as possible, *provided* full access to information is still possible. In practice, successful O.R. groups have been assigned to presidents, executive vice presidents, other vice presidents, and department heads or their counterparts.

In our experience, the most effective organization is one in which the team reports to an advisory board made up of managers from each of the principal departments of the company. This should be a permanent board that continues from project to project, meeting with the team for periodic reviews of progress every 4 to 8 weeks. One member of the board, the manager of the department most involved in the study, should serve as chairman and be the one approached by the team for assistance when it is needed.

In addition, it is very desirable to have an operating committee consisting of those persons below the departmental management level who will be most affected by the study. This committee should also meet regularly with the team, but its personnel should change as changes in study areas occur.

The existence of these boards removes the need for frequent written reports. Ideally, only one report should be prepared per project—at the end, to provide a historical record of what has been done. To the extent that all reporting can be done orally to the people involved on a periodic basis, results will be absorbed in small doses and implementation can be made gradually as results become available. Such meetings make participants out of those who must eventually take the recommended actions, and resistance to change is minimized. Occasional brief memoranda may be helpful in allowing more detailed consideration of results or methods that are difficult to grasp at one meeting. Presentations to the advisory board and operating committee should be as carefully prepared as written reports are prepared. Liberal use should be made of visual aids.

The O.R. group itself should be as small as possible and the tendency to enlarge merely because there is plenty of work to be done should be resisted. At the same time, the group should be large enough to allow for the representation of specialties most likely to be needed and large enough to provide for mutual stimulation and generation of ideas within the group.

Initially, there should be considerable stability of assignment, partly to reduce the problems of training, partly to facilitate the group's task of building up as much detailed data as possible about the organization which it is serving.

If all members of the group are equally experienced or inexperienced, no leader need be designated. If one member is more experienced than the rest, he can be designated formally as group leader, but even this is not usually necessary unless the team includes about five members or more. Organization for O.R. should be as free-wheeling as possible this side of anarchy.

In almost every organization in which an O.R. group has been established, various executives, operating personnel, and technicians will begin to call on the various specialists on the O.R. team for advice or assistance on problems involving their specialty. Provision of such a service can be an important role of the group, but not more than a small portion of its effort should be devoted to stopgap advising and assistance. Through such opportunities to serve the company, acceptance is accelerated and organizational exposure is increased. But the team must have the right to refuse when such demand becomes excessive.

What kind of problem should the team begin with? In general, initial problems should be ones that will not be very difficult or require too much time, and should be such that results are demonstrable. This will give the team and management a chance to build up confidence in themselves and in O.R. Gradually more difficult problems can be confronted.

Problems in production and inventory control usually fill the requirements for an initial effort. Methods and tools are well developed. Many successful applications have been made in this area and have been reported in the literature.

Eventually the team should move into marketing and organizational areas, and into problems with longer range significance. The team will generate new and more general problems as it proceeds. It is not likely that there will be lack of problems, once the first has been solved.

Finally, it should be remembered that the development of O.R. teams to conduct management research is still a matter for judgment and creativeness. One wants to find a team that:

1. Understands and can apply scientific method.
2. Is intensely interested in management-type problems.

3. Can communicate with and gain the confidence of company personnel.

4. Has had experience with O.R. and knows the latest developments in O.R.

One also knows that no such team exists or is likely to exist. As our experience grows, we will be able to make more definitive statements about how this ideal team can best be approximated; indeed, we may look forward eventually to applying O.R. to the construction of O.R. industrial teams.

BIBLIOGRAPHY

1. Ackoff, R. L., *The Design of Social Research*, University of Chicago Press, Chicago, 1953.
2. Bush, G. P., and Hattery, L. H., *Teamwork in Research*, American University Press, Washington, 1953.
3. Gander, R. S., "Training for Operations Research at the University of Birmingham," *J. Opns. Res. Soc. Am.*, *3*, 215–216 (1955).
4. Hertz, D. B., and Rubinstein, A. H., *Research Operations in Industry*, King's Crown Press, New York, 1953.
5. ――― (eds.), *Selection, Training, and Use of Personnel in Industrial Research*, King's Crown Press, New York, 1953.
6. McCloskey, J. F., "Training for Operations Research," *J. Opns. Res. Soc. Am.*, *2*, 386–392 (1954).
7. ―――, and Trefethen, F. N., *Operations Research for Management*, The Johns Hopkins Press, Baltimore, 1954.
8. Morse, P. M., "Report on the First Summer Program in Operations Research at the Massachusetts Institute of Technology," *J. Opns. Res. Soc. Am.*, *1*, 303–305 (1953).
9. "Report of The Education Committee," *J. Opns. Res. Soc. Am.*, *1*, 248–251 (1953).
10. Rinehart, R. F., "Threats to the Growth of Operations Research in Business and Industry," *J. Opns. Res. Soc. Am.*, *2*, 229–233 (1953).
11. Schultz, Andrew, Jr., "A Discussion of Education for Operations Research," *J. Opns. Res. Soc. Am.*, *3*, 91–100 (1955).

Author Index

637

Subject Index